CUMULATIVE PROBABILITIES FOR THE STANDARD NORMAL DISTRIBUTION

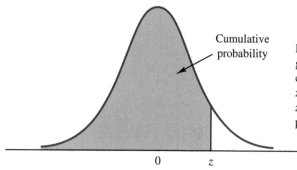

Cumulative probability

Entries in the table give the area under the curve to the left of the z value. For example, for z = 1.25, the cumulative probability is .8944.

z	.00	.01	.02	.03	.04	.05	.06	.07	.08	.09
.0	.5000	.5040	.5080	.5120	.5160	.5199	.5239	.5279	.5319	.5359
.1	.5398	.5438	.5478	.5517	.5557	.5596	.5636	.5675	.5714	.5753
.2	.5793	.5832	.5871	.5910	.5948	.5987	.6026	.6064	.6103	.6141
.3	.6179	.6217	.6255	.6293	.6331	.6368	.6406	.6443	.6480	.6517
.4	.6554	.6591	.6628	.6664	.6700	.6736	.6772	.6808	.6844	.6879
.5	.6915	.6950	.6985	.7019	.7054	.7088	.7123	.7157	.7190	.7224
.6	.7257	.7291	.7324	.7357	.7389	.7422	.7454	.7486	.7517	.7549
.7	.7580	.7611	.7642	.7673	.7704	.7734	.7764	.7794	.7823	.7852
.8	.7881	.7910	.7939	.7967	.7995	.8023	.8051	.8078	.8106	.8133
.9	.8159	.8186	.8212	.8238	.8264	.8289	.8315	.8340	.8365	.8389
1.0	.8413	.8438	.8461	.8485	.8508	.8531	.8554	.8577	.8599	.8621
1.1	.8643	.8665	.8686	.8708	.8729	.8749	.8770	.8790	.8810	.8830
1.2	.8849	.8869	.8888	.8907	.8925	.8944	.8962	.8980	.8997	.9015
1.3	.9032	.9049	.9066	.9082	.9099	.9115	.9131	.9147	.9162	.9177
1.4	.9192	.9207	.9222	.9236	.9251	.9265	.9279	.9292	.9306	.9319
1.5	.9332	.9345	.9357	.9370	.9382	.9394	.9406	.9418	.9429	.9441
1.6	.9452	.9463	.9474	.9484	.9495	.9505	.9515	.9525	.9535	.9545
1.7	.9554	.9564	.9573	.9582	.9591	.9599	.9608	.9616	.9625	.9633
1.8	.9641	.9649	.9656	.9664	.9671	.9678	.9686	.9693	.9699	.9706
1.9	.9713	.9719	.9726	.9732	.9738	.9744	.9750	.9756	.9761	.9767
2.0	.9772	.9778	.9783	.9788	.9793	.9798	.9803	.9808	.9812	.9817
2.1	.9821	.9826	.9830	.9834	.9838	.9842	.9846	.9850	.9854	.9857
2.2	.9861	.9864	.9868	.9871	.9875	.9878	.9881	.9884	.9887	.9890
2.3	.9893	.9896	.9898	.9901	.9904	.9906	.9909	.9911	.9913	.9913
2.4	.9918	.9920	.9922	.9925	.9927	.9929	.9931	.9932	.9934	.9936
2.5	.9938	.9940	.9941	.9943	.9945	.9946	.9948	.9949	.9951	.9952
2.6	.9953	.9955	.9956	.9957	.9959	.9960	.9961	.9962	.9963	.9964
2.7	.9965	.9966	.9967	.9968	.9969	.9970	.9971	.9972	.9973	.9974
2.8	.9974	.9975	.9976	.9977	.9977	.9978	.9979	.9979	.9980	.9981
2.9	.9981	.9982	.9982	.9983	.9984	.9984	.9985	.9985	.9986	.9986
3.0	.9986	.9987	.9987	.9988	.9988	.9989	.9989	.9989	.9990	.9990

Dedicated to
Krista, Justin, Mark, and Colleen
Mark, Linda, Brad, Tim, Scott, and Lisa
Cathy, David, and Kristin

Brief Contents

Contents

Chapter 6 Continuous Probability Distributions 240

Chapter 7 Sampling and Sampling Distributions 271

Chapter 13 Multiple Regression   559

Chapter 14 Statistical Methods for Quality Control 609

Preface

The purpose of *Essentials of Modern Business Statistics with Microsoft® Excel* is to give students, primarily in the fields of business administration and economics, an introduction to the field of statistics and its many applications. The text is applications oriented and written with the needs of the nonmathematician in mind; the mathematical prerequisite is knowledge of algebra.

Applications of data analysis and statistical methodology are an integral part of the organization and presentation of the text material. The discussion and development of each technique is presented in an application setting, with the statistical results providing insights to decisions and solutions to problems.

Although the book is applications oriented, we have taken care to provide a sound methodological development and to use notation that is generally accepted for the topic being covered. Hence, students will find that this text provides good preparation for the study of more advanced material. A bibliography to guide further study is included in an appendix.

Use of Microsoft® Excel for Statistical Analysis

Essentials of Modern Business Statistics with Microsoft® Excel is first and foremost a statistics textbook that emphasizes statistical concepts and applications. But, since most practical problems are too large to be solved using hand calculations, some type of statistical software package is required to solve these problems. There are several excellent statistical packages available today. However, because most students and potential employers value spreadsheet experience, many colleges and universities now use a spreadsheet package in their statistics courses. Microsoft Excel is the most widely used spreadsheet package in business as well as in colleges and universities. We have written *Essentials of Modern Business Statistics with Microsoft® Excel* especially for statistics courses in which Excel is used as the software package.

Excel has been integrated within each of the chapters and plays an integral part in providing an application orientation. We assume that readers using this text are familiar with Excel basics such as selecting cells, entering formulas, copying, and so on. We build on that familiarity by showing how to use the appropriate Excel statistical functions and data analysis tools.

The discussion of using Excel to perform a statistical procedure appears in a subsection immediately following the discussion of the statistical procedure. We believe that this style enables us to fully integrate the use of Excel throughout the text, but still maintain the primary emphasis on the statistical methodology being discussed. In each of these subsections, we use a standard format for setting up a worksheet for statistical analysis. There are three primary tasks: Enter Data, Enter Functions and Formulas, and Apply Tools. We believe a consistent framework for applying Excel helps users to focus on the statistical methodology without getting bogged down in the details of using Excel.

In presenting worksheet figures, we often use a nested approach in which the worksheet shown in the background of the figure displays the formulas and the worksheet shown in the foreground shows the values computed using the formulas.

Following is Figure 2.1 from the text, which is displayed to explain use of color in Excel figures. We use lavender to highlight the data from the sample (soft drink purchases in this figure) and green to highlight the cells containing Excel functions and formulas. The green

FIGURE 2.1   FREQUENCY DISTRIBUTION FOR SOFT DRINK PURCHASES CONSTRUCTED USING EXCEL'S COUNTIF FUNCTION

	A	B	C	D	E
1	Brand Purchased		Soft Drink	Frequency	
2	Coke Classic		Coke Classic	=COUNTIF($A$2:$A$51,C2)	
3	Diet Coke		Diet Coke	=COUNTIF($A$2:$A$51,C3)	
4	Pepsi-Cola		Dr. Pepper	=COUNTIF($A$2:$A$51,C4)	
5	Diet Coke		Pepsi-Cola	=COUNTIF($A$2:$A$51,C5)	
6	Coke Classic		Sprite	=COUNTIF($A$2:$A$51,C6)	
7	Coke Classic				
8	Dr. Pepper				
9	Diet Coke				
10	Pepsi-Cola				
45	Pepsi-Cola				
46	Pepsi-Cola				
47	Pepsi-Cola				
48	Coke Classic				
49	Dr. Pepper				
50	Pepsi-Cola				
51	Sprite				
52					

	A	B	C	D	E
1	Brand Purchased		Soft Drink	Frequency	
2	Coke Classic		Coke Classic	19	
3	Diet Coke		Diet Coke	8	
4	Pepsi-Cola		Dr. Pepper	5	
5	Diet Coke		Pepsi-Cola	13	
6	Coke Classic		Sprite	5	
7	Coke Classic				
8	Dr. Pepper				
9	Diet Coke				
10	Pepsi-Cola				
45	Pepsi-Cola				
46	Pepsi-Cola				
47	Pepsi-Cola				
48	Coke Classic				
49	Dr. Pepper				
50	Pepsi-Cola				
51	Sprite				
52					

Note: Rows 11–44 are hidden.

cells show the functions and formulas in the background worksheet and they show the values obtained using the formulas in the foreground worksheet. A third color (gold) is used in certain figures to highlight material that is printed by Excel as a result of using one of the data analysis tools.

Changes in the Third Edition

We appreciate the acceptance and positive response to the previous editions of *Essentials of Modern Business Statistics with Microsoft Excel*. Accordingly, in making modifications for this new edition, we have maintained the presentation style and readability of the previous editions. The significant changes in the new edition are summarized here.

Content Revisions

- **Descriptive Statistics:** New sections have been added on the shape of distributions in Chapters 2 and 3. Skewness is introduced as an important measure of the shape of a distribution. In later chapters, we now mention the need for larger sample sizes in interval estimation and hypothesis-testing applications involving a skewed population. Crosstabulation material has been expanded to include more discussion of percentage distributions. Simpson's paradox is used to point out a source of potentially erroneous conclusions when working with crosstabulations.

- **Probability Distributions:** The cumulative standard normal probability table has been expanded to show cumulative probabilities from $z = -3.09$ to $z = 3.09$. This enables hand calculations to parallel the approach that Excel uses to compute probabilities using the NORMSDIST and NORMDIST functions, and it makes it much easier to compute lower tail p-values. A discussion of the mean, variance, and standard deviation has been added for the Poisson and hypergeometric distributions in Chapter 5 and the exponential distribution in Chapter 6.

- **Interval Estimation:** In the second edition, we followed a large sample/small sample approach for interval estimation of a population mean in Chapter 8. In this third edition, we present interval estimation using the σ known and σ unknown paradigm. The standard normal distribution is used in all cases where the population standard deviation can be assumed known. The t distribution is used in all cases where the population standard deviation is estimated by the sample standard deviation. This approach simplifies the methodology for the student and is consistent with computer-based procedures provided by most statistical packages and Excel. In the σ unknown case, the new approach provides slightly improved results over the previous large-sample approximation. A t distribution table with up to 100 degrees of freedom is included as Table 2 of Appendix B. This change carries into hypothesis tests about a population mean in Chapter 9 and statistical inferences about the means of two populations in Chapter 10.

- **Hypothesis Testing Using p-values:** Another change in the new edition is the emphasis on the use of p-values for hypothesis testing. With more and more use of statistical software packages for data analysis, p-values are clearly preferred to the traditional test statistic and rejection region approach. As a result, we now use p-values as the primary method for hypothesis testing applications in Chapters 9 to 13.

- **New Procedure for Two Sample Inferences:** We provide new methodology for inferences about the means of two populations when the population standard deviations are unknown. The methodology is based on the t distribution and is more general in that it can be applied whether or not the population variances are equal. The student no longer has to consider making the equal population variance assumption and making the pooled variance calculation.

Solutions Manual

In response to suggestions from users, we have revised the solutions manual extensively. In conjunction with the hand solution of exercises, the use of Excel functions and formulas is shown where appropriate. In particular, results provided using Excel's probability distribution functions (e.g., BINOMDIST, NORMDIST, and so on) and data analysis tools are shown.

New Examples and Exercises Based on Real Data

We have added more than 200 new examples and exercises based on real data and recent reference sources of statistical information. Using data pulled from sources also used by the *Wall Street Journal, USA Today, Fortune, Barron's,* and a variety of other sources, we draw from actual studies to develop explanations and to create exercises that demonstrate many uses of statistics in business and economics. We believe that the use of real data helps generate more student interest in the material and enables the student to learn about both the statistical methodology and its application.

New Case Problems

We have added several new case problems to this edition, bringing the total number of case problems in the text to 21. The new case problems appear in the chapters on descriptive statistics, probability distributions, and regression analysis. These case problems provide students with the opportunity to analyze somewhat larger data sets and prepare managerial reports based on the results of the analysis.

New Statistics in Practice

Each chapter begins with a Statistics in Practice article that describes an application of the statistical methodology to be covered in the chapter. Statistics in Practice have been provided by practitioners at companies such as Colgate-Palmolive, Citibank, Procter & Gamble, Monsanto, and others. This edition includes two new Statistics in Practice: Food Lion (Chapter 8) and John Morrell & Company (Chapter 9).

New Materials for Microsoft Excel

All Excel materials have been updated to be consistent with Microsoft Excel 2003, and two options have been added to enhance learning and extend the use of Excel.

- **EasyStat: Digital Tutor for Microsoft® Excel, Version 2.** This online tutorial will make it easier for students to learn how to use Excel to perform statistical analysis. In each digital video, one of the textbook authors demonstrates how Excel can be used to perform a particular statistical procedure. Students may purchase an online subscription for the Excel version of EasyStat Digital Tutor at *http://asw. swlearning.com.*
- **Coverage of Excel Add-in SWStat+, Version 2.** *SWStat+* is now covered in the appendixes of relevant chapters, giving you the option of incorporating this Excel add-in in your course. *SWStat+ V.2* may be bundled with the text.

Features and Pedagogy

Anderson, Sweeney, and Williams have continued many of the features that appeared in the second edition. Some of the important ones are noted here.

Methods Exercises and Applications Exercises

The end-of-section exercises are split into two parts: Methods and Applications. The Methods exercises require users to use the formulas and make computations. The Applications exercises require students to apply the chapter material in real-world situations. Thus, students focus on the computational "nuts and bolts" and then move on to the subtleties of statistical applications and the interpretation of the statistical output.

Self-Test Exercises

Some exercises are identified as self-test exercises. Completely worked-out solutions for these exercises are provided in an appendix at the end of the book. Students can attempt the self-text exercises and immediately check the solutions to evaluate their understanding of the concepts presented in the chapter.

Margin Annotations and Notes & Comments

Margin annotations that highlight key points and provide additional insights for the student are a key feature of this text. These annotations, which appear in the margins, are designed to provide emphasis and enhance understanding of the terms and concepts being presented in the text.

At the end of many sections, we provide "Notes & Comments" designed to give the reader additional insights about the statistical methodology and its application. These notes include warnings about limitations of the methodology, recommendations for application, brief descriptions of technical considerations, and other matters.

Data Files Accompany the Text

Approximately 200 data files are available on the Student CD packaged with new copies of the text. Data sets for all case problems, as well as data sets and worksheets for larger exercises, are included.

Get Choice and Flexibility with ThomsonNOW

You envisioned it, we developed it. Designed *by* instructors and students *for* instructors and students, *ThomsonNOW for ASW's Essentials of Modern Business Statistics* is the most reliable, flexible, and easy-to-use online suite of services and resources. With efficient and immediate paths to success, ThomsonNOW delivers the results you expect. ThomsonNOW will be available in the fall of 2006.

- **Automatic grading and easy-to-use grade book.** Assigning chapters in ThomsonNOW takes just seconds and student results flow automatically into the instructor's online grade book.
- **At your service.** Thomson South-Western offers integration of ThomsonNOW with many course management platforms, including WebCT and Blackboard. Students can log in at their school's course management platform, access all the ThomsonNOW content with no additional login, and see their grades in a single grade book.
- **Personalized learning plans.** For every chapter, personalized learning plans allow students to focus on what they still need to learn and to select the activities that best match their learning styles (such as the relevant EasyStat tutorials, animations, step-by-step problem demonstrations, and text pages).
- **Control and flexibility.** Control exactly how and when students will complete a homework assignment, quiz, or test. Edit questions. Author your own questions and/or create entire tests or assessments.
- **Variety of problem types.** Choose from multiple choice, free entry, true/false, fill in the blank, and data analysis.
- **More study options.** Students can choose how they read the textbook—via integrated digital eBook or by reading the print version.

To ensure the results you desire, we offer a dedicated service and training program: Thomson Learning Connects. This program includes a 24/7 ThomsonNOW service and support Web site, a lead teacher program, and an extensive first day of class services. For details, contact your Thomson South-Western representative.

1Pass™ Online Resources. Thomson South-Western's new 1Pass program allows students to access a wide range of media using a single username and password—no more multiple URLs and login information to remember! To register, students use the 1Pass access code included on the card packaged with their textbooks. Students can use their 1Pass accounts to access e-resources for their courses year after year.

The 1Pass program is available for your students only if you choose to order a package that contains the text *Essentials of Modern Business Statistics* and ThomsonNOW. If you do not choose to order the 1Pass package, students will need to purchase these multimedia resources at an additional cost by ordering them at *http://www.thomsonedu.com.*

Ancillaries for Instructors

- **New for the Third Edition: JoinIn™**
  Authors Anderson, Sweeney, and Williams will help you turn your lecture into an interactive experience for your students. Thomson South-Western is pleased to offer you book-specific JoinIn content with *Essentials of Modern Business Statistics,* 3e for Student Classroom Response Systems, allowing you to transform your classroom and assess your students' progress with instant in-class quizzes and polls. In partnership with TurningPoint™ our software lets you pose book-specific questions and display students' answers seamlessly within the Microsoft® PowerPoint slides of your own lecture, in conjunction with the "clicker" hardware of your choice. Enhance how your students interact with you, your lecture, and each other. You will see better student interaction, better attendance, and better results. This product is available to college and university adopters only. Contact your local Thomson representative to learn more.

- **Instructor's Resource CD-Rom**
  Instructor support materials are available to adopters from the Thomson Learning™ Academic Resource Center at 800-423-0563 or through http://www.thomsonedu.com. Most instructor ancillaries are provided on a single Instructor's Resource CD-Rom (ISBN: 0-324-31278-4). Included in this convenient format are:
  1. **Solutions Manual**—The *Solutions Manual,* prepared by authors Anderson, Sweeney, and Williams, includes solutions for all exercises in the text. Also, at the request of the instructor, a print version of the *Solutions Manual* can be packaged with the text for student purchase.
  2. **Solutions for Case Problems**—Also prepared by the authors, it contains solutions to all case problems presented in the text.
  3. **Microsoft® PowerPoint Presentation Slides**—Prepared by John Loucks of St. Edward's University, the animated presentation slides contain a teaching outline that incorporates graphics to help instructors create even more stimulating lectures. The slides may be adapted using PowerPoint software to facilitate classroom use.
  4. **Test Bank**—Prepared also by John Loucks, the *Test Bank* in Microsoft® Word files includes multiple choice questions and problems for each chapter.

- **ExamView™**
  Available separately, the *Test Bank* presented in ExamView (ISBN 0-324-31282-2) computerized testing software allows instructors to create, edit, store and print exams.

Ancillaries for Students

- A **Student CD** is packaged free with each new text. It provides Excel worksheets for all text examples, exercises and Case problems, and a PredInt add-in with directions for computing confidence and predication intervals in regression analysis. If necessary, the Student CD may be purchased at the text's website.

- The **Study Guide** (ISBN 0-324-31279-2) prepared by John Loucks of St. Edward's University, will provide the student with significant supplementary study materials. For each chapter, it contains key concepts, review materials, example problems worked out in full detail, exercises with answers, and self-test questions with answers.
- **EasyStat Digital Tutor for Microsoft® Excel, Version 2.** These online tutorials make it easier than ever for students to learn how to use Excel to perform statistical analysis. For more information, visit *http://easystat.swlearning.com*.

Acknowledgments

We would like to acknowledge the work of our reviewers who provided comments and suggestions of ways to continue to improve our text. Thanks to:

Eddine Dahel, Monterey Institute of International Studies

Joan Donohue, University of South Carolina

Jianjun Du, University of Houston–Victoria

Thomas J. Dudley, Pepperdine University

Swarna Dutt, University of West Georgia

Robert Escudero, Pepperdine University

Stacy Everly, Delaware County Community College

Soheila Kahkashan Fardanesh, Towson University

Charles Harrington, University of Southern Indiana

Carl H. Hess, Marymount University

Woodrow W. Hughes, Jr., Converse College

Homayoun Khamooshi, George Washington University

Daniel M. Light, Northwest State College

Timothy McDaniel, Buena Vista University

Barry J. Monk, Macon State College

Von Roderick Plessner, Northwest State University

Robert D. Potter, University of Central Florida

Avuthu Rami Reddy, University of Wisconsin–Platteville

Ahmad Saranjam, Bridgewater State College

Ahmad Syamil, Arkansas State University

Elizabeth Wark, Springfield College

Nancy A. Williams, Loyola College in Maryland

Larry Woodward, University of Mary Hardin-Baylor

We would like to recognize the following individuals who have helped us in the past and continue to influence our writing.

Glen Archibald, University of Mississippi

Darl Bien, University of Denver

Thomas W. Bolland, Ohio University

Mike Bourke, Houston Baptist University

Peter Bryant, University of Colorado

Terri L. Byczkowski, University of Cincinnati

Robert Carver, Stonehill College

Ying Chien, University of Scranton

Robert Cochran, University of Wyoming

Murray Côté, University of Florida

David W. Cravens, Texas Christian University

Tom Dahlstrom, Eastern College

Terry Dielman, Texas Christian University

Ronald Ehresman, Baldwin-Wallace College

Mohammed A. El-Saidi, Ferris State University

Nicholas Farnum, California State University–Fullerton

Abe Feinberg, California State University, Northridge

Michael Ford, Rochester Institute of Technology

Phil Fry, Boise State University

V. Daniel Guide, Duquesne University

Paul Guy, California State University-Chico

Alan Humphrey, University of Rhode Island

Ann Hussein, Philadelphia College of Textiles and Science

Ben Isselhardt, Rochester Institute of Technology

Jeffery Jarrett, University of Rhode Island

Barry Kadets, Bryant College

Kenneth Klassen, California State University Northridge

David Krueger, St. Cloud State University

June Lapidus, Roosevelt University

Martin S. Levy, University of Cincinnati

Ka-sing Man, Georgetown University

Don Marx, University of Alaska, Anchorage

Tom McCullough, University of California–Berkeley

Mario Miranda, The Ohio State University

Mitchell Muesham, Sam Houston State University

Richard O'Connell, Miami University of Ohio

Alan Olinsky, Bryant College

Lynne Pastor, Carnegie Mellon University

Tom Pray, Rochester Institute of Technology

Harold Rahmlow, St. Joseph's University

Derrick Reagle, Fordham University

Tom Ryan, Case Western Reserve University

Bill Seaver, University of Tennessee

Alan Smith, Robert Morris College

William Struning, Seton Hall University

David Tufte, University of New Orleans

Jack Vaughn, University of Texas–El Paso

Ari Wijetunga, Morehead State University

J. E. Willis, Louisiana State University

Mustafa Yilmaz, Northeastern University

Special thanks are owed to our associates from business and industry who supplied the "Statistics in Practice" features. We recognize them individually by a credit line in each of the articles. Finally, we are also indebted to our senior acquisitions editor Charles McCormick, Jr., our senior developmental editor Alice Denny, our senior production editor Deanna Quinn, our senior marketing manager Larry Qualls, and others at Thomson Business and Economics for their editorial counsel and support during the preparation of this text.

David R. Anderson
Dennis J. Sweeney
Thomas A. Williams

About the Authors

David R. Anderson. David R. Anderson is Professor of Quantitative Analysis in the College of Business Administration at the University of Cincinnati. Born in Grand Forks, North Dakota, he earned his B.S., M.S., and Ph.D. degrees from Purdue University. Professor Anderson has served as Head of the Department of Quantitative Analysis and Operations Management and as Associate Dean of the College of Business Administration. In addition, he was the coordinator of the College's first Executive Program.

At the University of Cincinnati, Professor Anderson has taught introductory statistics for business students as well as graduate-level courses in regression analysis, multivariate analysis, and management science. He has also taught statistical courses at the Department of Labor in Washington, D.C. He has been honored with nominations and awards for excellence in teaching and excellence in service to student organizations.

Professor Anderson has coauthored 10 textbooks in the areas of statistics, management science, linear programming, and production and operations management. He is an active consultant in the field of sampling and statistical methods.

Dennis J. Sweeney. Dennis J. Sweeney is Professor of Quantitative Analysis and Founder of the Center for Productivity Improvement at the University of Cincinnati. Born in Des Moines, Iowa, he earned a B.S.B.A. degree from Drake University and his M.B.A. and D.B.A. degrees from Indiana University where he was an NDEA Fellow. During 1978–79, Professor Sweeney worked in the management science group at Procter & Gamble; during 1981–82, he was a visiting professor at Duke University. Professor Sweeney served as Head of the Department of Quantitative Analysis and as Associate Dean of the College of Business Administration at the University of Cincinnati.

Professor Sweeney has published more than 30 articles and monographs in the area of management science and statistics. The National Science Foundation, IBM, Procter & Gamble, Federated Department Stores, Kroger, and Cincinnati Gas & Electric have funded his research, which has been published in *Management Science*, *Operations Research*, *Mathematical Programming*, *Decision Sciences*, and other journals.

Professor Sweeney has coauthored 10 textbooks in the areas of statistics, management science, linear programming, and production and operations management.

Thomas A. Williams. Thomas A. Williams is Professor of Management Science in the College of Business at Rochester Institute of Technology. Born in Elmira, New York, he earned his B.S. degree at Clarkson University. He did his graduate work at Rensselaer Polytechnic Institute, where he received his M.S. and Ph.D. degrees.

Before joining the College of Business at RIT, Professor Williams served for seven years as a faculty member in the College of Business Administration at the University of Cincinnati, where he developed the undergraduate program in Information Systems and then served as its coordinator. At RIT, he was the first chairman of the Decision Sciences Department. He teaches courses in management science and statistics, as well as graduate courses in regression and decision analysis.

Professor Williams is the coauthor of 11 textbooks in the areas of management science, statistics, production and operations management, and mathematics. He has been a consultant for numerous *Fortune* 500 companies and has worked on projects ranging from the use of data analysis to the development of large-scale regression models.

CHAPTER 1

Data and Statistics

CONTENTS

BUSINESSWEEK*
NEW YORK, NEW YORK

With a global circulation of more than 1 million, *BusinessWeek* is the most widely read business magazine in the world. More than 200 dedicated reporters and editors in 26 bureaus worldwide deliver a variety of articles of interest to the business and economic community. Along with feature articles on current topics, the magazine contains regular sections on International Business, Economic Analysis, Information Processing, and Science & Technology. Information in the feature articles and the regular sections helps readers stay abreast of current developments and assess the impact of those developments on business and economic conditions.

Most issues of *BusinessWeek* provide an in-depth report on a topic of current interest. Often, the in-depth reports contain statistical facts and summaries that help the reader understand the business and economic information. For example, the December 6, 2004, issue included a special report on the pricing of goods made in China; the January 3, 2005, issue provided information about where to invest in 2005; and the April 4, 2005, issue provided an overview of the *BusinessWeek* 50, a diverse group of top-performing companies. In addition, the weekly *BusinessWeek Investor* provides statistics about the state of the economy, including production indexes, stock prices, mutual funds, and interest rates.

BusinessWeek also uses statistics and statistical information in managing its own business. For example, an annual survey of subscribers helps the company learn about subscriber demographics, reading habits, likely purchases, lifestyles, and so on. *BusinessWeek* managers use statistical summaries from the survey to provide better services to subscribers and advertisers. One

BusinessWeek uses statistical facts and summaries in many of its articles. © Terri Miller/E-Visual Communications, Inc.

recent North American subscriber survey indicated that 90% of *BusinessWeek* subscribers use a personal computer at home and that 64% of *BusinessWeek* subscribers are involved with computer purchases at work. Such statistics alert *BusinessWeek* managers to subscriber interest in articles about new developments in computers. The results of the survey are also made available to potential advertisers. The high percentage of subscribers using personal computers at home and the high percentage of subscribers involved with computer purchases at work would be an incentive for a computer manufacturer to consider advertising in *BusinessWeek*.

In this chapter, we discuss the types of data available for statistical analysis and describe how the data are obtained. We introduce descriptive statistics and statistical inference as ways of converting data into meaningful and easily interpreted statistical information.

---

*The authors are indebted to Charlene Trentham, Research Manager at *BusinessWeek*, for providing this Statistics in Practice.

Frequently, we see the following kinds of statements in newspaper and magazine articles:

- A Jupiter Media survey found that 31% of adult males spend 10 or more hours a week watching television. For adult women, it was 26% (*The Wall Street Journal,* January 26, 2004).
- General Motors, the leader in automotive cash rebates, provided an average cash incentive of $4300 per vehicle during 2003 (*USA Today,* January 23, 2004).

- More than 40% of Marriott International managers work their way up through the ranks (*Fortune,* January 20, 2003).
- Employees in management and finance had a median annual salary of $49,712 for 2003 (*The World Almanac,* 2004).
- Genentech was rated number 1 in Fortune's "100 Best Companies to Work For". Genentech's average annual pay for salaried and hourly workers respectively was $69,425 and $47,817 (*Fortune,* January 23, 2006).
- The New York Yankees have the highest payroll in major league baseball. In 2003, the team payroll was $152,749,814 with a median of $4,575,000 per player (*USA Today,* September 1, 2003).
- The Dow Jones Industrial Average closed at 10,960 on January 13, 2006 (*The Wall Street Journal,* January 14, 2006).

The numerical facts in the preceding statements (31%; 26%; $4300; 40%; $49,712; $69,425; $47,817; $152,749,814; $4,575,000; and 10,960) are called statistics. Thus, in everyday usage, the term *statistics* refers to numerical facts. However, the field, or subject, of statistics involves much more than numerical facts. In a broad sense, **statistics** is the art and science of collecting, analyzing, presenting, and interpreting data. Particularly in business and economics, the information provided by collecting, analyzing, presenting, and interpreting data gives managers and decision makers a better understanding of the business and economic environment and thus enables them to make more informed and better decisions. In this text, we emphasize the use of statistics for business and economic decision making.

Chapter 1 begins with some illustrations of the applications of statistics in business and economics. In Section 1.2 we define the term *data* and introduce the concept of a data set. This section also introduces key terms such as *variables* and *observations,* discusses the difference between quantitative and qualitative data, and illustrates the uses of cross-sectional and time series data. Section 1.3 discusses how data can be obtained from existing sources or through survey and experimental studies designed to obtain new data. The important role that the Internet now plays in obtaining data is also highlighted. The uses of data in developing descriptive statistics and in making statistical inferences are described in Sections 1.4 and 1.5.

Applications in Business and Economics

In today's global business and economic environment, anyone can access vast amounts of statistical information. The most successful managers and decision makers understand the information and know how to use it effectively. In this section, we provide examples that illustrate some of the uses of statistics in business and economics.

Accounting

Public accounting firms use statistical sampling procedures when conducting audits for their clients. For instance, suppose an accounting firm wants to determine whether the amount of accounts receivable shown on a client's balance sheet fairly represents the actual amount of accounts receivable. Usually the large number of individual accounts receivable makes reviewing and validating every account too time-consuming and expensive. As common practice in such situations, the audit staff selects a subset of the accounts called a sample. After reviewing the accuracy of the sampled accounts, the auditors draw a conclusion as to whether the accounts receivable amount shown on the client's balance sheet is acceptable.

Finance

Financial analysts use a variety of statistical information to guide their investment recommendations. In the case of stocks, the analysts review a variety of financial data including price/earnings ratios and dividend yields. By comparing the information for an individual stock with information about the stock market averages, a financial analyst can begin to draw a conclusion as to whether an individual stock is over- or underpriced. For example, *Barron's* (September 12, 2005) reported that the average price/earnings ratio for the 30 stocks in the Dow Jones Industrial Average was 16.5. JPMorgan showed a price/earnings ratio of 11.8. In this case, the statistical information on price/earnings ratios indicated a lower price in comparison to earnings for JPMorgan than the average for the Dow Jones stocks. Therefore, a financial analyst might conclude that JPMorgan was underpriced. This and other information about JPMorgan would help the analyst make a buy, sell, or hold recommendation for the stock.

Marketing

Electronic scanners at retail checkout counters collect data for a variety of marketing research applications. For example, data suppliers such as ACNielsen and Information Resources, Inc., purchase point-of-sale scanner data from grocery stores, process the data, and then sell statistical summaries of the data to manufacturers. Manufacturers spend hundreds of thousands of dollars per product category to obtain this type of scanner data. Manufacturers also purchase data and statistical summaries on promotional activities such as special pricing and the use of in-store displays. Brand managers can review the scanner statistics and the promotional activity statistics to gain a better understanding of the relationship between promotional activities and sales. Such analyses often prove helpful in establishing future marketing strategies for the various products.

Production

Today's emphasis on quality makes quality control an important application of statistics in production. A variety of statistical quality control charts are used to monitor the output of a production process. In particular, an x-bar chart can be used to monitor the average output. Suppose, for example, that a machine fills containers with 12 ounces of a soft drink. Periodically, a production worker selects a sample of containers and computes the average number of ounces in the sample. This average, or x-bar value, is plotted on an x-bar chart. A plotted value above the chart's upper control limit indicates overfilling, and a plotted value below the chart's lower control limit indicates underfilling. The process is termed "in control" and allowed to continue as long as the plotted x-bar values fall between the chart's upper and lower control limits. Properly interpreted, an x-bar chart can help determine when adjustments are necessary to correct a production process.

Economics

Economists frequently provide forecasts about the future of the economy or some aspect of it. They use a variety of statistical information in making such forecasts. For instance, in forecasting inflation rates, economists use statistical information on such indicators as the Producer Price Index, the unemployment rate, and manufacturing capacity utilization. Often these statistical indicators are entered into computerized forecasting models that predict inflation rates.

Applications of statistics such as those described in this section are an integral part of this text. Such examples provide an overview of the breadth of statistical applications. To supplement these examples, practitioners in the fields of business and economics provided chapter-opening Statistics in Practice articles that introduce the material covered in each chapter. The Statistics in Practice applications show the importance of statistics in a wide variety of business and economic situations.

Data

Data are the facts and figures collected, analyzed, and summarized for presentation and interpretation. All the data collected in a particular study are referred to as the **data set** for the study. Table 1.1 shows a data set containing information for 25 companies that are part of the S&P 500. The S&P 500 is made up of 500 companies selected by Standard & Poor's. These companies account for 76% of the market capitalization of all U.S. stocks. These stocks are closely followed by investors and Wall Street analysts.

TABLE 1.1   DATA SET FOR 25 S&P 500 COMPANIES

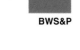

Company	Exchange	Ticker	*Business Week* Rank	Share Price ($)	Earnings per Share ($)
Abbott Laboratories	N	ABT	90	46	2.02
Altria Group	N	MO	148	66	4.57
Apollo Group	NQ	APOL	174	74	0.90
Bank of New York	N	BK	305	30	1.85
Bristol-Myers Squibb	N	BMY	346	26	1.21
Cincinnati Financial	NQ	CINF	161	45	2.73
Comcast	NQ	CMCSA	296	32	0.43
Deere	N	DE	36	71	5.77
eBay	NQ	EBAY	19	43	0.57
Federated Dept. Stores	N	FD	353	56	3.86
Hasbro	N	HAS	373	21	0.96
IBM	N	IBM	216	93	4.94
International Paper	N	IP	370	37	0.98
Knight-Ridder	N	KRI	397	66	4.13
Manor Care	N	HCR	285	34	1.90
Medtronic	N	MDT	53	52	1.79
National Semiconductor	N	NSM	155	20	1.03
Novellus Systems	NQ	NVLS	386	30	1.06
Pitney Bowes	N	PBI	339	46	2.05
Pulte Homes	N	PHM	12	78	7.67
SBC Communications	N	SBC	371	24	1.52
St. Paul Travelers	N	STA	264	38	1.53
Teradyne	N	TER	412	15	0.84
UnitedHealth Group	N	UNH	5	91	3.94
Wells Fargo	N	WFC	159	59	4.09

Source: BusinessWeek (April 4, 2005).

Elements, Variables, and Observations

Elements are the entities on which data are collected. For the data set in Table 1.1, each individual company's stock is an element; the element names appear in the first column. With 25 stocks, the data set contains 25 elements.

A **variable** is a characteristic of interest for the elements. The data set in Table 1.1 includes the following five variables:

- *Exchange:* Where the stock is traded—N (New York Stock Exchange) and NQ (Nasdaq National Market)
- *Ticker Symbol:* The abbreviation used to identify the stock on the exchange listing
- *BusinessWeek Rank:* A number from 1 to 500 that is a measure of company strength
- *Share Price ($):* The closing price (February 28, 2005)
- *Earnings per Share ($):* The earnings per share for the most recent 12 months

Measurements collected on each variable for every element in a study provide the data. The set of measurements obtained for a particular element is called an **observation**. Referring to Table 1.1, we see that the set of measurements for the first observation (Abbott Laboratories) is N, ABT, 90, 46, and 2.02. The set of measurements for the second observation (Altria Group) is N, MO, 148, 66, and 4.57, and so on. A data set with 25 elements contains 25 observations.

Scales of Measurement

Data collection requires one of the following scales of measurement: nominal, ordinal, interval, or ratio. The scale of measurement determines the amount of information contained in the data and indicates the most appropriate data summarization and statistical analyses.

When the data for a variable consist of labels or names used to identify an attribute of the element, the scale of measurement is considered a **nominal scale**. For example, referring to the data in Table 1.1, we see that the scale of measurement for the exchange variable is nominal because N and NQ are labels used to identify where the company's stock is traded. In cases where the scale of measurement is nominal, a numeric code as well as nonnumeric labels may be used. For example, to facilitate data collection and to prepare the data for entry into a computer database, we might use a numeric code by letting 1 denote the New York Stock Exchange and 2 denote the Nasdaq National Market. In this case the numeric values 1 and 2 provide the labels used to identify where the stock is traded. The scale of measurement is nominal even though the data appear as numeric values.

The scale of measurement for a variable is called an **ordinal scale** if the data exhibit the properties of nominal data and the order or rank of the data is meaningful. For example, Eastside Automotive sends customers a questionnaire designed to obtain data on the quality of its automotive repair service. Each customer provides a repair service rating of excellent, good, or poor. Because the data obtained are the labels—excellent, good, or poor—the data have the properties of nominal data. In addition, the data can be ranked, or ordered, with respect to the service quality. Data recorded as excellent indicate the best service, followed by good and then poor. Thus, the scale of measurement is ordinal. Note that the ordinal data can also be recorded using a numeric code. For example, the *BusinessWeek* rank for the data in Table 1.1 is ordinal data. It provides a rank from 1 to 500 based on *BusinessWeek*'s assessment of the company's strength.

The scale of measurement for a variable becomes an **interval scale** if the data show the properties of ordinal data and the interval between values is expressed in terms of a fixed unit of measure. Interval data are always numeric. Scholastic Aptitude Test (SAT) scores are an example of interval-scaled data. For example, three students with SAT scores of 1120, 1050, and 970 can be ranked or ordered in terms of best performance to poorest performance. In addition, the differences between the scores are meaningful. For instance, student 1 scored $1120 - 1050 = 70$ points more than student 2, while student 2 scored $1050 - 970 = 80$ points more than student 3.

The scale of measurement for a variable is a **ratio scale** if the data have all the properties of interval data and the ratio of two values is meaningful. Variables such as distance, height, weight, and time use the ratio scale of measurement. This scale requires that a zero value be included to indicate that nothing exists for the variable at the zero point. For example, consider the cost of an automobile. A zero value for the cost would indicate that the automobile has no cost and is free. In addition, if we compare the cost of $30,000 for one automobile to the cost of $15,000 for a second automobile, the ratio property shows that the first automobile is $30,000/$15,000 = 2 times, or twice, the cost of the second automobile.

Qualitative and Quantitative Data

Qualitative data are often referred to as categorical data.

Data can also be classified as either qualitative or quantitative. **Qualitative data** include labels or names used to identify an attribute of each element. Qualitative data use either the nominal or ordinal scale of measurement and may be nonnumeric or numeric. **Quantitative data** require numeric values that indicate how much or how many. Quantitative data are obtained using either the interval or ratio scale of measurement.

The statistical method appropriate for summarizing data depends upon whether the data are qualitative or quantitative.

A **qualitative variable** is a variable with qualitative data, and a **quantitative variable** is a variable with quantitative data. The statistical analysis appropriate for a particular variable depends upon whether the variable is qualitative or quantitative. If the variable is qualitative, the statistical analysis is rather limited. We can summarize qualitative data by counting the number of observations in each qualitative category or by computing the proportion of the observations in each qualitative category. However, even when the qualitative data use a numeric code, arithmetic operations such as addition, subtraction, multiplication, and division do not provide meaningful results. Section 2.1 discusses ways for summarizing qualitative data.

On the other hand, arithmetic operations often provide meaningful results for a quantitative variable. For example, for a quantitative variable, the data may be added and then divided by the number of observations to compute the average value. This average is usually meaningful and easily interpreted. In general, more alternatives for statistical analysis are possible when the data are quantitative. Section 2.2 and Chapter 3 provide ways of summarizing quantitative data.

Cross-Sectional and Time Series Data

For purposes of statistical analysis, distinguishing between cross-sectional data and time series data is important. **Cross-sectional data** are data collected at the same or approximately the same point in time. The data in Table 1.1 are cross-sectional because they describe the five variables for the 25 S&P 500 companies at the same point in time. **Time series data** are data collected over several time periods. For example, Figure 1.1 provides a graph of the U.S. city average price per gallon for unleaded regular gasoline. The graph shows gasoline prices in a fairly stable band between $1.80 and $2.00 from May, 2004, through

FIGURE 1.1   U.S. CITY AVERAGE PRICE PER GALLON FOR CONVENTIONAL REGULAR GASOLINE

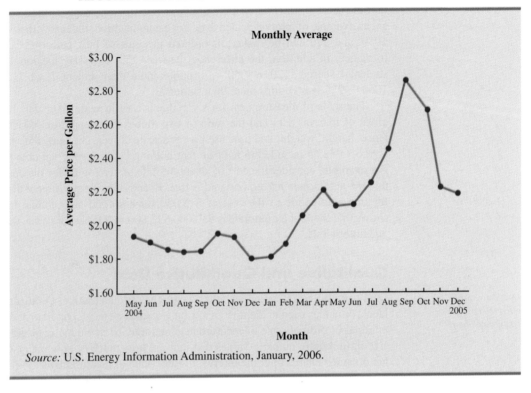

Source: U.S. Energy Information Administration, January, 2006.

February, 2005. After that they become very volatile. They rise significantly culminating with a sharp spike in September, 2005. After that, they ease sharply. Most of the statistical methods presented in this text apply to cross-sectional rather than time series data.

NOTES AND COMMENTS

1. An observation is the set of measurements obtained for each element in a data set. Hence, the number of observations is always the same as the number of elements. The number of measurements obtained for each element equals the number of variables. Hence, the total number of data items can be determined by multiplying the number of observations by the number of variables.

2. Quantitative data may be discrete or continuous. Quantitative data that measure how many (e.g., number of calls received in 5 minutes) are discrete. Quantitative data that measure how much (e.g., weight or time) are continuous because no separation occurs between the possible data values.

 1.3   # Data Sources

Data can be obtained from existing sources or from surveys and experimental studies designed to collect new data.

Existing Sources

In some cases, data needed for a particular application already exist. Companies maintain a variety of databases about their employees, customers, and business operations. Data on employee salaries, ages, and years of experience can usually be obtained from internal person-

TABLE 1.2   EXAMPLES OF DATA AVAILABLE FROM INTERNAL COMPANY RECORDS

Source	Some of the Data Typically Available
Employee records	Name, address, social security number, salary, number of vacation days, number of sick days, and bonus
Production records	Part or product number, quantity produced, direct labor cost, and materials cost
Inventory records	Part or product number, number of units on hand, reorder level, economic order quantity, and discount schedule
Sales records	Product number, sales volume, sales volume by region, and sales volume by customer type
Credit records	Customer name, address, phone number, credit limit, and accounts receivable balance
Customer profile	Age, gender, income level, household size, address, and preferences

nel records. Other internal records contain data on sales, advertising expenditures, distribution costs, inventory levels, and production quantities. Most companies also maintain detailed data about their customers. Table 1.2 shows some of the data commonly available from internal company records.

Organizations that specialize in collecting and maintaining data make available substantial amounts of business and economic data. Companies access these external data sources through leasing arrangements or by purchase. Dun & Bradstreet, Bloomberg, and Dow Jones & Company are three firms that provide extensive business database services to clients. ACNielsen and Information Resources, Inc., built successful businesses collecting and processing data that they sell to advertisers and product manufacturers.

Data are also available from a variety of industry associations and special interest organizations. The Travel Industry Association of America maintains travel-related information such as the number of tourists and travel expenditures by states. Such data would be of interest to firms and individuals in the travel industry. The Graduate Management Admission Council maintains data on test scores, student characteristics, and graduate management education programs. Most of the data from these types of sources are available to qualified users at a modest cost.

The Internet continues to grow as an important source of data and statistical information. Almost all companies maintain Web sites that provide general information about the company as well as data on sales, number of employees, number of products, product prices, and product specifications. In addition, a number of companies now specialize in making information available over the Internet. As a result, one can obtain access to stock quotes, meal prices at restaurants, salary data, and an almost infinite variety of information.

Government agencies are another important source of existing data. For instance, the U.S. Department of Labor maintains considerable data on employment rates, wage rates, size of the labor force, and union membership. Table 1.3 lists selected governmental agencies and some of the data they provide. Most government agencies that collect and process data also make the results available through a Web site. For instance, the U.S. Census Bureau has a wealth of data at its Web site, www.census.gov. Figure 1.2 shows the homepage for the U.S. Census Bureau.

Statistical Studies

Sometimes the data needed for a particular application are not available through existing sources. In such cases, the data can often be obtained by conducting a statistical study. Statistical studies can be classified as either *experimental* or *observational*.

TABLE 1.3   EXAMPLES OF DATA AVAILABLE FROM SELECTED GOVERNMENT AGENCIES

Government Agency	Some of the Data Available
Census Bureau *http://www.census.gov*	Population data, number of households, and household income
Federal Reserve Board *http://www.federalreserve.gov*	Data on the money supply, installment credit, exchange rates, and discount rates
Office of Management and Budget *http://www.whitehouse.gov/omb*	Data on revenue, expenditures, and debt of the federal government
Department of Commerce *http://www.doc.gov*	Data on business activity, value of shipments by industry, level of profits by industry, and growing and declining industries
Bureau of Labor Statistics *http://www.bls.gov*	Consumer spending, hourly earnings, unemployment rate, safety records, and international statistics

FIGURE 1.2   U.S. CENSUS BUREAU HOMEPAGE

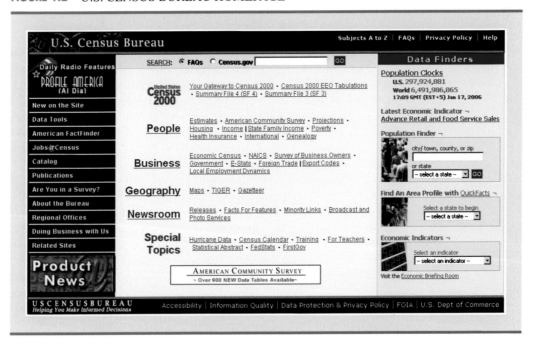

In an experimental study, a variable of interest is first identified. Then one or more other variables are identified and controlled so that data can be obtained about how they influence the variable of interest. For example, a pharmaceutical firm might be interested in conducting an experiment to learn about how a new drug affects blood pressure. Blood pressure is the variable of interest in the study. The dosage level of the new drug is another variable that is hoped to have a causal effect on blood pressure. To obtain data about the effect of the new drug, researchers select a sample of individuals. The dosage level of the new drug is controlled, as different groups of individuals are given different dosage levels. Before and after data on blood pressure are collected for each group. Statistical analysis of the experimental data can help determine how the new drug affects blood pressure.

Nonexperimental, or observational, statistical studies make no attempt to control the variables of interest. A survey is perhaps the most common type of observational study. For instance, in a personal interview survey, research questions are first identified. Then a questionnaire is designed and administered to a sample of individuals. Some restaurants use observational studies to obtain data about their customers' opinions of the quality of food, service, atmosphere, and so on. A questionnaire used by the Lobster Pot Restaurant in Redington Shores, Florida, is shown in Figure 1.3. Note that the customers completing the questionnaire are asked to provide ratings for five variables: food quality, friendliness of service, promptness of service, cleanliness, and management. The response categories of excellent,

FIGURE 1.3   CUSTOMER OPINION QUESTIONNAIRE USED BY THE LOBSTER POT RESTAURANT, REDINGTON SHORES, FLORIDA good, satisfactory, and unsatisfactory provide ordinal data that enable Lobster Pot's managers to assess the quality of the restaurant's operation.

Managers wanting to use data and statistical analyses as aids to decision making must be aware of the time and cost required to obtain the data. The use of existing data sources is desirable when data must be obtained in a relatively short period of time. If important data are not readily available from an existing source, the additional time and cost involved in obtaining the data must be taken into account. In all cases, the decision maker should consider the contribution of the statistical analysis to the decision-making process. The cost of data acquisition and the subsequent statistical analysis should not exceed the savings generated by using the information to make a better decision.

Data Acquisition Errors

Managers should always be aware of the possibility of data errors in statistical studies. Using erroneous data can be worse than not using any data at all. An error in data acquisition occurs whenever the data value obtained is not equal to the true or actual value that would be obtained with a correct procedure. Such errors can occur in a number of ways. For example, an interviewer might make a recording error, such as a transposition in writing the age of a 24-year-old person as 42, or the person answering an interview question might misinterpret the question and provide an incorrect response.

Experienced data analysts take great care in collecting and recording data to ensure that errors are not made. Special procedures can be used to check for internal consistency of the data. For instance, such procedures would indicate that the analyst should review the accuracy of data for a respondent shown to be 22 years of age but reporting 20 years of work experience. Data analysts also review data with unusually large and small values, called outliers, which are candidates for possible data errors. In Chapter 3 we present some of the methods statisticians use to identify outliers.

Errors often occur during data acquisition. Blindly using any data that happen to be available or using data that were acquired with little care can result in misleading information and bad decisions. Thus, taking steps to acquire accurate data can help ensure reliable and valuable decision-making information.

1.4 Descriptive Statistics

Most of the statistical information in newspapers, magazines, company reports, and other publications consists of data that are summarized and presented in a form that is easy for the reader to understand. Such summaries of data, which may be tabular, graphical, or numerical, are referred to as **descriptive statistics**.

Refer again to the data set in Table 1.1 showing data on 25 S&P 500 companies. Methods of descriptive statistics can be used to provide summaries of the information in this data set. For example, a tabular summary of the data for the qualitative variable Exchange is shown in Table 1.4. A graphical summary of the same data, called a bar graph, is shown in Figure 1.4. These types of tabular and graphical summaries generally make the data easier to interpret. Referring to Table 1.4 and Figure 1.4, we can see easily that the majority of the stocks in the data set are traded on the New York Stock Exchange. On a percentage basis, 80% are traded on the New York Stock Exchange and 20% are traded on the Nasdaq National Market.

TABLE 1.4   FREQUENCIES AND PERCENT FREQUENCIES FOR THE EXCHANGE VARIABLE

Exchange	Frequency	Percent Frequency
New York Stock Exchange	20	80
Nasdaq National Market	5	20
Totals	25	100

A graphical summary of the data for the quantitative variable Share Price for the S&P stocks, called a histogram, is provided in Figure 1.5. The histogram makes it easy to see that the share prices range from $0 to $100, with the highest concentrations between $20 and $60.

In addition to tabular and graphical displays, numerical descriptive statistics are used to summarize data. The most common numerical descriptive statistic is the average, or mean. Using the data on the variable Earnings per Share for the S&P stocks in Table 1.1, we can compute the average by adding the earnings per share for all 25 stocks and dividing the sum by 25. Doing so provides an average earnings per share of $2.49. This average demonstrates a measure of the central tendency, or central location, of the data for that variable.

In a number of fields, interest continues to grow in statistical methods that can be used for developing and presenting descriptive statistics. Chapters 2 and 3 devote attention to the tabular, graphical, and numerical methods of descriptive statistics.

FIGURE 1.4   BAR GRAPH FOR THE EXCHANGE VARIABLE

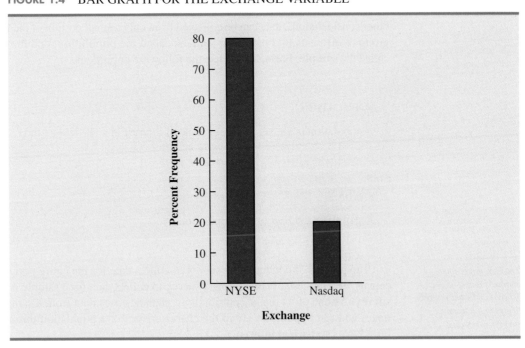

FIGURE 1.5   HISTOGRAM OF SHARE PRICE FOR 25 S&P STOCKS

Statistical Inference

Many situations require information about a large group of elements (individuals, companies, voters, households, products, customers, and so on). But, because of time, cost, and other considerations, data can be collected from only a small portion of the group. The larger group of elements in a particular study is called the **population**, and the smaller group is called the **sample**. Formally, we use the following definitions.

> **POPULATION**
>
> A population is the set of all elements of interest in a particular study.

> **SAMPLE**
>
> A sample is a subset of the population.

The U.S. government conducts a census every 10 years. Market research firms conduct sample surveys every day.

The process of conducting a survey to collect data for the entire population is called a **census**. The process of conducting a survey to collect data for a sample is called a **sample survey**. As one of its major contributions, statistics uses data from a sample to make estimates and test hypotheses about the characteristics of a population through a process referred to as **statistical inference**.

As an example of statistical inference, let us consider the study conducted by Norris Electronics. Norris manufactures a high-intensity lightbulb used in a variety of electrical

TABLE 1.5   HOURS UNTIL BURNOUT FOR A SAMPLE OF 200 LIGHTBULBS FOR THE NORRIS ELECTRONICS EXAMPLE

Norris

107	73	68	97	76	79	94	59	98	57
54	65	71	70	84	88	62	61	79	98
66	62	79	86	68	74	61	82	65	98
62	116	65	88	64	79	78	79	77	86
74	85	73	80	68	78	89	72	58	69
92	78	88	77	103	88	63	68	88	81
75	90	62	89	71	71	74	70	74	70
65	81	75	62	94	71	85	84	83	63
81	62	79	83	93	61	65	62	92	65
83	70	70	81	77	72	84	67	59	58
78	66	66	94	77	63	66	75	68	76
90	78	71	101	78	43	59	67	61	71
96	75	64	76	72	77	74	65	82	86
66	86	96	89	81	71	85	99	59	92
68	72	77	60	87	84	75	77	51	45
85	67	87	80	84	93	69	76	89	75
83	68	72	67	92	89	82	96	77	102
74	91	76	83	66	68	61	73	72	76
73	77	79	94	63	59	62	71	81	65
73	63	63	89	82	64	85	92	64	73

products. In an attempt to increase the useful life of the lightbulb, the product design group developed a new lightbulb filament. In this case, the population is defined as all lightbulbs that could be produced with the new filament. To evaluate the advantages of the new filament, 200 bulbs with the new filament were manufactured and tested. Data collected from this sample showed the number of hours each lightbulb operated before filament burnout. See Table 1.5.

Suppose Norris wants to use the sample data to make an inference about the average hours of useful life for the population of all lightbulbs that could be produced with the new filament. Adding the 200 values in Table 1.5 and dividing the total by 200 provides the sample average lifetime for the lightbulbs: 76 hours. We can use this sample result to estimate that the average lifetime for the lightbulbs in the population is 76 hours. Figure 1.6 provides a graphical summary of the statistical inference process for Norris Electronics.

Whenever statisticians use a sample to estimate a population characteristic of interest, they usually provide a statement of the quality, or precision, associated with the estimate. For the Norris example, the statistician might state that the point estimate of the average lifetime for the population of new lightbulbs is 76 hours with a margin of error of ± 4 hours. Thus, an interval estimate of the average lifetime for all lightbulbs produced with the new filament is 72 hours to 80 hours. The statistician can also state how confident he or she is that the interval from 72 hours to 80 hours contains the population average.

1.6 Statistical Analysis Using Microsoft Excel

Because statistical analysis typically involves working with large amounts of data, computer software is frequently used to conduct the analysis. Often the data to be analyzed reside in a spreadsheet. Given the data management, data analysis, and presentation capabilities of modern spreadsheet packages, it is now possible to conduct statistical analyses using them. In this book we show how statistical analysis can be performed using Microsoft Excel. In

FIGURE 1.6   THE PROCESS OF STATISTICAL INFERENCE FOR THE NORRIS
ELECTRONICS EXAMPLE

selected cases where Excel does not contain statistical analysis functions or data analysis tools that can be used to perform a statistical procedure discussed in the text, we have included chapter appendixes that show how to use SWStat+, an add-in for Excel that provides an extended range of statistical and graphical options. The appendix to Chapter 1 provides an introduction to SWStat+.

We want to emphasize that this book is about statistics; it is not a book about spreadsheets. Thus our focus is on showing the appropriate statistical procedures for collecting, analyzing, presenting, and interpreting data. Because Excel is widely available in business organizations, you can expect to put the knowledge gained here to use in the setting where you currently, or soon will, work. If, in the process of studying this material, you become more proficient in Excel, so much the better.

We stress statistical applications, therefore we begin most sections with an application scenario in which a statistical procedure is useful. After showing what the statistical procedure is and how it is used, we turn to showing how to implement the procedure using Excel. Thus, you should gain an understanding of what the procedure is, the situations in which it is useful, and how to implement it using the capabilities of Excel.

Data Sets and Excel Worksheets

Data sets are organized in Excel worksheets in much the same way as the data set for the 25 S&P 500 companies that appears in Table 1.1. Figure 1.7 shows an Excel worksheet for that data set. Note that row 1 and column A contain labels. Cells B1:F1 contain the variable names and cells A2:A26 contain the observation names. Cells B2:F26 contain the data that were collected. A purple screen highlights the data. The data are the focus of the statistical analysis. Except for the headings in row 1, each row in the worksheet corresponds to an observation and, except for the labels in column A, each column corresponds to a variable. For instance, row 2 of the worksheet contains the data for the first observation, Abbott

FIGURE 1.7   EXCEL WORKSHEET FOR THE S&P STOCK DATA SET

	A	B	C	D	E	F	G
1	Company	Exchange	Ticker	*Business Week* Rank	Share Price ($)	Earnings per Share ($)	
2	Abbott Laboratories	N	ABT	90	46	2.02	
3	Altria Group	N	MO	148	66	4.57	
4	Apollo Group	NQ	APOL	174	74	0.90	
5	Bank of New York	N	BK	305	30	1.85	
6	Bristol-Myers Squibb	N	BMY	346	26	1.21	
7	Cincinnati Financial	NQ	CINF	161	45	2.73	
8	Comcast	NQ	CMCSA	296	32	0.43	
9	Deere	N	DE	36	71	5.77	
10	eBay	NQ	EBAY	19	43	0.57	
11	Federated Dept. Stores	N	FD	353	56	3.86	
12	Hasbro	N	HAS	373	21	0.96	
13	IBM	N	IBM	216	93	4.94	
14	International Paper	N	IP	370	37	0.98	
15	Knight-Ridder	N	KRI	397	66	4.13	
16	Manor Care	N	HCR	285	34	1.90	
17	Medtronic	N	MDT	53	52	1.79	
18	National Semiconductor	N	NSM	155	20	1.03	
19	Novellus Systems	NQ	NVLS	386	30	1.06	
20	Pitney Bowes	N	PBI	339	46	2.05	
21	Pulte Homes	N	PHM	12	78	7.67	
22	SBC Communications	N	SBC	371	24	1.52	
23	St. Paul Travelers	N	STA	264	38	1.53	
24	Teradyne	N	TER	412	15	0.84	
25	UnitedHealth Group	N	UNH	5	91	3.94	
26	Wells Fargo	N	WFC	159	59	4.09	
27							

Laboratories, row 3 contains the data for the second observation, Altria Group, and so on. Thus, the names in column A provide a convenient way to refer to each of the 25 observations in the study. Note that column 2 of the worksheet contains the data for the variable Exchange, column 3 contains the data for the variable Ticker, and so on.

Suppose now that we want to use Excel to analyze the Norris Electronics data shown in Table 1.5. The data in Table 1.5 are organized into 10 columns with 20 data values in each column so that it would fit nicely on a single page of the text. Even though the table has several columns, it shows data for only one variable (hours until burnout). In statistical worksheets, it is customary to put all the data for each variable in a single column. Refer to the Excel worksheet shown in Figure 1.8. To make it easier to identify each observation in the data set, we entered the heading Observation into cell A1 and the numbers 1–200 into cells A2:A201. The heading Hours Until Burnout has been entered into cell B1, and the data for the 200 observations have been entered into cells B2:B201. Displaying a worksheet with this many rows on a single page of a textbook is not practical. In such cases we will hide selected rows to conserve space. In the Excel worksheet for the

FIGURE 1.8   EXCEL WORKSHEET FOR THE NORRIS ELECTRONICS DATA SET

	A	B	C
1	Observation	Hours until Burnout	
2	1	107	
3	2	54	
4	3	66	
5	4	62	
6	5	74	
196	195	45	
197	196	75	
198	197	102	
199	198	76	
200	199	65	
201	200	73	
202			

Note: Rows 7–195 are hidden.

Norris Electronics problem we have hidden rows 7 through 195 (observations 6 through 194) to conserve space.*

Using Excel for Statistical Analysis

In this text, we are careful to separate the discussion of a statistical procedure from the discussion of using Excel to implement the procedure. The material that discusses the use of Excel will usually be set apart in sections with headings such as Using Excel's COUNTIF Function to Construct a Frequency Distribution, Using Excel's Chart Wizard to Construct Bar Graphs and Pie Charts, and so on. In using Excel for statistical analysis, three tasks may be needed: Enter Data; Enter Functions and Formulas; and Apply Tools.

Enter Data: Select cell locations for the data and enter the data along with appropriate descriptive labels.

Enter Functions and Formulas: Select cell locations, enter Excel functions and formulas, and provide descriptive material to identify the results.

Apply Tools: Use Excel's tools for data management, data analysis, and presentation.

Our approach will be to describe how these tasks are performed each time we use Excel to implement a statistical procedure. It will always be necessary to enter data. But, depending upon the complexity of the statistical analysis, only one of the last two tasks may be needed.

To illustrate how the discussion of using Excel will appear throughout the book, we will show how to use Excel's AVERAGE function to compute the average lifetime for the 200 burnout times in Table 1.5. Refer to Figure 1.9 as we describe the tasks involved. The worksheet shown in the foreground of Figure 1.9 displays the data for the problem and shows the results of the analysis. It is called a **value worksheet**. The worksheet shown in the background displays the Excel formula used to compute the average lifetime and is

---

*To hide rows 7 through 195 in the Excel worksheet, first select rows 7 through 195. Then, right-click and choose the Hide option. To redisplay rows 7 through 195, just select rows 6 and 196, right-click, and select the Unhide option.

FIGURE 1.9   COMPUTING THE AVERAGE LIFETIME OF LIGHTBULBS FOR NORRIS ELECTRONICS
USING EXCEL'S AVERAGE FUNCTION

	A	B	C	D	E	F
1	Observation	Hours Until Burnout				
2	1	107		Average Lifetime	=AVERAGE(B2:B201)	
3	2	54				
4	3	66				
5	4	62				
6	5	74				
196	195	45				
197	196	75				
198	197	102				
199	198	76				
200	199	65				
201	200	73				
202						

	A	B	C	D	E	F
1	Observation	Hours Until Burnout				
2	1	107		Average Lifetime	76	
3	2	54				
4	3	66				
5	4	62				
6	5	74				
196	195	45				
197	196	75				
198	197	102				
199	198	76				
200	199	65				
201	200	73				
202						

Note: Rows 7–195 are hidden.

called the **formula worksheet.** A purple screen is used to highlight the data in both worksheets. In addition, a green screen is used to highlight functions and formulas in the formula worksheet and the corresponding results in the value worksheet.

Enter Data: The labels Observation and Hours Until Burnout are entered into cells A1:B1. The numbers 1–200 are entered into cells A2:A201 to identify each of the observations, and the data showing the hours until burnout for each observation are entered into cells B2:B201 of the worksheet.

Enter Functions and Formulas: Excel's AVERAGE function can be used to compute the average lifetime for the 200 lightbulbs. We can compute the average lifetime by entering the following formula into cell E2:

$$=AVERAGE(B2:B201)$$

To identify the result, the label Average Lifetime is entered into cell D2. Note that for this problem, the Apply Tools task was not required. The value worksheet shows that the value computed using the AVERAGE function is 76 hours.

Summary

Statistics is the art and science of collecting, analyzing, presenting, and interpreting data. Nearly every college student majoring in business or economics is required to take a course in statistics. We began the chapter by describing typical statistical applications for business and economics.

Data consist of the facts and figures that are collected and analyzed. Four scales of measurement used to obtain data on a particular variable include nominal, ordinal, interval, and ratio. The scale of measurement for a variable is nominal when the data are labels or names used to identify an attribute of an element. The scale is ordinal if the data demonstrate the properties of nominal data and the order or rank of the data is meaningful. The scale is interval if the data demonstrate the properties of ordinal data and the interval between values is expressed in terms of a fixed unit of measure. Finally, the scale of measurement is ratio if the data show all the properties of interval data and the ratio of two values is meaningful.

For purposes of statistical analysis, data can be classified as qualitative or quantitative. Qualitative data use labels or names to identify an attribute of each element. Qualitative data use either the nominal or ordinal scale of measurement and may be nonnumeric or numeric. Quantitative data are numeric values that indicate how much or how many. Quantitative data use either the interval or ratio scale of measurement. Ordinary arithmetic operations are meaningful only if the data are quantitative. Therefore, statistical computations used for quantitative data are not always appropriate for qualitative data.

In Sections 1.4 and 1.5 we introduced the topics of descriptive statistics and statistical inference. Descriptive statistics are the tabular, graphical, and numerical methods used to summarize data. The process of statistical inference uses data obtained from a sample to make estimates or test hypotheses about the characteristics of a population.

In the last section of the chapter we provided an introduction to the use of Excel for statistical analysis. We showed that data sets are organized in Excel worksheets in much the same way as the data set for the 25 S&P 500 companies presented in Table 1.1. That is, the columns in the worksheet correspond to variables in the data set and the rows correspond to observations. We also introduced the approach that will be used throughout the text to describe the use of Excel for statistical analysis. Three tasks may be needed: Enter Data; Enter Functions and Formulas; and Apply Tools. As an illustration, we showed how Excel's AVERAGE function could be used to compute the average lifetime for the 200 observations in the Norris Electronics data set.

Glossary

Statistics The art and science of collecting, analyzing, presenting, and interpreting data.

Data The facts and figures collected, analyzed, and summarized for presentation and interpretation.

Data set All the data collected in a particular study.

Elements The entities on which data are collected.

Variable A characteristic of interest for the elements.

Observation The set of measurements obtained for a particular element.

Nominal scale The scale of measurement for a variable when the data are labels or names used to identify an attribute of an element. Nominal data may be nonnumeric or numeric.

Ordinal scale The scale of measurement for a variable if the data exhibit the properties of nominal data and the order or rank of the data is meaningful. Ordinal data may be nonnumeric or numeric.

Interval scale The scale of measurement for a variable if the data demonstrate the properties of ordinal data and the interval between values is expressed in terms of a fixed unit of measure. Interval data are always numeric.

Ratio scale The scale of measurement for a variable if the data demonstrate all the properties of interval data and the ratio of two values is meaningful. Ratio data are always numeric.

Qualitative data Labels or names used to identify an attribute of each element. Qualitative data use either the nominal or ordinal scale of measurement and may be nonnumeric or numeric.

Quantitative data Numeric values that indicate how much or how many of something. Quantitative data are obtained using either the interval or ratio scale of measurement.
Qualitative variable A variable with qualitative data.
Quantitative variable A variable with quantitative data.
Cross-sectional data Data collected at the same or approximately the same point in time.
Time series data Data collected over several time periods.
Descriptive statistics Tabular, graphical, and numerical summaries of data.
Population The set of all elements of interest in a particular study.
Sample A subset of the population.
Census A survey to collect data on the entire population.
Sample survey A survey to collect data on a sample.
Statistical inference The process of using data obtained from a sample to make estimates or test hypotheses about the characteristics of a population.
Value worksheet A worksheet that displays the data for the problem and shows the results of the analysis.
Formula worksheet A worksheet that displays the Excel formulas used to create the results shown in the value worksheet.

Supplementary Exercises

1. Discuss the differences between statistics as numerical facts and statistics as a discipline or field of study.

2. *Condé Nast Traveler* magazine conducts an annual survey of subscribers in order to determine the best places to stay throughout the world. Table 1.6 shows a sample of nine European hotels (*Condé Nast Traveler,* January 2000). The price of a standard double room during the hotel's high season ranges from $ (lowest price) to $$$$ (highest price). The overall score includes subscribers' evaluations of each hotel's rooms, service, restaurants, location/atmosphere, and public areas; a higher overall score corresponds to a higher level of satisfaction.
   a. How many elements are in this data set?
   b. How many variables are in this data set?
   c. Which variables are qualitative and which variables are quantitative?
   d. What type of measurement scale is used for each of the variables?

3. Refer to Table 1.6.
   a. What is the average number of rooms for the nine hotels?
   b. Compute the average overall score.

TABLE 1.6   RATINGS FOR NINE PLACES TO STAY IN EUROPE

Hotel

Name of Property	Country	Room Rate	Number of Rooms	Overall Score
Graveteye Manor	England	$$	18	83.6
Villa d'Este	Italy	$$$$	166	86.3
Hotel Prem	Germany	$	54	77.8
Hotel d'Europe	France	$$	47	76.8
Palace Luzern	Switzerland	$$	326	80.9
Royal Crescent Hotel	England	$$$	45	73.7
Hotel Sacher	Austria	$$$	120	85.5
Duc de Bourgogne	Belgium	$	10	76.9
Villa Gallici	France	$$	22	90.6

Source: Condé Nast Traveler, January 2000.

c. What is the percentage of hotels located in England?

d. What is the percentage of hotels with a room rate of $$?

4. All-in-one sound systems, called minisystems, typically include an AM/FM tuner, a dual-cassette tape deck, and a CD changer in a book-sized box with two separate speakers. The data in Table 1.7 show the retail price, sound quality, CD capacity, FM tuning sensitivity and selectivity, and the number of tape decks for a sample of 10 minisystems (*Consumer Reports Buying Guide 2002*).

a. How many elements does this data set contain?

b. What is the population?

c. Compute the average price for the sample.

d. Using the results in part (c), estimate the average price for the population.

5. Consider the data set for the sample of 10 minisystems in Table 1.7.

a. How many variables are in the data set?

b. Which of the variables are quantitative and which are qualitative?

c. What is the average CD capacity for the sample?

d. What percentage of the minisystems provides an FM tuning rating of very good or excellent?

e. What percentage of the minisystems includes two tape decks?

6. Columbia House provides CDs to its mail-order club members. A Columbia House Music Survey asked new club members to complete an 11-question survey. Some of the questions asked were:

a. How many CDs have you bought in the last 12 months?

b. Are you currently a member of a national mail-order book club? (Yes or No)

c. What is your age?

d. Including yourself, how many people (adults and children) are in your household?

e. What kind of music are you interested in buying? Fifteen categories were listed, including hard rock, soft rock, adult contemporary, heavy metal, rap, and country.

Comment on whether each question provides qualitative or quantitative data.

7. A *Barron's* subscriber survey (September 15, 2000) asked subscribers to indicate their employment status. The data were recorded with 1 denoting employed full-time, 2 denoting employed part-time, 3 denoting retired, and 4 denoting unemployed (homemaker, student, etc.).

a. The variable is employment status. Is it a qualitative or quantitative variable?

b. What type of measurement scale is being used for this variable?

TABLE 1.7   A SAMPLE OF 10 MINISYSTEMS

CD file

Minisystems

Brand and Model	Price ($)	Sound Quality	CD Capacity	FM Tuning	Tape Decks
Aiwa NSX-AJ800	250	Good	3	Fair	2
JVC FS-SD1000	500	Good	1	Very Good	0
JVC MX-G50	200	Very Good	3	Excellent	2
Panasonic SC-PM11	170	Fair	5	Very Good	1
RCA RS 1283	170	Good	3	Poor	0
Sharp CD-BA2600	150	Good	3	Good	2
Sony CHC-CL1	300	Very Good	3	Very Good	1
Sony MHC-NX1	500	Good	5	Excellent	2
Yamaha GX-505	400	Very Good	3	Excellent	1
Yamaha MCR-E100	500	Very Good	1	Excellent	0

8. The Gallup organization conducted a telephone survey with a randomly selected national sample of 1005 adults, 18 years and older. The survey asked the respondents, "How would you describe your own physical health at this time?" (http://www.gallup.com, February 7, 2002). Response categories were Excellent, Good, Only Fair, Poor, and No Opinion.
   a. What was the sample size for this survey?
   b. Are the data qualitative or quantitative?
   c. Would it make more sense to use averages or percentages as a summary of the data for this question?
   d. Of the respondents, 29% said their personal health was excellent. How many individuals provided this response?

9. The Commerce Department reported receiving the following applications for the Malcolm Baldrige National Quality Award: 23 from large manufacturing firms, 18 from large service firms, and 30 from small businesses.
   a. Is type of business a qualitative or quantitative variable?
   b. What percentage of the applications came from small businesses?

10. *The Wall Street Journal* subscriber survey (October 13, 2003) asked 46 questions about subscriber characteristics and interests. State whether each of the following questions provided qualitative or quantitative data and indicate the measurement scale appropriate for each.
    a. What is your age?
    b. Are you male or female?
    c. When did you first start reading the *WSJ*? High school, college, early career, mid-career, late career, or retirement?
    d. How long have you been in your present job or position?
    e. What type of vehicle are you considering for your next purchase? Nine response categories include sedan, sports car, SUV, minivan, and so on.

11. State whether each of the following variables is qualitative or quantitative and indicate its measurement scale.
    a. Annual sales
    b. Soft drink size (small, medium, large)
    c. Employee classification (GS1 through GS18)
    d. Earnings per share
    e. Method of payment (cash, check, credit card)

12. The Hawaii Visitors Bureau collects data on visitors to Hawaii. The following questions were among 16 asked in a questionnaire handed out to passengers during incoming airline flights in June 2003.
    * This trip to Hawaii is my: 1st, 2nd, 3rd, 4th, etc.
    * The primary reason for this trip is: (10 categories including vacation, convention, honeymoon)
    * Where I plan to stay: (11 categories including hotel, apartment, relatives, camping)
    * Total days in Hawaii
    a. What is the population being studied?
    b. Is the use of a questionnaire a good way to reach the population of passengers on incoming airline flights?
    c. Comment on each of the four questions in terms of whether it will provide qualitative or quantitative data.

13. Figure 1.10 provides a bar graph summarizing the earnings and estimated earnings for Volkswagen for the years 1997 to 2002 (*BusinessWeek,* July 23, 2001).
    a. Are the data qualitative or quantitative?
    b. Are the data time series or cross-sectional?

FIGURE 1.10   EARNINGS FOR VOLKSWAGEN

c.   What is the variable of interest?

d.   Comment on the trend in Volkswagen's earnings over time. Would you expect to see an increase or decrease in 2003?

14.   The Recording Industry of America keeps track of recorded music sales by type of music, format, and age group. The following data show the percentage of music sales by type (*The New York Times 2002 Almanac*).

Music

Type	1996	1997	1998	1999	2000
Rock	32.6	32.5	25.7	25.2	24.8
Country	12.1	11.2	12.8	10.8	10.7
R&B	12.1	11.2	12.8	10.5	9.7
Pop	9.3	9.4	10.0	10.3	11.0
Rap	8.9	10.1	9.7	10.8	12.9
Gospel	4.3	4.5	6.3	5.1	4.8
Classical	3.4	2.8	3.3	3.5	2.7
Jazz	3.3	2.8	1.9	3.0	2.9
Other	14.0	15.5	17.5	20.8	20.5

a.   Is the type of music a qualitative or quantitative variable?

b.   Construct a graph of rock music sales over the five-year period; use the horizontal axis to display the year and the vertical axis to display the percentage of music sales. Is this graph based on cross-sectional data or time series data?

c.   Construct a bar graph for type of music sales in 2000. Is this graph based on cross-sectional data or time series data?

15.   The Food and Drug Administration (FDA) reported the number of new drugs approved over an eight-year period (*The Wall Street Journal,* January 12, 2004). Figure 1.11 provides a bar graph summarizing the number of new drugs approved each year.

a.   Are the data qualitative or quantitative?

b.   Are the data time series or cross-sectional?

c.   How many new drugs were approved in 2003?

d.   In what year were the fewest new drugs approved? How many?

e.   Comment on the trend in the number of new drugs approved by the FDA over the eight-year period.

FIGURE 1.11 NUMBER OF NEW DRUGS APPROVED BY THE FOOD AND DRUG ADMINISTRATION

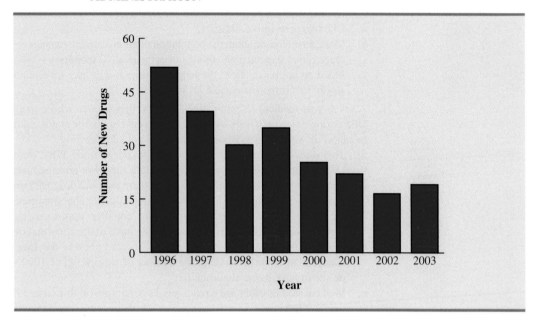

16. The marketing group at your company developed a new diet soft drink that it claims will capture a large share of the young adult market.
   a. What data would you want to see before deciding to invest substantial funds in introducing the new product into the marketplace?
   b. How would you expect the data mentioned in part (a) to be obtained?

17. A manager of a large corporation recommends a $10,000 raise be given to keep a valued subordinate from moving to another company. What internal and external sources of data might be used to decide whether such a salary increase is appropriate?

18. A survey of 430 business travelers found 155 business travelers used a travel agent to make the travel arrangements (*USA Today*, November 20, 2003).
   a. Develop a descriptive statistic that can be used to estimate the percentage of all business travelers who use a travel agent to make travel arrangements.
   b. The survey reported that the most frequent way business travelers make travel arrangements is by using an online travel site. If 44% of business travelers surveyed made their arrangements this way, how many of the 430 business travelers used an online travel site?
   c. Are the data on how travel arrangements are made qualitative or quantitative?

19. A *BusinessWeek* North American subscriber study collected data from a sample of 2861 subscribers. Fifty-nine percent of the respondents indicated an annual income of $75,000 or more, and 50% reported having an American Express credit card.
   a. What is the population of interest in this study?
   b. Is annual income a qualitative or quantitative variable?
   c. Is ownership of an American Express card a qualitative or quantitative variable?
   d. Does this study involve cross-sectional or time series data?
   e. Describe any statistical inferences *BusinessWeek* might make on the basis of the survey.

20. A survey of 131 investment managers in *Barron's* Big Money poll revealed the following (*Barron's*, October 28, 2002):
   - 43% of managers classified themselves as bullish or very bullish on the stock market.
   - The average expected return over the next 12 months for equities was 11.2%.

- 21% selected health care as the sector most likely to lead the market in the next 12 months.
- When asked to estimate how long it would take for technology and telecom stocks to resume sustainable growth, the managers' average response was 2.5 years.
  a. Cite two descriptive statistics.
  b. Make an inference about the population of all investment managers concerning the average return expected on equities over the next 12 months.
  c. Make an inference about the length of time it will take for technology and telecom stocks to resume sustainable growth.

21. A seven-year medical research study reported that women whose mothers took the drug DES during pregnancy were *twice* as likely to develop tissue abnormalities that might lead to cancer as were women whose mothers did not take the drug.
  a. This study involved the comparison of two populations. What were the populations?
  b. Do you suppose the data were obtained in a survey or an experiment?
  c. For the population of women whose mothers took the drug DES during pregnancy, a sample of 3980 women showed 63 developed tissue abnormalities that might lead to cancer. Provide a descriptive statistic that could be used to estimate the number of women out of 1000 in this population who have tissue abnormalities.
  d. For the population of women whose mothers did not take the drug DES during pregnancy, what is the estimate of the number of women out of 1000 who would be expected to have tissue abnormalities?
  e. Medical studies often use a relatively large sample (in this case, 3980). Why?

22. In the fall of 2003, Arnold Schwarzenegger challenged Governor Gray Davis for the governorship of California. A Policy Institute of California survey of registered voters reported Arnold Schwarzenegger in the lead with an estimated 54% of the vote (*Newsweek,* September 8, 2003).
  a. What was the population for this survey?
  b. What was the sample for this survey?
  c. Why was a sample used in this situation? Explain.

23. Nielsen Media Research conducts weekly surveys of television viewing throughout the United States, publishing both rating and market share data. The Nielsen rating is the percentage of households with televisions watching a program, while the Nielsen share is the percentage of households watching a program among those households with televisions in use. For example, Nielsen Media Research results for the 2003 Baseball World Series between the New York Yankees and the Florida Marlins showed a rating of 12.8% and a share of 22% (Associated Press, October 27, 2003). Thus, 12.8% of households with televisions were watching the World Series and 22% of households with televisions in use were watching the World Series. Based on the rating and share data for major television programs, Nielsen publishes a weekly ranking of television programs as well as a weekly ranking of the four major networks: ABC, CBS, NBC, and Fox.
  a. What is Nielsen Media Research attempting to measure?
  b. What is the population?
  c. Why would a sample be used in this situation?
  d. What kinds of decisions or actions are based on the Nielsen rankings?

24. A sample of midterm grades for five students showed the following results: 72, 65, 82, 90, 76. Which of the following statements are correct, and which should be challenged as being too generalized?
  a. The average midterm grade for the sample of five students is 77.
  b. The average midterm grade for all students who took the exam is 77.
  c. An estimate of the average midterm grade for all students who took the exam is 77.
  d. More than half of the students who take this exam will score between 70 and 85.
  e. If five other students are included in the sample, their grades will be between 65 and 90.

25. Table 1.8 shows a data set containing information for 25 of the shadow stocks tracked by the American Association of Individual Investors (aaii.com, February 2002). Shadow stocks

TABLE 1.8   A DATA SET FOR 25 SHADOW STOCKS

CD file

Shadow02

Company	Exchange	Ticker Symbol	Market Cap ($ millions)	Price/ Earnings Ratio	Gross Profit Margin (%)
DeWolfe Companies	AMEX	DWL	36.4	8.4	36.7
North Coast Energy	OTC	NCEB	52.5	6.2	59.3
Hansen Natural Corp.	OTC	HANS	41.1	14.6	44.8
MarineMax, Inc.	NYSE	HZO	111.5	7.2	23.8
Nanometrics Incorporated	OTC	NANO	228.6	38.0	53.3
TeamStaff, Inc.	OTC	TSTF	92.1	33.5	4.1
Environmental Tectonics	AMEX	ETC	51.1	35.8	35.9
Measurement Specialties	AMEX	MSS	101.8	26.8	37.6
SEMCO Energy, Inc.	NYSE	SEN	193.4	18.7	23.6
Party City Corporation	OTC	PCTY	97.2	15.9	36.4
Embrex, Inc.	OTC	EMBX	136.5	18.9	59.5
Tech/Ops Sevcon, Inc.	AMEX	TO	23.2	20.7	35.7
ARCADIS NV	OTC	ARCAF	173.4	8.8	9.6
Qiao Xing Universal Tele.	OTC	XING	64.3	22.1	30.8
Energy West Incorporated	OTC	EWST	29.1	9.7	16.3
Barnwell Industries, Inc.	AMEX	BRN	27.3	7.4	73.4
Innodata Corporation	OTC	INOD	66.1	11.0	29.6
Medical Action Industries	OTC	MDCI	137.1	26.9	30.6
Instrumentarium Corp.	OTC	INMRY	240.9	3.6	52.1
Petroleum Development	OTC	PETD	95.9	6.1	19.4
Drexler Technology Corp.	OTC	DRXR	233.6	45.6	53.6
Gerber Childrenswear Inc.	NYSE	GCW	126.9	7.9	25.8
Gaiam, Inc.	OTC	GAIA	295.5	68.2	60.7
Artesian Resources Corp.	OTC	ARTNA	62.8	20.5	45.5
York Water Company	OTC	YORW	92.2	22.9	74.2

are common stocks of smaller companies that are not closely followed by Wall Street analysts. The data set is also on the CD accompanying the text in the file named Shadow02.

a. How many variables are in the data set? Name them.

b. Which of the variables are qualitative and which are quantitative?

c. For the Exchange variable, count the number of observations and compute the percent frequencies corresponding to NYSE, AMEX, and OTC. Construct a bar graph similar to Figure 1.4 for the Exchange variable.

d. Count the number of observations for the Gross Profit Margin variable that fall within the following five intervals: 0–15, 15–30, 30–45, 45–60, and 60–75. Using these intervals for the base of each bar, construct a histogram similar to Figure 1.5.

e. Use Excel to compute the average for the Market Cap variable.

f. Use Excel to compute the average for the Price/Earnings Ratio.

Appendix 1.1   An Introduction to SWStat+

Excel 2003 does not contain statistical functions or data analysis tools to perform all of the statistical procedures discussed in the text. SWStat+ is an Excel add-in that extends the range of statistical and graphical options. In some cases, we include a chapter appendix that shows the steps required to accomplish a statistical procedure using SWStat+. For those students who want to make more extensive use of the software, SWStat+ offers an excellent Help facility. The SWStat+ Help system includes detailed explanations of the statistical and graphical options available, as well as descriptions and definitions of the types of output provided.

The purpose of this appendix is to explain how to install SWStat+ so that it can be accessed from an Excel worksheet, and to provide a brief introduction to its use.

Installing and Running SWStat+

The label on the SWStat+ CD provides instructions for installing the SWStat+ software on your computer. After installing the SWStat+ software, you must perform the following steps to use it as an Excel add-in.

When you perform the steps to make SWStat+ a permanent add-in, you will be asked whether you want to enable macros. You must enable macros to run SWStat+.

Step 1. Open Excel
Step 2. Select the **Tools** menu
Step 3. Choose **Add-Ins**
Step 4. Click the **Browse** button
Step 5. When the Browse dialog box appears:
　　　　Locate the **SWStat2** folder and double-click
　　　　Double-click the **SWStat2** icon

These steps will add SWStat2 (version 2) to the list of add-ins available in Excel, and SWStat+ will appear on the menu bar each time you run Excel. If you decide later that you do not want SWStat+ to be loaded each time you open Excel, choose **Tools**, then **Add-Ins**, and remove the check in the SWStat2 box.

Using SWStat+

More information can be found quickly using the Search/Index function of the SWStat+ Help system.

To use SWStat+ for a particular application you must first create a Data Area for the data set you will be working with. We will use the Excel worksheet for the S&P 500 data set that appeared in Figure 1.7 to show how to create a data area that tells SWStat+ where the data to be analyzed reside. Then we will show how to do some simple statistical analysis with that data.

Creating a Data Area   The purpose of creating a data area is to tell SWStat+ where the data to be analyzed reside and whether row or column labels are present. The following steps will create a data area for the S&P 500 data.

Step 1. Open the BWS&P workbook on the CD accompanying the text
Step 2. Select any cell in the data set (say, C5)
Step 3. Select the **SWStat+** menu
Step 4. Choose **Data Area**
Step 5. Choose **Set New Data Area** from the list of Data Area options
Step 6. When the SWStat+ Data Area dialog box appears:
　　　　Select the **Set New** tab
　　　　Select **With column headers**
　　　　Select **With row headers**
　　　　Click **Set data area**

Note that the row and column labels are highlighted in yellow and the entire data area (including labels) is enclosed by a blue border. In addition, a Results worksheet has been added to the workbook. All the output generated using SWStat+ will be placed in this worksheet.

The SWStat+ toolbar in the right margin of your window contains shortcuts for many SWStat+ tasks. For instance, steps 3, 4, and 5 above can be replaced by clicking the second button from the top on the toolbar: Set Data Area with both Column and Row Headers.

TABLE 2.2

FREQUENCY
DISTRIBUTION OF
SOFT DRINK
PURCHASES

Soft Drink	Frequency
Coke Classic	19
Diet Coke	8
Dr. Pepper	5
Pepsi-Cola	13
Sprite	5
Total	50

To develop a frequency distribution for these data, we count the number of times each soft drink appears in Table 2.1. Coke Classic appears 19 times, Diet Coke appears 8 times, Dr. Pepper appears 5 times, Pepsi-Cola appears 13 times, and Sprite appears 5 times. These counts are summarized in the frequency distribution in Table 2.2.

This frequency distribution provides a summary of how the 50 soft drink purchases are distributed across the five soft drinks. It offers more insight than the original data shown in Table 2.1. Viewing the frequency distribution, we see that Coke Classic is the leader, Pepsi-Cola is second, Diet Coke is third, and Sprite and Dr. Pepper are tied for fourth. The frequency distribution summarizes information about the popularity of the five best-selling soft drinks.

Let us examine how Excel can be used to count the frequencies and construct a frequency distribution for the soft drink data in Table 2.1.

Using Excel's COUNTIF Function to Construct a Frequency Distribution

Two tasks are involved in using Excel's COUNTIF function to construct a frequency distribution: Enter Data and Enter Functions and Formulas. Refer to Figure 2.1 as we describe the tasks involved. The formula worksheet is in the background; the value worksheet is in the foreground.

FIGURE 2.1 FREQUENCY DISTRIBUTION FOR SOFT DRINK PURCHASES
CONSTRUCTED USING EXCEL'S COUNTIF FUNCTION

	A	B	C	D	E
1	**Brand Purchased**		**Soft Drink**	**Frequency**	
2	Coke Classic		Coke Classic	=COUNTIF($A$2:$A$51,C2)	
3	Diet Coke		Diet Coke	=COUNTIF($A$2:$A$51,C3)	
4	Pepsi-Cola		Dr. Pepper	=COUNTIF($A$2:$A$51,C4)	
5	Diet Coke		Pepsi-Cola	=COUNTIF($A$2:$A$51,C5)	
6	Coke Classic		Sprite	=COUNTIF($A$2:$A$51,C6)	
7	Coke Classic				
8	Dr. Pepper				
9	Diet Coke				
10	Pepsi-Cola				
45	Pepsi-Cola				
46	Pepsi-Cola				
47	Pepsi-Cola				
48	Coke Classic				
49	Dr. Pepper				
50	Pepsi-Cola				
51	Sprite				
52					

	A	B	C	D	E
1	**Brand Purchased**		**Soft Drink**	**Frequency**	
2	Coke Classic		Coke Classic	19	
3	Diet Coke		Diet Coke	8	
4	Pepsi-Cola		Dr. Pepper	5	
5	Diet Coke		Pepsi-Cola	13	
6	Coke Classic		Sprite	5	
7	Coke Classic				
8	Dr. Pepper				
9	Diet Coke				
10	Pepsi-Cola				
45	Pepsi-Cola				
46	Pepsi-Cola				
47	Pepsi-Cola				
48	Coke Classic				
49	Dr. Pepper				
50	Pepsi-Cola				
51	Sprite				
52					

Note: Rows 11–44 are hidden.

Enter Data: The label "Brand Purchased" and the data for the 50 soft drink purchases are entered into cells A1:A51.

Enter Functions and Formulas: Excel's COUNTIF function can be used to count the number of times each soft drink appears in cells A2:A51. We first entered a label and the soft drink names into cells C1:C6 and D1. Then, to count the number of times that Coke Classic appears, we entered the following formula into cell D2:

$$=COUNTIF(\$A\$2:\$A\$51,C2)$$

To count the number of times the other soft drinks appear, we copied the same formula into cells D3:D6.

The value worksheet, in the foreground of Figure 2.1, shows the values computed using these cell formulas; we see that the Excel worksheet shows the same frequency distribution that we developed in Table 2.2.

Relative Frequency and Percent Frequency Distributions

A frequency distribution shows the number (frequency) of items in each of several nonoverlapping classes. However, we are often interested in the proportion, or percentage, of items in each class. The *relative frequency* of a class equals the fraction or proportion of items belonging to a class. For a data set with n observations, the relative frequency of each class can be determined as follows:

RELATIVE FREQUENCY

$$\text{Relative frequency of a class} = \frac{\text{Frequency of the class}}{n} \qquad (2.1)$$

The *percent frequency* of a class is the relative frequency multiplied by 100.

A **relative frequency distribution** gives a tabular summary of data showing the relative frequency for each class. A **percent frequency distribution** summarizes the percent frequency of the data for each class. Table 2.3 shows a relative frequency distribution and a percent frequency distribution for the soft drink data. In Table 2.3 we see that the relative frequency for Coke Classic is 19/50 = .38, the relative frequency for Diet Coke is 8/50 = .16, and so on. From the percent frequency distribution, we see that 38% of the purchases were Coke Classic, 16% of the purchases were Diet Coke, and so on. We can also note that 38% + 26% + 16% = 80% of the purchases were the top three soft drinks.

TABLE 2.3   RELATIVE AND PERCENT FREQUENCY DISTRIBUTIONS
OF SOFT DRINK PURCHASES

Soft Drink	Relative Frequency	Percent Frequency
Coke Classic	.38	38
Diet Coke	.16	16
Dr. Pepper	.10	10
Pepsi-Cola	.26	26
Sprite	.10	10
Total	1.00	100

Using Excel to Construct Relative Frequency and Percent Frequency Distributions

Extending the worksheet shown in Figure 2.1, we can develop the relative frequency and percent frequency distributions shown in Table 2.3. Refer to Figure 2.2 as we describe the tasks involved. The formula worksheet is in the background; the value worksheet is in the foreground.

Enter Data: The label "Brand Purchased" and the data for the 50 soft drink purchases are entered into cells A1:A51.

Enter Functions and Formulas: The information in cells C1:D6 is the same as in Figure 2.1. Excel's SUM function is used in cell D7 to compute the sum of the frequencies in cells D2:D6. The resulting value of 50 is the number of observations in the data set. To compute the relative frequency for Coke Classic using equation (2.1), we entered the formula =D2/$D$7 into cell E2; the result, 0.38, is the relative frequency for Coke Classic. Copying cell E2 to cells E3:E6 computes the relative frequencies for each of the other soft drinks.

To compute the percent frequency for Coke Classic we entered the formula =E2*100 into cell F2. The result, 38, indicates that 38% of the soft drink purchases were Coke Classic. Copying cell F2 to cells F3:F6 computes the percent frequencies for each of the other soft drinks. Finally, copying cell D7 to cells E7:F7 computes the total of the relative frequencies (1.00) and the total of the percent frequencies (100).

FIGURE 2.2   RELATIVE FREQUENCY AND PERCENT FREQUENCY DISTRIBUTIONS OF SOFT DRINK PURCHASES CONSTRUCTED USING EXCEL

	A	B	C	D	E	F	G
1	Brand Purchased		Soft Drink	Frequency	Relative Frequency	Percent Frequency	
2	Coke Classic		Coke Classic	=COUNTIF($A$2:$A$51,C2)	=D2/$D$7	=E2*100	
3	Diet Coke		Diet Coke	=COUNTIF($A$2:$A$51,C3)	=D3/$D$7	=E3*100	
4	Pepsi-Cola		Dr. Pepper	=COUNTIF($A$2:$A$51,C4)	=D4/$D$7	=E4*100	
5	Diet Coke		Pepsi-Cola	=COUNTIF($A$2:$A$51,C5)	=D5/$D$7	=E5*100	
6	Coke Classic		Sprite	=COUNTIF($A$2:$A$51,C6)	=D6/$D$7	=E6*100	
7	Coke Classic		Total	=SUM(D2:D6)	=SUM(E2:E6)	=SUM(F2:F6)	
8	Dr. Pepper						

	A	B	C	D	E	F	G
9	Diet Coke						
10	Pepsi-Cola	1	Brand Purchased		Soft Drink	Frequency	Relative Frequency	Percent Frequency	
45	Pepsi-Cola	2	Coke Classic		Coke Classic	19	0.38	38	
46	Pepsi-Cola	3	Diet Coke		Diet Coke	8	0.16	16	
47	Pepsi-Cola	4	Pepsi-Cola		Dr. Pepper	5	0.1	10	
48	Coke Classic	5	Diet Coke		Pepsi-Cola	13	0.26	26	
49	Dr. Pepper	6	Coke Classic		Sprite	5	0.1	10	
50	Pepsi-Cola	7	Coke Classic		Total	50	1.00	100	
51	Sprite	8	Dr. Pepper						
52		9	Diet Coke						
		10	Pepsi-Cola						
		45	Pepsi-Cola						
		46	Pepsi-Cola						
		47	Pepsi-Cola						
		48	Coke Classic						
		49	Dr. Pepper						
		50	Pepsi-Cola						
		51	Sprite						
		52							

Note: Rows 11–44 are hidden.

Bar Graphs and Pie Charts

A **bar graph**, or bar chart, is a graphical device for depicting qualitative data summarized in a frequency, relative frequency, or percent frequency distribution. On one axis of the graph (usually the horizontal axis), we specify the labels that are used for the classes (categories). A frequency, relative frequency, or percent frequency scale can be used for the other axis of the graph (usually the vertical axis). Then, using a bar of fixed width drawn above each class label, we extend the length of the bar until we reach the frequency, relative frequency, or percent frequency of the class. For qualitative data, the bars should be separated to emphasize the fact that each class is separate. Figure 2.3 shows a bar graph of the frequency distribution for the 50 soft drink purchases. Note how the graphical presentation shows Coke Classic, Pepsi-Cola, and Diet Coke to be the most preferred brands.

In quality control applications, bar graphs are used to identify the most important causes of problems. When the bars are arranged in descending order of height from left to right with the most frequently occurring cause appearing first, the bar graph is called a pareto diagram. *This diagram is named for its founder, Vilfredo Pareto, an Italian economist.*

The **pie chart** provides another graphical device for presenting relative frequency and percent frequency distributions for qualitative data. To construct a pie chart, we first draw a circle to represent all of the data. Then we use the relative frequencies to subdivide the circle into sectors, or parts, that correspond to the relative frequency for each class. For example, because a circle contains 360 degrees and Coke Classic shows a relative frequency of .38, the sector of the pie chart labeled Coke Classic consists of .38(360) = 136.8 degrees. The sector of the pie chart labeled Diet Coke consists of .16(360) = 57.6 degrees. Similar calculations for the other classes yield the pie chart in Figure 2.4. The numerical values shown for each sector can be frequencies, relative frequencies, or percent frequencies.

Using Excel's Chart Wizard to Construct Bar Graphs and Pie Charts

Excel's Chart Wizard provides a general tool for constructing a variety of graphical displays, including bar graphs and pie charts. We illustrate its use by showing how to construct the bar graph for soft drink purchases. The Chart Wizard tool allows us to go beyond what can be done with functions and formulas alone. When such tools are used, a third task is needed for worksheet construction: Apply Tools.

The same data and functions and formulas that were used in Figure 2.1 are used here. Thus, the chart we are going to develop is an extension of that worksheet. Refer to Fig-

FIGURE 2.3   BAR GRAPH OF SOFT DRINK PURCHASES

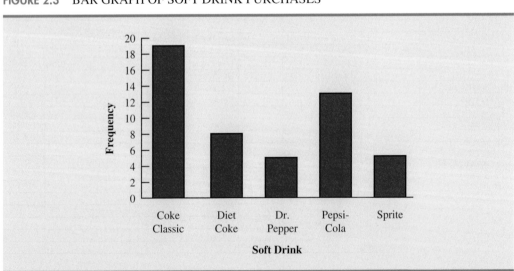

FIGURE 2.4   PIE CHART OF SOFT DRINK PURCHASES

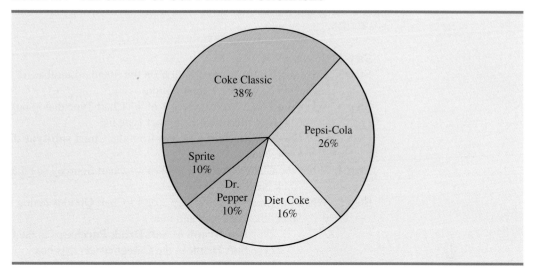

ure 2.5 as we describe the Apply Tools task. The value worksheet is in the background; the chart developed using the Excel Chart Wizard is in the foreground.

Enter Data: Same as in Figure 2.1.

Enter Functions and Formulas: Same as in Figure 2.1.

FIGURE 2.5   BAR GRAPH OF SOFT DRINK PURCHASES CONSTRUCTED USING EXCEL'S CHART WIZARD

	A	B	C	D	E	F	G	H	I	J
1	Brand Purchased		Soft Drink	Frequency						
2	Coke Classic		Coke Classic	19						
3	Diet Coke		Diet Coke	8						
4	Pepsi-Cola		Dr. Pepper	5						
5	Diet Coke		Pepsi-Cola	13						
6	Coke Classic		Sprite	5						
7	Coke Classic									
8	Dr. Pepper									
9	Diet Coke									
10	Pepsi-Cola									
45	Pepsi-Cola									
46	Pepsi-Cola									
47	Pepsi-Cola									
48	Coke Classic									
49	Dr. Pepper									
50	Pepsi-Cola									
51	Sprite									
52										
53										
54										
55										
56										
57										

Bar Graph of Soft Drink Purchases

Apply Tools: The following steps describe how to use Excel's Chart Wizard to construct a bar graph for the soft drink data using the frequency distribution appearing in cells C1:D6.

Step 1. Select cells C1:D6
Step 2. Click the **Chart Wizard** button on the Standard toolbar (or select the **Insert** menu and choose the **Chart** option)
Step 3. When the Chart Wizard - Step 1 of 4 - Chart Type dialog box appears:
  Choose **Column** in the **Chart type** list
  Choose **Clustered Column** from the **Chart sub-type** display
  Click **Next >**
Step 4. When the Chart Wizard - Step 2 of 4 - Chart Source Data dialog box appears:
  Click **Next >**
Step 5. When the Chart Wizard - Step 3 of 4 - Chart Options dialog box appears:
  Select the **Titles** tab and then
    Type **Bar Graph of Soft Drink Purchases** in the **Chart title** box
    Type **Soft Drink** in the **Category (X)** axis box
    Type **Frequency** in the **Value (Y)** axis box
  Select the **Legend** tab and then
    Remove the check in the **Show legend** box
    Click **Next >**
Step 6. When the Chart Wizard - Step 4 of 4 - Chart Location dialog box appears:
  Specify a location for the new chart (we used the default setting of the current worksheet)
  Click **Finish**

The resulting bar graph (chart) is shown in Figure 2.5.*

Excel's Chart Wizard can produce a pie chart for the soft drink data in a similar fashion. The major difference is that in step 3 we would choose **Pie** in the Chart type list.

NOTES AND COMMENTS

1. Often the number of classes in a frequency distribution is the same as the number of categories found in the data, as is the case for the soft drink purchase data in this section. The data involve only five soft drinks, and a separate frequency distribution class was defined for each one. Data that included all soft drinks would require many categories, most of which would have a small number of purchases. Most statisticians recommend that classes with smaller frequencies be grouped into an aggregate class called "other." Categories with frequencies of 5% or less would most often be treated in this fashion.

2. The sum of the frequencies in any frequency distribution always equals the number of observations. The sum of the relative frequencies in any relative frequency distribution always equals 1.00, and the sum of the percentages in a percent frequency distribution always equals 100.

---

*The bar graph in Figure 2.5 is slightly different than what was provided by Excel after selecting **Finish**. Resizing an Excel chart is not difficult. First, select the chart. Small black squares, called sizing handles, will appear on the chart border. Click on the sizing handles and drag them to resize the figure to your preference.

Exercises

Methods

1. The response to a question has three alternatives: A, B, and C. A sample of 120 responses provides 60 A, 24 B, and 36 C. Show the frequency and relative frequency distributions.

2. A partial relative frequency distribution is given.

Class	Relative Frequency
A	.22
B	.18
C	.40
D	

   a. What is the relative frequency of class D?
   b. The total sample size is 200. What is the frequency of class D?
   c. Show the frequency distribution.
   d. Show the percent frequency distribution.

3. A questionnaire provides 58 Yes, 42 No, and 20 No Opinion answers.
   a. In the construction of a pie chart, how many degrees would be in the section of the pie showing the Yes answers?
   b. How many degrees would be in the section of the pie showing the No answers?
   c. Construct a pie chart.
   d. Construct a bar graph.

Applications

4. The top four primetime television shows were *CSI, ER, Everybody Loves Raymond,* and *Friends* (Nielsen Media Research, January 11, 2004). Data indicating the preferred shows for a sample of 50 viewers follow.

CSI	Friends	CSI	CSI	CSI
CSI	CSI	Raymond	ER	ER
Friends	CSI	ER	Friends	CSI
ER	ER	Friends	CSI	Raymond
CSI	Friends	CSI	CSI	Friends
ER	ER	ER	Friends	Raymond
CSI	Friends	Friends	CSI	Raymond
Friends	Friends	Raymond	Friends	CSI
Raymond	Friends	ER	Friends	CSI
CSI	ER	CSI	Friends	ER

   a. Are these data qualitative or quantitative?
   b. Provide frequency and percent frequency distributions.
   c. Construct a bar graph and a pie chart.
   d. On the basis of the sample, which television show has the largest viewing audience? Which one is second?

5. In alphabetical order, the six most common last names in the United States are Brown, Davis, Johnson, Jones, Smith, and Williams (*Time Almanac 2001*). Assume that a sample of 50 individuals with one of these last names provided the following data.

Names

Brown	Williams	Williams	Williams	Brown
Smith	Jones	Smith	Johnson	Smith
Davis	Smith	Brown	Williams	Johnson
Johnson	Smith	Smith	Johnson	Brown
Williams	Davis	Johnson	Williams	Johnson
Williams	Johnson	Jones	Smith	Brown
Johnson	Smith	Smith	Brown	Jones
Jones	Jones	Smith	Smith	Davis
Davis	Jones	Williams	Davis	Smith
Jones	Johnson	Brown	Johnson	Davis

Summarize the data by constructing the following:
a. Relative and percent frequency distributions
b. A bar graph
c. A pie chart
d. Based on these data, what are the three most common last names?

6. The eight best-selling paperback business books are listed in Table 2.4 (*BusinessWeek*, April 3, 2000). Suppose a sample of book purchases provided the following data:

BWBooks

7 Habits	Dad	7 Habits	Millionaire	Millionaire	WSJ Guide
Motley	Millionaire	Tax Guide	7 Habits	Dad	Dummies
Millionaire	Motley	Dad	Dad	Parachute	Dad
Dad	7 Habits	WSJ Guide	WSJ Guide	WSJ Guide	7 Habits
Motley	WSJ Guide	Millionaire	7 Habits	Millionaire	Millionaire
Millionaire	7 Habits	Millionaire	7 Habits	Motley	Motley
Motley	7 Habits	Dad	Dad	Dad	Dad
7 Habits	WSJ Guide	Tax Guide	Millionaire	Motley	Tax Guide
Motley	Motley	Millionaire	Millionaire	Dad	Dummies
Millionaire	Millionaire	Millionaire	Dad	Millionaire	Dad

a. Construct frequency and percent frequency distributions for the data. Group any books with a frequency of 5% or less in an "other" category.
b. Rank the best-selling books.
c. What percentage of the sales are represented by *The Millionaire Next Door* and *Rich Dad, Poor Dad*?

7. Leverock's Waterfront Steakhouse in Maderia Beach, Florida, uses a questionnaire to ask customers how they rate the server, food quality, cocktails, prices, and atmosphere at the restaurant. Each characteristic is rated on a scale of outstanding (O), very good (V), good (G), average (A), and poor (P). Use descriptive statistics to summarize the following data collected on food quality. What is your feeling about the food quality ratings at the restaurant?

G	O	V	G	A	O	V	O	V	G	O	V	A
V	O	P	V	O	G	A	O	O	O	G	O	V
V	A	G	O	V	P	V	O	O	G	O	O	V
O	G	A	O	V	O	O	G	V	A	G		

8. Data for a sample of 55 members of the Baseball Hall of Fame in Cooperstown, New York, are shown here. Each observation indicates the primary position played by the Hall of Famers: pitcher (P), catcher (H), 1st base (1), 2nd base (2), 3rd base (3), shortstop (S), left field (L), center field (C), and right field (R).

Baseball

L	P	C	H	2	P	R	1	S	S	1	L	P	R	P
P	P	P	R	C	S	L	R	P	C	C	P	P	R	P
2	3	P	H	L	P	1	C	P	P	S	1	L	R
R	1	2	H	S	3	H	2	L	P				

TABLE 2.4

THE EIGHT
BEST-SELLING
PAPERBACK
BUSINESS BOOKS

* *The 7 Habits of Highly Effective People*
* *Investing for Dummies*
* *The Ernst & Young Tax Guide 2000*
* *The Millionaire Next Door*
* *The Motley Fool Investment Guide*
* *Rich Dad, Poor Dad*
* *The Wall Street Journal Guide to Understanding Money and Investing*
* *What Color Is Your Parachute? 2000*

a. Use frequency and relative frequency distributions to summarize the data.
b. What position provides the most Hall of Famers?
c. What position provides the fewest Hall of Famers?
d. What outfield position (L, C, or R) provides the most Hall of Famers?
e. Compare infielders (1, 2, 3, and S) to outfielders (L, C, and R).

9. About 60% of small and medium-sized businesses are family-owned. A TEC International Inc. survey asked the chief executive officers (CEOs) of family-owned businesses how they became the CEO (*The Wall Street Journal,* December 16, 2003). Responses were that the CEO inherited the business, the CEO built the business, or the CEO was hired by the family-owned firm. A sample of 26 CEOs of family-owned businesses provided the following data on how each became the CEO.

CEOs

Built	Built	Built	Inherited
Inherited	Built	Inherited	Built
Inherited	Built	Built	Built
Built	Hired	Hired	Hired
Inherited	Inherited	Inherited	Built
Built	Built	Built	Hired
Built	Inherited		

a. Provide a frequency distribution.
b. Provide a percent frequency distribution.
c. Construct a bar graph.
d. What percentage of CEOs of family-owned businesses became the CEO because they inherited the business? What is the primary reason a person becomes the CEO of a family-owned business?

10. A 2001 Merrill Lynch Client Satisfaction Survey asked clients to indicate how satisfied they were with their financial consultant. Client responses were coded 1 to 7, with 1 indicating "not at all satisfied" and 7 indicating "extremely satisfied." Assume that the following data are from a sample of 60 responses for a particular financial consultant.

Client

5	7	6	6	7	5	5	7	3	6
7	7	6	6	6	5	5	6	7	7
6	6	4	4	7	6	7	6	7	6
5	7	5	7	6	4	7	5	7	6
6	5	3	7	7	6	6	6	6	5
5	6	6	7	7	5	6	4	6	6

a. Comment on why these data are qualitative.
b. Provide a frequency distribution and a relative frequency distribution for the data.
c. Provide a bar graph.
d. On the basis of your summaries, comment on the clients' overall evaluation of the financial consultant.

2.2 Summarizing Quantitative Data

Frequency Distribution

As defined in Section 2.1, a frequency distribution is a tabular summary of data showing the number (frequency) of items in each of several nonoverlapping classes. This definition holds for quantitative as well as qualitative data. However, with quantitative data we must be more careful in defining the nonoverlapping classes to be used in the frequency distribution.

For example, consider the quantitative data in Table 2.5. These data show the time in days required to complete year-end audits for a sample of 20 clients of Sanderson and Clifford,

TABLE 2.5

YEAR-END AUDIT
TIMES (IN DAYS)

12	14	19	18
15	15	18	17
20	27	22	23
22	21	33	28
14	18	16	13

a small public accounting firm. The three steps necessary to define the classes for a frequency distribution with quantitative data are:

1. Determine the number of nonoverlapping classes.
2. Determine the width of each class.
3. Determine the class limits.

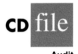

Audit

Let us demonstrate these steps by developing a frequency distribution for the audit time data in Table 2.5.

Number of Classes Classes are formed by specifying ranges that will be used to group the data. As a general guideline, we recommend using between 5 and 20 classes. For a small number of data items, as few as five or six classes may be used to summarize the data. For a larger number of data items, a larger number of classes is usually required. The goal is to use enough classes to show the variation in the data, but not so many classes that some contain only a few data items. Because the number of data items in Table 2.5 is relatively small ($n = 20$), we chose to develop a frequency distribution with five classes.

Making the classes the same width reduces the chance of inappropriate interpretations by the user.

Width of the Classes The second step in constructing a frequency distribution for quantitative data is to choose a width for the classes. As a general guideline, we recommend that the width be the same for each class. Thus the choices of the number of classes and the width of classes are not independent decisions. A larger number of classes means a smaller class width, and vice versa. To determine an approximate class width, we begin by identifying the largest and smallest data values. Then, with the desired number of classes specified, we can use the following expression to determine the approximate class width.

$$\text{Approximate class width} = \frac{\text{Largest data value} - \text{Smallest data value}}{\text{Number of classes}} \qquad \textbf{(2.2)}$$

The approximate class width given by equation (2.2) can be rounded to a more convenient value based on the preference of the person developing the frequency distribution. For example, an approximate class width of 9.28 might be rounded to 10 simply because 10 is a more convenient class width to use in presenting a frequency distribution.

For the data involving the year-end audit times, the largest data value is 33 and the smallest data value is 12. Because we decided to summarize the data with five classes, using equation (2.2) provides an approximate class width of $(33 - 12)/5 = 4.2$. We therefore decided to round up and use a class width of five days in the frequency distribution.

No single frequency distribution is best for a data set. Different people may construct different, but equally acceptable, frequency distributions. The goal is to reveal the natural grouping and variation in the data.

In practice, the number of classes and the appropriate class width are determined by trial and error. Once a possible number of classes is chosen, equation (2.2) is used to find the approximate class width. The process can be repeated for a different number of classes. Ultimately, the analyst uses judgment to determine the combination of the number of classes and class width that provides the best frequency distribution for summarizing the data.

For the audit time data in Table 2.5, after deciding to use five classes, each with a width of five days, the next task is to specify the class limits for each of the classes.

Class Limits Class limits must be chosen so that each data item belongs to one and only one class. The *lower class limit* identifies the smallest possible data value assigned to the class. The *upper class limit* identifies the largest possible data value assigned to the class. In developing frequency distributions for qualitative data, we did not need to specify class limits because each data item naturally fell into a separate class. But with quantitative data, such as the audit times in Table 2.5, class limits are necessary to determine where each data value belongs.

Using the audit time data in Table 2.5, we selected 10 days as the lower class limit and 14 days as the upper class limit for the first class. This class is denoted 10–14 in Table 2.6. The smallest data value, 12, is included in the 10–14 class. We then selected 15 days as the

TABLE 2.6   FREQUENCY DISTRIBUTION FOR THE AUDIT TIME DATA

Audit Time (days)	Frequency
10–14	4
15–19	8
20–24	5
25–29	2
30–34	1
Total	20

lower class limit and 19 days as the upper class limit of the next class. We continued defining the lower and upper class limits to obtain a total of five classes: 10–14, 15–19, 20–24, 25–29, and 30–34. The largest data value, 33, is included in the 30–34 class. The difference between the lower class limits of adjacent classes is the class width. Using the first two lower class limits of 10 and 15, we see that the class width is $15 - 10 = 5$.

With the number of classes, class width, and class limits determined, a frequency distribution can be obtained by counting the number of data values belonging to each class. For example, the data in Table 2.5 show that four values—12, 14, 14, and 13—belong to the 10–14 class. Thus, the frequency for the 10–14 class is 4. Continuing this counting process for the 15–19, 20–24, 25–29, and 30–34 classes provides the frequency distribution in Table 2.6. Using this frequency distribution, we can observe the following:

1. The most frequently occurring audit times are in the class of 15–19 days. Eight of the 20 audit times belong to this class.
2. Only one audit required 30 or more days.

Other conclusions are possible, depending on the interests of the person viewing the frequency distribution. The value of a frequency distribution is that it provides insights about the data that are not easily obtained by viewing the data in their original unorganized form.

Class Midpoint   In some applications, we want to know the midpoints of the classes in a frequency distribution for quantitative data. The **class midpoint** is the value halfway between the lower and upper class limits. For the audit time data, the five class midpoints are 12, 17, 22, 27, and 32.

Using Excel's FREQUENCY Function to Construct a Frequency Distribution

Constructing a frequency distribution for quantitative data using Excel's COUNTIF function is cumbersome. Here we show how to use Excel's FREQUENCY function to construct a frequency distribution for quantitative data. The FREQUENCY function has two inputs: the range for the data, and the upper limits for the classes used. Unlike most Excel functions, it provides multiple values (in this case the class frequencies) as output. Because of the multiple output values, we must enter the FREQUENCY function in a special way as an array formula.

Refer to Figure 2.6 as we describe the tasks involved in using the FREQUENCY function to create a frequency distribution for the audit time data. The formula worksheet is in the background; the value worksheet is in the foreground.

Enter Data: The label Audit Time and the 20 audit times have been entered into cells A1:A21. Descriptive headings have been entered into cells C1:E1, and labels to identify the chosen classes have been entered using text format into cells C2:C6. The class upper limits used by Excel's FREQUENCY function have been entered into cells D2:D6.

FIGURE 2.6 FREQUENCY DISTRIBUTION FOR AUDIT TIME DATA CONSTRUCTED USING EXCEL'S FREQUENCY FUNCTION

	A	B	C	D	E	F
1	**Audit Time**		**Audit Time**	**Upper Limit**	**Frequency**	
2	12		10-14	14	=FREQUENCY(A2:A21,D2:D6)	
3	15		15-19	19	=FREQUENCY(A2:A21,D2:D6)	
4	20		20-24	24	=FREQUENCY(A2:A21,D2:D6)	
5	22		25-29	29	=FREQUENCY(A2:A21,D2:D6)	
6	14		30-34	34	=FREQUENCY(A2:A21,D2:D6)	
7	14					
8	15					
9	27					
10	21					
11	18					
12	19					
13	18					
14	22					
15	33					
16	16					
17	18					
18	17					
19	23					
20	28					
21	13					
22						

	A	B	C	D	E	F
1	**Audit Time**		**Audit Time**	**Upper Limit**	**Frequency**	
2	12		10-14	14	4	
3	15		15-19	19	8	
4	20		20-24	24	5	
5	22		25-29	29	2	
6	14		30-34	34	1	
7	14					
8	15					
9	27					
10	21					
11	18					
12	19					
13	18					
14	22					
15	33					
16	16					
17	18					
18	17					
19	23					
20	28					
21	13					
22						

Enter Functions and Formulas: Excel's FREQUENCY function is used in cells E2:E6 to compute the class frequencies. The following steps describe how to create and enter an array formula that uses the FREQUENCY function to develop a frequency distribution for the audit time data.

Step 1. Select cells E2:E6, the cells where we want the frequencies to appear

Step 2. Type, but do not enter, the following formula:
=FREQUENCY(A2:A21,D2:D6)

You must hold down the Ctrl and Shift keys while pressing the Enter key to enter an array formula.

Step 3. Press CTRL+SHIFT+ENTER and the array formula will be entered into each of the cells E2:E6

The results are shown in Figure 2.6. Because we entered an array formula into cells E2:E6, the formula that Excel displays in each of these cells is the same, but the values calculated are not. They are the frequencies for each class. The range of cells for the upper class limits (D2:D6) used as the second input for the FREQUENCY function tells Excel which frequency to put into each cell of the output range (E2:E6). The frequency for the class with an upper limit of 14 is placed in the first cell (E2), the frequency for the class with an upper limit of 19 is placed in the second cell (E3), and so on.

TABLE 2.7 RELATIVE AND PERCENT FREQUENCY DISTRIBUTIONS FOR THE AUDIT TIME DATA

Audit Time (days)	Relative Frequency	Percent Frequency
10–14	.20	20
15–19	.40	40
20–24	.25	25
25–29	.10	10
30–34	.05	5
Total	1.00	100

Relative Frequency and Percent Frequency Distributions

We define the relative frequency and percent frequency distributions for quantitative data in the same manner as for qualitative data. First, recall that the relative frequency is the proportion of the observations belonging to a class. With n observations,

$$\text{Relative frequency of class} = \frac{\text{Frequency of the class}}{n}$$

The percent frequency of a class is the relative frequency multiplied by 100.

Based on the class frequencies in Table 2.6 and with $n = 20$, Table 2.7 shows the relative frequency distribution and percent frequency distribution for the audit time data. Note that .40 of the audits, or 40%, required from 15 to 19 days. Only .05 of the audits, or 5%, required 30 or more days. Again, additional interpretations and insights can be obtained by using Table 2.7.

Histogram

A common graphical presentation of quantitative data is a **histogram**. This graphical summary can be prepared for data previously summarized in either a frequency, relative frequency, or percent frequency distribution. A histogram is constructed by placing the variable of interest on the horizontal axis and the frequency, relative frequency, or percent frequency on the vertical axis. The frequency, relative frequency, or percent frequency of each class is shown by drawing a rectangle whose base is determined by the class limits on the horizontal axis and whose height is the corresponding frequency, relative frequency, or percent frequency.

Figure 2.7 is a histogram for the audit time data.* Note that the class with the greatest frequency is shown by the rectangle appearing above the class of 15–19 days. The height of the rectangle shows that the frequency of this class is 8. A histogram for the relative or percent frequency distribution of these data would look the same as the histogram in Figure 2.7 with the exception that the vertical axis would be labeled with relative or percent frequency values.

As Figure 2.7 shows, the adjacent rectangles of a histogram touch one another. Unlike a bar graph, a histogram contains no natural separation between the rectangles of adjacent classes. This format is the usual convention for histograms. Because the classes for the audit time data are stated as 10–14, 15–19, 20–24, 25–29, and 30–34, one-unit spaces of 14 to 15, 19 to 20, 24 to 25, and 29 to 30 would seem to be needed between the classes. These spaces are eliminated when constructing a histogram. Eliminating the spaces between

---

*In Figure 2.7 the labels used to identify each rectangle are the same as the labels we used to identify each class in the frequency distribution. Another commonly used convention is to label the horizontal axis using the class midpoints. In this case, the first rectangle would be labelled at 12, the midpoint of the first class; the second rectangle would be labelled at 17, the midpoint of the second class; and so on.

FIGURE 2.7   HISTOGRAM FOR THE AUDIT TIME DATA

classes in a histogram for the audit time data helps show that all values between the lower limit of the first class and the upper limit of the last class are possible.

One of the most important uses of a histogram is to provide information about the shape, or form, of a distribution. Figure 2.8 contains four histograms constructed from relative frequency distributions. Panel A shows the histogram for a set of data moderately skewed to the left. A histogram is said to be skewed to the left if its tail extends farther to the left. This histogram is typical for exam scores, with no scores above 100%, most of the scores above 70%, and only a few really low scores. Panel B shows the histogram for a set of data moderately skewed to the right. A histogram is said to be skewed to the right if its tail extends farther to the right. An example of this type of histogram would be for data such as housing prices; a few very expensive houses create the skewness in the right tail.

Panel C shows a symmetric histogram. In a symmetric histogram, the left tail mirrors the shape of the right tail. Histograms for data found in applications are never perfectly symmetric, but the histogram for many applications may be roughly symmetric. Data for SAT scores, heights and weights of people, and so on lead to histograms that are roughly symmetric. Panel D shows a histogram highly skewed to the right. This histogram was constructed from data on the amount of customer purchases over one day at a women's apparel store. Data from applications in business and economics often lead to histograms that are skewed to the right. For instance, data on housing prices, salaries, purchase amounts, and so on often result in histograms skewed to the right.

Using Excel's Chart Wizard to Construct a Histogram

We can use Excel's Chart Wizard to construct a histogram for the audit time data. Refer to Figures 2.9, 2.10, and 2.11 as we describe the tasks involved.

Enter Data: Same as in Figure 2.6.

Enter Functions and Formulas: Same as in Figure 2.6.

Apply Tools: The following steps describe how to use Excel's Chart Wizard to produce a histogram for the audit time data using the class frequencies appearing in cells E2:E6 of the worksheet shown in Figure 2.9.

   Step 1. Select cells E2:E6
   Step 2. Click the **Chart Wizard** button on the Standard toolbar (or select the **Insert** menu and choose the **Chart** option)

FIGURE 2.8   HISTOGRAMS SHOWING DIFFERING LEVELS OF SKEWNESS

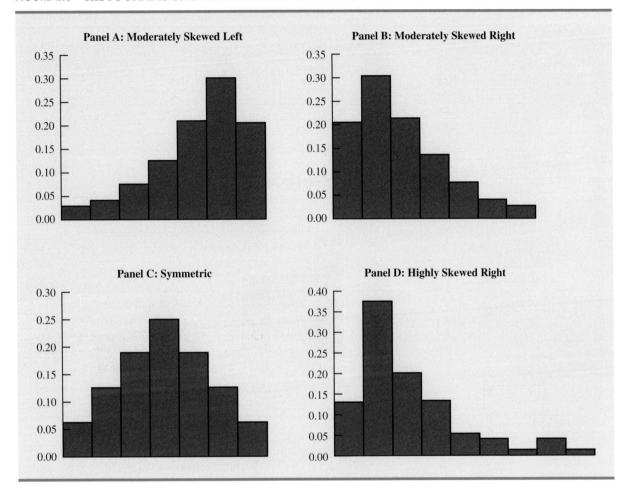

Step 3. When the Chart Wizard - Step 1 of 4 - Chart Type dialog box appears:
   Choose **Column** in the **Chart type** list
   Choose **Clustered Column** from the **Chart sub-type** display
   Click **Next >**

Step 4. When the Chart Wizard - Step 2 of 4 - Chart Source Data dialog box appears:
   Select the **Series** tab and then
   Click in the **Category (X) axis labels** box
   Select C2:C6
   Click **Next >**

Step 5. When the Chart Wizard - Step 3 of 4 - Chart Options dialog box appears:
   Select the **Titles** tab and then
      Type **Histogram for Audit Time Data** in the **Chart title** box
      Type **Audit Time in Days** in the **Category (X)** axis box
      Type **Frequency** in the **Value (Y)** axis box
   Select the **Legend** tab and then
      Remove the check in the **Show legend** box
   Click **Next >**

FIGURE 2.9   INITIAL HISTOGRAM CONSTRUCTED USING EXCEL'S CHART WIZARD
FOR THE AUDIT TIME DATA

	A	B	C	D	E	F	G	H	I	J
1	Audit Time		Audit Time	Upper Limit	Frequency					
2	12		10-14	14	4					
3	15		15-19	19	8					
4	20		20-24	24	5					
5	22		25-29	29	2					
6	14		30-34	34	1					
7	14									
8	15									
9	27									
10	21									
11	18									
12	19									
13	18									
14	22									
15	33									
16	16									
17	18									
18	17									
19	23									
20	28									
21	13									
22										
23										
24										

Step 6. When the Chart Wizard - Step 4 of 4 - Chart Location dialog box appears:
Specify a location for the chart (we used the default setting of the current worksheet)
Click **Finish**

The worksheet displayed in Figure 2.9 shows the column chart produced by Excel. Note the gaps between the rectangles. Because the adjacent rectangles in a histogram must touch, we need to edit the chart in order to eliminate the gap between each of the rectangles. The following steps describe this process. Refer to Figure 2.10 as we describe the steps.

Step 1. Right-click on any rectangle in the column chart to produce a list of options
Step 2. Select the **Format Data Series** option
Step 3. When the Format Data Series dialog box appears:
Select the **Options** tab and then
Enter **0** in the **Gap width** box
Click **OK**

Figure 2.11 displays the histogram produced by Excel. It is the same histogram that we developed earlier in Figure 2.7. The size of the chart can now be adjusted to suit user preference.

Cumulative Distributions

A variation of the frequency distribution that provides another tabular summary of quantitative data is the **cumulative frequency distribution**. The cumulative frequency distribution uses the number of classes, class widths, and class limits developed for the frequency distribution. However, rather than showing the frequency of each class, the cumulative fre-

FIGURE 2.10 REMOVING THE GAPS BETWEEN CLASSES TO DISPLAY A HISTOGRAM FOR THE AUDIT TIME DATA

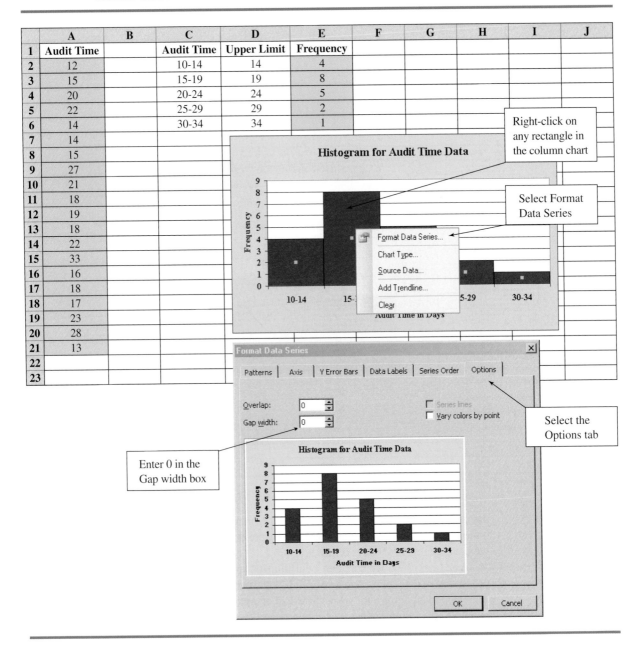

quency distribution shows the number of data items with values *less than or equal to the upper class limit* of each class. The first two columns of Table 2.8 provide the cumulative frequency distribution for the audit time data.

To understand how the cumulative frequencies are determined, consider the class with the description "less than or equal to 24." The cumulative frequency for this class is simply the sum of the frequencies for all classes with data values less than or equal to 24. For the frequency distribution in Table 2.6, the sum of the frequencies for classes 10–14, 15–19, and 20–24 indicates that $4 + 8 + 5 = 17$ data values are less than or equal to 24. Hence,

FIGURE 2.11 FINAL HISTOGRAM CONSTRUCTED USING EXCEL'S CHART WIZARD FOR THE AUDIT TIME DATA

the cumulative frequency for this class is 17. In addition, the cumulative frequency distribution in Table 2.8 shows that four audits were completed in 14 days or less and 19 audits were completed in 29 days or less.

As a final point, we note that a **cumulative relative frequency distribution** shows the proportion of data items, and a **cumulative percent frequency distribution** shows the percentage of data items with values less than or equal to the upper limit of each class. The cumulative relative frequency distribution can be computed either by summing the relative frequencies in the relative frequency distribution or by dividing the cumulative frequencies by the total number of items. Using the latter approach, we found the cumulative relative frequencies in column 3 of Table 2.8 by dividing the cumulative frequencies in column 2 by the total number of items ($n = 20$). The cumulative percent frequencies were again computed by multiplying the relative frequencies by 100. The cumulative relative and percent frequency distributions show that .85 of the audits, or 85%, were completed in 24 days or less; .95 of the audits, or 95%, were completed in 29 days or less; and so on.

A graph of a cumulative distribution, called an **ogive**, shows data values on the horizontal axis and either the cumulative frequencies, the cumulative relative frequencies, or the cumulative percent frequencies on the vertical axis. Figure 2.12 illustrates an ogive for the cumulative frequencies of the audit time data in Table 2.8.

TABLE 2.8   CUMULATIVE FREQUENCY, CUMULATIVE RELATIVE FREQUENCY,
AND CUMULATIVE PERCENT FREQUENCY DISTRIBUTIONS
FOR THE AUDIT TIME DATA

Audit Time (days)	Cumulative Frequency	Cumulative Relative Frequency	Cumulative Percent Frequency
Less than or equal to 14	4	.20	20
Less than or equal to 19	12	.60	60
Less than or equal to 24	17	.85	85
Less than or equal to 29	19	.95	95
Less than or equal to 34	20	1.00	100

The ogive is constructed by plotting a point corresponding to the cumulative frequency of each class. Because the classes for the audit time data are 10–14, 15–19, 20–24, and so on, one-unit gaps appear from 14 to 15, 19 to 20, and so on. These gaps are eliminated by plotting points halfway between the class limits. Thus, 14.5 is used for the 10–14 class, 19.5 is used for the 15–19 class, and so on. The "less than or equal to 14" class with a cumulative frequency of 4 is shown on the ogive in Figure 2.12 by the point located at 14.5 on the horizontal axis and 4 on the vertical axis. The "less than or equal to 19" class with a cumulative frequency of 12 is shown by the point located at 19.5 on the horizontal axis and 12 on the vertical axis. Note that one additional point is plotted at the left end of the ogive. This point starts the ogive by showing that no data values fall below the 10–14 class. It is plotted at 9.5 on the horizontal axis and 0 on the vertical axis. The plotted points are connected by straight lines to complete the ogive.

Using Excel's Histogram Tool to Construct a Frequency Distribution and Histogram

In illustrating how to use Excel to summarize quantitative data, we used the FREQUENCY function to construct a frequency distribution and the Chart Wizard to construct a histogram. Microsoft Excel also provides a set of data analysis tools that can be accessed through

FIGURE 2.12   OGIVE FOR THE AUDIT TIME DATA

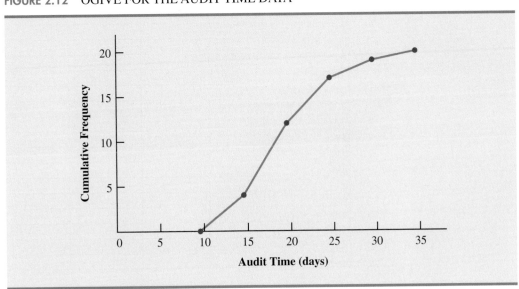

the Tools menu. The data analysis tool for constructing frequency distributions and histograms is the Histogram tool. It can save steps when both a frequency distribution and a histogram are desired. Here we show how it is used by constructing a frequency distribution and a histogram for the audit time data in Table 2.5.

Enter Data: The label Audit Time and the data for the 20 audit times have been entered into cells A1:A21 of the worksheet shown in Figure 2.13.

Enter Functions and Formulas: No functions and formulas are needed.

Apply Tools: Excel's Histogram tool requires the identification of what are called *bins* for each class in the frequency distribution using the class upper limits. Hence, five bins with upper limits of 14, 19, 24, 29, and 34 are needed for the audit time data. The bin upper limits must be entered in ascending order in a column or row of the worksheet. Descriptive labels have been entered into cells C1:D1, the class limits 10–14, 15–19, and so on, have been entered using text format into cells C2:C6, and the bin upper limits have been entered into cells D2:D6 of the worksheet in Figure 2.13.

The following steps describe how to use the Histogram tool to produce a frequency distribution and a histogram consisting of five classes, or bins, for the audit time data.

*Note: If the **Data Analysis** option does not appear when you select the **Tools** menu, choose **Add-Ins**, and check **Analysis ToolPak** to install it.*

Step 1. Select the **Tools** menu
Step 2. Choose the **Data Analysis** option
Step 3. Choose **Histogram** from the list of Analysis Tools
Step 4. When the Histogram dialog box appears (see Figure 2.14):
  Enter A1:A21 in the **Input Range** box
  Enter D1:D6 in the **Bin Range** box

FIGURE 2.13 WORKSHEET FOR AUDIT TIME DATA AFTER CREATING BINS USING UPPER CLASS LIMITS

	A	B	C	D	E
1	**Audit Time**		**Audit Time**	**Upper Limit**	
2	12		10-14	14	
3	15		15-19	19	
4	20		20-24	24	
5	22		25-29	29	
6	14		30-34	34	
7	14				
8	15				
9	27				
10	21				
11	18				
12	19				
13	18				
14	22				
15	33				
16	16				
17	18				
18	17				
19	23				
20	28				
21	13				
22					

FIGURE 2.14   DIALOG BOX FOR HISTOGRAM TOOL

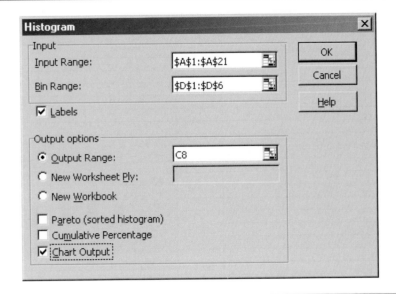

Select **Labels**
Select **Output Range**
Enter C8 in the **Output Range** box (it tells Excel where to display the frequency distribution)
Select **Chart Output** (to request a histogram)
Click **OK**

The worksheet shown in Figure 2.15 displays the frequency distribution and the histogram created using these steps. The frequency distribution is displayed in cells C8:D14. Note that Excel added a row to the frequency distribution with a label of "More" in order to provide for the possibility that we might have entered too few bin values.

To present the frequency distribution in the format of Table 2.6, some editing is required. Paste the contents of cells C1:C6 into cells C8:C13 and clear the contents of cells C14:D14. To present the histogram in the form of Figure 2.7 some editing of it is also required.

Step 1. Right-click on the legend title (Frequency) and select **Clear**
Step 2. Left-click on the horizontal axis title (Upper Limit), type **Audit Time**, and press **Enter**
Step 3. Remove the gaps between bars the same way as when using the Chart Wizard (see Figure 2.9)

The worksheet now appears as shown in Figure 2.16.

As we have just seen, the Histogram tool can be used to construct both a frequency distribution and histogram in one series of steps. Previously, we showed how to use the FREQUENCY function and the Chart Wizard to accomplish the same thing. The advantage of using the FREQUENCY function and Chart Wizard is that the results remain linked to the data. Thus, a change in the data will prompt an automatic update of the frequency distribution and histogram. With the Histogram tool, the results are not linked to the data so a change in the data requires that we reconstruct the frequency distribution and histogram.

FIGURE 2.15   INITIAL FREQUENCY DISTRIBUTION AND HISTOGRAM CONSTRUCTED USING HISTOGRAM TOOL

	A	B	C	D	E	F	G	H	I	J	K	L
1	Audit Time		Audit Time	Upper Limit								
2	12		10-14	14								
3	15		15-19	19								
4	20		20-24	24								
5	22		25-29	29								
6	14		30-34	34								
7	14											
8	15		*Upper Limit*	*Frequency*								
9	27		14	4								
10	21		19	8								
11	18		24	5								
12	19		29	2								
13	18		34	1								
14	22		More	0								
15	33											
16	16											
17	18											
18	17											
19	23											
20	28											
21	13											
22												

FIGURE 2.16   FINAL FREQUENCY DISTRIBUTION AND HISTOGRAM CONSTRUCTED USING HISTOGRAM TOOL

	A	B	C	D	E	F	G	H	I	J	K
1	Audit Time		Audit Time	Upper Limit							
2	12		10-14	14							
3	15		15-19	19							
4	20		20-24	24							
5	22		25-29	29							
6	14		30-34	34							
7	14										
8	15		Audit Time	*Frequency*							
9	27		10-14	4							
10	21		15-19	8							
11	18		20-24	5							
12	19		25-29	2							
13	18		30-34	1							
14	22										
15	33										
16	16										
17	18										
18	17										
19	23										
20	28										
21	13										
22											

NOTES AND COMMENTS

1. A bar graph and a histogram are essentially the same thing; both are graphical presentations of the data in a frequency distribution. A histogram is just a bar graph with no separation between bars. For some discrete quantitative data, a separation between bars is also appropriate. Consider, for example, the number of classes in which a college student is enrolled. The data may only assume integer values. Intermediate values such as 1.5, 2.73, and so on are not possible. With continuous quantitative data, however, such as the audit times in Table 2.5, a separation between bars is not appropriate.

2. The appropriate values for the class limits with quantitative data depend on the level of accuracy of the data. For instance, with the audit time data of Table 2.5 the limits used were integer values. If the data were rounded to the nearest tenth of a day (e.g., 12.3, 14.4, and so on), then the limits would be stated in tenths of days. For instance, the first class would be 10.0–14.9. If the data were recorded to the nearest hundredth of a day (e.g., 12.34, 14.45, and so on), the limits would be stated in hundredths of days. For instance, the first class would be 10.00–14.99.

3. An *open-end* class requires only a lower class limit or an upper class limit. For example, in the audit time data of Table 2.5, suppose two of the audits had taken 58 and 65 days. Rather than continue with the classes of width 5 with classes 35–39, 40–44, 45–49, and so on, we could simplify the frequency distribution to show an open-end class of "35 or more." This class would have a frequency of 2. Most often the open-end class appears at the upper end of the distribution. Sometimes an open-end class appears at the lower end of the distribution, and occasionally such classes appear at both ends.

4. The last entry in a cumulative frequency distribution always equals the total number of observations. The last entry in a cumulative relative frequency distribution always equals 1.00 and the last entry in a cumulative percent frequency distribution always equals 100.

Exercises

Methods

11. Consider the following data.

14	21	23	21	16
19	22	25	16	16
24	24	25	19	16
19	18	19	21	12
16	17	18	23	25
20	23	16	20	19
24	26	15	22	24
20	22	24	22	20

CD file

Frequency

a. Develop a frequency distribution using classes of 12–14, 15–17, 18–20, 21–23, and 24–26.
b. Develop a relative frequency distribution and a percent frequency distribution using the classes in part (a).

12. Consider the following frequency distribution.

SELF test

Class	Frequency
10–19	10
20–29	14
30–39	17
40–49	7
50–59	2

Construct a cumulative frequency distribution and a cumulative relative frequency distribution.

13. Construct a histogram and an ogive for the data in exercise 12.
14. Consider the following data.

8.9	10.2	11.5	7.8	10.0	12.2	13.5	14.1	10.0	12.2
6.8	9.5	11.5	11.2	14.9	7.5	10.0	6.0	15.8	11.5

a. Construct a frequency distribution.
b. Construct a percent frequency distribution.

Applications

15. A doctor's office staff studied the waiting times for patients who arrive at the office with a request for emergency service. The following data with waiting times in minutes were collected over a one-month period.

2 5 10 12 4 4 5 17 11 8 9 8 12 21 6 8 7 13 18 3

Use classes of 0–4, 5–9, and so on in the following:
a. Show the frequency distribution.
b. Show the relative frequency distribution.
c. Show the cumulative frequency distribution.
d. Show the cumulative relative frequency distribution.
e. What proportion of patients needing emergency service wait 9 minutes or less?

16. Consider the following two frequency distributions. The first frequency distribution shows the annual adjusted gross income in the United States for individuals earning less than $200,000 (Internal Revenue Service, March 2003). The second frequency distribution shows exam scores for students in a college statistics course.

Income ($1000s)	Frequency (millions)	Exam Score	Frequency
0–24	60	Below 30	2
25–49	33	30–39	5
50–74	20	40–49	6
75–99	6	50–59	13
100–124	4	60–69	32
125–149	2	70–79	78
150–174	1	80–89	43
175–199	1	90–99	21
Total	**127**	**Total**	**200**

a. Develop a histogram for the annual income data. What evidence of skewness does it show? Does this skewness make sense? Explain.
b. Develop a histogram for the exam score data. What evidence of skewness does it show? Explain.
c. Develop a histogram for the data in exercise 11. What evidence of skewness does it show? What is the general shape of the distribution?

17. Mendelsohn Media Research provided survey data on the annual amount of household purchases by families with an annual income of $75,000 or more (*Money*, 2001). Assume that the following data from a sample of 25 households show the dollars spent in the past year on books and magazines.

Spending

280	496	382	202	287
266	119	10	385	135
475	255	379	267	24
42	25	283	110	423
160	123	16	243	363

a. Construct a frequency distribution and relative frequency distribution for the data.

b. Provide a histogram. Comment on the shape of the distribution.

c. Comment on the annual spending on books and magazines for families in the sample.

18. Wageweb conducts surveys of salary data and presents summaries on its Web site. Wageweb reported annual salaries of marketing vice presidents ranged from $85,090 to $190,054 (http://www.Wageweb.com, April 12, 2000). Assume the following data come from a sample of the annual salaries for 50 marketing vice presidents. Data are in thousands of dollars.

Wageweb

145	95	148	112	132
140	162	118	170	144
145	127	148	165	138
173	113	104	141	142
116	178	123	141	138
127	143	134	136	137
155	93	102	154	142
134	165	123	124	124
138	160	157	138	131
114	135	151	138	157

a. What are the lowest and highest salaries?

b. Use a class width of $15,000 and prepare tabular summaries of the annual salary data.

c. What proportion of the annual salaries are $135,000 or less?

d. What percentage of the annual salaries are more than $150,000?

e. Prepare a histogram. Comment on the shape of the distribution.

19. Sorting through unsolicited e-mail and spam affects the productivity of office workers. An InsightExpress survey monitored office workers to determine the unproductive time per day devoted to unsolicited e-mail and spam (*USA Today,* November 13, 2003). The following data show a sample of time in minutes devoted to this task.

2	4	8	4
8	1	2	32
12	1	5	7
5	5	3	4
24	19	4	14

Summarize the data by constructing the following:

a. A frequency distribution (classes 1–5, 6–10, 11–15, 16–20, and so on)

b. A relative frequency distribution

c. A cumulative frequency distribution

d. A cumulative relative frequency distribution

e. An ogive

f. What percentage of office workers spend 5 minutes or less on unsolicited e-mail and spam? What percentage of office workers spend more than 10 minutes a day on this task?

20. The top 20 concert tours and their average ticket price for shows in North America are shown here. The list is based on data provided to the trade publication *Pollstar* by concert promoters and venue managers (Associated Press, November 21, 2003).

Concerts

Concert Tour	Ticket Price	Concert Tour	Ticket Price
Bruce Springsteen	$72.40	Toby Keith	$37.76
Dave Matthews Band	44.11	James Taylor	44.93
Aerosmith/KISS	69.52	Alabama	40.83
Shania Twain	61.80	Harper/Johnson	33.70
Fleetwood Mac	78.34	50 Cent	38.89
Radiohead	39.50	Steely Dan	36.38
Cher	64.47	Red Hot Chili Peppers	56.82
Counting Crows	36.48	R.E.M.	46.16
Timberlake/Aguilera	74.43	American Idols Live	39.11
Mana	46.48	Mariah Carey	56.08

Summarize the data by constructing the following:
a. A frequency distribution and a percent frequency distribution
b. A histogram
c. What concert had the most expensive average ticket price? What concert had the least expensive average ticket price?
d. Comment on what the data indicate about the average ticket prices of the top concert tours.

21. The *Nielsen Home Technology Report* provided information about home technology and its usage by persons age 12 and older. The following data are the hours of personal computer usage during one week for a sample of 50 persons.

Computer

4.1	1.5	10.4	5.9	3.4	5.7	1.6	6.1	3.0	3.7
3.1	4.8	2.0	14.8	5.4	4.2	3.9	4.1	11.1	3.5
4.1	4.1	8.8	5.6	4.3	3.3	7.1	10.3	6.2	7.6
10.8	2.8	9.5	12.9	12.1	0.7	4.0	9.2	4.4	5.7
7.2	6.1	5.7	5.9	4.7	3.9	3.7	3.1	6.1	3.1

Summarize the data by constructing the following:
a. A frequency distribution (use a class width of 3 hours)
b. A relative frequency distribution
c. A histogram
d. An ogive
e. Comment on what the data indicate about personal computer usage at home.

(2.3) Exploratory Data Analysis: The Stem-and-Leaf Display

The techniques of **exploratory data analysis** consist of simple arithmetic and easy-to-draw graphs that can be used to summarize data quickly. One technique—referred to as a **stem-and-leaf display**—can be used to show both the rank order and shape of a data set simultaneously.

To illustrate the use of a stem-and-leaf display, consider the data in Table 2.9. These data result from a 150-question aptitude test given to 50 individuals recently interviewed for a position at Haskens Manufacturing. The data indicate the number of questions answered correctly.

To develop a stem-and-leaf display, we first arrange the leading digits of each data value to the left of a vertical line. To the right of the vertical line, we record the last digit for each

TABLE 2.9   NUMBER OF QUESTIONS ANSWERED CORRECTLY ON AN APTITUDE TEST

ApTest

112	72	69	97	107
73	92	76	86	73
126	128	118	127	124
82	104	132	134	83
92	108	96	100	92
115	76	91	102	81
95	141	81	80	106
84	119	113	98	75
68	98	115	106	95
100	85	94	106	119

data value. Based on the top row of data in Table 2.9 (112, 72, 69, 97, and 107), the first five entries in constructing a stem-and-leaf display would be as follows:

```
 6 | 9
 7 | 2
 8 |
 9 | 7
10 | 7
11 | 2
12 |
13 |
14 |
```

For example, the data value 112 shows the leading digits 11 to the left of the line and the last digit 2 to the right of the line. Similarly, the data value 72 shows the leading digit 7 to the left of the line and last digit 2 to the right of the line. Continuing to place the last digit of each data value on the line corresponding to its leading digit(s) provides the following:

```
 6 | 9  8
 7 | 2  3  6  3  6  5
 8 | 6  2  3  1  1  0  4  5
 9 | 7  2  2  6  2  1  5  8  8  5  4
10 | 7  4  8  0  2  6  6  0  6
11 | 2  8  5  9  3  5  9
12 | 6  8  7  4
13 | 2  4
14 | 1
```

With this organization of the data, sorting the digits on each line into rank order is simple. Doing so provides the stem-and-leaf display shown here.

```
 6 | 8  9
 7 | 2  3  3  5  6  6
 8 | 0  1  1  2  3  4  5  6
 9 | 1  2  2  2  4  5  5  6  7  8  8
10 | 0  0  2  4  6  6  6  7  8
11 | 2  3  5  5  8  9  9
12 | 4  6  7  8
13 | 2  4
14 | 1
```

The numbers to the left of the vertical line (6, 7, 8, 9, 10, 11, 12, 13, and 14) form the *stem*, and each digit to the right of the vertical line is a *leaf*. For example, consider the first row with a stem value of 6 and leaves of 8 and 9.

```
6 | 8  9
```

This row indicates that two data values have a first digit of six. The leaves show that the data values are 68 and 69. Similarly, the second row

$$7 \mid 2 \quad 3 \quad 3 \quad 5 \quad 6 \quad 6$$

indicates that six data values have a first digit of seven. The leaves show that the data values are 72, 73, 73, 75, 76, and 76.

To focus on the shape indicated by the stem-and-leaf display, let us use a rectangle to contain the leaves of each stem. Doing so, we obtain the following.

```
 6 | 8  9
 7 | 2  3  3  5  6  6
 8 | 0  1  1  2  3  4  5  6
 9 | 1  2  2  2  4  5  5  6  7  8  8
10 | 0  0  2  4  6  6  6  7  8
11 | 2  3  5  5  8  9  9
12 | 4  6  7  8
13 | 2  4
14 | 1
```

Rotating this page counterclockwise onto its side provides a picture of the data that is similar to a histogram with classes of 60–69, 70–79, 80–89, and so on.

Although the stem-and-leaf display may appear to offer the same information as a histogram, it has two primary advantages.

1. The stem-and-leaf display is easier to construct by hand.
2. Within a class interval, the stem-and-leaf display provides more information than the histogram because the stem-and-leaf shows the actual data.

In a stretched stem-and-leaf display, whenever a stem value is stated twice, the first value corresponds to leaf values of 0–4, and the second value corresponds to leaf values of 5–9.

Just as a frequency distribution or histogram has no absolute number of classes, neither does a stem-and-leaf display have an absolute number of rows or stems. If we believe that our original stem-and-leaf display condensed the data too much, we can easily stretch the display by using two or more stems for each leading digit. For example, to use two stems for each leading digit, we would place all data values ending in 0, 1, 2, 3, and 4 in one row and all values ending in 5, 6, 7, 8, and 9 in a second row. The following stretched stem-and-leaf display illustrates this approach.

```
 6 | 8  9
 7 | 2  3  3
 7 | 5  6  6
 8 | 0  1  1  2  3  4
 8 | 5  6
 9 | 1  2  2  2  4
 9 | 5  5  6  7  8  8
10 | 0  0  2  4
10 | 6  6  6  7  8
11 | 2  3
11 | 5  5  8  9  9
12 | 4
12 | 6  7  8
13 | 2  4
13 |
14 | 1
```

Note that values 72, 73, and 73 have leaves in the 0–4 range and are shown with the first stem value of 7. The values 75, 76, and 76 have leaves in the 5–9 range and are shown with the second stem value of 7. This stretched stem-and-leaf display is similar to a frequency distribution with intervals of 65–69, 70–74, 75–79, and so on.

The preceding example showed a stem-and-leaf display for data with as many as three digits. Stem-and-leaf displays for data with more than three digits are possible. For example, consider the following data on the number of hamburgers sold by a fast-food restaurant for each of 15 weeks.

1565	1852	1644	1766	1888	1912	2044	1812
1790	1679	2008	1852	1967	1954	1733	

A stem-and-leaf display of these data follows.

Leaf unit = 10

```
15 | 6
16 | 4  7
17 | 3  6  9
18 | 1  5  5  8
19 | 1  5  6
20 | 0  4
```

A single digit is used to define each leaf in a stem-and-leaf display. The leaf unit indicates how to multiply the stem-and-leaf numbers in order to approximate the original data. Leaf units may be 100, 10, 1, 0.1, and so on.

Note that a single digit is used to define each leaf and that only the first three digits of each data value have been used to construct the display. At the top of the display we have specified Leaf unit = 10. To illustrate how to interpret the values in the display, consider the first stem, 15, and its associated leaf, 6. Combining these numbers, we obtain 156. To reconstruct an approximation of the original data value, we must multiply this number by 10, the value of the *leaf unit*. Thus, $156 \times 10 = 1560$ is an approximation of the original data value used to construct the stem-and-leaf display. Although it is not possible to reconstruct the exact data value from this stem-and-leaf display, the convention of using a single digit for each leaf enables stem-and-leaf displays to be constructed for data having a large number of digits. For stem-and-leaf displays where the leaf unit is not shown, the leaf unit is assumed to equal 1.

Exercises

Methods

22. Construct a stem-and-leaf display for the following data.

70	72	75	64	58	83	80	82
76	75	68	65	57	78	85	72

23. Construct a stem-and-leaf display for the following data.

11.3	9.6	10.4	7.5	8.3	10.5	10.0
9.3	8.1	7.7	7.5	8.4	6.3	8.8

24. Construct a stem-and-leaf display for the following data. Use a leaf unit of 10.

1161	1206	1478	1300	1604	1725	1361	1422
1221	1378	1623	1426	1557	1730	1706	1689

Applications

25. A psychologist developed a new test of adult intelligence. The test was administered to 20 individuals, and the following data were obtained.

| 114 | 99 | 131 | 124 | 117 | 102 | 106 | 127 | 119 | 115 |
| 98 | 104 | 144 | 151 | 132 | 106 | 125 | 122 | 118 | 118 |

Construct a stem-and-leaf display for the data.

26. The American Association of Individual Investors conducts an annual survey of discount brokers. The following prices charged are from a sample of 24 discount brokers (*AAII Journal*, January 2003). The two types of trades are a broker-assisted trade of 100 shares at $50 per share and an online trade of 500 shares at $50 per share.

Broker

Broker	Broker-Assisted 100 Shares at $50/Share	Online 500 Shares at $50/Share	Broker	Broker-Assisted 100 Shares at $50/Share	Online 500 Shares at $50/Share
Accutrade	30.00	29.95	Merrill Lynch Direct	50.00	29.95
Ameritrade	24.99	10.99	Muriel Siebert	45.00	14.95
Banc of America	54.00	24.95	NetVest	24.00	14.00
Brown & Co.	17.00	5.00	Recom Securities	35.00	12.95
Charles Schwab	55.00	29.95	Scottrade	17.00	7.00
CyberTrader	12.95	9.95	Sloan Securities	39.95	19.95
E*TRADE Securities	49.95	14.95	Strong Investments	55.00	24.95
First Discount	35.00	19.75	TD Waterhouse	45.00	17.95
Freedom Investments	25.00	15.00	T. Rowe Price	50.00	19.95
Harrisdirect	40.00	20.00	Vanguard	48.00	20.00
Investors National	39.00	62.50	Wall Street Discount	29.95	19.95
MB Trading	9.95	10.55	York Securities	40.00	36.00

a. Round the trading prices to the nearest dollar and develop a stem-and-leaf display for 100 shares at $50 per share. Comment on what you learned about broker-assisted trading prices.

b. Round the trading prices to the nearest dollar and develop a stretched stem-and-leaf display for 500 shares online at $50 per share. Comment on what you learned about online trading prices.

27. The prices per share for the 30 companies making up the Dow Jones Industrial Average are shown here (*The Wall Street Journal*, April 9, 2004).

StockPrices

Company	$/Share	Company	$/Share
Alcoa	$34	Honeywell	$35
Altria Group	55	IBM	93
American Express	52	Intel	27
American International	76	Johnson & Johnson	51
Boeing	41	JPMorgan Chase	41
Caterpillar	82	McDonald's	29
Citigroup	52	Merck	45
Coca-Cola	51	Microsoft	25
Disney	26	Pfizer	36
DuPont	43	Procter & Gamble	106
ExxonMobil	42	SBE Communications	24
General Electric	31	3M	82
General Motors	47	United Technologies	90
Hewlett-Packard	23	Verizon	37
Home Depot	36	Wal-Mart Stores	57

   a. Develop a stem-and-leaf display.
   b. Use the stem-and-leaf display to answer the following questions:
   - What does the grouping of the data in the stem-and-leaf display tell you about the prices per share for the 30 Dow Jones companies?
   - What is the price-per-share range for the majority of the companies?
   - How many companies have a price per share of $36?
   - What is the most frequently appearing price per share?
   - What should be considered a relatively high price per share? What percentage of the companies have a price per share in this range? Which companies have a price per share in this range, and what is the price per share for each?
   c. Use *The Wall Street Journal* or another business publication to find the current price per share for each of the 30 Dow Jones Industrial Average companies. Construct a stem-and-leaf display for these data and use the display to comment on any changes in the prices per share since April 2004.

28. The 2004 Naples, Florida, mini marathon (13.1 miles) had 1228 registrants (*The Naples Daily News,* January 17, 2004). Competition was held in six age groups. The following data show the ages for a sample of 40 individuals who participated in the marathon.

Marathon

49	33	40	37	56
44	46	57	55	32
50	52	43	64	40
46	24	30	37	43
31	43	50	36	61
27	44	35	31	43
52	43	66	31	50
72	26	59	21	47

   a. Show a stretched stem-and-leaf display.
   b. What age group had the largest number of runners?
   c. What age occurred most frequently?
   d. A *Naples Daily News* feature article emphasized the number of runners who were "20-something." What percentage of the runners were in the 20-something age group? What do you suppose was the focus of the article?

(2.4) Crosstabulations and Scatter Diagrams

Crosstabulations and scatter diagrams are used to summarize data in a way that reveals the relationship between two variables.

Thus far in this chapter, we focused on tabular and graphical methods used to summarize the data for *one variable at a time.* Often a manager or decision maker requires tabular and graphical methods that will assist in the understanding of the *relationship between two variables.* Crosstabulations and scatter diagrams are two such methods.

Crosstabulation

A **crosstabulation** is a tabular summary of data for two variables. Let us illustrate the use of a crosstabulation by considering the following application based on data from Zagat's Restaurant Survey. The quality rating and the meal price data were collected for a sample of 300 restaurants located in the Los Angeles area. Table 2.10 shows the data for the first 10 restaurants. Data on a restaurant's quality rating and typical meal price are reported. Quality rating is a qualitative variable with rating categories of good, very good, and excellent. Meal price is a quantitative variable that ranges from $10 to $49.

A crosstabulation of the data for this application is shown in Table 2.11. The left and top margin labels define the classes for the two variables. In the left margin, the row labels (good, very good, and excellent) correspond to the three classes of the quality rating variable. In the top margin, the column labels ($10–19, $20–29, $30–39, and $40–49) correspond to the four classes of the meal price variable. Each restaurant in the sample provides a quality

TABLE 2.10   QUALITY RATING AND MEAL PRICE FOR 300 LOS ANGELES RESTAURANTS

Restaurant

Restaurant	Quality Rating	Meal Price ($)
1	Good	18
2	Very Good	22
3	Good	28
4	Excellent	38
5	Very Good	33
6	Good	28
7	Very Good	19
8	Very Good	11
9	Very Good	23
10	Good	13
.	.	.
.	.	.
.	.	.

rating and a meal price. Thus, each restaurant in the sample is associated with a cell appearing in one of the rows and one of the columns of the crosstabulation. For example, restaurant 5 is identified as having a very good quality rating and a meal price of $33. This restaurant belongs to the cell in row 2 and column 3 of Table 2.11. In constructing a crosstabulation, we simply count the number of restaurants that belong to each of the cells in the crosstabulation table.

In reviewing Table 2.11, we see that the greatest number of restaurants in the sample (64) have a very good rating and a meal price in the $20–29 range. Only two restaurants have an excellent rating and a meal price in the $10–19 range. Similar interpretations of the other frequencies can be made. In addition, note that the right and bottom margins of the cross-tabulation provide the frequency distributions for quality rating and meal price separately. From the frequency distribution in the right margin, we see that data on quality ratings show that 84 of the restaurants were rated good, 150 were rated very good, and 66 were rated excellent. Similarly, the bottom margin shows the frequency distribution for the meal price variable.

Dividing the totals in the right margin of the crosstabulation by the total for that column provides a relative and percent frequency distribution for the quality rating variable.

Quality Rating	Relative Frequency	Percent Frequency
Good	.28	28
Very Good	.50	50
Excellent	.22	22
Total	1.00	100

TABLE 2.11   CROSSTABULATION OF QUALITY RATING AND MEAL PRICE
FOR 300 LOS ANGELES RESTAURANTS

Quality Rating	Meal Price				Total
	$10–19	$20–29	$30–39	$40–49	
Good	42	40	2	0	84
Very Good	34	64	46	6	150
Excellent	2	14	28	22	66
Total	78	118	76	28	300

From the percent frequency distribution we see that 28% of the restaurants were rated good, 50% were rated very good, and 22% were rated excellent.

Dividing the totals in the bottom row of the crosstabulation by the total for that row provides a relative and percent frequency distribution for the meal price variable.

Meal Price	Relative Frequency	Percent Frequency
$10–19	.26	26
$20–29	.39	39
$30–39	.25	25
$40–49	.09	9
Total	1.00	100

Note that the sum of the values in each column does not add up exactly to the column total, because the values being summed are rounded. From the percent frequency distribution we see that 26% of the meal prices are in the lowest price class ($10–19), 39% are in the next higher class, and so on.

The frequency and relative frequency distributions constructed from the margins of a crosstabulation provide information about each of the variables individually, but they do not shed any light on the relationship between the variables. The primary value of a crosstabulation lies in the insight it offers about the relationship between the variables. A review of the crosstabulation in Table 2.11 reveals that higher meal prices are associated with the higher quality restaurants, and the lower meal prices are associated with the lower quality restaurants.

Converting the entries in a crosstabulation into row percentages or column percentages can provide more insight into the relationship between the two variables. For row percentages, the results of dividing each frequency in Table 2.11 by its corresponding row total are shown in Table 2.12. Each row of Table 2.12 is a percent frequency distribution of meal price for one of the quality rating categories. Of the restaurants with the lowest quality rating (good), we see that the greatest percentages are for the less expensive restaurants (50% have $10–19 meal prices and 47.6% have $20–29 meal prices). Of the restaurants with the highest quality rating (excellent), we see that the greatest percentages are for the more expensive restaurants (42.4% have $30–39 meal prices and 33.4% have $40–49 meal prices). Thus, we continue to see that the more expensive meals are associated with the higher quality restaurants.

Crosstabulation is widely used for examining the relationship between two variables. In practice, the final reports for many statistical studies include a large number of crosstabulation tables. In the Los Angeles restaurant survey, the crosstabulation is based on one qualitative variable (quality rating) and one quantitative variable (meal price). Crosstabulations can also be developed when both variables are qualitative and when both variables are quantitative. When quantitative variables are used, however, we must first create classes for the values of the variable. For instance, in the restaurant example we grouped the meal prices into four classes ($10–19, $20–29, $30–39, and $40–49).

TABLE 2.12   ROW PERCENTAGES FOR EACH QUALITY RATING CATEGORY

Quality Rating	Meal Price				Total
	$10–19	**$20–29**	**$30–39**	**$40–49**	
Good	50.0	47.6	2.4	0.0	100
Very Good	22.7	42.7	30.6	4.0	100
Excellent	3.0	21.2	42.4	33.4	100

Using Excel's PivotTable Report to Construct a Crosstabulation

Excel's PivotTable Report provides a general tool for summarizing the data for two or more variables simultaneously. We will illustrate the use of Excel's PivotTable Report by showing how to develop a crosstabulation of quality ratings and meal prices for the sample of 300 restaurants located in the Los Angeles area.

Enter Data: The labels "Restaurant," "Quality Rating," and "Meal Price ($)" have been entered into cells A1:C1 of the worksheet shown in Figure 2.17. The data for each of the 300 restaurants in the sample have been entered into cells B2:C301.

Enter Functions and Formulas: No functions and formulas are needed.

Apply Tools: Starting with the worksheet in Figure 2.17, the following steps will produce a crosstabulation.

Step 1. Select the **Data** menu
Step 2. Choose **PivotTable and PivotChart Report**
Step 3. When the PivotTable and PivotChart Wizard - Step 1 of 3 dialog box appears:
  Choose **Microsoft Office Excel list or database**
  Choose **PivotTable**
  Click **Next**
Step 4. When the PivotTable and PivotChart Wizard - Step 2 of 3 dialog box appears:
  Enter A1:C301 in the **Range:** box
  Click **Next**

FIGURE 2.17   EXCEL WORKSHEET CONTAINING RESTAURANT DATA

CD file

Restaurant

Note: Rows 12–291 are hidden.

	A	B	C	D
1	Restaurant	Quality Rating	Meal Price ($)	
2	1	Good	18	
3	2	Very Good	22	
4	3	Good	28	
5	4	Excellent	38	
6	5	Very Good	33	
7	6	Good	28	
8	7	Very Good	19	
9	8	Very Good	11	
10	9	Very Good	23	
11	10	Good	13	
292	291	Very Good	23	
293	292	Very Good	24	
294	293	Excellent	45	
295	294	Good	14	
296	295	Good	18	
297	296	Good	17	
298	297	Good	16	
299	298	Good	15	
300	299	Very Good	38	
301	300	Very Good	31	
302				

a. Develop a crosstabulation for the data, with x as the row variable and y as the column variable.
b. Compute the row percentages.
c. Compute the column percentages.
d. What is the relationship, if any, between x and y?

30. The following 20 observations are for two quantitative variables, x and y.

Scatter

Observation	x	y	Observation	x	y
1	-22	22	11	-37	48
2	-33	49	12	34	-29
3	2	8	13	9	-18
4	29	-16	14	-33	31
5	-13	10	15	20	-16
6	21	-28	16	-3	14
7	-13	27	17	-15	18
8	-23	35	18	12	17
9	14	-5	19	-20	-11
10	3	-3	20	-7	-22

a. Develop a scatter diagram for the relationship between x and y.
b. What is the relationship, if any, between x and y?

Applications

31. The following crosstabulation shows household income by educational level of the head of household (*Statistical Abstract of the United States: 2002*).

Educational Level	Household Income ($1000s)					Total
	Under 25	25.0–49.9	50.0–74.9	75.0–99.9	100 or more	
Not H.S. graduate	9285	4093	1589	541	354	15862
H.S. graduate	10150	9821	6050	2737	2028	30786
Some college	6011	8221	5813	3215	3120	26380
Bachelor's degree	2138	3985	3952	2698	4748	17521
Beyond bach. deg.	813	1497	1815	1589	3765	9479
Total	28397	27617	19219	10780	14015	100028

a. Compute the row percentages and identify the percent frequency distributions of income for households in which the head of household is a high school graduate and in which the head of household holds a bachelor's degree.
b. What percentage of households headed by high school graduates earn $75,000 or more? What percentage of households headed by bachelor's degree recipients earn $75,000 or more?
c. Construct percent frequency histograms of income for households headed by persons with a high school degree and for those headed by persons with a bachelor's degree. Is any relationship evident between household income and educational level?

32. Refer again to the crosstabulation of household income by educational level shown in exercise 31.
a. Compute column percentages and identify the percent frequency distributions displayed. What percentage of the heads of households did not graduate from high school?
b. What percentage of the households earning $100,000 or more were headed by a person having schooling beyond a bachelor's degree? What percentage of the households

headed by a person with schooling beyond a bachelor's degree earned over $100,000? Why are these two percentages different?

c. Compare the percent frequency distributions for those households earning "Under 25," "100 or more," and for "Total." Comment on the relationship between household income and educational level of the head of household.

33. Recently, management at Oak Tree Golf Course received a few complaints about the condition of the greens. Several players complained that the greens are too fast. Rather than react to the comments of just a few players, the Golf Association conducted a survey of 100 male and 100 female golfers. The survey results are summarized here.

Male Golfers

	Greens Condition	
Handicap	Too Fast	Fine
Under 15	10	40
15 or more	25	25

Female Golfers

	Greens Condition	
Handicap	Too Fast	Fine
Under 15	1	9
15 or more	39	51

a. Combine these two crosstabulations into one with Male, Female as the row labels and the column labels Too Fast and Fine. Which group shows the highest percentage saying that the greens are too fast?

b. Refer to the initial crosstabulations. For those players with handicaps under 15 (better players), which group (male or female) shows the highest percentage saying the greens are too fast?

c. Refer to the initial crosstabulations. For those players with handicaps 15 or more, which group (male or female) shows the highest percentage saying the greens are too fast?

d. What conclusions can you draw about the preferences of men and women concerning the speed of the greens? Are the conclusions you draw from part (a) as compared with parts (b) and (c) consistent? Explain any apparent inconsistencies.

34. Table 2.14 provides financial data for a sample of 36 companies whose stock trades on the New York Stock Exchange (*Investor's Business Daily,* April 7, 2000). The data on Sales/Margins/ROE are a composite rating based on a company's sales growth rate, its profit margins, and its return on equity (ROE). EPS Rating is a measure of growth in earnings per share for the company.

a. Prepare a crosstabulation of the data on Sales/Margins/ROE (rows) and EPS Rating (columns). Use classes of 0–19, 20–39, 40–59, 60–79, and 80–99 for EPS Rating.

b. Compute row percentages and comment on any relationship between the variables.

35. Refer to the data in Table 2.14.

a. Prepare a crosstabulation of the data on Sales/Margins/ROE and Industry Group Relative Strength.

b. Prepare a frequency distribution for the data on Sales/Margins/ROE.

c. Prepare a frequency distribution for the data on Industry Group Relative Strength.

d. How has the crosstabulation helped in preparing the frequency distributions in parts (b) and (c)?

36. Refer to the data in Table 2.14.

a. Prepare a scatter diagram of the data on EPS Rating and Relative Price Strength.

b. Comment on the relationship, if any, between the variables. (The meaning of the EPS Rating is described in exercise 34. Relative Price Strength is a measure of the change in the stock's price over the past 12 months. Higher values indicate greater strength.)

c. Compare the stem-and-leaf displays from parts (a) and (b), and make some comments about the differences between daily high and low temperatures.
d. Use the stem-and-leaf display from part (a) to determine the number of cities having a high temperature of 80 degrees or above.
e. Provide frequency distributions for both high and low temperature data.

47. Refer to the data set in exercise 46.
a. Develop a scatter diagram to show the relationship between the two variables, high temperature and low temperature.
b. Comment on the relationship between high and low temperatures.

48. A study of job satisfaction was conducted for four occupations. Job satisfaction was measured using an 18-item questionnaire with each question receiving a response score of 1 to 5 with higher scores indicating greater satisfaction. The sum of the 18 scores provides the job satisfaction score for each individual in the sample. The data are as follow.

CD file

OccupSat

Occupation	Satisfaction Score	Occupation	Satisfaction Score	Occupation	Satisfaction Score
Lawyer	42	Physical Therapist	78	Systems Analyst	60
Physical Therapist	86	Systems Analyst	44	Physical Therapist	59
Lawyer	42	Systems Analyst	71	Cabinetmaker	78
Systems Analyst	55	Lawyer	50	Physical Therapist	60
Lawyer	38	Lawyer	48	Physical Therapist	50
Cabinetmaker	79	Cabinetmaker	69	Cabinetmaker	79
Lawyer	44	Physical Therapist	80	Systems Analyst	62
Systems Analyst	41	Systems Analyst	64	Lawyer	45
Physical Therapist	55	Physical Therapist	55	Cabinetmaker	84
Systems Analyst	66	Cabinetmaker	64	Physical Therapist	62
Lawyer	53	Cabinetmaker	59	Systems Analyst	73
Cabinetmaker	65	Cabinetmaker	54	Cabinetmaker	60
Lawyer	74	Systems Analyst	76	Lawyer	64
Physical Therapist	52				

a. Provide a crosstabulation of occupation and job satisfaction score.
b. Compute the row percentages for your crosstabulation in part (a).
c. What observations can you make concerning the level of job satisfaction for these occupations?

49. Do larger companies generate more revenue? The following data show the number of employees and annual revenue for a sample of 20 *Fortune* 1000 companies (*Fortune*, April 17, 2000).

CD file

RevEmps

Company	Employees	Revenue ($ millions)	Company	Employees	Revenue ($ millions)
Sprint	77,600	19,930	American Financial	9,400	3,334
Chase Manhattan	74,801	33,710	Fluor	53,561	12,417
Computer Sciences	50,000	7,660	Phillips Petroleum	15,900	13,852
Wells Fargo	89,355	21,795	Cardinal Health	36,000	25,034
Sunbeam	12,200	2,398	Borders Group	23,500	2,999
CBS	29,000	7,510	MCI Worldcom	77,000	37,120
Time Warner	69,722	27,333	Consolidated Edison	14,269	7,491
Steelcase	16,200	2,743	IBP	45,000	14,075
Georgia-Pacific	57,000	17,796	Super Value	50,000	17,421
Toro	1,275	4,673	H&R Block	4,200	1,669

a. Prepare a scatter diagram to show the relationship between the variables Revenue and Employees.
b. Comment on any relationship between the variables.

50. A survey of commercial buildings served by the Cincinnati Gas & Electric Company asked what main heating fuel was used and what year the building was constructed. A partial crosstabulation of the findings follows.

Year Constructed	Fuel Type				
	Electricity	Natural Gas	Oil	Propane	Other
1973 or before	40	183	12	5	7
1974–1979	24	26	2	2	0
1980–1986	37	38	1	0	6
1987–1991	48	70	2	0	1

a. Complete the crosstabulation by showing the row totals and column totals.
b. Show the frequency distributions for year constructed and for fuel type.
c. Prepare a crosstabulation showing column percentages.
d. Prepare a crosstabulation showing row percentages.
e. Comment on the relationship between year constructed and fuel type.

51. Table 2.18 contains a portion of the data on the file named Fortune on the CD that accompanies the text. It provides data on stockholders' equity, market value, and profits for a sample of 50 *Fortune* 500 companies.
a. Prepare a crosstabulation for the variables Stockholders' Equity and Profit. Use classes of 0–200, 200–400, . . . , 1000–1200 for Profit, and classes of 0–1200, 1200–2400, . . . , 4800–6000 for Stockholders' Equity.
b. Compute the row percentages for your crosstabulation in part (a).
c. What relationship, if any, do you notice between Profit and Stockholders' Equity?

52. Refer to the data set in Table 2.18.
a. Prepare a crosstabulation for the variables Market Value and Profit.
b. Compute the row percentages for your crosstabulation in part (a).
c. Comment on any relationship between the variables.

TABLE 2.18   DATA FOR A SAMPLE OF 50 *FORTUNE* 500 COMPANIES

Fortune

Company	Stockholders' Equity ($1000s)	Market Value ($1000s)	Profit ($1000s)
AGCO	982.1	372.1	60.6
AMP	2698.0	12017.6	2.0
Apple Computer	1642.0	4605.0	309.0
Baxter International	2839.0	21743.0	315.0
Bergen Brunswick	629.1	2787.5	3.1
Best Buy	557.7	10376.5	94.5
Charles Schwab	1429.0	35340.6	348.5
.	.	.	.
.	.	.	.
.	.	.	.
Walgreen	2849.0	30324.7	511.0
Westvaco	2246.4	2225.6	132.0
Whirlpool	2001.0	3729.4	325.0
Xerox	5544.0	35603.7	395.0

53. Refer to the data set in Table 2.18.
    a. Prepare a scatter diagram to show the relationship between the variables Profit and
       Stockholders' Equity.
    b. Comment on any relationship between the variables.
54. Refer to the data set in Table 2.18.
    a. Prepare a scatter diagram to show the relationship between the variables Market Value
       and Stockholders' Equity.
    b. Comment on any relationship between the variables.

Case Problem   Pelican Stores

Pelican Stores, a division of National Clothing, is a chain of women's apparel stores operating throughout the country. The chain recently ran a promotion in which discount
coupons were sent to customers of other National Clothing stores. Data collected for a
sample of 100 in-store credit card transactions at Pelican Stores during one day while the
promotion was running are contained in the file named PelicanStores. Table 2.19 shows a
portion of the data set. The Proprietary Card method of payment refers to charges made
using a National Clothing charge card. Customers who made a purchase using a discount
coupon are referred to as promotional customers and customers who made a purchase but
did not use a discount coupon are referred to as regular customers. Because the promotional coupons were not sent to regular Pelican Stores customers, management considers
the sales made to people presenting the promotional coupons as sales it would not otherwise make. Of course, Pelican also hopes that the promotional customers will continue to
shop at its stores.

    Most of the variables shown in Table 2.19 are self-explanatory, but two of the variables
require some clarification.

| Items | The total number of items purchased |
| Net Sales | The total amount ($) charged to the credit card |

    Pelican's management would like to use this sample data to learn about its customer
base and to evaluate the promotion involving discount coupons.

TABLE 2.19   DATA FOR A SAMPLE OF 100 CREDIT CARD PURCHASES AT PELICAN STORES

PelicanStores

Customer	Type of Customer	Items	Net Sales	Method of Payment	Gender	Marital Status	Age
1	Regular	1	39.50	Discover	Male	Married	32
2	Promotional	1	102.40	Proprietary Card	Female	Married	36
3	Regular	1	22.50	Proprietary Card	Female	Married	32
4	Promotional	5	100.40	Proprietary Card	Female	Married	28
5	Regular	2	54.00	MasterCard	Female	Married	34
.	.	.	.	.	.	.	.
.	.	.	.	.	.	.	.
.	.	.	.	.	.	.	.
96	Regular	1	39.50	MasterCard	Female	Married	44
97	Promotional	9	253.00	Proprietary Card	Female	Married	30
98	Promotional	10	287.59	Proprietary Card	Female	Married	52
99	Promotional	2	47.60	Proprietary Card	Female	Married	30
100	Promotional	1	28.44	Proprietary Card	Female	Married	44

Managerial Report

Use the tabular and graphical methods of descriptive statistics to help management develop a customer profile and to evaluate the promotional campaign. At a minimum, your report should include the following:

1. Percent frequency distribution for key variables.
2. A bar graph or pie chart showing the number of customer purchases attributable to the method of payment.
3. A crosstabulation of type of customer (regular or promotional) versus net sales. Comment on any similarities or differences present.
4. A scatter diagram to explore the relationship between net sales and customer age.

CHAPTER 3

Descriptive Statistics: Numerical Measures

SMALL FRY DESIGN*
SANTA ANA, CALIFORNIA

Founded in 1997, Small Fry Design is a toy and accessory company that designs and imports products for infants. The company's product line includes teddy bears, mobiles, musical toys, rattles, and security blankets and features high-quality soft toy designs with an emphasis on color, texture, and sound. The products are designed in the United States and manufactured in China.

Small Fry Design uses independent representatives to sell the products to infant furnishing retailers, children's accessory and apparel stores, gift shops, upscale department stores, and major catalog companies. Currently, Small Fry Design products are distributed in more than 1000 retail outlets throughout the United States.

Cash flow management is one of the most critical activities in the day-to-day operation of this company. Ensuring sufficient incoming cash to meet both current and ongoing debt obligations can mean the difference between business success and failure. A critical factor in cash flow management is the analysis and control of accounts receivable. By measuring the average age and dollar value of outstanding invoices, management can predict cash availability and monitor changes in the status of accounts receivable. The company set the following goals: the average age for outstanding invoices should not exceed 45 days, and the dollar value of invoices more than 60 days old should not exceed 5% of the dollar value of all accounts receivable.

In a recent summary of accounts receivable status, the following descriptive statistics were provided for the age of outstanding invoices:

Mean	40 days
Median	35 days
Mode	31 days

A Small Fry Design mobile. © Photo courtesy of Small Fry Design, Inc.

Interpretation of these statistics shows that the mean or average age of an invoice is 40 days. The median shows that half of the invoices remain outstanding 35 days or more. The mode of 31 days, the most frequent invoice age, indicates that the most common length of time an invoice is outstanding is 31 days. The statistical summary also showed that only 3% of the dollar value of all accounts receivable was more than 60 days old. Based on the statistical information, management was satisfied that accounts receivable and incoming cash flow were under control.

In this chapter, you will learn how to compute and interpret some of the statistical measures used by Small Fry Design. In addition to the mean, median, and mode, you will learn about other descriptive statistics such as the range, variance, standard deviation, percentiles, and correlation. These numerical measures will assist in the understanding and interpretation of data.

*The authors are indebted to John A. McCarthy, President of Small Fry Design, for providing this Statistics in Practice.

In Chapter 2 we discussed tabular and graphical presentations used to summarize data. In this chapter, we present several numerical measures that provide additional alternatives for summarizing data.

We start by developing numerical summary measures for data sets consisting of a single variable. When a data set contains more than one variable, the same numerical measures can be computed separately for each variable. However, in the two-variable case, we will also develop measures of the relationship between the variables.

Numerical measures of location, dispersion, shape, and association are introduced. If the measures are computed for data from a sample, they are called **sample statistics**. If the measures are computed for data from a population, they are called **population parameters**. In statistical inference, a sample statistic is referred to as the **point estimator** of the corresponding population parameter. In Chapter 7 we will discuss in more detail the process of point estimation.

Several more of Excel's statistical functions are introduced in this chapter. In most cases we introduce them with little digression from the flow of the statistical material. But, at the end of Section 3.2, we pause to show how Excel's Descriptive Statistics tool can be used to perform the work of several functions by providing a summary of the most commonly used descriptive statistics. If you experience trouble using any of the statistical functions, recall that Excel's Insert Function dialog box is designed to provide help (see Appendix E: Using Excel Functions).

3.1   Measures of Location

Mean

Perhaps the most important measure of location is the **mean**, or average value, for a variable. The mean provides a measure of central location for the data. If the data are from a sample, the mean is denoted by $\bar{x}$; if the data are from a population, the mean is denoted by the Greek letter μ (mu).

In statistical formulas, it is customary to denote the value of variable x for the first observation by x_1, the value of variable x for the second observation by x_2, and so on. In general, the value of variable x for the ith observation is denoted by x_i. For a sample with n observations, the formula for the sample mean is as follows.

The sample mean $\bar{x}$ is a sample statistic.

SAMPLE MEAN

$$\bar{x} = \frac{\Sigma x_i}{n} \tag{3.1}$$

In the preceding formula, the numerator is the sum of the values of the n observations. That is,

$$\Sigma x_i = x_1 + x_2 + \cdots + x_n$$

The Greek letter Σ is the summation sign.

To illustrate the computation of a sample mean, let us consider the following class size data for a sample of five college classes.

$$46 \quad 54 \quad 42 \quad 46 \quad 32$$

We use the notation x_1, x_2, x_3, x_4, x_5 to represent the number of students in each of the five classes.

$$x_1 = 46 \qquad x_2 = 54 \qquad x_3 = 42 \qquad x_4 = 46 \qquad x_5 = 32$$

Hence, to compute the sample mean, we can write

$$\bar{x} = \frac{\Sigma x_i}{n} = \frac{x_1 + x_2 + x_3 + x_4 + x_5}{5} = \frac{46 + 54 + 42 + 46 + 32}{5} = 44$$

The sample mean class size is 44 students.

Another illustration of the computation of a sample mean is given in the following situation. Suppose that a college placement office sent a questionnaire to a sample of business

TABLE 3.1 MONTHLY STARTING SALARIES FOR A SAMPLE OF 12 BUSINESS SCHOOL GRADUATES

Graduate	Monthly Starting Salary ($)	Graduate	Monthly Starting Salary ($)
1	2850	7	2890
2	2950	8	3130
3	3050	9	2940
4	2880	10	3325
5	2755	11	2920
6	2710	12	2880

school graduates requesting information on monthly starting salaries. Table 3.1 shows the collected data. The mean monthly starting salary for the sample of 12 business college graduates is computed as

$$\bar{x} = \frac{\Sigma x_i}{n} = \frac{x_1 + x_2 + \cdots + x_{12}}{12}$$

$$= \frac{2850 + 2950 + \cdots + 2880}{12}$$

$$= \frac{35{,}280}{12} = 2940$$

Equation (3.1) shows how the mean is computed for a sample with n observations. The formula for computing the mean of a population remains the same, but we use different notation to indicate that we are working with the entire population. The number of observations in a population is denoted by N and the symbol for a population mean is μ.

The sample mean $\bar{x}$ is a point estimator of the population mean μ.

POPULATION MEAN

$$\mu = \frac{\Sigma x_i}{N} \tag{3.2}$$

Median

The **median** is another measure of central location for a variable. The median is the value in the middle when the data are arranged in ascending order (smallest value to largest value). With an odd number of observations, the median is the middle value. An even number of observations has no single middle value. In this case, we follow convention and define the median as the average of the values for the middle two observations. For convenience the definition of the median is restated as follows.

MEDIAN

Arrange the data in ascending order (smallest value to largest value).

(a) For an odd number of observations, the median is the middle value.
(b) For an even number of observations, the median is the average of the two middle values.

Let us apply this definition to compute the median class size for the sample of five college classes. Arranging the data in ascending order provides the following list.

$$32 \quad 42 \quad 46 \quad 46 \quad 54$$

Because $n = 5$ is odd, the median is the middle value. Thus the median class size is 46 students. Even though this data set contains two observations with values of 46, each observation is treated separately when we arrange the data in ascending order.

Suppose we also compute the median starting salary for the 12 business college graduates in Table 3.1. We first arrange the data in ascending order.

$$2710 \quad 2755 \quad 2850 \quad 2880 \quad 2880 \quad \underbrace{2890 \quad 2920}_{\text{Middle Two Values}} \quad 2940 \quad 2950 \quad 3050 \quad 3130 \quad 3325$$

Because $n = 12$ is even, we identify the middle two values: 2890 and 2920. The median is the average of these values.

$$\text{Median} = \frac{2890 + 2920}{2} = 2905$$

The median is the measure of location most often reported for annual income and property value data because a few extremely large incomes or property values can inflate the mean. In such cases, the median is the preferred measure of central location.

Although the mean is the more commonly used measure of central location, in some situations the median is preferred. The mean is influenced by extremely small and large data values. For instance, suppose that one of the graduates (see Table 3.1) had a starting salary of $10,000 per month (maybe the individual's family owns the company). If we change the highest monthly starting salary in Table 3.1 from $3325 to $10,000 and recompute the mean, the sample mean changes from $2940 to $3496. The median of $2905, however, is unchanged, because $2890 and $2920 are still the middle two values. With the extremely high starting salary included, the median provides a better measure of central location than the mean. We can generalize to say that whenever a data set contains extreme values, the median is often the preferred measure of central location.

Mode

A third measure of location is the **mode**. The mode is defined as follows.

MODE

The mode is the value that occurs with greatest frequency.

To illustrate the identification of the mode, consider the sample of five class sizes. The only value that occurs more than once is 46. Because this value, occurring with a frequency of 2, has the greatest frequency, it is the mode. As another illustration, consider the sample of starting salaries for the business school graduates. The only monthly starting salary that occurs more than once is $2880. Because this value has the greatest frequency, it is the mode.

Situations can arise for which the greatest frequency occurs at two or more different values. In these instances more than one mode exists. If the data contain exactly two modes, we say that the data are *bimodal.* If data contain more than two modes, we say that the data are *multimodal.* In multimodal cases the mode is almost never reported because listing three or more modes would not be particularly helpful in describing a location for the data.

The mode is an important measure of location for qualitative data. For example, the qualitative data set in Table 2.2 resulted in the following frequency distribution for soft drink purchases.

Soft Drink	Frequency
Coke Classic	19
Diet Coke	8
Dr. Pepper	5
Pepsi-Cola	13
Sprite	5
Total	50

The mode, or most frequently purchased soft drink, is Coke Classic. For this type of data it obviously makes no sense to speak of the mean or median. The mode provides the information of interest, the most frequently purchased soft drink.

Using Excel to Compute the Mean, Median, and Mode

Excel provides functions for computing the mean, median, and mode. We illustrate the use of these Excel functions by computing the mean, median, and mode for the starting salary data in Table 3.1. Refer to Figure 3.1 as we describe the tasks involved. The formula worksheet is in the background; the value worksheet is in the foreground.

FIGURE 3.1   EXCEL WORKSHEET USED TO COMPUTE THE MEAN, MEDIAN, AND MODE
FOR STARTING SALARIES

	A	B	C	D	E	F
1	Graduate	Starting Salary		Mean	=AVERAGE(B2:B13)	
2	1	2850		Median	=MEDIAN(B2:B13)	
3	2	2950		Mode	=MODE(B2:B13)	
4	3	3050				
5	4	2880				

	A	B	C	D	E	F
6	5	2755				
7	6	2710	1	Graduate	Starting Salary		Mean	2940	
8	7	2890	2	1	2850		Median	2905	
9	8	3130	3	2	2950		Mode	2880	

	A	B	C	D	E	F
1	Graduate	Starting Salary		Mean	2940	
2	1	2850		Median	2905	
3	2	2950		Mode	2880	
4	3	3050				
5	4	2880				
6	5	2755				
7	6	2710				
8	7	2890				
9	8	3130				
10	9	2940				
11	10	3325				
12	11	2920				
13	12	2880				
14						

Background formula worksheet (rows 6–14):

	A	B
6	5	2755
7	6	2710
8	7	2890
9	8	3130
10	9	2940
11	10	3325
12	11	2920
13	12	2880
14		

Enter Data: Labels and the starting salary data are entered into cells A1:B13 of the worksheet.

Enter Functions and Formulas: Excel's AVERAGE function can be used to compute the mean by entering the following formula into cell E1:

$$=\text{AVERAGE(B2:B13)}$$

If the data are bimodal or multimodal, Excel's MODE function will incorrectly identify a single mode.

Similarly, the formulas =MEDIAN(B2:B13) and =MODE(B2:B13) are entered into cells E2 and E3, respectively, to compute the median and the mode. The labels Mean, Median, and Mode are entered into cells D1:D3 to identify the output.

The formulas in cells E1:E3 are displayed in the formula worksheet in the background of Figure 3.1. The worksheet in the foreground shows the values computed using the Excel functions. Note that the mean (2940), median (2905), and mode (2880) are the same as we computed earlier.

Percentiles

A **percentile** provides information about how the data are spread over the interval from the smallest value to the largest value. For data that do not contain numerous repeated values, the pth percentile divides the data into two parts. Approximately p percent of the observations have values less than the pth percentile; approximately $(100 - p)$ percent of the observations have values greater than the pth percentile. The pth percentile is formally defined as follows.

> PERCENTILE
>
> The pth percentile is a value such that *at least* p percent of the observations are less than or equal to this value and *at least* $(100 - p)$ percent of the observations are greater than or equal to this value.

Colleges and universities frequently report admission test scores in terms of percentiles. For instance, suppose an applicant obtains a raw score of 54 on the verbal portion of an admission test. How this student performed in relation to other students taking the same test may not be readily apparent. However, if the raw score of 54 corresponds to the 70th percentile, we know that approximately 70% of the students scored lower than this individual and approximately 30% of the students scored higher than this individual.

The following procedure can be used to compute the pth percentile.

> CALCULATING THE pTH PERCENTILE
>
> *Following these steps makes it easy to calculate percentiles.*
>
> **Step 1.** Arrange the data in ascending order (smallest value to largest value).
> **Step 2.** Compute an index i
>
> $$i = \left(\frac{p}{100}\right)n$$
>
> where p is the percentile of interest and n is the number of observations.

Step 3. (a) If *i is not an integer, round up*. The next integer *greater* than *i* denotes the position of the *p*th percentile.
(b) If *i is an integer*, the *p*th percentile is the average of the values in positions *i* and *i* + 1.

As an illustration of this procedure, let us determine the 85th percentile for the starting salary data in Table 3.1.

Step 1. Arrange the data in ascending order.

2710   2755   2850   2880   2880   2890   2920   2940   2950   3050   3130   3325

Step 2.

$$i = \left(\frac{p}{100}\right)n = \left(\frac{85}{100}\right)12 = 10.2$$

Step 3. Because *i* is not an integer, *round up*. The position of the 85th percentile is the next integer greater than 10.2, the 11th position.

Returning to the data, we see that the 85th percentile is the data value in the 11th position, or 3130.

As another illustration of this procedure, let us consider the calculation of the 50th percentile for the starting salary data. Applying step 2, we obtain

$$i = \left(\frac{50}{100}\right)12 = 6$$

Because *i* is an integer, step 3(b) states that the 50th percentile is the average of the sixth and seventh data values; thus, the 50th percentile is (2890 + 2920)/2 = 2905. Note that the *50th percentile is also the median.*

Quartiles

Quartiles are just specific percentiles; thus, the steps for computing percentiles can be applied directly in the computation of quartiles.

It is often desirable to divide data into four parts, with each part containing approximately one-fourth, or 25%, of the observations. Figure 3.2 shows a data distribution divided into four parts. The division points are referred to as the **quartiles** and are defined as

Q_1 = first quartile, or 25th percentile
Q_2 = second quartile, or 50th percentile (also the median)
Q_3 = third quartile, or 75th percentile

The starting salary data are again arranged in ascending order. We already identified Q_2, the second quartile (median), as 2905.

2710   2755   2850   2880   2880   2890   2920   2940   2950   3050   3130   3325

The computations of quartiles Q_1 and Q_3 require the use of the rule for finding the 25th and 75th percentiles. These calculations follow.
For Q_1,

$$i = \left(\frac{p}{100}\right)n = \left(\frac{25}{100}\right)12 = 3$$

FIGURE 3.2 LOCATION OF THE QUARTILES

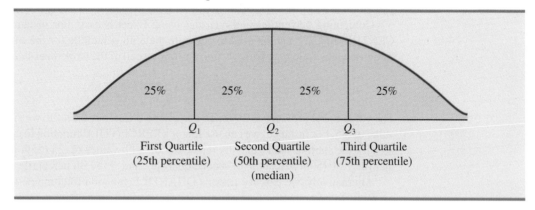

Because i is an integer, step 3(b) indicates that the first quartile, or 25th percentile, is the average of the third and fourth data values; thus, $Q_1 = (2850 + 2880)/2 = 2865$.

For Q_3,

$$i = \left(\frac{p}{100}\right)n = \left(\frac{75}{100}\right)12 = 9$$

Again, because i is an integer, step 3(b) indicates that the third quartile, or 75th percentile, is the average of the ninth and tenth data values; thus, $Q_3 = (2950 + 3050)/2 = 3000$.

The quartiles divide the starting salary data into four parts, with each part containing 25% of the observations.

| 2710 | 2755 | 2850 | 2880 | 2880 | 2890 | 2920 | 2940 | 2950 | 3050 | 3130 | 3325 |

$Q_1 = 2865$ $\qquad$ $Q_2 = 2905$ $\qquad$ $Q_3 = 3000$
$\qquad\qquad\qquad\qquad$ (Median)

We defined the quartiles as the 25th, 50th, and 75th percentiles. Thus, we computed the quartiles in the same way as percentiles. However, other conventions are sometimes used to compute quartiles, and the actual values reported for quartiles may vary slightly depending on the convention used. Nevertheless, the objective of all procedures for computing quartiles is to divide the data into four equal parts.

Using Excel's Rank and Percentile Tool to Compute Percentiles and Quartiles

Computer software packages do not all use the same method to compute percentiles and quartiles. The formula Excel uses to compute the location (L_p) of the pth percentile is

$$L_p = \left(\frac{p}{100}\right)n + \left(1 - \frac{p}{100}\right)$$

For instance, Excel would compute the location of the 85th percentile for the starting salary data as follows:

$$L_{85} = (.85)12 + (1 - .85) = 10.20 + .15 = 10.35$$

The value of $L_{85} = 10.35$ indicates that the 85th percentile is between the 10th and the 11th observations in rank order from the bottom up. It is the value of observation 10 (3050) plus

.35 of the difference between observation 10 and observation 11 (3130). Therefore, the 85th percentile is $3050 + .35(3130 - 3050) = 3050 + .35(80) = 3078.$*

Computing percentiles and quartiles using Excel is easy. For instance, Excel's PERCENTILE function can be used to compute the 85th percentile for the starting salary data by entering the following formula into any empty cell of the worksheet shown in Figure 3.1:

$$=PERCENTILE(B2:B13,.85)$$

The value Excel provides is 3078. To compute a different percentile we simply change the value of .85. For instance, we can use Excel's PERCENTILE function to compute the quartiles for the starting salary data by replacing .85 with values of .25 (25th percentile or first quartile), .50 (50th percentile or second quartile), and .75 (75th percentile or third quartile).

Alternatively, we can use Excel's QUARTILE function to compute the quartiles. For example, to compute the first quartile for the starting salary data we would enter the following formula into an empty cell of the worksheet in Figure 3.1.

$$=QUARTILE(B2:B13,1)$$

If the value of 1 in the QUARTILE function is changed to 0, Excel computes the minimum value in the data set. If the value of 1 is changed to 4, Excel computes the maximum value.

The value Excel provides is 2872.5. We can compute the second quartile or median by replacing the value of 1 with 2, and the third quartile by replacing the value of 1 with 3.

Computing percentiles and quartiles is useful for a data analyst who is interested in getting a feel for how the values in a data set are distributed. However, if you are a student who wants to know how the starting salary you received ranks compared to all the other starting salaries, then what you would like to do is to take your salary and compute its rank and percentile. Or perhaps you know your raw score on an exam and would like to know its rank and percentile. Excel's Rank and Percentile tool can be used to provide this information for an entire data set.

We illustrate the use of Excel's Rank and Percentile tool by computing the ranks and percentiles for the starting salaries in Table 3.1. Refer to Figure 3.3 as we present the steps involved.

Enter Data: Labels and the starting salary data are entered into cells A1:B13.

Enter Functions and Formulas: No functions and formulas are needed.

Apply Tools: The following steps will compute the rank and percentile for each observation.

Note: If the Data Analysis option does not appear when you select the Tools menu, choose Add-Ins, and check Analysis ToolPak to install it.

Step 1. Select the **Tools** menu
Step 2. Choose **Data Analysis**
Step 3. Choose **Rank and Percentile** from the list of Analysis Tools
Step 4. When the Rank and Percentile dialog box appears:
　　　　　Enter B1:B13 in the **Input Range** box
　　　　　Select **Grouped by Columns**
　　　　　Select **Labels in First Row**
　　　　　Select **Output Range**
　　　　　Enter D1 in the **Output Range** box
　　　　　　(Any cell where the upper left corner of the output is desired may be entered here.)
　　　　　Click **OK**

*The value Excel computed for the 85th percentile does not strictly satisfy the definition of the 85th percentile because only 83% of the values are less than or equal to 3078. Our procedure would round up in this case to obtain 3130 as the value satisfying the definition of the 85th percentile. For larger data sets, the difference between the approximate value provided by Excel and the value computed using our three-step procedure is not of practical significance.

FIGURE 3.3   USING EXCEL'S RANK AND PERCENTILE TOOL FOR STARTING SALARIES

	A	B	C	D	E	F	G	H
1	Graduate	Starting Salary		*Point*	*Starting Salary*	*Rank*	*Percent*	
2	1	2850		10	3325	1	100.00%	
3	2	2950		8	3130	2	90.90%	
4	3	3050		3	3050	3	81.80%	
5	4	2880		2	2950	4	72.70%	
6	5	2755		9	2940	5	63.60%	
7	6	2710		11	2920	6	54.50%	
8	7	2890		7	2890	7	45.40%	
9	8	3130		4	2880	8	27.20%	
10	9	2940		12	2880	8	27.20%	
11	10	3325		1	2850	10	18.10%	
12	11	2920		5	2755	11	9.00%	
13	12	2880		6	2710	12	0.00%	
14								

Excel interpolates over the interval from 0 to n when computing percentiles for a data set.

The output from using the Rank and Percentile tool appears in cells D1:G13. Cells F2:F13 contain the rank of each observation. The highest salary is given a rank of 1 and the lowest salary is given a rank of 12. Cells G2:G13 show the percentile each salary represents. For instance, the percentile for 2850 is 18.1% because 2 of the other 11 salaries are smaller than 2850. The lowest salary is the 0th percentile and the highest salary is the 100th percentile. The percentiles increase by $(1/11)100\%$ as we move up from the lowest salary to the highest, except for ties. In the case of a tie, Excel gives the tied values the same rank and percentile. Note that the two observations with the same value (2880) both received a rank of 8 and a percentile of 27.20%.

NOTES AND COMMENTS

It is better to use the median than the mean as a measure of central location when a data set contains extreme values. Another measure, sometimes used when extreme values are present, is the *trimmed mean*. It is obtained by deleting a percentage of the smallest and largest values from a data set and then computing the mean of the remaining values. For example, the 5% trimmed mean is obtained by removing the smallest 5% and the largest 5% of the data values and then computing the mean of the remaining values. Using the sample with $n = 12$ starting salaries, $0.05(12) = 0.6$. Rounding this value to 1 indicates that the 5% trimmed mean would remove the 1 smallest data value and the 1 largest data value. The 5% trimmed mean using the 10 remaining observations is 2924.50.

Exercises

Methods

1. Consider a sample with data values of 10, 20, 12, 17, and 16. Compute the mean and median.

2. Consider a sample with data values of 10, 20, 21, 17, 16, and 12. Compute the mean and median.

3. Consider a sample with data values of 27, 25, 20, 15, 30, 34, 28, and 25. Compute the 20th, 25th, 65th, and 75th percentiles.

4. Consider a sample with data values of 53, 55, 70, 58, 64, 57, 53, 69, 57, 68, and 53. Compute the mean, median, and mode.

Applications

Hotels

5. The Dow Jones Travel Index reported what business travelers pay for hotel rooms per night in major U.S. cities (*The Wall Street Journal,* January 16, 2004). The hotel room rates for 20 cities are as follows:

Atlanta	$163	Minneapolis	$125
Boston	177	New Orleans	167
Chicago	166	New York	245
Cleveland	126	Orlando	146
Dallas	123	Phoenix	139
Denver	120	Pittsburgh	134
Detroit	144	San Francisco	167
Houston	173	Seattle	162
Los Angeles	160	St. Louis	145
Miami	192	Washington, D.C.	207

   a. What is the mean hotel room rate?
   b. What is the median hotel room rate?
   c. What is the mode?
   d. What is the first quartile?
   e. What is the third quartile?

6. J. D. Powers and Associates surveyed cell phone users in order to learn about the minutes of cell phone usage per month (Associated Press, June 2002). Minutes per month for a sample of 15 cell phone users are shown here.

615	135	395
430	830	1180
690	250	420
265	245	210
180	380	105

   a. What is the mean number of minutes of usage per month?
   b. What is the median number of minutes of usage per month?
   c. What is the 85th percentile?
   d. J. D. Powers and Associates reported that the average wireless subscriber plan allows up to 750 minutes of usage per month. What do the data suggest about cell phone subscribers' utilization of their monthly plan?

7. The American Association of Individual Investors conducted an annual survey of discount brokers (*AAII Journal,* January 2003). The commissions charged by 24 discount brokers for two types of trades, a broker-assisted trade of 100 shares at $50 per share and an on-line trade of 500 shares at $50 per share, are shown in Table 3.2.
   a. Compute the mean, median, and mode for the commission charged on a broker-assisted trade of 100 shares at $50 per share.
   b. Compute the mean, median, and mode for the commission charged on an online trade of 500 shares at $50 per share.
   c. Which costs more, a broker-assisted trade of 100 shares at $50 per share or an online trade of 500 shares at $50 per share?
   d. Is the cost of a transaction related to the amount of the transaction?

TABLE 3.2 COMMISSIONS CHARGED BY DISCOUNT BROKERS

Broker

Broker	Broker-Assisted 100 Shares at $50/Share	Online 500 Shares at $50/Share	Broker	Broker-Assisted 100 Shares at $50/Share	Online 500 Shares at $50/Share
Accutrade	30.00	29.95	Merrill Lynch Direct	50.00	29.95
Ameritrade	24.99	10.99	Muriel Siebert	45.00	14.95
Banc of America	54.00	24.95	NetVest	24.00	14.00
Brown & Co.	17.00	5.00	Recom Securities	35.00	12.95
Charles Schwab	55.00	29.95	Scottrade	17.00	7.00
CyberTrader	12.95	9.95	Sloan Securities	39.95	19.95
E*TRADE Securities	49.95	14.95	Strong Investments	55.00	24.95
First Discount	35.00	19.75	TD Waterhouse	45.00	17.95
Freedom Investments	25.00	15.00	T. Rowe Price	50.00	19.95
Harrisdirect	40.00	20.00	Vanguard	48.00	20.00
Investors National	39.00	62.50	Wall Street Discount	29.95	19.95
MB Trading	9.95	10.55	York Securities	40.00	36.00

Source: AAII Journal, January 2003.

8. Millions of Americans get up each morning and telecommute to work from offices in their home. Following is a sample of age data for individuals working at home.

18 54 20 46 25 48 53 27 26 37
40 36 42 25 27 33 28 40 45 25

a. Compute the mean and mode.
b. The median age of the population of all adults is 35.5 years (*The World Almanac,* 2004). Use the median age of the preceding data to comment on whether the at-home workers tend to be younger or older than the population of all adults.
c. Compute the first and third quartiles.
d. Compute and interpret the 32nd percentile.

9. Media Matrix collected data showing the most popular Web sites when browsing at home and at work (*Business 2.0,* January 2000). The following data show the number of unique visitors (thousands) for the top 25 Web sites when browsing at home.

Websites

Web Site	Unique Visitors (1000s)
about.com	5538
altavista.com	7391
amazon.com	7986
angelfire.com	8917
aol.com	23863
bluemountainarts.com	6786
ebay.com	8296
excite.com	10479
geocities.com	15321
go.com	14330
hotbot.com	5760
hotmail.com	11791
icq.com	5052

(*continued*)

Web Site	Unique Visitors (1000s)
looksmart.com	5984
lycos.com	9950
microsoft.com	15593
msn.com	23505
netscape.com	14470
passport.com	11299
real.com	6785
snap.com	5730
tripod.com	7970
xoom.com	5652
yahoo.com	26796
zdnet.com	5133

a. Compute the mean and median.
b. Do you think it would be better to use the mean or the median as the measure of central location for these data? Explain.
c. Compute the first and third quartiles.
d. Compute and interpret the 85th percentile.

10. An American Hospital Association survey found that most hospital emergency rooms are operating at full capacity (Associated Press, April 9, 2002). The survey collected data on the emergency room waiting times for hospitals where the emergency room is operating at full capacity and for hospitals where the emergency room is in balance and rarely operates at capacity. Sample data showing waiting times in minutes are as follows.

ER Waiting Times for Hospitals at Full Capacity		ER Waiting Times for Hospitals in Balance	
87	59	60	39
80	110	54	32
47	83	18	56
73	79	29	26
50	50	45	37
93	66	34	38
72	115		

a. Compute the mean and median emergency room waiting times for hospitals operating at full capacity.
b. Compute the mean and median emergency room waiting times for hospitals operating in balance.
c. What observations can you make about emergency room waiting times based on these results? Would the American Hospital Association express concern with the statistical results shown here?

11. In automobile mileage and gasoline-consumption testing, 13 automobiles were road tested for 300 miles in both city and highway driving conditions. The following data were recorded for miles-per-gallon performance.

City: 16.2 16.7 15.9 14.4 13.2 15.3 16.8 16.0 16.1 15.3 15.2 15.3 16.2
Highway: 19.4 20.6 18.3 18.6 19.2 17.4 17.2 18.6 19.0 21.1 19.4 18.5 18.7

Use the mean, median, and mode to make a statement about the difference in performance for city and highway driving.

12. The following data show the price, picture capacity, and battery life (minutes) for 20 digital cameras (*PC World,* January 2000).

Cameras

Camera	Price ($)	Picture Capacity	Battery Life (minutes)
Agfa Ephoto CL30	349	36	25
Canon PowerShot A50	499	106	75
Canon PowerShot Pro70	999	96	118
Epson PhotoPC 800	699	120	99
Fujifilm DX-10	299	30	229
Fujifilm MX-2700	699	141	124
Fujifilm MX-2900 Zoom	899	141	88
HP PhotoSmart C200	299	80	68
Kodak DC215 Zoom	399	54	159
Kodak DC265 Zoom	899	180	186
Kodak DC280 Zoom	799	245	143
Minolta Dimage EX Zoom 1500	549	105	38
Nikon Coolpix 950	999	32	88
Olympus D-340R	299	122	161
Olympus D-450 Zoom	499	122	62
Ricoh RDC-500	699	99	56
Sony Cybershot DSC-F55	699	63	69
Sony Mavica MVC-FD73	599	40	186
Sony Mavica MVC-FD88	999	40	88
Toshiba PDR-M4	599	124	142

a. Compute the mean price.
b. Compute the mean picture capacity.
c. Compute the mean battery life.
d. If you had to select one camera from this list, which camera would you choose? Explain.

3.2 Measures of Variability

In addition to measures of location, it is often desirable to consider measures of variability, or dispersion. For example, suppose that you are a purchasing agent for a large manufacturing firm and that you regularly place orders with two different suppliers. After several months of operation, you find that the mean number of days required to fill orders is 10 days for both of the suppliers. The histograms summarizing the number of working days required to fill orders from the suppliers are shown in Figure 3.4. Although the mean number of days is 10 for both suppliers, do the two suppliers demonstrate the same degree of reliability in terms of making deliveries on schedule? Note the dispersion, or variability, in delivery times indicated by the histograms. Which supplier would you prefer?

For most firms, receiving materials and supplies on schedule is important. The seven- or eight-day deliveries shown for J.C. Clark Distributors might be viewed favorably; however, a few of the slow 13- to 15-day deliveries could be disastrous in terms of keeping a workforce busy and production on schedule. This example illustrates a situation in which the variability in the delivery times may be an overriding consideration in selecting a supplier. For most purchasing agents, the lower variability shown for Dawson Supply, Inc., would make Dawson the preferred supplier.

We turn now to a discussion of some commonly used measures of variability.

FIGURE 3.4   HISTORICAL DATA SHOWING THE NUMBER OF DAYS REQUIRED TO FILL ORDERS

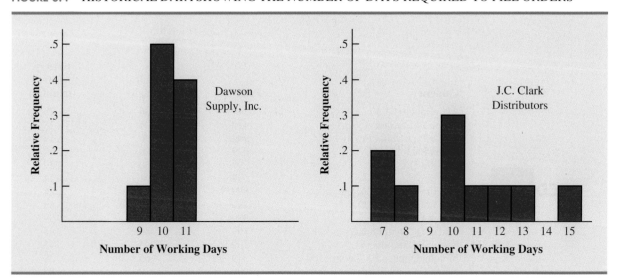

Range

The simplest measure of variability is the **range**.

> RANGE
>
> $$\text{Range} = \text{Largest value} - \text{Smallest value}$$

Let us refer to the data on starting salaries for business school graduates in Table 3.1. The largest starting salary is 3325 and the smallest is 2710. The range is $3325 - 2710 = 615$.

Although the range is the easiest of the measures of variability to compute, it is seldom used as the only measure. The reason is that the range is based on only two of the observations and thus is highly influenced by extreme values. Suppose one of the graduates received a starting salary of \$10,000 per month. In this case, the range would be $10,000 - 2710 = 7290$ rather than 615. This large value for the range would not be especially descriptive of the variability in the data because 11 of the 12 starting salaries are closely grouped between 2710 and 3130.

Interquartile Range

A measure of variability that overcomes the dependency on extreme values is the **interquartile range (IQR)**. This measure of variability is the difference between the third quartile, Q_3, and the first quartile, Q_1. In other words, the interquartile range is the range for the middle 50% of the data.

> INTERQUARTILE RANGE
>
> $$IQR = Q_3 - Q_1 \tag{3.3}$$

For the data on monthly starting salaries, the quartiles are $Q_3 = 3000$ and $Q_1 = 2865$. Thus, the interquartile range is $3000 - 2865 = 135$.

Variance

The **variance** is a measure of variability that utilizes all the data. The variance is based on the difference between the value of each observation (x_i) and the mean. The difference between each x_i and the mean ($\bar{x}$ for a sample, μ for a population) is called a *deviation about the mean*. For a sample, a deviation about the mean is written ($x_i - \bar{x}$); for a population, it is written ($x_i - \mu$). In the computation of the variance, the deviations about the mean are *squared*.

If the data are for a population, the average of the squared deviations is called the *population variance*. The population variance is denoted by the Greek symbol σ^2 (sigma squared). For a population of N observations and with μ denoting the population mean, the definition of the population variance is as follows.

POPULATION VARIANCE

$$\sigma^2 = \frac{\Sigma(x_i - \mu)^2}{N} \qquad (3.4)$$

In most statistical applications, the data being analyzed are for a sample. When we compute a sample variance, we are often interested in using it to estimate the population variance σ^2. Although a detailed explanation is beyond the scope of this text, it can be shown that if the sum of the squared deviations about the sample mean is divided by $n - 1$, and not n, the resulting sample variance provides an unbiased estimate of the population variance. For this reason, the *sample variance,* denoted by s^2, is defined as follows.

The sample variance s^2 is the estimator of the population variance σ^2.

SAMPLE VARIANCE

$$s^2 = \frac{\Sigma(x_i - \bar{x})^2}{n - 1} \qquad (3.5)$$

To illustrate the computation of the sample variance, we will use the data on class size for the sample of five college classes as presented in Section 3.1. A summary of the data, including the computation of the deviations about the mean and the squared deviations about the mean, is shown in Table 3.3. The sum of squared deviations about the mean is $\Sigma(x_i - \bar{x})^2 = 256$. Hence, with $n - 1 = 4$, the sample variance is

$$s^2 = \frac{\Sigma(x_i - \bar{x})^2}{n - 1} = \frac{256}{4} = 64$$

Before moving on, let us note that the units associated with the sample variance often cause confusion. Because the values being summed in the variance calculation $(x_i - \bar{x})^2$ are squared, the units associated with the sample variance are also *squared.* For instance, the sample variance for the class size data is $s^2 = 64$ (students)^2. The squared units associated with variance make it difficult to obtain an intuitive understanding and interpretation of the numerical value of the variance. We recommend that you think of the variance as a measure useful in comparing the amount of variability for two or more variables. In a comparison of the variables, the one with the largest variance shows the most variability. Further interpretation of the value of the variance may not be necessary.

The variance is useful in comparing the variability of two or more variables.

As another illustration of computing a sample variance, consider the starting salaries listed in Table 3.1 for the 12 business school graduates. In Section 3.1, we showed that the

TABLE 3.3 COMPUTATION OF DEVIATIONS AND SQUARED DEVIATIONS ABOUT THE MEAN FOR THE CLASS SIZE DATA

Number of Students in Class (x_i)	Mean Class Size ($\bar{x}$)	Deviation About the Mean ($x_i - \bar{x}$)	Squared Deviation About the Mean ($x_i - \bar{x})^2$
46	44	2	4
54	44	10	100
42	44	−2	4
46	44	2	4
32	44	−12	144
		0	256
		$\Sigma(x_i - \bar{x})$	$\Sigma(x_i - \bar{x})^2$

sample mean starting salary was 2940. A summary of the data, including the computation of the deviations about the mean and the squared deviations about the mean, is shown in Figure 3.5. The worksheet in the background shows the Excel formulas used to compute the results shown in the value worksheet in the foreground. The sum of the squared deviations about the mean is $\Sigma(x_i - \bar{x})^2 = 301{,}850$ (see cell E14). Hence, with $n - 1 = 11$, the sample variance is

$$s^2 = \frac{\Sigma(x_i - \bar{x})^2}{n - 1} = \frac{301{,}850}{11} = 27{,}440.91$$

Using the definition to compute the sample variance helps us to realize that the variance measures variability as a function of the squared deviations about the mean.

The method we used for computing the sample variance for starting salaries is the same method that we used to compute the sample variance for the class size data (see Table 3.3). We used the definition as given by equation (3.5). The only difference is that this time we use an Excel worksheet to ease the computational burden. Later we will see that Excel provides a function for obtaining the sample variance directly without entering all the formulas needed to compute the sum of the squared deviations about the mean.

Note that in Table 3.3 and Figure 3.5 we show both the sum of the deviations about the mean and the sum of the squared deviations about the mean. For any data set, the sum of the deviations about the mean will *always equal zero*. Note that in Table 3.3 and Figure 3.5, $\Sigma(x_i - \bar{x}) = 0$. The positive deviations and negative deviations cancel each other, causing the sum of the deviations about the mean to equal zero.

Standard Deviation

The **standard deviation** is defined to be the positive square root of the variance. Following the notation we adopted for a sample variance and a population variance, we use s to denote the sample standard deviation and σ to denote the population standard deviation. The standard deviation is derived from the variance in the following way.

STANDARD DEVIATION

The sample standard deviation s is the estimator of the population standard deviation σ.

$$\text{Sample standard deviation} = s = \sqrt{s^2} \tag{3.6}$$

$$\text{Population standard deviation} = \sigma = \sqrt{\sigma^2} \tag{3.7}$$

may introduce errors when a calculator is used in the computation of the variance and standard deviation. To reduce rounding errors, we recommend carrying at least six significant digits during intermediate calculations. The resulting variance or standard deviation can then be rounded to fewer digits.

3. An alternative formula for the computation of the sample variance is

$$s^2 = \frac{\Sigma x_i^2 - n\bar{x}^2}{n - 1}$$

where $\Sigma x_i^2 = x_1^2 + x_2^2 + \cdots + x_n^2$.

Exercises

Methods

13.   Consider a sample with data values of 10, 20, 12, 17, and 16. Compute the range and interquartile range.

14.   Consider a sample with data values of 10, 20, 12, 17, and 16. Compute the variance and standard deviation.

15.   Consider a sample with data values of 27, 25, 20, 15, 30, 34, 28, and 25. Compute the range, interquartile range, variance, and standard deviation.

Applications

16.   A bowler's scores for six games were 182, 168, 184, 190, 170, and 174. Using these data as a sample, compute the following descriptive statistics.
    a.   Range
    b.   Variance
    c.   Standard deviation
    d.   Coefficient of variation

17.   A home theater in a box is the easiest and cheapest way to provide surround sound for a home entertainment center. A sample of prices is shown here (*Consumer Reports Buying Guide,* 2004). The prices are for models with a DVD player and for models without a DVD player.

Models with DVD Player	Price ($)	Models without DVD Player	Price ($)
Sony HT-1800DP	450	Pioneer HTP-230	300
Pioneer HTD-330DV	300	Sony HT-DDW750	300
Sony HT-C800DP	400	Kenwood HTB-306	360
Panasonic SC-HT900	500	RCA RT-2600	290
Panasonic SC-MTI	400	Kenwood HTB-206	300

    a.   Compute the mean price for models with a DVD player and the mean price for models without a DVD player. What is the additional price paid to have a DVD player included in a home theater unit?
    b.   Compute the range, variance, and standard deviation for the two samples. What does this information tell you about the prices for models with and without a DVD player?

18.   Car rental rates per day for a sample of seven eastern U.S. cities are as follows (*The Wall Street Journal,* January 16, 2004).

City	Daily Rate ($)
Boston	43
Atlanta	35
Miami	34

(continued)

City	Daily Rate ($)
New York	58
Orlando	30
Pittsburgh	30
Washington, D.C.	36

    a. Compute the mean, variance, and standard deviation for the car rental rates.

    b. A similar sample of seven western U.S. cities showed a sample mean car rental rate of $38 per day. The variance and standard deviation were 12.3 and 3.5, respectively. Discuss any difference between the car rental rates in eastern and western U.S. cities.

19. The *Los Angeles Times* regularly reports the air quality index for various areas of Southern California. A sample of air quality index values for Pomona provided the following data: 28, 42, 58, 48, 45, 55, 60, 49, and 50.

    a. Compute the range and interquartile range.

    b. Compute the sample variance and sample standard deviation.

    c. A sample of air quality index readings for Anaheim provided a sample mean of 48.5, a sample variance of 136, and a sample standard deviation of 11.66. What comparisons can you make between the air quality in Pomona and that in Anaheim on the basis of these descriptive statistics?

Orders

20. The following data were used to construct the histograms of the number of days required to fill orders for Dawson Supply, Inc., and J.C. Clark Distributors (see Figure 3.4).

Dawson Supply Days for Delivery: 11   10   9   10   11   11   10   11   10   10

Clark Distributors Days for Delivery: 8   10   13   7   10   11   10   7   15   12

Use the range and standard deviation to support the previous observation that Dawson Supply provides the more consistent and reliable delivery times.

21. How do grocery costs compare across the country? Using a market basket of 10 items including meat, milk, bread, eggs, coffee, potatoes, cereal, and orange juice, *Where to Retire* magazine calculated the cost of the market basket in six cities and in six retirement areas across the country (*Where to Retire,* November/December 2003). The data with market basket cost to the nearest dollar are as follows:

City	Cost ($)	Retirement Area	Cost ($)
Buffalo, NY	33	Biloxi-Gulfport, MS	29
Des Moines, IA	27	Asheville, NC	32
Hartford, CT	32	Flagstaff, AZ	32
Los Angeles, CA	38	Hilton Head, SC	34
Miami, FL	36	Fort Myers, FL	34
Pittsburgh, PA	32	Santa Fe, NM	31

    a. Compute the mean, variance, and standard deviation for the sample of cities and the sample of retirement areas.

    b. What observations can be made based on the two samples?

22. The American Association of Individual Investors conducted an annual survey of discount brokers (*AAII Journal,* January 2003). The commissions charged by 24 discount brokers for two types of trades, a broker-assisted trade of 100 shares at $50 per share and an on-line trade of 500 shares at $50 per share, are shown in Table 3.2.

Broker

    a. Compute the range and interquartile range for each type of trade.

    b. Compute the variance and standard deviation for each type of trade.

c. Compute the coefficient of variation for each type of trade.
d. Compare the variability of cost for the two types of trades.

23. *PC World* provided ratings for 15 notebook PCs (*PC World*, February 2000). A 100-point scale was used to provide an overall rating for each notebook. A score in the 90s is exceptional, while one in the 70s is good. The overall ratings for the 15 notebooks are shown here.

Notebook

Notebook	Overall Rating
AMS Tech Roadster 15CTA380	67
Compaq Armada M700	78
Compaq Prosignia Notebook 150	79
Dell Inspiron 3700 C466GT	80
Dell Inspiron 7500 R500VT	84
Dell Latitude Cpi A366XT	76
Enpower ENP-313 Pro	77
Gateway Solo 9300LS	92
HP Pavilion Notebook PC	83
IBM ThinkPad I Series 1480	78
Micro Express NP7400	77
Micron TransPort NX PII-400	78
NEC Versa SX	78
Sceptre Soundx 5200	73
Sony VAIO PCG-F340	77

Compute the range, interquartile range, variance, and standard deviation for this sample of notebook PCs.

24. The following times were recorded by the quarter-mile and mile runners of a university track team (times are in minutes).

Quarter-Mile Times:	.92	.98	1.04	.90	.99
Mile Times:	4.52	4.35	4.60	4.70	4.50

After viewing this sample of running times, one of the coaches commented that the quarter-milers turned in the more consistent times. Use the standard deviation and the coefficient of variation to summarize the variability in the data. Does the use of the coefficient of variation indicate that the coach's statement should be qualified?

3.3 Measures of Distribution Shape, Relative Location, and Detecting Outliers

We have described several measures of location and variability for data. In addition, it is often important to have a measure of the shape of a distribution. In Chapter 2 we noted that a histogram provides a graphical display showing the shape of a distribution. An important numerical measure of the shape of a distribution is called **skewness**.

Distribution Shape

Shown in Figure 3.9 are four histograms constructed from relative frequency distributions. The histograms in Panels A and B are moderately skewed. The one in Panel A is skewed to the left; its skewness is −.85. The histogram in Panel B is skewed to the right; its skewness is +.85. The histogram in Panel C is symmetric; its skewness is zero. The histogram in Panel D is highly skewed to the right; its skewness is 1.62. For data skewed to the left, the skewness is negative; for data skewed to the right, the skewness is positive. If the data are symmetric, the skewness is zero.

FIGURE 3.9   HISTOGRAMS SHOWING THE SKEWNESS FOR FOUR DISTRIBUTIONS

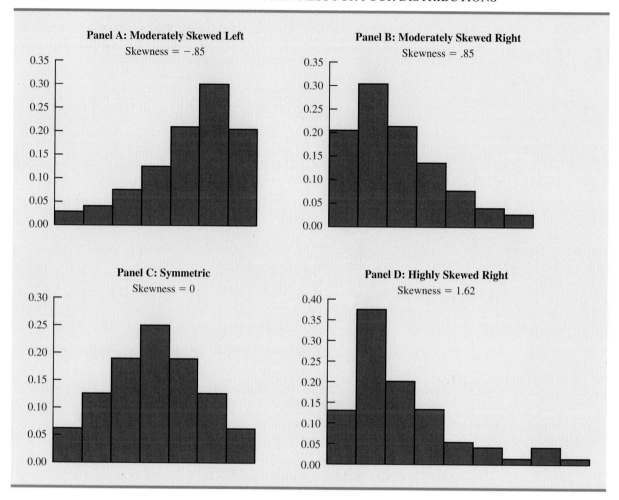

The formula used to compute skewness is somewhat complex.* However, the skewness can be easily computed using Excel. In Section 3.2 we showed how Excel's Descriptive Statistics tool can be used to compute descriptive statistics for the starting salary data in Table 3.1; the results were shown in the worksheet in Figure 3.8. The label Skewness in cell D10 and the corresponding value of 1.0911 in cell E10 indicates that the starting salary data are moderately to highly skewed to the right.

Excel's SKEW function can also be used to compute the skewness by entering the following formula into any empty cell of the worksheet in Figure 3.8: =SKEW(B2:B13).

For a symmetric distribution, the mean and the median are equal. When the data are positively skewed, the mean will usually be greater than the median; when the data are negatively skewed, the mean will usually be less than the median. The data used to construct the histogram in Panel D are customer purchases at a women's apparel store. The mean purchase amount is $77.60 and the median purchase amount is $59.70. The relatively few large purchase amounts tend to increase the mean, while the median remains unaffected by the large purchase amounts. The median provides the preferred measure of location when the data are highly skewed.

---

*The formula for the skewness of sample data:

$$\text{Skewness} = \frac{n}{(n-1)(n-2)} \sum \left(\frac{x_i - \bar{x}}{s} \right)^3$$

z-Scores

In addition to measures of location, variability, and shape, we are also interested in the relative location of values within a data set. Measures of relative location help us determine how far a particular value is from the mean.

By using both the mean and standard deviation, we can determine the relative location of any observation. Suppose we have a sample of n observations, with the values denoted by $x_1, x_2, \ldots, x_n$. In addition, assume that the sample mean, $\bar{x}$, and the sample standard deviation, s, are already computed. Associated with each value, x_i, is another value called its **z-score**. Equation (3.9) shows how the z-score is computed for each x_i.

Excel's STANDARDIZE function can be used to compute the z-score. But it is just as easy to enter a cell formula to compute z_i.

z-SCORE

$$z_i = \frac{x_i - \bar{x}}{s} \tag{3.9}$$

where

z_i = the z-score for x_i
$\bar{x}$ = the sample mean
s = the sample standard deviation

The z-score is often called the *standardized value*. The z-score, z_i, can be interpreted as the *number of standard deviations x_i is from the mean $\bar{x}$*. For example, $z_1 = 1.2$ would indicate that x_1 is 1.2 standard deviations greater than the sample mean. Similarly, $z_2 = -.5$ would indicate that x_2 is .5, or 1/2, standard deviation less than the sample mean. A z-score greater than zero occurs for observations with a value greater than the mean, and a z-score less than zero occurs for observations with a value less than the mean. A z-score of zero indicates that the value of the observation is equal to the mean.

The z-score for any observation can be interpreted as a measure of the relative location of the observation in a data set. Thus, observations in two different data sets with the same z-score can be said to have the same relative location in terms of being the same number of standard deviations from the mean.

The z-scores for the class size data are computed in Table 3.4. Recall the previously computed sample mean, $\bar{x} = 44$, and sample standard deviation, $s = 8$. The z-score of -1.50 for the fifth observation shows it is farthest from the mean; it is 1.50 standard deviations below the mean.

TABLE 3.4   z-SCORES FOR THE CLASS SIZE DATA

Number of Students in Class (x_i)	Deviation About the Mean ($x_i - \bar{x}$)	z-Score $\left(\dfrac{x_i - \bar{x}}{s}\right)$
46	2	2/8 = .25
54	10	10/8 = 1.25
42	−2	−2/8 = −.25
46	2	2/8 = .25
32	−12	−12/8 = −1.50

Chebyshev's Theorem

Chebyshev's theorem enables us to make statements about the proportion of data values that must be within a specified number of standard deviations of the mean.

> CHEBYSHEV'S THEOREM
>
> At least $(1 - 1/z^2)$ of the data values must be within z standard deviations of the mean, where z is any value greater than 1.

Some of the implications of this theorem, with $z = 2, 3,$ and 4 standard deviations, follow.

- At least .75, or 75%, of the data values must be within $z = 2$ standard deviations of the mean.
- At least .89, or 89%, of the data values must be within $z = 3$ standard deviations of the mean.
- At least .94, or 94%, of the data values must be within $z = 4$ standard deviations of the mean.

For an example using Chebyshev's theorem, suppose that the midterm test scores for 100 students in a college business statistics course had a mean of 70 and a standard deviation of 5. How many students had test scores between 60 and 80? How many students had test scores between 58 and 82?

For the test scores between 60 and 80, we note that 60 is two standard deviations below the mean and 80 is two standard deviations above the mean. Using Chebyshev's theorem, we see that at least .75, or at least 75%, of the observations must have values within two standard deviations of the mean. Thus, at least 75% of the students must have scored between 60 and 80.

Chebyshev's theorem requires z > 1; but z need not be an integer.

For the test scores between 58 and 82, we see that $(58 - 70)/5 = -2.4$ indicates 58 is 2.4 standard deviations below the mean and that $(82 - 70)/5 = +2.4$ indicates 82 is 2.4 standard deviations above the mean. Applying Chebyshev's theorem with $z = 2.4$, we have

$$\left(1 - \frac{1}{z^2}\right) = \left(1 - \frac{1}{(2.4)^2}\right) = .826$$

At least 82.6% of the students must have test scores between 58 and 82.

Empirical Rule

The empirical rule is based on the normal probability distribution, which will be discussed in Chapter 6. The normal distribution is used extensively throughout the text.

One of the advantages of Chebyshev's theorem is that it applies to any data set regardless of the shape of the distribution of the data. Indeed, it could be used with any of the distributions in Figure 3.9. In many practical applications, however, data exhibit a symmetric mound-shaped or bell-shaped distribution like the one shown in Figure 3.10. When the data are believed to approximate this distribution, the **empirical rule** can be used to determine the percentage of data values that must be within a specified number of standard deviations of the mean.

> EMPIRICAL RULE
>
> For data having a bell-shaped distribution:
>
> - Approximately 68% of the data values will be within one standard deviation of the mean.
> - Approximately 95% of the data values will be within two standard deviations of the mean.
> - Almost all of the data values will be within three standard deviations of the mean.

FIGURE 3.10   SYMMETRIC MOUND-SHAPED OR BELL-SHAPED DISTRIBUTION

For example, liquid detergent cartons are filled automatically on a production line. Filling weights frequently have a bell-shaped distribution. If the mean filling weight is 16 ounces and the standard deviation is .25 ounces, we can use the empirical rule to draw the following conclusions.

- Approximately 68% of the filled cartons will have weights between 15.75 and 16.25 ounces (within one standard deviation of the mean).
- Approximately 95% of the filled cartons will have weights between 15.50 and 16.50 ounces (within two standard deviations of the mean).
- Almost all filled cartons will have weights between 15.25 and 16.75 ounces (within three standard deviations of the mean).

Detecting Outliers

Sometimes a data set will have one or more observations with unusually large or unusually small values. These extreme values are called **outliers**. Experienced statisticians take steps to identify outliers and then review each one carefully. An outlier may be a data value that has been incorrectly recorded. If so, it can be corrected before further analysis. An outlier may also be from an observation that was incorrectly included in the data set; if so, it can be removed. Finally, an outlier may be an unusual data value that has been recorded correctly and belongs in the data set.

It is a good idea to check for outliers before making decisions based on data analysis. Errors are often made in recording data and entering data into the computer. Outliers should not necessarily be deleted, but their accuracy and appropriateness should be verified.

Standardized values (*z*-scores) can be used to identify outliers. Recall that the empirical rule allows us to conclude that for data with a bell-shaped distribution, almost all the data values will be within three standard deviations of the mean. Hence, in using *z*-scores to identify outliers, we recommend treating any data value with a *z*-score less than -3 or greater than $+3$ as an outlier. Such data values can then be reviewed for accuracy and to determine whether they belong in the data set.

Refer to the *z*-scores for the class size data in Table 3.4. The *z*-score of -1.50 shows the fifth class size is farthest from the mean. However, this standardized value is well within the -3 to $+3$ guideline for outliers. Thus, the *z*-scores do not indicate that outliers are present in the class size data.

NOTES AND COMMENTS

1. Chebyshev's theorem is applicable for any data set and can be used to state the minimum number of data values that will be within a certain number of standard deviations of the mean. If the data are known to be approximately bell-shaped, more can be said. For instance, the empirical rule allows us to say that *approximately* 95% of the data values will be within two standard deviations of the mean; Chebyshev's theorem allows us to conclude only that at least 75% of the data values will be in that interval.

2. Before analyzing a data set, statisticians usually make a variety of checks to ensure the validity of data. In a large study it is not uncommon for errors to be made in recording data values or in entering the values into a computer. Identifying outliers is one tool used to check the validity of the data.

Exercises

Methods

25. Consider a sample with data values of 10, 20, 12, 17, and 16. Compute the z-score for each of the five observations.

26. Consider a sample with a mean of 500 and a standard deviation of 100. What are the z-scores for the following data values: 520, 650, 500, 450, and 280?

27. Consider a sample with a mean of 30 and a standard deviation of 5. Use Chebyshev's theorem to determine the percentage of the data within each of the following ranges.
    a. 20 to 40
    b. 15 to 45
    c. 22 to 38
    d. 18 to 42
    e. 12 to 48

28. Suppose the data have a bell-shaped distribution with a mean of 30 and a standard deviation of 5. Use the empirical rule to determine the percentage of data within each of the following ranges.
    a. 20 to 40
    b. 15 to 45
    c. 25 to 35

Applications

29. The results of a national survey showed that on average, adults sleep 6.9 hours per night (2000 Omnibus Sleep in America Poll). Suppose that the standard deviation is 1.2 hours.
    a. Use Chebyshev's theorem to calculate the percentage of individuals who sleep between 4.5 and 9.3 hours.
    b. Use Chebyshev's theorem to calculate the percentage of individuals who sleep between 3.9 and 9.9 hours.
    c. Assume that the number of hours of sleep follows a bell-shaped distribution. Use the empirical rule to calculate the percentage of individuals who sleep between 4.5 and 9.3 hours per day. How does this result compare to the value that you obtained using Chebyshev's theorem in part (a)?

30. The Energy Information Administration reported that the mean retail price per gallon of regular grade gasoline was $1.47 (*The Wall Street Journal,* January 30, 2003). Suppose that the standard deviation was $.08 and that the retail price per gallon has a bell-shaped distribution.
    a. What percentage of regular grade gasoline sold between $1.39 and $1.55 per gallon?
    b. What percentage of regular grade gasoline sold between $1.39 and $1.63 per gallon?
    c. What percentage of regular grade gasoline sold for more than $1.63 per gallon?

31. The national average for the verbal portion of the College Board's Scholastic Aptitude Test (SAT) is 507 (*The World Almanac,* 2004). The College Board periodically rescales the test scores such that the standard deviation is approximately 100. Answer the following questions using a bell-shaped distribution and the empirical rule for the verbal test scores.

a. What percentage of students have an SAT verbal score greater than 607?
b. What percentage of students have an SAT verbal score greater than 707?
c. What percentage of students have an SAT verbal score between 407 and 507?
d. What percentage of students have an SAT verbal score between 307 and 607?

32. The high costs in the California real estate market have caused families who cannot afford to buy bigger homes to consider backyard sheds as an alternative form of housing expansion. Many are using the backyard structures for home offices, art studios, and hobby areas as well as for additional storage. The mean price of a customized wooden, shingled backyard structure is $3100 (*Newsweek,* September 29, 2003). Assume that the standard deviation is $1200.
    a. What is the *z*-score for a backyard structure costing $2300?
    b. What is the *z*-score for a backyard structure costing $4900?
    c. Interpret the *z*-scores in parts (a) and (b). Comment on whether either should be considered an outlier.
    d. The *Newsweek* article described a backyard shed-office combination built in Albany, California, for $13,000. Should this structure be considered an outlier? Explain.

33. Wageweb conducts surveys of salary data and presents summaries on its Web site. Salaries reported for benefits managers ranged from $50,935 to $79,577 (http://www.Wageweb.com, April 12, 2000). Assume the following data are a sample of the annual salaries for 30 benefits managers. Data are in thousands of dollars.

WageWeb

57.7	64.4	62.1	59.1	71.1
63.0	64.7	61.2	66.8	61.8
64.2	63.3	62.2	61.2	59.4
63.0	66.7	60.3	74.0	62.8
68.7	63.8	59.2	60.3	56.6
59.3	69.5	61.7	58.9	63.1

a. Compute the mean and standard deviation for the sample data.
b. Using the mean and standard deviation computed in part (a) as estimates of the mean and standard deviation of salary for the population of benefits managers, use Chebyshev's theorem to determine the percentage of benefits managers with an annual salary between $55,000 and $71,000.
c. Develop a histogram for the sample data. Computer software provides .97 as the measure of skewness. Does it appear reasonable to assume that the distribution of annual salary can be approximated by a bell-shaped distribution?
d. Assume that the distribution of annual salary is bell-shaped. Using the mean and standard deviation computed in part (a) as estimates of the mean and standard deviation of salary for the population of benefits managers, use the empirical rule to determine the percentage of benefits managers with an annual salary between $55,000 and $71,000. Compare your answer with the value computed in part (b).
e. Do the sample data contain any outliers?

34. A sample of 10 NCAA college basketball game scores provided the following data (*USA Today,* January 26, 2004).

NCAA

Winning Team	Points	Losing Team	Points	Winning Margin
Arizona	90	Oregon	66	24
Duke	85	Georgetown	66	19
Florida State	75	Wake Forest	70	5
Kansas	78	Colorado	57	21
Kentucky	71	Notre Dame	63	8
Louisville	65	Tennessee	62	3

(*continued*)

Winning Team	Points	Losing Team	Points	Winning Margin
Oklahoma State	72	Texas	66	6
Purdue	76	Michigan State	70	6
Stanford	77	Southern Cal	67	10
Wisconsin	76	Illinois	56	20

a. Compute the mean and standard deviation for the points scored by the winning team.
b. Assume that the points scored by the winning teams for all NCAA games follow a bell-shaped distribution. Using the mean and standard deviation found in part (a), estimate the percentage of all NCAA games in which the winning team scores 84 or more points. Estimate the percentage of NCAA games in which the winning team scores more than 90 points.
c. Compute the mean and standard deviation for the winning margin. Do the data contain outliers? Explain.

35. *Consumer Review* posts reviews and ratings of a variety of products on the Internet. The following is a sample of 20 speaker systems and their ratings (http://www.audioreview.com). The ratings are on a scale of 1 to 5, with 5 being best.

Speakers

Speaker	Rating	Speaker	Rating
Infinity Kappa 6.1	4.00	ACI Sapphire III	4.67
Allison One	4.12	Bose 501 Series	2.14
Cambridge Ensemble II	3.82	DCM KX-212	4.09
Dynaudio Contour 1.3	4.00	Eosone RSF1000	4.17
Hsu Rsch. HRSW12V	4.56	Joseph Audio RM7si	4.88
Legacy Audio Focus	4.32	Martin Logan Aerius	4.26
Mission 73li	4.33	Omni Audio SA 12.3	2.32
PSB 400i	4.50	Polk Audio RT12	4.50
Snell Acoustics D IV	4.64	Sunfire True Subwoofer	4.17
Thiel CS1.5	4.20	Yamaha NS-A636	2.17

a. Compute the mean and the median.
b. Compute the first and third quartiles.
c. Compute the standard deviation.
d. The skewness of this data is -1.67. Comment on the shape of the distribution.
e. What are the z-scores associated with Allison One and Omni Audio?
f. Do the data contain any outliers? Explain.

3.4 Exploratory Data Analysis

In Chapter 2 we introduced the stem-and-leaf display as a technique of exploratory data analysis. Recall that exploratory data analysis enables us to use simple arithmetic and easy-to-draw pictures to summarize data. In this section we continue exploratory data analysis by considering five-number summaries and box plots.

Five-Number Summary

In a **five-number summary**, the following five numbers are used to summarize the data.

1. Smallest value
2. First quartile (Q_1)
3. Median (Q_2)

4. Third quartile (Q_3)

5. Largest value

The easiest way to develop a five-number summary is to first place the data in ascending order. Then it is easy to identify the smallest value, the three quartiles, and the largest value. The monthly starting salaries shown in Table 3.1 for a sample of 12 business school graduates are repeated here in ascending order.

2710 2755 2850 │ 2880 2880 2890 │ 2920 2940 2950 │ 3050 3130 3325

$Q_1 = 2865$ $Q_2 = 2905$ $Q_3 = 3000$
                          (Median)

The median of 2905 and the quartiles $Q_1 = 2865$ and $Q_3 = 3000$ were computed in Section 3.1. Reviewing the data shows a smallest value of 2710 and a largest value of 3325. Thus, the five-number summary for the salary data is 2710, 2865, 2905, 3000, 3325. Approximately one-fourth, or 25%, of the observations are between adjacent numbers in a five-number summary.

Box Plot

A **box plot** is a graphical summary of data that is based on a five-number summary. A key to the development of a box plot is the computation of the median and the quartiles, Q_1 and Q_3. The interquartile range, IQR = $Q_3 - Q_1$, is also used. Figure 3.11 is the box plot for the monthly starting salary data. The steps used to construct the box plot follow.

1. A box is drawn with the ends of the box located at the first and third quartiles. For the salary data, $Q_1 = 2865$ and $Q_3 = 3000$. This box contains the middle 50% of the data.

Box plots provide another way to identify outliers. But they do not necessarily identify the same values as those with a z-score less than −3 or greater than +3. Either or both procedures may be used.

2. A vertical line is drawn in the box at the location of the median (2905 for the salary data).

3. By using the interquartile range, IQR = $Q_3 - Q_1$, *limits* are located. The limits for the box plot are 1.5(IQR) below Q_1 and 1.5(IQR) above Q_3. For the salary data, IQR = $Q_3 - Q_1 = 3000 - 2865 = 135$. Thus, the limits are 2865 − 1.5(135) = 2662.5 and 3000 + 1.5(135) = 3202.5. Data outside these limits are considered *outliers*.

4. The dashed lines in Figure 3.11 are called *whiskers*. The whiskers are drawn from the ends of the box to the smallest and largest values *inside the limits* computed in step 3. Thus, the whiskers end at salary values of 2710 and 3130.

5. Finally, the location of each outlier is shown with the symbol *. In Figure 3.11 we see one outlier, 3325.

FIGURE 3.11 BOX PLOT OF THE STARTING SALARY DATA WITH LINES SHOWING THE LOWER AND UPPER LIMITS

FIGURE 3.12 BOX PLOT OF THE STARTING SALARY DATA

In Figure 3.11 we included lines showing the location of the upper and lower limits. These lines were drawn to show how the limits are computed and where they are located for the salary data. Although the limits are always computed, generally they are not drawn on the box plots. Figure 3.12 shows the usual appearance of a box plot for the salary data.

NOTES AND COMMENTS

1. An advantage of the exploratory data analysis procedures is that they are easy to use; few numerical calculations are necessary. We simply sort the data values into ascending order and identify the five-number summary. The box plot can then be constructed. It is not necessary to compute the mean and the standard deviation for the data.

2. Excel 2003 does not contain a procedure for constructing box plots. In Appendix 3.1, we show how to construct a box plot for the starting salary data using SWStat+, an Excel add-in.

Exercises

Methods

36. Consider a sample with data values of 27, 25, 20, 15, 30, 34, 28, and 25. Provide the five-number summary for the data.

37. Show the box plot for the data in exercise 36.

38. Show the five-number summary and the box plot for the following data: 5, 15, 18, 10, 8, 12, 16, 10, 6.

39. A data set has a first quartile of 42 and a third quartile of 50. Compute the lower and upper limits for the corresponding box plot. Should a data value of 65 be considered an outlier?

Applications

40. Ebby Halliday Realtors provide advertisements for distinctive properties and estates located throughout the United States. The prices listed for 22 distinctive properties and estates are shown here (*The Wall Street Journal*, January 16, 2004). Prices are in thousands.

Property

1500	700	2995
895	619	880
719	725	3100
619	739	1699
625	799	1120
4450	2495	1250
2200	1395	912
1280		

a. Provide a five-number summary.
b. Compute the lower and upper limits.
c. The highest priced property, $4,450,000, is listed as an estate overlooking White Rock Lake in Dallas, Texas. Should this property be considered an outlier? Explain.
d. Should the second highest priced property listed for $3,100,000 be considered an outlier? Explain.
e. Show a box plot.

41. Annual sales, in millions of dollars, for 21 pharmaceutical companies follow.

8408	1374	1872	8879	2459	11413
608	14138	6452	1850	2818	1356
10498	7478	4019	4341	739	2127
3653	5794	8305			

a. Provide a five-number summary.
b. Compute the lower and upper limits.
c. Do the data contain any outliers?
d. Johnson & Johnson's sales are the largest on the list at $14,138 million. Suppose a data entry error (a transposition) had been made and the sales had been entered as $41,138 million. Would the method of detecting outliers in part (c) identify this problem and allow for correction of the data entry error?
e. Show a box plot.

42. Major League Baseball payrolls continue to escalate. Team payrolls in millions are as follows (*The Miami Herald,* May 22, 2002).

Payroll

Team	Payroll ($)	Team	Payroll ($)
Anaheim	62	Milwaukee	50
Arizona	103	Minnesota	40
Atlanta	93	Montreal	39
Baltimore	60	NY Mets	95
Boston	108	NY Yankees	126
Chi Cubs	76	Oakland	40
Chi White Sox	57	Philadelphia	58
Cincinnati	45	Pittsburgh	42
Cleveland	79	San Diego	41
Colorado	57	San Francisco	78
Detroit	55	Seattle	90
Florida	42	St. Louis	74
Houston	63	Tampa Bay	34
Kansas City	47	Texas	105
Los Angeles	95	Toronto	77

a. What is the median team payroll?
b. Provide a five-number summary.
c. Is the $126 million payroll for the New York Yankees an outlier? Explain.
d. Show a box plot.

43. New York Stock Exchange (NYSE) Chairman Richard Grasso and NYSE Board of Directors came under fire for the large compensation package being paid to Grasso. When it comes to salary plus bonus, Grasso's $8.5 million out-earned the top executives of all major financial services companies. The data that follow show total annual salary plus bonus paid

to the top executives of 14 financial services companies (*The Wall Street Journal*, September 17, 2003). Data are in millions.

Company	Salary and Bonus ($)	Company	Salary and Bonus ($)
Aetna	3.5	Fannie Mae	4.3
AIG	6.0	Federal Home Loan	0.8
Allstate	4.1	Fleet Boston	1.0
American Express	3.8	Freddie Mac	1.2
Chubb	2.1	Mellon Financial	2.0
Cigna	1.0	Merrill Lynch	7.7
Citigroup	1.0	Wells Fargo	8.0

a. What is the median annual salary plus bonus paid to the top executive of the 14 financial service companies?
b. Provide a five-number summary.
c. Should Grasso's $8.5 million annual salary plus bonus be considered an outlier for this group of top executives? Explain.
d. Show a box plot.

44. A listing of 46 mutual funds and their 12-month total return percentage is shown in Table 3.5 (*Smart Money*, February 2004).

Mutual

a. What are the mean and median return percentages for these mutual funds?
b. What are the first and third quartiles?
c. Provide a five-number summary.
d. Do the data contain any outliers? Show a box plot.

TABLE 3.5   TWELVE-MONTH RETURN FOR MUTUAL FUNDS

Mutual Fund	Return (%)	Mutual Fund	Return (%)
Alger Capital Appreciation	23.5	Nations Small Company	21.4
Alger LargeCap Growth	22.8	Nations SmallCap Index	24.5
Alger MidCap Growth	38.3	Nations Strategic Growth	10.4
Alger SmallCap	41.3	Nations Value Inv	10.8
AllianceBernstein Technology	40.6	One Group Diversified Equity	10.0
Federated American Leaders	15.6	One Group Diversified Int'l	10.9
Federated Capital Appreciation	12.4	One Group Diversified Mid Cap	15.1
Federated Equity-Income	11.5	One Group Equity Income	6.6
Federated Kaufmann	33.3	One Group Int'l Equity Index	13.2
Federated Max-Cap Index	16.0	One Group LargeCap Growth	13.6
Federated Stock	16.9	One Group LargeCap Value	12.8
Janus Adviser Int'l Growth	10.3	One Group MidCap Growth	18.7
Janus Adviser Worldwide	3.4	One Group MidCap Value	11.4
Janus Enterprise	24.2	One Group SmallCap Growth	23.6
Janus High-Yield	12.1	PBHG Growth	27.3
Janus Mercury	20.6	Putnam Europe Equity	20.4
Janus Overseas	11.9	Putnam Int'l Capital Opportunity	36.6
Janus Worldwide	4.1	Putnam International Equity	21.5
Nations Convertible Securities	13.6	Putnam Int'l New Opportunity	26.3
Nations Int'l Equity	10.7	Strong Advisor MidCap Growth	23.7
Nations LargeCap Enhd. Core	13.2	Strong Growth 20	11.7
Nations LargeCap Index	13.5	Strong Growth Inv	23.2
Nation MidCap Index	19.5	Strong LargeCap Growth	14.5

3.5

Measures of Association Between Two Variables

Thus far we examined numerical methods used to summarize the data for *one variable at a time*. Often a manager or decision maker is interested in the *relationship between two variables*. In this section we present covariance and correlation as measures of the relationship between two variables.

We begin by reconsidering the application concerning a stereo and sound equipment store in San Francisco as presented in Section 2.4. The store's manager wants to determine the relationship between the number of weekend television commercials shown and the sales at the store during the following week. Sample data with sales expressed in hundreds of dollars are provided in Table 3.6. It shows 10 observations ($n = 10$), one for each week. The scatter diagram and trendline in Figure 3.13 shows a positive relationship, with higher sales (y) associated with a greater number of commercials (x). In fact, the trendline suggests that a straight line could be used as an approximation of the relationship. In the following discussion, we introduce **covariance** as a measure of the linear association between two variables.

Covariance

For a sample of size n with the observations (x_1, y_1), (x_2, y_2), and so on, the sample covariance is defined as follows:

SAMPLE COVARIANCE

$$s_{xy} = \frac{\Sigma(x_i - \bar{x})(y_i - \bar{y})}{n - 1}$$

(3.10)

This formula pairs each x_i with a y_i. We then sum the products obtained by multiplying the deviation of each x_i from its sample mean $\bar{x}$ by the deviation of the corresponding y_i from its sample mean $\bar{y}$; this sum is then divided by $n - 1$.

TABLE 3.6   SAMPLE DATA FOR THE STEREO AND SOUND EQUIPMENT STORE

Week	Number of Commercials x	Sales Volume ($100s) y
1	2	50
2	5	57
3	1	41
4	3	54
5	4	54
6	1	38
7	5	63
8	3	48
9	4	59
10	2	46

FIGURE 3.13   SCATTER DIAGRAM AND TRENDLINE FOR THE STEREO AND SOUND EQUIPMENT STORE

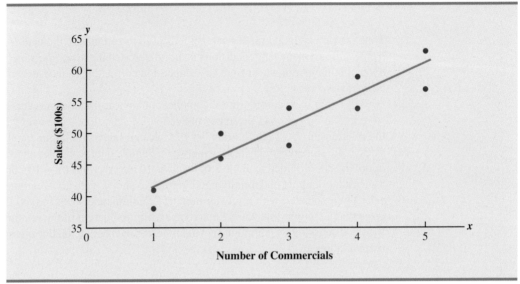

To measure the strength of the linear relationship between the number of commercials x and the sales volume y in the stereo and sound equipment store problem, we use equation (3.10) to compute the sample covariance. The calculations in Table 3.7 show the computation of $\Sigma(x_i - \bar{x})(y_i - \bar{y})$. Note that $\bar{x} = 30/10 = 3$ and $\bar{y} = 510/10 = 51$. Using equation (3.10), we obtain a sample covariance of

$$s_{xy} = \frac{\Sigma(x_i - \bar{x})(y_i - \bar{y})}{n - 1} = \frac{99}{9} = 11$$

TABLE 3.7   CALCULATIONS FOR THE SAMPLE COVARIANCE

	x_i	y_i	$x_i - \bar{x}$	$y_i - \bar{y}$	$(x_i - \bar{x})(y_i - \bar{y})$
	2	50	-1	-1	1
	5	57	2	6	12
	1	41	-2	-10	20
	3	54	0	3	0
	4	54	1	3	3
	1	38	-2	-13	26
	5	63	2	12	24
	3	48	0	-3	0
	4	59	1	8	8
	2	46	-1	-5	5
Totals	30	510	0	0	99

$$s_{xy} = \frac{\Sigma(x_i - \bar{x})(y_i - \bar{y})}{n - 1} = \frac{99}{10 - 1} = 11$$

The formula for computing the covariance of a population of size N is similar to equation (3.10), but we use different notation to indicate that we are working with the entire population.

POPULATION COVARIANCE

$$\sigma_{xy} = \frac{\Sigma(x_i - \mu_x)(y_i - \mu_y)}{N}$$

(3.11)

In equation (3.11) we use the notation μ_x for the population mean of the variable x and μ_y for the population mean of the variable y. The population covariance σ_{xy} is defined for a population of size N.

Interpretation of the Covariance

To aid in the interpretation of the sample covariance, consider Figure 3.14. It is the same as the scatter diagram of Figure 3.13 with a vertical dashed line at $\bar{x} = 3$ and a horizontal dashed line at $\bar{y} = 51$. The lines divide the graph into four quadrants. Points in quadrant I correspond to x_i greater than $\bar{x}$ and y_i greater than $\bar{y}$, points in quadrant II correspond to x_i less than $\bar{x}$ and y_i greater than $\bar{y}$, and so on. Thus, the value of $(x_i - \bar{x})(y_i - \bar{y})$ must be positive for points in quadrant I, negative for points in quadrant II, positive for points in quadrant III, and negative for points in quadrant IV.

The covariance is a measure of the linear association between two variables.

If the value of s_{xy} is positive, the points with the greatest influence on s_{xy} must be in quadrants I and III. Hence, a positive value for s_{xy} indicates a positive linear association between x and y; that is, as the value of x increases, the value of y increases. If the value of s_{xy} is negative, however, the points with the greatest influence on s_{xy} are in quadrants II and IV. Hence, a negative value for s_{xy} indicates a negative linear association between x and y; that is, as the value of x increases, the value of y decreases. Finally, if the points are evenly distributed across all four quadrants, the value of s_{xy} will be close to zero, indicating no linear association between x and y. Figure 3.15 shows the values of s_{xy} that can be expected with three different types of scatter diagrams.

FIGURE 3.14   PARTITIONED SCATTER DIAGRAM FOR THE STEREO AND SOUND EQUIPMENT STORE

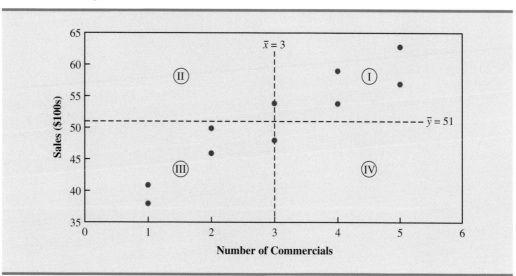

FIGURE 3.15 INTERPRETATION OF SAMPLE COVARIANCE

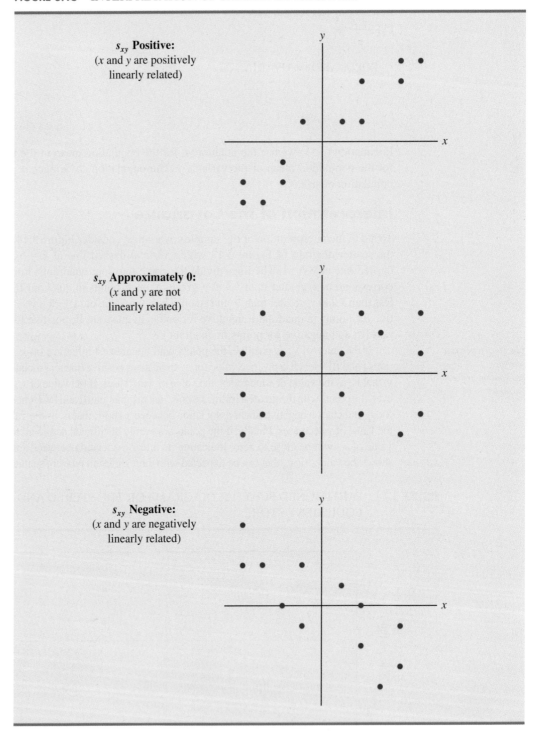

Referring again to Figure 3.14, we see that the scatter diagram for the stereo and sound equipment store follows the pattern in the top panel of Figure 3.15. As we should expect, the value of the sample covariance indicates a positive linear relationship with $s_{xy} = 11$.

From the preceding discussion, it might appear that a large positive value for the co-variance indicates a strong positive linear relationship and that a large negative value indicates a strong negative linear relationship. However, one problem with using covariance as a measure of the strength of the linear relationship is that the value of the covariance depends on the units of measurement for x and y. For example, suppose we are interested in the relationship between height x and weight y for individuals. Clearly the strength of the relationship should be the same whether we measure height in feet or inches. Measuring the height in inches, however, gives us much larger numerical values for $(x_i - \bar{x})$ than when we measure height in feet. Thus, with height measured in inches, we would obtain a larger value for the numerator $\Sigma(x_i - \bar{x})(y_i - \bar{y})$ in equation (3.10)—and hence a larger covariance—when in fact the relationship does not change. A measure of the relationship between two variables that is not affected by the units of measurement for x and y is the **correlation coefficient**.

Correlation Coefficient

For sample data, the Pearson product moment correlation coefficient is defined as follows.

PEARSON PRODUCT MOMENT CORRELATION COEFFICIENT: SAMPLE DATA

$$r_{xy} = \frac{s_{xy}}{s_x s_y} \tag{3.12}$$

where

r_{xy} = sample correlation coefficient
s_{xy} = sample covariance
s_x = sample standard deviation of x
s_y = sample standard deviation of y

Equation (3.12) shows that the Pearson product moment correlation coefficient for sample data (commonly referred to more simply as the *sample correlation coefficient*) is computed by dividing the sample covariance by the product of the sample standard deviation of x and the sample standard deviation of y.

Let us now compute the sample correlation coefficient for the stereo and sound equipment store. Using the data in Table 3.7, we can compute the sample standard deviations for the two variables.

$$s_x = \sqrt{\frac{\Sigma(x_i - \bar{x})^2}{n - 1}} = \sqrt{\frac{20}{9}} = 1.49$$

$$s_y = \sqrt{\frac{\Sigma(y_i - \bar{y})^2}{n - 1}} = \sqrt{\frac{566}{9}} = 7.93$$

Now, because $s_{xy} = 11$, the sample correlation coefficient equals

$$r_{xy} = \frac{s_{xy}}{s_x s_y} = \frac{11}{(1.49)(7.93)} = +.93$$

The formula for computing the correlation coefficient for a population, denoted by the Greek letter ρ_{xy} (*rho*, pronounced "row"), follows.

PEARSON PRODUCT MOMENT CORRELATION COEFFICIENT: POPULATION DATA

The sample correlation coefficient r_{xy} is the estimator of the population correlation coefficient ρ_{xy}.

$$\rho_{xy} = \frac{\sigma_{xy}}{\sigma_x \sigma_y} \qquad (3.13)$$

where

ρ_{xy} = population correlation coefficient
σ_{xy} = population covariance
σ_x = population standard deviation for x
σ_y = population standard deviation for y

The sample correlation coefficient r_{xy} provides an estimate of the population correlation coefficient ρ_{xy}.

Interpretation of the Correlation Coefficient

First let us consider a simple example that illustrates the concept of a perfect positive linear relationship. The scatter diagram in Figure 3.16 depicts the relationship between x and y based on the following sample data.

x_i	y_i
5	10
10	30
15	50

FIGURE 3.16   SCATTER DIAGRAM DEPICTING A PERFECT POSITIVE LINEAR RELATIONSHIP

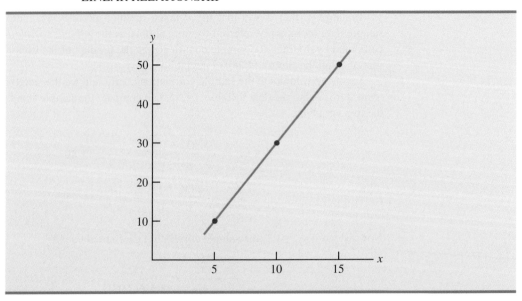

The straight line drawn through each of the three points shows a perfect linear relationship between x and y. In order to apply equation (3.12) to compute the sample correlation we must first compute s_{xy}, s_x, and s_y. Some of the computations are shown in Table 3.8. Using the results in Table 3.8, we find

$$s_{xy} = \frac{\Sigma(x_i - \bar{x})(y_i - \bar{y})}{n - 1} = \frac{200}{2} = 100$$

$$s_x = \sqrt{\frac{\Sigma(x_i - \bar{x})^2}{n - 1}} = \sqrt{\frac{50}{2}} = 5$$

$$s_y = \sqrt{\frac{\Sigma(y_i - \bar{y})^2}{n - 1}} = \sqrt{\frac{800}{2}} = 20$$

$$r_{xy} = \frac{s_{xy}}{s_x s_y} = \frac{100}{5(20)} = 1$$

The correlation coefficient ranges from −1 to +1. Values close to −1 or +1 indicate a strong linear relationship. The closer the correlation is to zero, the weaker the relationship.

Thus, we see that the value of the sample correlation coefficient is 1.

In general, it can be shown that if all the points in a data set fall on a positively sloped straight line, the value of the sample correlation coefficient is +1; that is, a sample correlation coefficient of +1 corresponds to a perfect positive linear relationship between x and y. Moreover, if the points in the data set fall on a straight line having negative slope, the value of the sample correlation coefficient is −1; that is, a sample correlation coefficient of −1 corresponds to a perfect negative linear relationship between x and y.

Let us now suppose that a certain data set indicates a positive linear relationship between x and y but that the relationship is not perfect. The value of r_{xy} will be less than 1, indicating that the points in the scatter diagram are not all on a straight line. As the points deviate more and more from a perfect positive linear relationship, the value of r_{xy} becomes smaller and smaller. A value of r_{xy} equal to zero indicates no linear relationship between x and y, and values of r_{xy} near zero indicate a weak linear relationship.

For the data involving the stereo and sound equipment store, recall that $r_{xy} = +.93$. Therefore, we conclude that a strong positive linear relationship exists between the number of commercials and sales. More specifically, an increase in the number of commercials is associated with an increase in sales.

In closing, we note that correlation provides a measure of linear association and not necessarily causation. A high correlation between two variables does not mean that changes in one variable will cause changes in the other variable. For example, we may find that the quality rating and the typical meal price of restaurants are positively correlated. However, simply increasing the meal price at a restaurant will not cause the quality rating to increase.

TABLE 3.8   COMPUTATIONS USED IN CALCULATING THE SAMPLE CORRELATION COEFFICIENT

	x_i	y_i	$x_i - \bar{x}$	$(x_i - \bar{x})^2$	$y_i - \bar{y}$	$(y_i - \bar{y})^2$	$(x_i - \bar{x})(y_i - \bar{y})$
	5	10	−5	25	−20	400	100
	10	30	0	0	0	0	0
	15	50	5	25	20	400	100
Totals	30	90	0	50	0	800	200

$\bar{x} = 10$ $\bar{y} = 30$

Using Excel to Compute the Covariance and Correlation Coefficient

Excel's COVAR function is designed for a population and Excel's CORREL function is designed for a sample.

Excel provides functions that can be used to compute the covariance and correlation coefficient. But you must be careful when using these functions because the covariance function treats the data as a population and the correlation function treats the data as a sample. Thus, the result obtained using Excel's covariance function must be adjusted to provide the sample covariance. We show here how these functions can be used to compute the sample covariance and the sample correlation coefficient for the stereo and sound equipment store data. Refer to Figure 3.17 as we present the steps involved. The formula worksheet is in the background; the value worksheet is in the foreground.

Enter Data: Labels and data on commercials and sales are entered into cells A1:C11 of the worksheet.

Enter Functions and Formulas: Excel's covariance function, COVAR, can be used to compute the population covariance by entering the following formula into cell F1:

$$=COVAR(B2:B11,C2:C11)$$

Similarly, the formula =CORREL(B2:B11,C2:C11) is entered into cell F2 to compute the sample correlation coefficient. The labels Population Covariance and Sample Correlation are entered into cells E1 and E2 to identify the output.

The formulas in cells F1:F2 are displayed in the worksheet in the background of Figure 3.17. The worksheet in the foreground shows the values computed using the Excel functions. Note that, except for rounding, the value of the sample correlation coefficient (.9305) is the same as we computed earlier using equation (3.12). However, the result provided by the COVAR function, 9.9, was obtained by treating the data as a population. Thus, we must adjust the Excel result of 9.9 to obtain the sample covariance. The adjustment is rather simple. First, note that the formula for the population covariance, equation (3.11), re-

FIGURE 3.17   EXCEL WORKSHEET USED TO COMPUTE THE COVARIANCE AND CORRELATION COEFFICIENT

	A	B	C	D	E	F	G
1	Week	Commercials	Sales		Population Covariance	=COVAR(B2:B11,C2:C11)	
2	1	2	50		Sample Correlation	=CORREL(B2:B11,C2:C11)	
3	2	5	57				

	A	B	C	D	E	F	G
4	3	1	41	1	Week	Commercials	Sales		Population Covariance	9.9	

	A	B	C	D	E	F	G
1	Week	Commercials	Sales		Population Covariance	9.9	
2	1	2	50		Sample Correlation	0.9305	
3	2	5	57				
4	3	1	41				
5	4	3	54				
6	5	4	54				
7	6	1	38				
8	7	5	63				
9	8	3	48				
10	9	4	59				
11	10	2	46				
12							

Left worksheet:

	A	B	C	D
1	Week	Commercials	Sales	
2	1	2	50	
3	2	5	57	
4	3	1	41	
5	4	3	54	
6	5	4	54	
7	6	1	38	
8	7	5	63	
9	8	3	48	
10	9	4	59	
11	10	2	46	
12				

quires dividing by the total number of observations in the data set. But the formula for the sample covariance, equation (3.10), requires dividing by the total number of observations minus 1. So to use the Excel result of 9.9 to compute the sample covariance, we simply multiply 9.9 by $n/(n - 1)$. With $n = 10$, we obtain

$$s_{xy} = \left(\frac{10}{9}\right)9.9 = 11$$

Thus, the sample covariance for the stereo and sound equipment data is 11.

Exercises

Methods

45. Five observations taken for two variables follow.

x_i	4	6	11	3	16
y_i	50	50	40	60	30

a. Develop a scatter diagram with x on the horizontal axis.
b. What does the scatter diagram developed in part (a) indicate about the relationship between the two variables?
c. Compute and interpret the sample covariance.
d. Compute and interpret the sample correlation coefficient.

46. Five observations taken for two variables follow.

x_i	6	11	15	21	27
y_i	6	9	6	17	12

a. Develop a scatter diagram for these data.
b. What does the scatter diagram indicate about a relationship between x and y?
c. Compute and interpret the sample covariance.
d. Compute and interpret the sample correlation coefficient.

Applications

47. Nielsen Media Research provides two measures of the television viewing audience: a television program *rating,* which is the percentage of households with televisions watching a program, and a television program *share,* which is the percentage of households watching a program among those with televisions in use. The following data show the Nielsen television ratings and share data for the Major League Baseball World Series over a nine-year period (Associated Press, October 27, 2003).

Rating	19	17	17	14	16	12	15	12	13
Share	32	28	29	24	26	20	24	20	22

a. Develop a scatter diagram with rating on the horizontal axis.
b. What is the relationship between rating and share? Explain.
c. Compute and interpret the sample covariance.
d. Compute the sample correlation coefficient. What does this value tell us about the relationship between rating and share?

48. A department of transportation's study on driving speed and mileage for midsize automobiles resulted in the following data.

Driving Speed	30	50	40	55	30	25	60	25	50	55
Mileage	28	25	25	23	30	32	21	35	26	25

Compute and interpret the sample correlation coefficient.

49. *PC World* provided ratings for 15 notebook PCs (*PC World*, February 2000). The performance score is a measure of how fast a PC can run a mix of common business applications as compared to a baseline machine. For example, a PC with a performance score of 200 is twice as fast as the baseline machine. A 100-point scale was used to provide an overall rating for each notebook tested in the study. A score in the 90s is exceptional, while one in the 70s is good. Table 3.9 shows the performance scores and the overall ratings for the 15 notebooks.
    a. Compute the sample correlation coefficient.
    b. What does the sample correlation coefficient tell about the relationship between the performance score and the overall rating?

50. The Dow Jones Industrial Average (DJIA) and the Standard & Poor's (S&P) 500 Index are both used as measures of overall movement in the stock market. The DJIA is based on the price movements of 30 large companies; the S&P 500 is an index composed of 500 stocks. Some say the S&P 500 is a better measure of stock market performance because it is broader based. The closing price for the DJIA and the S&P 500 for 10 weeks, beginning with February 11, 2000, are shown (*Barron's*, April 17, 2000).

CD **file**

DowS&P

Date	Dow Jones	S&P 500	Date	Dow Jones	S&P 500
February 11	10425	1387	March 17	10595	1464
February 18	10220	1346	March 24	11113	1527
February 25	9862	1333	March 31	10922	1499
March 3	10367	1409	April 7	11111	1516
March 10	9929	1395	April 14	10306	1357

a. Compute the sample correlation coefficient for these data.
b. Discuss the association between the DJIA and the S&P 500 Index.

TABLE 3.9   PERFORMANCE SCORES AND OVERALL RATINGS FOR 15 NOTEBOOK PCs

CD **file**

PCs

Notebook	Performance Score	Overall Rating
AMS Tech Roadster 15CTA380	115	67
Compaq Armada M700	191	78
Compaq Prosignia Notebook 150	153	79
Dell Inspiron 3700 C466GT	194	80
Dell Inspiron 7500 R500VT	236	84
Dell Latitude Cpi A366XT	184	76
Enpower ENP-313 Pro	184	77
Gateway Solo 9300LS	216	92
HP Pavilion Notebook PC	185	83
IBM ThinkPad I Series 1480	183	78
Micro Express NP7400	189	77
Micron TransPort NX PII-400	202	78
NEC Versa SX	192	78
Sceptre Soundx 5200	141	73
Sony VAIO PCG-F340	187	77

51. The daily high and low temperatures for 12 U.S. cities are as follows (Weather Channel, January 25, 2004).

Temperature

City	High	Low	City	High	Low
Albany	9	−8	Los Angeles	62	47
Boise	32	26	New Orleans	71	55
Cleveland	21	19	Portland	43	36
Denver	37	10	Providence	18	8
Des Moines	24	16	Raleigh	28	24
Detroit	20	17	Tulsa	55	38

a. What is the sample mean daily high temperature?
b. What is the sample mean daily low temperature?
c. What is the correlation between the high and low temperatures?

3.6 The Weighted Mean and Working with Grouped Data

In Section 3.1, we presented the mean as one of the most important measures of central location. The formula for the mean of a sample with n observations is restated as follows.

$$\bar{x} = \frac{\Sigma x_i}{n} = \frac{x_1 + x_2 + \cdots + x_n}{n} \tag{3.14}$$

In this formula, each x_i is given equal importance or weight. Although this practice is most common, in some instances, the mean is computed by giving each observation a weight that reflects its importance. A mean computed in this manner is referred to as a **weighted mean**.

Weighted Mean

The weighted mean is computed as follows:

WEIGHTED MEAN

$$\bar{x} = \frac{\Sigma w_i x_i}{\Sigma w_i} \tag{3.15}$$

where

$$x_i = \text{value of observation } i$$
$$w_i = \text{weight for observation } i$$

When the data are from a sample, equation (3.15) provides the weighted sample mean. When the data are from a population, μ replaces $\bar{x}$ and equation (3.15) provides the weighted population mean.

As an example of the need for a weighted mean, consider the following sample of five purchases of a raw material over the past three months.

Purchase	Cost per Pound ($)	Number of Pounds
1	3.00	1200
2	3.40	500
3	2.80	2750
4	2.90	1000
5	3.25	800

Note that the cost per pound varies from $2.80 to $3.40, and the quantity purchased varies from 500 to 2750 pounds. Suppose that a manager asked for information about the mean cost per pound of the raw material. Because the quantities ordered vary, we must use the formula for a weighted mean. The five cost-per-pound data values are $x_1 = 3.00$, $x_2 = 3.40$, $x_3 = 2.80$, $x_4 = 2.90$, and $x_5 = 3.25$. The weighted mean cost per pound is found by weighting each cost by its corresponding quantity. For this example, the weights are $w_1 = 1200$, $w_2 = 500$, $w_3 = 2750$, $w_4 = 1000$, and $w_5 = 800$. Using equation (3.15), the weighted mean is calculated as follows:

$$\bar{x} = \frac{1200(3.00) + 500(3.40) + 2750(2.80) + 1000(2.90) + 800(3.25)}{1200 + 500 + 2750 + 1000 + 800}$$

$$= \frac{18,500}{6250} = 2.96$$

Thus, the weighted mean computation shows that the mean cost per pound for the raw material is $2.96. Note that using equation (3.14) rather than the weighted mean formula would have provided misleading results. In this case, the mean of the five cost-per-pound values is $(3.00 + 3.40 + 2.80 + 2.90 + 3.25)/5 = 15.35/5 = \$3.07$, which overstates the actual mean cost per pound purchased.

The choice of weights for a particular weighted mean computation depends upon the application. An example that is well known to college students is the computation of a grade point average (GPA). In this computation, the data values generally used are 4 for an A grade, 3 for a B grade, 2 for a C grade, 1 for a D grade, and 0 for an F grade. The weights are the number of credits hours earned for each grade. Exercise 54 at the end of this section provides an example of this weighted mean computation. In other weighted mean computations, quantities such as pounds, dollars, or volume are frequently used as weights. In any case, when observations vary in importance, the analyst must choose the weight that best reflects the importance of each observation in the determination of the mean.

Computing a grade point average is a good example of the use of a weighted mean.

Grouped Data

In most cases, measures of location and variability are computed by using the individual data values. Sometimes, however, data are available only in a grouped or frequency distribution form. In the following discussion, we show how the weighted mean formula can be used to obtain approximations of the mean, variance, and standard deviation for **grouped data**.

In Section 2.2 we provided a frequency distribution of the time in days required to complete year-end audits for the public accounting firm of Sanderson and Clifford. The frequency distribution of audit times based on a sample of 20 clients is shown again in Table 3.10. Based on this frequency distribution, what is the sample mean audit time?

TABLE 3.10 FREQUENCY DISTRIBUTION OF AUDIT TIMES

Audit Time (days)	Frequency
10–14	4
15–19	8
20–24	5
25–29	2
30–34	1
Total	**20**

To compute the mean using only the grouped data, we treat the midpoint of each class as being representative of the items in the class. Let M_i denote the midpoint for class i and let f_i denote the frequency of class i. The weighted mean formula (3.15) is then used with the data values denoted as M_i and the weights given by the frequencies f_i. In this case, the denominator of equation (3.15) is the sum of the frequencies, which is the sample size n. That is, $\Sigma f_i = n$. Thus, the equation for the sample mean for grouped data is as follows.

SAMPLE MEAN FOR GROUPED DATA

$$\bar{x} = \frac{\Sigma f_i M_i}{n} \tag{3.16}$$

where

$$M_i = \text{the midpoint for class } i$$
$$f_i = \text{the frequency for class } i$$
$$n = \text{the sample size}$$

With the class midpoints, M_i, halfway between the class limits, the first class of 10–14 in Table 3.10 has a midpoint at $(10 + 14)/2 = 12$. The five class midpoints and the weighted mean computation for the audit time data are summarized in Table 3.11. As can be seen, the sample mean audit time is 19 days.

TABLE 3.11 COMPUTATION OF THE SAMPLE MEAN AUDIT TIME FOR GROUPED DATA

Audit Time (days)	Class Midpoint (M_i)	Frequency (f_i)	$f_i M_i$
10–14	12	4	48
15–19	17	8	136
20–24	22	5	110
25–29	27	2	54
30–34	32	1	32
		20	380

$$\text{Sample mean } \bar{x} = \frac{\Sigma f_i M_i}{n} = \frac{380}{20} = 19 \text{ days}$$

To compute the variance for grouped data, we use a slightly altered version of the formula for the variance provided in equation (3.5). In equation (3.5), the squared deviations of the data about the sample mean $\bar{x}$ were written $(x_i - \bar{x})^2$. However, with grouped data, the values are not known. In this case, we treat the class midpoint, M_i, as being representative of the x_i values in the corresponding class. Thus, the squared deviations about the sample mean, $(x_i - \bar{x})^2$, are replaced by $(M_i - \bar{x})^2$. Then, just as we did with the sample mean calculations for grouped data, we weight each value by the frequency of the class, f_i. The sum of the squared deviations about the mean for all the data is approximated by $\sum f_i(M_i - \bar{x})^2$. The term $n - 1$ rather than n appears in the denominator in order to make the sample variance the estimate of the population variance. Thus, the following formula is used to obtain the sample variance for grouped data.

SAMPLE VARIANCE FOR GROUPED DATA

$$s^2 = \frac{\sum f_i(M_i - \bar{x})^2}{n - 1}$$

(3.17)

The calculation of the sample variance for audit times based on the grouped data from Table 3.10 is shown in Table 3.12. As can be seen, the sample variance is 30.

The standard deviation for grouped data is simply the square root of the variance for grouped data. For the audit time data, the sample standard deviation is $s = \sqrt{30} = 5.48$.

Before closing this section on computing measures of location and dispersion for grouped data, we note that formulas (3.16) and (3.17) are for a sample. Population summary measures are computed similarly. The grouped data formulas for a population mean and variance follow.

POPULATION MEAN FOR GROUPED DATA

$$\mu = \frac{\sum f_i M_i}{N}$$

(3.18)

TABLE 3.12   COMPUTATION OF THE SAMPLE VARIANCE OF AUDIT TIMES FOR GROUPED DATA (SAMPLE MEAN $\bar{x} = 19$)

Audit Time (days)	Class Midpoint (M_i)	Frequency (f_i)	Deviation $(M_i - \bar{x})$	Squared Deviation $(M_i - \bar{x})^2$	$f_i(M_i - \bar{x})^2$
10–14	12	4	−7	49	196
15–19	17	8	−2	4	32
20–24	22	5	3	9	45
25–29	27	2	8	64	128
30–34	32	1	13	169	169
		20			570

$$\sum f_i(M_i - \bar{x})^2$$

$$\text{Sample variance } s^2 = \frac{\sum f_i(M_i - \bar{x})^2}{n - 1} = \frac{570}{19} = 30$$

POPULATION VARIANCE FOR GROUPED DATA

$$\sigma^2 = \frac{\Sigma f_i (M_i - \mu)^2}{N}$$ (3.19)

NOTES AND COMMENTS

In computing descriptive statistics for grouped data, the class midpoints are used to approximate the data values in each class. As a result, the descriptive statistics for grouped data approximate the descriptive statistics that would result from using the original data directly. We therefore recommend computing descriptive statistics from the original data rather than from grouped data whenever possible.

Exercises

Methods

52.   Consider the following data and corresponding weights.

x_i	Weight (w_i)
3.2	6
2.0	3
2.5	2
5.0	8

   a.   Compute the weighted mean.
   b.   Compute the sample mean of the four data values without weighting. Note the difference in the results provided by the two computations.

53.   Consider the sample data in the following frequency distribution.

Class	Midpoint	Frequency
3–7	5	4
8–12	10	7
13–17	15	9
18–22	20	5

   a.   Compute the sample mean.
   b.   Compute the sample variance and sample standard deviation.

Applications

54.   The grade point average for college students is based on a weighted mean computation. For most colleges, the grades are given the following data values: A (4), B (3), C (2), D (1), and F (0). After 60 credit hours of course work, a student at State University earned 9 credit hours of A, 15 credit hours of B, 33 credit hours of C, and 3 credit hours of D.
   a.   Compute the student's grade point average.
   b.   Students at State University must maintain a 2.5 grade point average for their first 60 credit hours of course work in order to be admitted to the business college. Will this student be admitted?

55. *Bloomberg Personal Finance* (July/August 2001) included the following companies in its recommended investment portfolio. For a portfolio value of $25,000, the recommended dollar amounts allocated to each stock are shown.

Company	Portfolio ($)	Estimated Growth Rate (%)	Dividend Yield (%)
Citigroup	3000	15	1.21
General Electric	5500	14	1.48
Kimberly-Clark	4200	12	1.72
Oracle	3000	25	0.00
Pharmacia	3000	20	0.96
SBC Communications	3800	12	2.48
WorldCom	2500	35	0.00

a. Using the portfolio dollar amounts as the weights, what is the weighted average estimated growth rate for the portfolio?
b. What is the weighted average dividend yield for the portfolio?

56. A service station recorded the following frequency distribution for the number of gallons of gasoline sold per car in a sample of 680 cars.

Gasoline (gallons)	Frequency
0–4	74
5–9	192
10–14	280
15–19	105
20–24	23
25–29	6
Total	680

Compute the mean, variance, and standard deviation for these grouped data. If the service station expects to service about 120 cars on a given day, estimate the total number of gallons of gasoline that will be sold.

57. A survey of subscribers to *Fortune* magazine asked the following question: "How many of the last four issues have you read?" Suppose that the following frequency distribution summarizes 500 responses.

Number Read	Frequency
0	15
1	10
2	40
3	85
4	350
Total	500

a. What is the mean number of issues read by a *Fortune* subscriber?
b. What is the standard deviation of the number of issues read?

Summary

In this chapter we introduced several descriptive statistics that can be used to summarize the location, variability, and shape of a data distribution. Unlike the tabular and graphical procedures introduced in Chapter 2, the measures introduced in this chapter summarize the data in terms of numerical values. When the numerical values obtained are for a sample, they are called sample statistics. When the numerical values obtained are for a population, they are called population parameters. Some of the sample statistics and population parameters discussed follow.

In statistical inference, the sample statistic is referred to as the point estimator of the population parameter.

	Sample Statistic	**Population Parameter**
Mean	$\bar{x}$	μ
Variance	s^2	σ^2
Standard deviation	s	σ
Covariance	s_{xy}	σ_{xy}
Correlation	r_{xy}	ρ_{xy}

As measures of central location, we defined the mean, median, and mode. Then the concept of percentiles was used to describe other locations in the data set. Next, we presented the range, interquartile range, variance, standard deviation, and coefficient of variation as measures of variability or dispersion. Our primary measure of the shape of a data distribution was the skewness. Negative values indicate a data distribution skewed to the left. Positive values indicate a data distribution skewed to the right. We then described how the mean and standard deviation could be used, applying Chebyshev's theorem and the empirical rule, to provide more information about the distribution of data and to identify outliers.

In Section 3.4 we showed how to develop a five-number summary and a box plot to provide simultaneous information about the location, variability, and shape of the distribution. In Section 3.5 we introduced covariance and the correlation coefficient as measures of association between two variables. In the final section, we showed how to compute a weighted mean and how to calculate a mean, variance, and standard deviation for grouped data.

Most of the descriptive statistics discussed in this chapter can be computed using the functions and tools available in Excel. We showed how to use many of these functions as well as the Descriptive Statistics tool.

Glossary

Sample statistic A numerical value used as a summary measure for a sample (e.g., the sample mean, $\bar{x}$, the sample variance, s^2, and the sample standard deviation, s).

Population parameter A numerical value used as a summary measure for a population (e.g., the population mean, μ, the population variance, σ^2, and the population standard deviation, σ).

Point estimator The sample statistic, such as $\bar{x}$, s^2, and s, used to estimate the corresponding population parameter.

Mean A measure of central location computed by summing the data values and dividing by the number of observations.

Median A measure of central location provided by the value in the middle when the data are arranged in ascending order.

Mode A measure of location, defined as the value that occurs with greatest frequency.

Percentile A value such that at least p percent of the observations are less than or equal to this value and at least $(100 - p)$ percent of the observations are greater than or equal to this value. The 50th percentile is the median.

Quartiles The 25th, 50th, and 75th percentiles, referred to as the first quartile, the second quartile (median), and third quartile, respectively. The quartiles can be used to divide a data set into four parts, with each part containing approximately 25% of the data.

Range A measure of variability, defined to be the largest value minus the smallest value.

Interquartile range (IQR) A measure of variability, defined to be the difference between the third and first quartiles.

Variance A measure of variability based on the squared deviations of the data values about the mean.

Standard deviation A measure of variability computed by taking the positive square root of the variance.

Coefficient of variation A measure of relative variability computed by dividing the standard deviation by the mean and multiplying by 100.

Skewness A measure of the shape of a data distribution. Data skewed to the left result in negative skewness; a symmetric data distribution results in zero skewness; and data skewed to the right result in positive skewness.

z-score A value computed by dividing the deviation about the mean $(x_i - \bar{x})$ by the standard deviation s. A z-score is referred to as a standardized value and denotes the number of standard deviations x_i is from the mean.

Chebyshev's theorem A theorem that can be used to make statements about the proportion of data values that must be within a specified number of standard deviations of the mean.

Empirical rule A rule that can be used to compute the percentage of data values that must be within one, two, and three standard deviations of the mean for data that exhibit a bell-shaped distribution.

Outlier An unusually small or unusually large data value.

Five-number summary An exploratory data analysis technique that uses five numbers to summarize the data: smallest value, first quartile, median, third quartile, and largest value.

Box plot A graphical summary of data based on a five-number summary.

Covariance A measure of linear association between two variables. Positive values indicate a positive relationship; negative values indicate a negative relationship.

Correlation coefficient A measure of linear association between two variables that takes on values between -1 and $+1$. Values near $+1$ indicate a strong positive linear relationship; values near -1 indicate a strong negative linear relationship; and values near zero indicate the lack of a linear relationship.

Weighted mean The mean obtained by assigning each observation a weight that reflects its importance.

Grouped data Data in a grouped or a frequency distribution form.

Key Formulas

Sample Mean

$$\bar{x} = \frac{\Sigma x_i}{n} \tag{3.1}$$

Population Mean

$$\mu = \frac{\Sigma x_i}{N} \tag{3.2}$$

Interquartile Range

$$IQR = Q_3 - Q_1 \tag{3.3}$$

Population Variance

$$\sigma^2 = \frac{\Sigma(x_i - \mu)^2}{N} \tag{3.4}$$

Sample Variance

$$s^2 = \frac{\Sigma(x_i - \bar{x})^2}{n - 1} \tag{3.5}$$

Standard Deviation

$$\text{Sample standard deviation} = s = \sqrt{s^2} \tag{3.6}$$

$$\text{Population standard deviation} = \sigma = \sqrt{\sigma^2} \tag{3.7}$$

Coefficient of Variation

$$\left(\frac{\text{Standard deviation}}{\text{Mean}} \times 100\right)\% \tag{3.8}$$

z-Score

$$z_i = \frac{x_i - \bar{x}}{s} \tag{3.9}$$

Sample Covariance

$$s_{xy} = \frac{\Sigma(x_i - \bar{x})(y_i - \bar{y})}{n - 1} \tag{3.10}$$

Population Covariance

$$\sigma_{xy} = \frac{\Sigma(x_i - \mu_x)(y_i - \mu_y)}{N} \tag{3.11}$$

Pearson Product Moment Correlation Coefficient: Sample Data

$$r_{xy} = \frac{s_{xy}}{s_x s_y} \tag{3.12}$$

Pearson Product Moment Correlation Coefficient: Population Data

$$\rho_{xy} = \frac{\sigma_{xy}}{\sigma_x \sigma_y} \tag{3.13}$$

Weighted Mean

$$\bar{x} = \frac{\Sigma w_i x_i}{\Sigma w_i} \tag{3.15}$$

Sample Mean for Grouped Data

$$\bar{x} = \frac{\Sigma f_i M_i}{n} \tag{3.16}$$

Sample Variance for Grouped Data

$$s^2 = \frac{\Sigma f_i(M_i - \bar{x})^2}{n - 1}$$

(3.17)

Population Mean for Grouped Data

$$\mu = \frac{\Sigma f_i M_i}{N}$$

(3.18)

Population Variance for Grouped Data

$$\sigma^2 = \frac{\Sigma f_i(M_i - \mu)^2}{N}$$

(3.19)

Supplementary Exercises

58. According to the 2003 Annual Consumer Spending Survey, the average monthly Bank of America Visa credit card charge was $1838 (*U.S. Airways Attaché Magazine,* December 2003). A sample of monthly credit card charges provides the following data.

236	1710	1351	825	7450
316	4135	1333	1584	387
991	3396	170	1428	1688

Visa

   a. Compute the mean and median.
   b. Compute the first and third quartiles.
   c. Compute the range and interquartile range.
   d. Compute the variance and standard deviation.
   e. The skewness measure for these data is 2.12. Comment on the shape of this distribution. Is it the shape you would expect? Why or why not?
   f. Do the data contain outliers?

59. The total annual compensation for a board member at one of the nation's 100 biggest public companies is based in part on the cash retainer, an annual payment for serving on the board. In addition to the cash retainer, a board member may receive a stock retainer, a stock grant, a stock option, and a fee for attending board meetings. The total compensation can easily exceed $100,000 even with an annual retainer as low as $15,000. The following data show the cash retainer (in $1000s) for a sample of 20 of the nation's biggest public companies (*USA Today,* April 17, 2000).

Retainer

Company	Cash Retainer
American Express	64
Bank of America	36
Boeing	26
Chevron	35
Dell Computer	40
DuPont	35
ExxonMobil	40
Ford Motor	30
General Motors	60
International Paper	36
Kroger	28
Lucent Technologies	50

Company	Cash Retainer
Motorola	20
Procter & Gamble	55
Raytheon	40
Sears Roebuck	30
Texaco	15
United Parcel Service	55
Wal-Mart Stores	25
Xerox	40

Compute the following descriptive statistics.
a. Mean, median, and mode
b. The first and third quartiles
c. The range and interquartile range
d. The variance and the standard deviation
e. Coefficient of variation

60. Dividend yield is the annual dividend per share a company pays divided by the current market price per share expressed as a percentage. A sample of 10 large companies provided the following dividend yield data (*The Wall Street Journal,* January 16, 2004).

Company	Yield %	Company	Yield %
Altria Group	5.0	General Motors	3.7
American Express	0.8	JPMorgan Chase	3.5
Caterpillar	1.8	McDonald's	1.6
Eastman Kodak	1.9	United Technology	1.5
ExxonMobil	2.5	Wal-Mart Stores	0.7

a. What are the mean and median dividend yields?
b. What are the variance and standard deviation?
c. Which company provides the highest dividend yield?
d. What is the z-score for McDonald's? Interpret this z-score.
e. What is the z-score for General Motors? Interpret this z-score.
f. Based on z-scores, do the data contain any outliers?

61. According to Forrester Research, Inc., approximately 19% of Internet users play games online. The following data show the number of unique users (in thousands) for the month of March for 10 game sites (*The Wall Street Journal,* April 17, 2000).

Site	Unique Users
aolgames.com	9416
extremelotto.com	3955
freelotto.com	12901
gamesville.com	4844
iwin.com	7410
prizecentral.com	4899
shockwave.com	5582
speedyclick.com	6628
uproar.com	8821
webstakes.com	7499

Using these data, compute the mean, median, variance, and standard deviation.

62. The typical household income for a sample of 20 cities follows (*Places Rated Almanac, 2000*). Data are in thousands of dollars.

Income

City	Income	City	Income
Akron, OH	74.1	Hartford, CT	89.1
Atlanta, GA	82.4	Lancaster, PA	75.2
Birmingham, AL	71.2	Madison, WI	78.8
Bismark, ND	62.8	Naples, FL	100.0
Cleveland, OH	79.2	Nashville, TN	77.3
Columbia, SC	66.8	Philadelphia, PA	87.0
Danbury, CT	132.3	Savannah, GA	67.8
Denver, CO	82.6	Toledo, OH	71.2
Detroit, MI	85.3	Trenton, NJ	106.4
Fort Lauderdale, FL	75.8	Washington, DC	97.4

a. Compute the mean and standard deviation for the sample data.
b. Using the mean and standard deviation computed in part (a) as estimates of the mean and standard deviation of household income for the population of all cities, use Chebyshev's theorem to determine the range within which 75% of the household incomes for the population of all cities must fall.
c. Assume that the distribution of household income is bell-shaped. Using the mean and standard deviation computed in part (a) as estimates of the mean and standard deviation of household income for the population of all cities, use the empirical rule to determine the range within which 95% of the household incomes for the population of all cities must fall. Compare your answer with the value in part (b).
d. Do the sample data contain any outliers?

63. Public transportation and the automobile are two methods an employee can use to get to work each day. Samples of times recorded for each method are shown. Times are in minutes.

Public Transportation:	28	29	32	37	33	25	29	32	41	34
Automobile:	29	31	33	32	34	30	31	32	35	33

a. Compute the sample mean time to get to work for each method.
b. Compute the sample standard deviation for each method.
c. On the basis of your results from parts (a) and (b), which method of transportation should be preferred? Explain.
d. Develop a box plot for each method. Does a comparison of the box plots support your conclusion in part (c)?

64. The typical household income and typical home price for a sample of 20 cities follow (*Places Rated Almanac, 2000*). Data are in thousands of dollars.

Cities

City	Income	Home Price
Bismark, ND	62.8	92.8
Columbia, SC	66.8	116.7
Savannah, GA	67.8	108.1
Birmingham, AL	71.2	130.9
Toledo, OH	71.2	101.1
Akron, OH	74.1	114.9
Lancaster, PA	75.2	125.9
Fort Lauderdale, FL	75.8	145.3
Nashville, TN	77.3	125.9
Madison, WI	78.8	145.2

City	Income	Home Price
Cleveland, OH	79.2	135.8
Atlanta, GA	82.4	126.9
Denver, CO	82.6	161.9
Detroit, MI	85.3	145.0
Philadelphia, PA	87.0	151.5
Hartford, CT	89.1	162.1
Washington, DC	97.4	191.9
Naples, FL	100.0	173.6
Trenton, NJ	106.4	168.1
Danbury, CT	132.3	234.1

    a.   What is the value of the sample covariance? Does it indicate a positive or a negative linear relationship between income and home price?

    b.   What is the sample correlation coefficient?

65.   The following data show the media expenditures ($ millions) and shipments in millions of barrels (bbls.) for 10 major brands of beer.

Beer

Brand	Media Expenditures ($ millions)	Shipments in bbls. (millions)
Budweiser	120.0	36.3
Bud Light	68.7	20.7
Miller Lite	100.1	15.9
Coors Light	76.6	13.2
Busch	8.7	8.1
Natural Light	0.1	7.1
Miller Genuine Draft	21.5	5.6
Miller High Life	1.4	4.4
Busch Lite	5.3	4.3
Milwaukee's Best	1.7	4.3

    a.   What is the sample covariance? Does it indicate a positive or negative relationship between media expenditures and shipments?

    b.   What is the sample correlation coefficient?

66.   *Road & Track* provided the following sample of the tire ratings and load-carrying capacity of automobiles tires.

Tire Rating	Load-Carrying Capacity
75	853
82	1047
85	1135
87	1201
88	1235
91	1356
92	1389
93	1433
105	2039

    a.   Develop a scatter diagram for the data with tire rating on the *x*-axis.

    b.   What is the sample correlation coefficient, and what does it tell you about the relationship between tire rating and load-carrying capacity?

67. The following data show the trailing 52-weeks primary share earnings and book values as reported by 10 companies (*The Wall Street Journal,* March 13, 2000).

Company	Book Value	Earnings	Company	Book Value	Earnings
Am Elec	25.21	2.69	Enron Cp.	7.44	1.27
Columbia En	23.20	3.01	Peco	13.61	3.15
Con Ed	25.19	3.13	Pub Sv Ent	21.86	3.29
Duke Energy	20.17	2.25	Southn Co.	8.77	1.86
Edison Int'l	13.55	1.79	Unicom	23.22	2.74

  a. Develop a scatter diagram for the data with book value on the *x*-axis.
  b. What is the sample correlation coefficient, and what does it tell you about the relationship between the earnings per share and the book value?

68. A forecasting technique referred to as moving averages uses the average or mean of the most recent *n* periods to forecast the next value for time series data. With a three-period moving average, the most recent three periods of data are used in the forecast computation. Consider a product with the following demand for the first three months of the current year: January (800 units), February (750 units), and March (900 units).
  a. What is the three-month moving average forecast for April?
  b. A variation of this forecasting technique is called weighted moving averages. The weighting allows the more recent time series data to receive more weight or more importance in the computation of the forecast. For example, a weighted three-month moving average might give a weight of 3 to data one month old, a weight of 2 to data two months old, and a weight of 1 to data three months old. Use the data given to provide a three-month weighted moving average forecast for April.

69. The days to maturity for a sample of five money market funds are shown here. The dollar amounts invested in the funds are provided. Use the weighted mean to determine the mean number of days to maturity for dollars invested in these five money market funds.

Days to Maturity	Dollar Value ($ millions)
20	20
12	30
7	10
5	15
6	10

70. Automobiles traveling on a road with a posted speed limit of 55 miles per hour are checked for speed by a state police radar system. Following is a frequency distribution of speeds.

Speed (miles per hour)	Frequency
45–49	10
50–54	40
55–59	150
60–64	175
65–69	75
70–74	15
75–79	10
Total	475

a. What is the mean speed of the automobiles traveling on this road?
b. Compute the variance and the standard deviation.

Case Problem 1   Pelican Stores

Pelican Stores, a division of National Clothing, is a chain of women's apparel stores operating throughout the country. The chain recently ran a promotion in which discount coupons were sent to customers of other National Clothing stores. Data collected for a sample of 100 in-store credit card transactions at Pelican Stores during one day while the promotion was running are contained in the file named PelicanStores. Table 3.13 shows a portion of the data set. The Proprietary Card method of payment refers to charges made using a National Clothing charge card. Customers who made a purchase using a discount coupon are referred to as promotional customers and customers who made a purchase but did not use a discount coupon are referred to as regular customers. Because the promotional coupons were not sent to regular Pelican Stores customers, management considers the sales made to people presenting the promotional coupons as sales it would not otherwise make. Of course, Pelican also hopes that the promotional customers will continue to shop at its stores.

Most of the variables shown in Table 3.13 are self-explanatory, but two of the variables require some clarification.

Items   The total number of items purchased
Net Sales   The total amount ($) charged to the credit card

Pelican's management would like to use this sample data to learn about its customer base and to evaluate the promotion involving discount coupons.

TABLE 3.13   DATA FOR A SAMPLE OF 100 CREDIT CARD PURCHASES AT PELICAN STORES

PelicanStores

Customer	Type of Customer	Items	Net Sales	Method of Payment	Gender	Marital Status	Age
1	Regular	1	39.50	Discover	Male	Married	32
2	Promotional	1	102.40	Proprietary Card	Female	Married	36
3	Regular	1	22.50	Proprietary Card	Female	Married	32
4	Promotional	5	100.40	Proprietary Card	Female	Married	28
5	Regular	2	54.00	MasterCard	Female	Married	34
6	Regular	1	44.50	MasterCard	Female	Married	44
7	Promotional	2	78.00	Proprietary Card	Female	Married	30
8	Regular	1	22.50	Visa	Female	Married	40
9	Promotional	2	56.52	Proprietary Card	Female	Married	46
10	Regular	1	44.50	Proprietary Card	Female	Married	36
.	.	.	.	.	.	.	.
.	.	.	.	.	.	.	.
.	.	.	.	.	.	.	.
96	Regular	1	39.50	MasterCard	Female	Married	44
97	Promotional	9	253.00	Proprietary Card	Female	Married	30
98	Promotional	10	287.59	Proprietary Card	Female	Married	52
99	Promotional	2	47.60	Proprietary Card	Female	Married	30
100	Promotional	1	28.44	Proprietary Card	Female	Married	44

Managerial Report

Use the methods of descriptive statistics presented in this chapter to summarize the data and comment on your findings. At a minimum, your report should include the following:

1. Descriptive statistics on net sales and descriptive statistics on net sales by various classifications of customers.
2. Descriptive statistics concerning the relationship between age and net sales.

Case Problem 2   National Health Care Association

The National Health Care Association is concerned about the shortage of nurses the health care profession is projecting for the future. To learn the current degree of job satisfaction among nurses, the association sponsored a study of hospital nurses throughout the country. As part of this study, 50 nurses in a sample indicated their degree of satisfaction with their work, their pay, and their opportunities for promotion. Each of the three aspects of satisfaction was measured on a scale from 0 to 100, with larger values indicating higher degrees of satisfaction. The data collected also showed the type of hospital employing the nurses. The types of hospitals were Private, Veterans Administration (VA), and University. A portion of the data is shown in Table 3.14. The complete data set can be found on the CD accompanying the text in the file named Health.

Managerial Report

Use methods of descriptive statistics to summarize the data. Present the summaries that will be beneficial in communicating the results to others. Discuss your findings. Specifically, comment on the following questions.

1. On the basis of the entire data set and the three job satisfaction variables, what aspect of the job is most satisfying for the nurses? What appears to be the least satisfying? In what area(s), if any, do you feel improvements should be made? Discuss.

TABLE 3.14   SATISFACTION SCORE DATA FOR A SAMPLE OF 50 NURSES

Health

Nurse	Hospital	Work	Pay	Promotion
1	Private	74	47	63
2	VA	72	76	37
3	University	75	53	92
4	Private	89	66	62
5	University	69	47	16
6	Private	85	56	64
7	University	89	80	64
8	Private	88	36	47
9	University	88	55	52
10	Private	84	42	66
.	.	.	.	.
.	.	.	.	.
.	.	.	.	.
45	University	79	59	41
46	University	84	53	63
47	University	87	66	49
48	VA	84	74	37
49	VA	95	66	52
50	Private	72	57	40

2. On the basis of descriptive measures of variability, what measure of job satisfaction appears to generate the greatest difference of opinion among the nurses? Explain.

3. What can be learned about the types of hospitals? Does any particular type of hospital seem to have better levels of job satisfaction than the other types? Do your results suggest any recommendations for learning about and improving job satisfaction? Discuss.

4. What additional descriptive statistics and insights can you use to learn about and possibly improve job satisfaction?

Case Problem 3 Business Schools of Asia-Pacific

CD file

Asian

The pursuit of a higher education degree in business is now international. A survey shows that more and more Asians choose the Master of Business Administration degree route to corporate success (*Asia, Inc.,* September 1997). The number of applicants for MBA courses at Asia-Pacific schools continues to increase about 30% a year. In 1997, the 74 business schools in the Asia-Pacific region reported a record 170,000 applications for the 11,000 full-time MBA degrees to be awarded in 1999. A main reason for the surge in demand is that an MBA can greatly enhance earning power.

Across the region, thousands of Asians show an increasing willingness to temporarily shelve their careers and spend two years in pursuit of a theoretical business qualification. Courses in these schools are notoriously tough and include economics, banking, marketing, behavioral sciences, labor relations, decision making, strategic thinking, business law, and more. *Asia, Inc.* provided the data set in Table 3.15, which shows some of the characteristics of the leading Asia-Pacific business schools.

Managerial Report

Use the methods of descriptive statistics to summarize the data in Table 3.15. Discuss your findings.

1. Include a summary for each variable in the data set. Make comments and interpretations based on maximums and minimums, as well as the appropriate means and proportions. What new insights do these descriptive statistics provide concerning Asia-Pacific business schools?

2. Summarize the data to compare the following:
   a. Any difference between local and foreign tuition costs.
   b. Any difference between mean starting salaries for schools requiring and not requiring work experience.
   c. Any difference between starting salaries for schools requiring and not requiring English tests.

3. Do starting salaries appear to be related to tuition?

4. Present any additional graphical and numerical summaries that will be beneficial in communicating the data in Table 3.15 to others.

Appendix 3.1 Constructing a Box Plot Using SWStat+

We discussed the box plot in Section 3.4. A box plot is a graphical display of data based on a five-number summary: smallest value, first quartile, median, third quartile, and largest value. Excel 2003 does not have a procedure for constructing a box plot. In this appendix we describe the steps required to construct a box plot for the starting salary data using SWStat+. First, we must create the data area.

TABLE 3.15   DATA FOR 25 ASIA-PACIFIC BUSINESS SCHOOLS

Business School	Full-Time Enrollment	Students per Faculty	Local Tuition ($)	Foreign Tuition ($)	Age	%Foreign	GMAT	English Test	Work Experience	Starting Salary ($)
Melbourne Business School	200	5	24,420	29,600	28	47	Yes	No	Yes	71,400
University of New South Wales (Sydney)	228	4	19,993	32,582	29	28	Yes	No	Yes	65,200
Indian Institute of Management (Ahmedabad)	392	5	4,300	4,300	22	0	No	No	No	7,100
Chinese University of Hong Kong	90	5	11,140	11,140	29	10	Yes	No	No	31,000
International University of Japan (Niigata)	126	4	33,060	33,060	28	60	Yes	Yes	No	87,000
Asian Institute of Management (Manila)	389	5	7,562	9,000	25	50	Yes	No	Yes	22,800
Indian Institute of Management (Bangalore)	380	5	3,935	16,000	23	1	Yes	No	No	7,500
National University of Singapore	147	6	6,146	7,170	29	51	Yes	Yes	Yes	43,300
Indian Institute of Management (Calcutta)	463	8	2,880	16,000	23	0	No	No	No	7,400
Australian National University (Canberra)	42	2	20,300	20,300	30	80	Yes	Yes	Yes	46,600
Nanyang Technological University (Singapore)	50	5	8,500	8,500	32	20	Yes	No	Yes	49,300
University of Queensland (Brisbane)	138	17	16,000	22,800	32	26	No	No	Yes	49,600
Hong Kong University of Science and Technology	60	2	11,513	11,513	26	37	Yes	No	Yes	34,000
Macquarie Graduate School of Management (Sydney)	12	8	17,172	19,778	34	27	No	No	Yes	60,100
Chulalongkorn University (Bangkok)	200	7	17,355	17,355	25	6	Yes	No	Yes	17,600
Monash Mt. Eliza Business School (Melbourne)	350	13	16,200	22,500	30	30	Yes	Yes	Yes	52,500
Asian Institute of Management (Bangkok)	300	10	18,200	18,200	29	90	No	Yes	Yes	25,000
University of Adelaide	20	19	16,426	23,100	30	10	No	No	Yes	66,000
Massey University (Palmerston North, New Zealand)	30	15	13,106	21,625	37	35	No	Yes	Yes	41,400
Royal Melbourne Institute of Technology Business Graduate School	30	7	13,880	17,765	32	30	No	Yes	Yes	48,900
Jamnalal Bajaj Institute of Management Studies (Bombay)	240	9	1,000	1,000	24	0	No	No	Yes	7,000
Curtin Institute of Technology (Perth)	98	15	9,475	19,097	29	43	Yes	No	Yes	55,000
Lahore University of Management Sciences	70	14	11,250	26,300	23	2.5	No	No	No	7,500
Universiti Sains Malaysia (Penang)	30	5	2,260	2,260	32	15	No	Yes	Yes	16,000
De La Salle University (Manila)	44	17	3,300	3,600	28	3.5	Yes	No	Yes	13,100

Creating the Data Area

Step 1. Select any cell in the starting salary data set
Step 2. Select the **SWStat+** menu
Step 3. Choose **Data Area**
Step 4. Choose **Set New Data Area** from the list of Data Area options
Step 5. When the SWStat+ Data Area dialog box appears:
> Select the **Set New** tab
> Select **With column headers**
> Select **With row headers**
> Click **Set data area**

After creating the data area, the row and column labels are highlighted in yellow and the entire data set (including labels) is surrounded by a blue border.

The worksheet in Figure 3.18 shows the starting salary data set with the SWStat+ data area highlighted. A Results worksheet has also been added to the workbook. (View the Worksheet tabs to see where the Results worksheet is located.)

Constructing a Box Plot

We are now ready to use SWStat+ to create a box plot for the starting salary data. The necessary steps are as follows:

Step 1. Select the **SWStat+** menu
Step 2. Choose **Charts and Graphs**
Step 3. When the SWStat+: Charts and Graphs dialog box appears:
> Select the **One Variable** tab
> Select **Box Plot**
> Select **Starting Salary** in the Variables list
> Select **Modified** in the Style list
> Click **Show Chart**

FIGURE 3.18   STARTING SALARY DATA AFTER SETTING THE DATA AREA USING SWStat+

	A	B	C	D
1	Graduate	Starting Salary		
2	1	2850		
3	2	2950		
4	3	3050		
5	4	2880		
6	5	2755		
7	6	2710		
8	7	2890		
9	8	3130		
10	9	2940		
11	10	3325		
12	11	2920		
13	12	2880		
14				
15				
16				

A box plot is now displayed in the Results worksheet. We can resize it as desired using the following steps.

Step 1. Position the mouse pointer over the horizontal axis and right-click
Step 2. Select **Format Axis**
Step 3. When the Format Axis dialog box appears:
    Select the **Scale** tab
    Enter 2400 in the **Minimum** box
    Enter 3400 in the **Maximum** box
    Click **OK**

The resulting box plot is shown in Figure 3.19. It is similar to the one shown in Figure 3.12.

FIGURE 3.19   SWStat+ RESULTS WORKSHEET SHOWING BOX PLOT

CHAPTER 4

Introduction to Probability

CONTENTS

MORTON INTERNATIONAL*
CHICAGO, ILLINOIS

Morton International is a company with businesses in salt, household products, rocket motors, and specialty chemicals. Carstab Corporation, a subsidiary of Morton International, produces specialty chemicals and offers a variety of chemicals designed to meet the unique specifications of its customers. For one particular customer, Carstab produced an expensive catalyst used in chemical processing. Some, but not all, of the lots produced by Carstab met the customer's specifications for the product.

Carstab's customer agreed to test each lot after receiving it and determine whether the catalyst would perform the desired function. Lots that did not pass the customer's test would be returned to Carstab. Over time, Carstab found that the customer was accepting 60% of the lots and returning 40%. In probability terms, each Carstab shipment to the customer had a .60 probability of being accepted and a .40 probability of being returned.

Neither Carstab nor its customer was pleased with these results. In an effort to improve service, Carstab explored the possibility of duplicating the customer's test prior to shipment. However, the high cost of the special testing equipment made that alternative infeasible. Carstab's chemists then proposed a new, relatively low-cost test designed to indicate whether a lot would pass the customer's test. The probability question of interest was: What is the probability that a lot will pass the customer's test if it has passed the new Carstab test?

Morton Salt: "When It Rains It Pours." © Joe Higgins/ South-Western.

A sample of lots was produced and subjected to the new Carstab test. Only lots that passed the new test were sent to the customer. Probability analysis of the data indicated that if a lot passed the Carstab test, it had a .909 probability of passing the customer's test and being accepted. Alternatively, if a lot passed the Carstab test, it had only a .091 probability of being returned. The probability analysis provided key supporting evidence for the adoption and implementation of the new testing procedure at Carstab. The new test resulted in an immediate improvement in customer service and a substantial reduction in shipping and handling costs for returned lots.

The probability of a lot being accepted by the customer after passing the new Carstab test is called a conditional probability. In this chapter, you will learn how to compute this and other probabilities that are helpful in decision making.

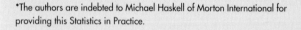

*The authors are indebted to Michael Haskell of Morton International for providing this Statistics in Practice.

Managers often base their decisions on an analysis of uncertainties such as the following:

1. What are the chances that sales will decrease if we increase prices?
2. What is the likelihood a new assembly method will increase productivity?
3. How likely is it that the project will be finished on time?
4. What is the chance that a new investment will be profitable?

Some of the earliest work on probability originated in a series of letters between Pierre de Fermat and Blaise Pascal in the 1650s.

Probability is a numerical measure of the likelihood that an event will occur. Thus, probabilities can be used as measures of the degree of uncertainty associated with the four events previously listed. If probabilities are available, we can determine the likelihood of each event occurring.

Probability values are always assigned on a scale from 0 to 1. A probability near zero indicates an event is unlikely to occur; a probability near 1 indicates an event is almost

FIGURE 4.1 PROBABILITY AS A NUMERICAL MEASURE OF THE LIKELIHOOD OF AN EVENT OCCURRING

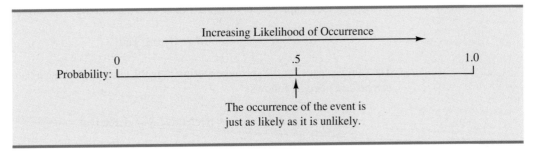

certain to occur. Other probabilities between 0 and 1 represent degrees of likelihood that an event will occur. For example, if we consider the event "rain tomorrow," we understand that when the weather report indicates "a near-zero probability of rain," it means almost no chance of rain. However, if a .90 probability of rain is reported, we know that rain is likely to occur. A .50 probability indicates that rain is just as likely to occur as not. Figure 4.1 depicts the view of probability as a numerical measure of the likelihood of an event occurring.

 ## Experiments, Counting Rules, and Assigning Probabilities

In discussing probability, we define an **experiment** as a process that generates well-defined outcomes. On any single repetition of an experiment, one and only one of the possible experimental outcomes will occur. Several examples of experiments and their associated outcomes follow.

Experiment	**Experimental Outcomes**
Toss a coin	Head, tail
Select a part for inspection	Defective, nondefective
Conduct a sales call	Purchase, no purchase
Roll a die	1, 2, 3, 4, 5, 6
Play a football game	Win, lose, tie

By specifying all possible experimental outcomes, we identify the **sample space** for an experiment.

SAMPLE SPACE

The sample space for an experiment is the set of all experimental outcomes.

Experimental outcomes are also called sample points.

An experimental outcome is also called a **sample point** to identify it as an element of the sample space.

Consider the first experiment in the preceding table—tossing a coin. The upward face of the coin—a head or a tail—determines the experimental outcomes (sample points). If we let S denote the sample space, we can use the following notation to describe the sample space.

$$S = \{Head, Tail\}$$

The sample space for the second experiment in the table—selecting a part for inspection—can be described as follows:

$$S = \{Defective, Nondefective\}$$

Both of the experiments just described have two experimental outcomes (sample points). However, suppose we consider the fourth experiment listed in the table—rolling a die. The possible experimental outcomes, defined as the number of dots appearing on the upward face of the die, are the six points in the sample space for this experiment.

$$S = \{1, 2, 3, 4, 5, 6\}$$

Counting Rules, Combinations, and Permutations

Being able to identify and count the experimental outcomes is a necessary step in assigning probabilities. We now discuss three useful counting rules.

Multiple-Step Experiments The first counting rule applies to multiple-step experiments. Consider the experiment of tossing two coins. Let the experimental outcomes be defined in terms of the pattern of heads and tails appearing on the upward faces of the two coins. How many experimental outcomes are possible for this experiment? The experiment of tossing two coins can be thought of as a two-step experiment in which step 1 is the tossing of the first coin and step 2 is the tossing of the second coin. If we use H to denote a head and T to denote a tail, (H, H) indicates the experimental outcome with a head on the first coin and a head on the second coin. Continuing this notation, we can describe the sample space (S) for this coin-tossing experiment as follows:

$$S = \{(H, H), (H, T), (T, H), (T, T)\}$$

Thus, we see that four experimental outcomes are possible. In this case, we can easily list all of the experimental outcomes.

The counting rule for multiple-step experiments makes it possible to determine the number of experimental outcomes without listing them.

COUNTING RULE FOR MULTIPLE-STEP EXPERIMENTS

If an experiment can be described as a sequence of k steps with n_1 possible outcomes on the first step, n_2 possible outcomes on the second step, and so on, then the total number of experimental outcomes is given by $(n_1) (n_2) \ldots (n_k)$.

Viewing the experiment of tossing two coins as a sequence of first tossing one coin ($n_1 = 2$) and then tossing the other coin ($n_2 = 2$), we can see from the counting rule that there are $(2)(2) = 4$ distinct experimental outcomes. As shown, they are $S = \{(H, H), (H, T), (T, H), (T, T)\}$. The number of experimental outcomes in an experiment involving tossing six coins is $(2)(2)(2)(2)(2)(2) = 64$.

A **tree diagram** is a graph that helps in visualizing a multiple-step experiment. Figure 4.2 shows a tree diagram for the experiment of tossing two coins. The sequence of steps moves from left to right through the tree. Step 1 corresponds to tossing the first coin, and step 2 corresponds to tossing the second coin. For each step, the two possible outcomes are head or tail. Note that for each possible outcome at step 1 two branches correspond to the two possible outcomes at step 2. Each of the points on the right end of the tree corresponds to an experimental outcome. Each path through the tree from the leftmost node to one of the nodes at the right side of the tree corresponds to a unique sequence of outcomes.

Let us now see how the counting rule for multiple-step experiments can be used in the analysis of a capacity expansion project for the Kentucky Power & Light Company (KP&L). KP&L is starting a project designed to increase the generating capacity of one of its plants in northern Kentucky. The project is divided into two sequential stages or steps: stage 1 (design) and stage 2 (construction). Even though each stage will be scheduled and controlled as closely as possible, management cannot predict beforehand the exact time required to complete each stage of the project. An analysis of similar construction projects revealed possible completion times for the design stage of 2, 3, or 4 months and possible completion times for the construction stage of 6, 7, or 8 months. In addition, because of the critical need for additional electrical power, management set a goal of 10 months for the completion of the entire project.

Because this project has three possible completion times for the design stage (step 1) and three possible completion times for the construction stage (step 2), the counting rule for multiple-step experiments can be used to show that there are (3)(3) = 9 experimental outcomes. To describe the experimental outcomes, we use a two-number notation; for instance, (2, 6) indicates that the design stage is completed in 2 months and the construction stage is completed in 6 months. This experimental outcome results in a total of 2 + 6 = 8 months to complete the entire project. Table 4.1 summarizes the nine experimental outcomes for the KP&L problem. The tree diagram in Figure 4.3 shows how the nine outcomes (sample points) occur.

The counting rule and tree diagram help the project manager identify the experimental outcomes and determine the possible project completion times. From the information in

FIGURE 4.2 TREE DIAGRAM FOR THE EXPERIMENT OF TOSSING TWO COINS

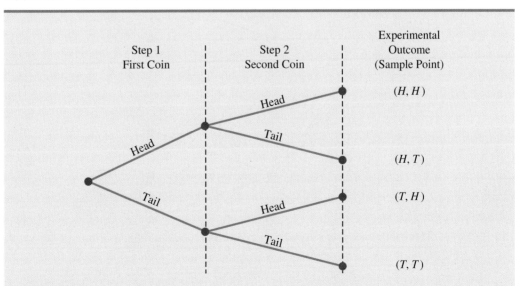

TABLE 4.1   EXPERIMENTAL OUTCOMES (SAMPLE POINTS) FOR THE KP&L PROJECT

Completion Time (months)

Stage 1 Design	Stage 2 Construction	Notation for Experimental Outcome	Total Project Completion Time (months)
2	6	(2, 6)	8
2	7	(2, 7)	9
2	8	(2, 8)	10
3	6	(3, 6)	9
3	7	(3, 7)	10
3	8	(3, 8)	11
4	6	(4, 6)	10
4	7	(4, 7)	11
4	8	(4, 8)	12

FIGURE 4.3   TREE DIAGRAM FOR THE KP&L PROJECT

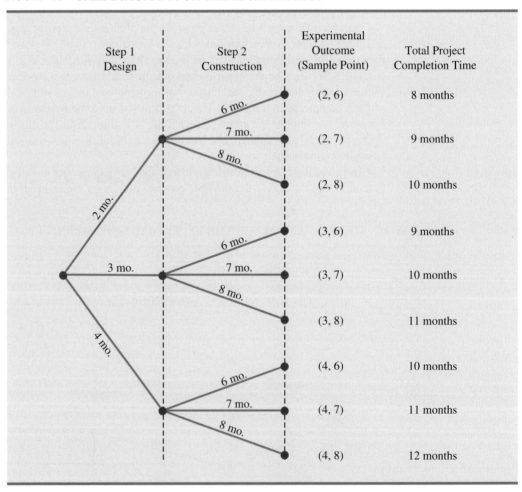

c. What is the probability of seat belt usage by region of the country? What region has the highest seat belt usage?

d. What proportion of the drivers in the sample came from each region of the country? What region had the most drivers selected? What region had the second most drivers selected?

e. Assuming the total number of drivers in each region is the same, do you see any reason why the probability estimate in part (a) might be too high? Explain.

12. The Powerball lottery is played twice each week in 23 states, the Virgin Islands, and the District of Columbia. To play Powerball a participant must purchase a ticket for $1 and then select five numbers from the digits 1 through 53 and a Powerball number from the digits 1 through 42. To determine the winning numbers for each game, lottery officials draw five white balls out of a drum with 53 white balls, and one red ball out of a drum with 42 red balls. To win the jackpot, a participant's numbers must match the numbers on the five white balls in any order and the number on the red Powerball. In August 2001, four winners shared a jackpot of $295 million by matching the numbers 8-17-22-42-47 plus Powerball number 21. In addition to the jackpot, a variety of other prizes is awarded each time the game is played. For instance, a prize of $100,000 is paid if the participant's five numbers match the numbers on the five white balls (http://www.powerball.com, March 25, 2003).

a. Compute the number of ways the first five numbers can be selected.

b. What is the probability of winning a prize of $100,000 by matching the numbers on the five white balls?

c. What is the probability of winning the Powerball jackpot?

13. A company that manufactures toothpaste is studying five different package designs. Assuming that one design is just as likely to be selected by a consumer as any other design, what selection probability would you assign to each of the package designs? In an actual experiment, 100 consumers were asked to pick the design they preferred. The following data were obtained. Do the data confirm the belief that one design is just as likely to be selected as another? Explain.

Design	Number of Times Preferred
1	5
2	15
3	30
4	40
5	10

4.2 Events and Their Probabilities

In the introduction to this chapter we used the term *event* much as it would be used in everyday language. Then, in Section 4.1 we introduced the concept of an experiment and its associated experimental outcomes or sample points. Sample points and events provide the foundation for the study of probability. As a result, we must now introduce the formal definition of an **event** as it relates to sample points. Doing so will provide the basis for determining the probability of an event.

EVENT

An event is a collection of sample points.

For an example, let us return to the KP&L project and assume that the project manager is interested in the event that the entire project can be completed in 10 months or less. Referring to Table 4.3, we see that six sample points—(2, 6), (2, 7), (2, 8), (3, 6), (3, 7), and (4, 6)—provide a project completion time of 10 months or less. Let C denote the event that the project is completed in 10 months or less; we write

$$C = \{(2, 6), (2, 7), (2, 8), (3, 6), (3, 7), (4, 6)\}$$

Event C is said to occur if *any one* of these six sample points appears as the experimental outcome.

Other events that might be of interest to KP&L management include the following.

L = The event that the project is completed in *less* than 10 months
M = The event that the project is completed in *more* than 10 months

Using the information in Table 4.3, we see that these events consist of the following sample points.

$$L = \{(2, 6), (2, 7), (3, 6)\}$$
$$M = \{(3, 8), (4, 7), (4, 8)\}$$

A variety of additional events can be defined for the KP&L project, but in each case the event must be identified as a collection of sample points for the experiment.

Given the probabilities of the sample points shown in Table 4.3, we can use the following definition to compute the probability of any event that KP&L management might want to consider.

PROBABILITY OF AN EVENT

The probability of any event is equal to the sum of the probabilities of the sample points in the event.

Using this definition, we calculate the probability of a particular event by adding the probabilities of the sample points (experimental outcomes) that make up the event. We can now compute the probability that the project will take 10 months or less to complete. Because this event is given by $C = \{(2, 6), (2, 7), (2, 8), (3, 6), (3, 7), (4, 6)\}$, the probability of event C, denoted $P(C)$, is given by

$$P(C) = P(2, 6) + P(2, 7) + P(2, 8) + P(3, 6) + P(3, 7) + P(4, 6)$$

Refer to the sample point probabilities in Table 4.3; we have

$$P(C) = .15 + .15 + .05 + .10 + .20 + .05 = .70$$

Similarly, because the event that the project is completed in less than 10 months is given by $L = \{(2, 6), (2, 7), (3, 6)\}$, the probability of this event is given by

$$P(L) = P(2, 6) + P(2, 7) + P(3, 6)$$
$$= .15 + .15 + .10 = .40$$

Finally, for the event that the project is completed in more than 10 months, we have $M = \{(3, 8), (4, 7), (4, 8)\}$ and thus

$$P(M) = P(3, 8) + P(4, 7) + P(4, 8)$$
$$= .05 + .10 + .15 = .30$$

Using these probability results, we can now tell KP&L management that there is a .70 probability that the project will be completed in 10 months or less, a .40 probability that the project will be completed in less than 10 months, and a .30 probability that the project will be completed in more than 10 months. This procedure of computing event probabilities can be repeated for any event of interest to the KP&L management.

Any time that we can identify all the sample points of an experiment and assign probabilities to each, we can compute the probability of an event using the definition. However, in many experiments the large number of sample points makes the identification of the sample points, as well as the determination of their associated probabilities, extremely cumbersome, if not impossible. In the remaining sections of this chapter, we present some basic probability relationships that can be used to compute the probability of an event without knowledge of all the sample point probabilities.

NOTES AND COMMENTS

1. The sample space, S, is an event. Because it contains all the experimental outcomes, it has a probability of 1; that is, $P(S) = 1$.
2. When the classical method is used to assign probabilities, the assumption is that the experimental outcomes are equally likely. In such cases, the probability of an event can be computed by counting the number of experimental outcomes in the event and dividing the result by the total number of experimental outcomes.

Exercises

Methods

14. An experiment has four equally likely outcomes: E_1, E_2, E_3, and E_4.
    a. What is the probability that E_2 occurs?
    b. What is the probability that any two of the outcomes occur (e.g., E_1 or E_3)?
    c. What is the probability that any three of the outcomes occur (e.g., E_1 or E_2 or E_4)?

15. Consider the experiment of selecting a playing card from a deck of 52 playing cards. Each card corresponds to a sample point with a 1/52 probability.
    a. List the sample points in the event an ace is selected.
    b. List the sample points in the event a club is selected.
    c. List the sample points in the event a face card (jack, queen, or king) is selected.
    d. Find the probabilities associated with each of the events in parts (a), (b), and (c).

16. Consider the experiment of rolling a pair of dice. Suppose that we are interested in the sum of the face values showing on the dice.
    a. How many sample points are possible? (*Hint:* Use the counting rule for multiple-step experiments.)
    b. List the sample points.
    c. What is the probability of obtaining a value of 7?
    d. What is the probability of obtaining a value of 9 or greater?
    e. Because each roll has six possible even values (2, 4, 6, 8, 10, and 12) and only five possible odd values (3, 5, 7, 9, and 11), the dice should show even values more often than odd values. Do you agree with this statement? Explain.
    f. What method did you use to assign the probabilities requested?

Applications

17. Refer to the KP&L sample points and sample point probabilities in Tables 4.2 and 4.3.
    a. The design stage (stage 1) will run over budget if it takes 4 months to complete. List the sample points in the event the design stage is over budget.
    b. What is the probability that the design stage is over budget?
    c. The construction stage (stage 2) will run over budget if it takes 8 months to complete. List the sample points in the event the construction stage is over budget.
    d. What is the probability that the construction stage is over budget?
    e. What is the probability that both stages are over budget?

18. Suppose that a manager of a large apartment complex provides the following subjective probability estimates about the number of vacancies that will exist next month.

Vacancies	Probability
0	.05
1	.15
2	.35
3	.25
4	.10
5	.10

Provide the probability of each of the following events.
    a. No vacancies
    b. At least four vacancies
    c. Two or fewer vacancies

19. The National Sporting Goods Association conducted a survey of persons 7 years of age or older about participation in sports activities (*Statistical Abstract of the United States: 2002*). The total population in this age group was reported at 248.5 million, with 120.9 million male and 127.6 million female. The number of participants for the top five sports activities appears here.

Activity	Participants (millions)	
	Male	**Female**
Bicycle riding	22.2	21.0
Camping	25.6	24.3
Exercise walking	28.7	57.7
Exercising with equipment	20.4	24.4
Swimming	26.4	34.4

    a. For a randomly selected female, estimate the probability of participation in each of the sports activities.
    b. For a randomly selected male, estimate the probability of participation in each of the sports activities.
    c. For a randomly selected person, what is the probability the person participates in exercise walking?
    d. Someone tells you they saw an exercise walker. What is the probability the walker is a woman? What is the probability the walker is a man?

20.   *Fortune* magazine publishes an annual issue containing information on *Fortune* 500 companies. The following data show the six states with the largest number of *Fortune* 500 companies as well as the number of companies headquartered in those states (*Fortune*, April 17, 2000).

State	Number of Companies
New York	56
California	53
Texas	43
Illinois	37
Ohio	28
Pennsylvania	28

Suppose a *Fortune* 500 company is chosen for a follow-up questionnaire. What are the probabilities of the following events?
   a.   Let N be the event the company is headquartered in New York. Find $P(N)$.
   b.   Let T be the event the company is headquartered in Texas. Find $P(T)$.
   c.   Let B be the event the company is headquartered in one of these six states. Find $P(B)$.

21.   The U.S. population by age is as follows (*The World Almanac 2004*). The data are in millions of people.

Age	Number
19 and under	80.5
20 to 24	19.0
25 to 34	39.9
35 to 44	45.2
45 to 54	37.7
55 to 64	24.3
65 and over	35.0

Assume that a person will be randomly chosen from this population.
   a.   What is the probability the person is 20 to 24 years old?
   b.   What is the probability the person is 20 to 34 years old?
   c.   What is the probability the person is 45 years or older?

Some Basic Relationships of Probability

Complement of an Event

Given an event A, the **complement of** A is defined to be the event consisting of all sample points that are *not* in A. The complement of A is denoted by A^c. Figure 4.4 is a diagram, known as a **Venn diagram**, which illustrates the concept of a complement. The rectangular area represents the sample space for the experiment and as such contains all possible sample points. The circle represents event A and contains only the sample points that belong to A. The shaded region of the rectangle contains all sample points not in event A and is by definition the complement of A.

In any probability application, either event A or its complement A^c must occur. Therefore, we have

$$P(A) + P(A^c) = 1$$

FIGURE 4.4   COMPLEMENT OF EVENT *A* IS SHADED

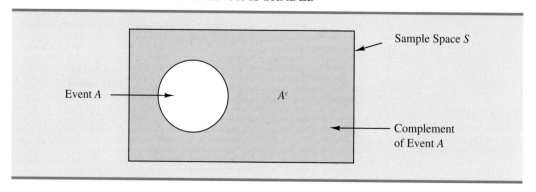

Solving for $P(A)$, we obtain the following result.

COMPUTING PROBABILITY USING THE COMPLEMENT

$$P(A) = 1 - P(A^c) \tag{4.5}$$

Equation (4.5) shows that the probability of an event *A* can be computed easily if the probability of its complement, $P(A^c)$, is known.

    As an example, consider the case of a sales manager who, after reviewing sales reports, states that 80% of new customer contacts result in no sale. By allowing *A* to denote the event of a sale and A^c to denote the event of no sale, the manager is stating that $P(A^c) = .80$. Using equation (4.5), we see that

$$P(A) = 1 - P(A^c) = 1 - .80 = .20$$

We can conclude that a new customer contact has a .20 probability of resulting in a sale.

    In another example, a purchasing agent states a .90 probability that a supplier will send a shipment that is free of defective parts. Using the complement, we can conclude that there is a $1 - .90 = .10$ probability that the shipment will contain defective parts.

Addition Law

The addition law is used to compute the probability that at least one of two events occurs. That is, with events *A* and *B* we are interested in knowing the probability that event *A* or event *B* or both occur.

    Before we present the addition law, we need to discuss two concepts related to the combination of events: the *union* of events and the *intersection* of events. Given two events *A* and *B*, the **union of *A* and *B*** is defined as follows.

UNION OF TWO EVENTS

The *union* of *A* and *B* is the event containing *all* sample points belonging to *A or B or both*. The union is denoted by $A \cup B$.

The Venn diagram in Figure 4.5 depicts the union of events *A* and *B*. Note that the two circles contain all the sample points in event *A* as well as all the sample points in event *B*.

FIGURE 4.5   UNION OF EVENTS *A* AND *B* IS SHADED

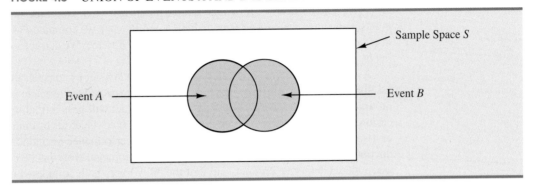

The fact that the circles overlap indicates that some sample points are contained in both *A* and *B*.

The definition of the **intersection of *A* and *B*** follows.

INTERSECTION OF TWO EVENTS

Given two events *A* and *B*, the *intersection* of *A* and *B* is the event containing the sample points belonging to *both A and B*. The intersection is denoted by $A \cap B$.

The Venn diagram depicting the intersection of events *A* and *B* is shown in Figure 4.6. The area where the two circles overlap is the intersection; it contains the sample points that are in both *A* and *B*.

Let us now continue with a discussion of the addition law. The **addition law** provides a way to compute the probability that event *A* or event *B* or both occur. In other words, the addition law is used to compute the probability of the union of two events. The addition law is written as follows.

ADDITION LAW

$$P(A \cup B) = P(A) + P(B) - P(A \cap B)$$ **(4.6)**

FIGURE 4.6   INTERSECTION OF EVENTS *A* AND *B* IS SHADED

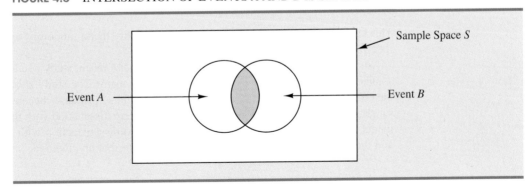

To understand the addition law intuitively, note that the first two terms in the addition law, $P(A) + P(B)$, account for all the sample points in $A \cup B$. However, because the sample points in the intersection $A \cap B$ are in both A and B, when we compute $P(A) + P(B)$, we are in effect counting each of the sample points in $A \cap B$ twice. We correct for this overcounting by subtracting $P(A \cap B)$.

As an example of an application of the addition law, let us consider the case of a small assembly plant with 50 employees. Each worker is expected to complete work assignments on time and in such a way that the assembled product will pass a final inspection. On occasion, some of the workers fail to meet the performance standards by completing work late or assembling a defective product. At the end of a performance evaluation period, the production manager found that 5 of the 50 workers completed work late, 6 of the 50 workers assembled a defective product, and 2 of the 50 workers both completed work late *and* assembled a defective product.

Let

$$L = \text{the event that the work is completed late}$$
$$D = \text{the event that the assembled product is defective}$$

The relative frequency information leads to the following probabilities.

$$P(L) = \frac{5}{50} = .10$$

$$P(D) = \frac{6}{50} = .12$$

$$P(L \cap D) = \frac{2}{50} = .04$$

After reviewing the performance data, the production manager decided to assign a poor performance rating to any employee whose work was either late or defective; thus the event of interest is $L \cup D$. What is the probability that the production manager assigned an employee a poor performance rating?

Note that the probability question is about the union of two events. Specifically, we want to know $P(L \cup D)$. Using equation (4.6), we have

$$P(L \cup D) = P(L) + P(D) - P(L \cap D)$$

Knowing values for the three probabilities on the right side of this expression, we can write

$$P(L \cup D) = .10 + .12 - .04 = .18$$

This calculation tells us that there is a .18 probability that a randomly selected employee received a poor performance rating.

As another example of the addition law, consider a recent study conducted by the personnel manager of a major computer software company. The study showed that 30% of the employees who left the firm within two years did so primarily because they were dissatisfied with their salary, 20% left because they were dissatisfied with their work assignments, and 12% of the former employees indicated dissatisfaction with *both* their salary and their work assignments. What is the probability that an employee who leaves within two years does so because of dissatisfaction with salary, dissatisfaction with the work assignment, or both?

Let

S = the event that the employee leaves because of dissatisfaction with salary

W = the event that the employee leaves because of dissatisfaction with the work assignment

We have $P(S) = .30$, $P(W) = .20$, and $P(S \cap W) = .12$. Using equation (4.6), the addition law, we have

$$P(S \cup W) = P(S) + P(W) - P(S \cap W) = .30 + .20 - .12 = .38$$

We find a .38 probability that an employee leaves for salary or work assignment reasons.

Before we conclude our discussion of the addition law, let us consider a special case that arises for **mutually exclusive events**.

MUTUALLY EXCLUSIVE EVENTS

Two events are said to be mutually exclusive if the events have no sample points in common.

Events A and B are mutually exclusive if, when one event occurs, the other cannot occur. Thus, a requirement for A and B to be mutually exclusive is that their intersection must contain no sample points. The Venn diagram depicting two mutually exclusive events A and B is shown in Figure 4.7. In this case $P(A \cap B) = 0$ and the addition law can be written as follows.

ADDITION LAW FOR MUTUALLY EXCLUSIVE EVENTS

$$P(A \cup B) = P(A) + P(B)$$

FIGURE 4.7   MUTUALLY EXCLUSIVE EVENTS

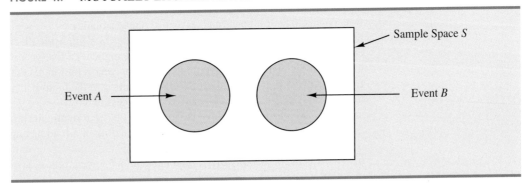

Exercises

Methods

22. Suppose that we have a sample space with five equally likely experimental outcomes: E_1, E_2, E_3, E_4, E_5. Let

$$A = \{E_1, E_2\}$$
$$B = \{E_3, E_4\}$$
$$C = \{E_2, E_3, E_5\}$$

a. Find $P(A)$, $P(B)$, and $P(C)$.
b. Find $P(A \cup B)$. Are A and B mutually exclusive?
c. Find A^c, C^c, $P(A^c)$, and $P(C^c)$.
d. Find $A \cup B^c$ and $P(A \cup B^c)$.
e. Find $P(B \cup C)$.

23. Suppose that we have a sample space $S = \{E_1, E_2, E_3, E_4, E_5, E_6, E_7\}$, where $E_1, E_2, \ldots$, E_7 denote the sample points. The following probability assignments apply: $P(E_1) = .05$, $P(E_2) = .20$, $P(E_3) = .20$, $P(E_4) = .25$, $P(E_5) = .15$, $P(E_6) = .10$, and $P(E_7) = .05$. Let

$$A = \{E_1, E_4, E_6\}$$
$$B = \{E_2, E_4, E_7\}$$
$$C = \{E_2, E_3, E_5, E_7\}$$

a. Find $P(A)$, $P(B)$, and $P(C)$.
b. Find $A \cup B$ and $P(A \cup B)$.
c. Find $A \cap B$ and $P(A \cap B)$.
d. Are events A and C mutually exclusive?
e. Find B^c and $P(B^c)$.

Applications

24. Clarkson University surveyed alumni to learn more about what they think of Clarkson. One part of the survey asked respondents to indicate whether their overall experience at Clarkson fell short of expectations, met expectations, or surpassed expectations. The results showed that 4% of the respondents did not provide a response, 26% said that their experience fell short of expectations, and 65% of the respondents said that their experience met expectations (*Clarkson Magazine,* Summer 2001).
    a. If we chose an alumnus at random, what is the probability that the alumnus would say the Clarkson experience surpassed expectations?
    b. If we chose an alumnus at random, what is the probability that the alumnus would say the Clarkson experience met or surpassed expectations?

25. Data on the 30 largest bond funds provided one-year and five-year percentage returns for the period ending March 31, 2000 (*The Wall Street Journal,* April 10, 2000). Suppose we consider a one-year return in excess of 2% to be high and a five-year return in excess of 44% to be high. One-half of the funds had a one-year return in excess of 2%, 12 of the funds had a five-year return in excess of 44%, and six of the funds had both a one-year return in excess of 2% and a five-year return in excess of 44%.
    a. Find the probability of a fund having a high one-year return, the probability of a fund having a high five-year return, and the probability of a fund having both a high one-year return and a high five-year return.
    b. What is the probability that a fund had a high one-year return or a high five-year return or both?
    c. What is the probability that a fund had neither a high one-year return nor a high five-year return?

26. Data on the 30 largest stock and balanced funds provided one-year and five-year percentage returns for the period ending March 31, 2000 (*The Wall Street Journal,* April 10, 2000). Suppose we consider a one-year return in excess of 50% to be high and a five-year return in excess of 300% to be high. Nine of the funds had one-year returns in excess of 50%, seven of the funds had five-year returns in excess of 300%, and five of the funds had both one-year returns in excess of 50% and five-year returns in excess of 300%.
    a. What is the probability of a high one-year return, and what is the probability of a high five-year return?
    b. What is the probability of both a high one-year return and a high five-year return?
    c. What is the probability of neither a high one-year return nor a high five-year return?

27. A 2001 preseason NCAA football poll asked respondents to answer the question, "Will the Big Ten or the Pac-10 have a team in this year's national championship game, the Rose Bowl?" Of the 13,429 respondents, 2961 said the Big Ten would, 4494 said the Pac-10 would, and 6823 said neither the Big Ten nor the Pac-10 would have a team in the Rose Bowl (http://www.yahoo.com, August 30, 2001).
    a. What is the probability that a respondent said neither the Big Ten nor the Pac-10 will have a team in the Rose Bowl?
    b. What is the probability that a respondent said either the Big Ten or the Pac-10 will have a team in the Rose Bowl?
    c. Find the probability that a respondent said both the Big Ten and the Pac-10 would have a team in the Rose Bowl.

28. A survey of magazine subscribers showed that 45.8% rented a car during the past 12 months for business reasons, 54% rented a car during the past 12 months for personal reasons, and 30% rented a car during the past 12 months for both business and personal reasons.
    a. What is the probability that a subscriber rented a car during the past 12 months for business or personal reasons?
    b. What is the probability that a subscriber did not rent a car during the past 12 months for either business or personal reasons?

29. High school seniors with strong academic records apply to the nation's most selective colleges in greater numbers each year. Because the number of slots remains relatively stable, some colleges reject more early applicants. The University of Pennsylvania received 2851 applications for early admission. Of this group, it admitted 1033 students, rejected 854 outright, and deferred 964 to the regular admissions pool. Penn admitted about 18% of the applicants in the regular admissions pool for a total class size (number of early admissions plus number of regular admissions) of 2375 students (*USA Today,* January 24, 2001). Let E, R, and D represent the events that a student who applies for early admission is admitted, rejected outright, or deferred to the regular admissions pool; and let A represent the event that a student in the regular admissions pool is admitted.
    a. Use the data to estimate $P(E)$, $P(R)$, and $P(D)$.
    b. Are events E and D mutually exclusive? Find $P(E \cap D)$.
    c. For the 2375 students admitted to Penn, what is the probability that a randomly selected student was accepted for early admission?
    d. Suppose a student applies to Penn for early admission. What is the probability the student will be admitted for early admission or be accepted for admission in the regular admissions pool?

Conditional Probability

Often, the probability of an event is influenced by whether a related event already occurred. Suppose we have an event A with probability $P(A)$. If we obtain new information and learn that a related event, denoted by B, already occurred, we will want to take advantage of this information by calculating a new probability for event A. This new probability of event A is called a **conditional probability** and is written $P(A \mid B)$. We use the notation | to indicate that we are considering the probability of event A *given* the condition that event B has occurred. Hence, the notation $P(A \mid B)$ reads "the probability of A given B."

As an illustration of the application of conditional probability, consider the situation of the promotion status of male and female officers of a major metropolitan police force in the eastern United States. The police force consists of 1200 officers, 960 men and 240 women. Over the past two years, 324 officers on the police force received promotions. The specific breakdown of promotions for male and female officers is shown in Table 4.4.

After reviewing the promotion record, a committee of female officers raised a discrimination case on the basis that 288 male officers had received promotions but only 36 female officers had received promotions. The police administration argued that the relatively low number of promotions for female officers was due not to discrimination, but to the fact that relatively few females are members of the police force. Let us show how conditional probability could be used to analyze the discrimination charge.

Let

$$M = \text{event an officer is a man}$$
$$W = \text{event an officer is a woman}$$
$$A = \text{event an officer is promoted}$$
$$A^c = \text{event an officer is not promoted}$$

Dividing the data values in Table 4.4 by the total of 1200 officers enables us to summarize the available information with the following probability values.

$P(M \cap A) = 288/1200 = .24 =$ probability that a randomly selected officer is a man *and* is promoted

$P(M \cap A^c) = 672/1200 = .56 =$ probability that a randomly selected officer is a man *and* is not promoted

$P(W \cap A) = 36/1200 = .03 =$ probability that a randomly selected officer is a woman *and* is promoted

$P(W \cap A^c) = 204/1200 = .17 =$ probability that a randomly selected officer is a woman *and* is not promoted

Because each of these values gives the probability of the intersection of two events, the probabilities are called **joint probabilities**. Table 4.5, which provides a summary of the probability information for the police officer promotion situation, is referred to as a *joint probability table*.

The values in the margins of the joint probability table provide the probabilities of each event separately. That is, $P(M) = .80$, $P(W) = .20$, $P(A) = .27$, and $P(A^c) = .73$. These

TABLE 4.4   PROMOTION STATUS OF POLICE OFFICERS OVER THE PAST TWO YEARS

	Men	Women	Total
Promoted	288	36	324
Not Promoted	672	204	876
Total	960	240	1200

TABLE 4.5   JOINT PROBABILITY TABLE FOR PROMOTION STATUS OF POLICE OFFICERS

Joint probabilities appear in the body of the table.	Men (*M*)	Women (*W*)	Total
Promoted (*A*)	.24	.03	.27
Not Promoted (*A^c*)	.56	.17	.73
Total	.80	.20	1.00

Marginal probabilities appear in the margins of the table.

probabilities are referred to as **marginal probabilities** because of their location in the margins of the joint probability table. We note that the marginal probabilities are found by summing the joint probabilities in the corresponding row or column of the joint probability table. For instance, the marginal probability of being promoted is $P(A) = P(M \cap A) + P(W \cap A) = .24 + .03 = .27$. From the marginal probabilities, we see that 80% of the force is male, 20% of the force is female, 27% of all officers received promotions, and 73% were not promoted.

Let us begin the conditional probability analysis by computing the probability that an officer is promoted given that the officer is a man. In conditional probability notation, we are attempting to determine $P(A \mid M)$. To calculate $P(A \mid M)$, we first realize that this notation simply means that we are considering the probability of the event A (promotion) given that the condition designated as event M (the officer is a man) is known to exist. Thus $P(A \mid M)$ tells us that we are now concerned only with the promotion status of the 960 male officers. Because 288 of the 960 male officers received promotions, the probability of being promoted given that the officer is a man is 288/960 = .30. In other words, given that an officer is a man, that officer had a 30% chance of receiving a promotion over the past two years.

This procedure was easy to apply because the values in Table 4.4 show the number of officers in each category. We now want to demonstrate how conditional probabilities such as $P(A \mid M)$ can be computed directly from related event probabilities rather than the frequency data of Table 4.4.

We have shown that $P(A \mid M) = 288/960 = .30$. Let us now divide both the numerator and denominator of this fraction by 1200, the total number of officers in the study.

$$P(A \mid M) = \frac{288}{960} = \frac{288/1200}{960/1200} = \frac{.24}{.80} = .30$$

We now see that the conditional probability $P(A \mid M)$ can be computed as .24/.80. Refer to the joint probability table (Table 4.5). Note in particular that .24 is the joint probability of events A and M; that is, $P(A \cap M) = .24$. Also note that .80 is the marginal probability that a randomly selected officer is a man; that is, $P(M) = .80$. Thus, the conditional probability $P(A \mid M)$ can be computed as the ratio of the joint probability $P(A \cap M)$ to the marginal probability $P(M)$.

$$P(A \mid M) = \frac{P(A \cap M)}{P(M)} = \frac{.24}{.80} = .30$$

The fact that conditional probabilities can be computed as the ratio of a joint probability to a marginal probability provides the following general formula for conditional probability calculations for two events A and B.

CONDITIONAL PROBABILITY

$$P(A \mid B) = \frac{P(A \cap B)}{P(B)} \tag{4.7}$$

or

$$P(B \mid A) = \frac{P(A \cap B)}{P(A)} \tag{4.8}$$

The Venn diagram in Figure 4.8 is helpful in obtaining an intuitive understanding of conditional probability. The circle on the right shows that event B has occurred; the portion of the circle that overlaps with event A denotes the event $(A \cap B)$. We know that once event B has occurred, the only way that we can also observe event A is for the event $(A \cap B)$ to occur. Thus, the ratio $P(A \cap B)/P(B)$ provides the conditional probability that we will observe event A given that event B has already occurred.

Let us return to the issue of discrimination against the female officers. The marginal probability in row 1 of Table 4.5 shows that the probability of promotion of an officer is $P(A) = .27$ (regardless of whether that officer is male or female). However, the critical issue in the discrimination case involves the two conditional probabilities $P(A \mid M)$ and $P(A \mid W)$. That is, what is the probability of a promotion *given* that the officer is a man, and what is the probability of a promotion *given* that the officer is a woman? If these two probabilities are equal, a discrimination argument has no basis because the chances of a promotion are the same for male and female officers. However, a difference in the two conditional probabilities will support the position that male and female officers are treated differently in promotion decisions.

We already determined that $P(A \mid M) = .30$. Let us now use the probability values in Table 4.5 and the basic relationship of conditional probability in equation (4.7) to compute

FIGURE 4.8   CONDITIONAL PROBABILITY $P(A \mid B) = P(A \cap B)/P(B)$

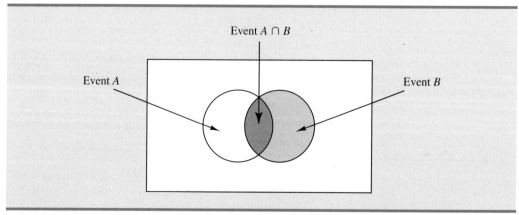

the probability that an officer is promoted given that the officer is a woman; that is, $P(A \mid W)$. Using equation (4.7), with W replacing B, we obtain

$$P(A \mid W) = \frac{P(A \cap W)}{P(W)} = \frac{.03}{.20} = .15$$

What conclusion do you draw? The probability of a promotion given that the officer is a man is .30, twice the .15 probability of a promotion given that the officer is a woman. Although the use of conditional probability does not in itself prove that discrimination exists in this case, the conditional probability values support the argument presented by the female officers.

Independent Events

In the preceding illustration, $P(A) = .27$, $P(A \mid M) = .30$, and $P(A \mid W) = .15$. We see that the probability of a promotion (event A) is affected or influenced by whether the officer is a man or a woman. Particularly, because $P(A \mid M) \neq P(A)$, we would say that events A and M are dependent events. That is, the probability of event A (promotion) is altered or affected by knowing that event M (the officer is a man) exists. Similarly, with $P(A \mid W) \neq P(A)$, we would say that events A and W are *dependent events*. However, if the probability of event A is not changed by the existence of event M—that is, $P(A \mid M) = P(A)$—we would say that events A and M are **independent events**. This situation leads to the following definition of the independence of two events.

INDEPENDENT EVENTS

Two events A and B are independent if

$$P(A \mid B) = P(A) \tag{4.9}$$

or

$$P(B \mid A) = P(B) \tag{4.10}$$

Otherwise, the events are dependent.

Multiplication Law

Whereas the addition law of probability is used to compute the probability of a union of two events, the multiplication law is used to compute the probability of the intersection of two events. The multiplication law is based on the definition of conditional probability. Using equations (4.7) and (4.8) and solving for $P(A \cap B)$, we obtain the **multiplication law**.

MULTIPLICATION LAW

$$P(A \cap B) = P(B)P(A \mid B) \tag{4.11}$$

or

$$P(A \cap B) = P(A)P(B \mid A) \tag{4.12}$$

To illustrate the use of the multiplication law, consider a newspaper circulation department where it is known that 84% of the households in a particular neighborhood subscribe to the daily edition of the paper. If we let D denote the event that a household subscribes to the daily edition, $P(D) = .84$. In addition, it is known that the probability that a household that already holds a daily subscription also subscribes to the Sunday edition (event S) is .75; that is, $P(S \mid D) = .75$.

What is the probability that a household subscribes to both the Sunday and daily editions of the newspaper? Using the multiplication law, we compute the desired $P(S \cap D)$ as

$$P(S \cap D) = P(D)P(S \mid D) = .84(.75) = .63$$

We now know that 63% of the households subscribe to both the Sunday and daily editions.

Before concluding this section, let us consider the special case of the multiplication law when the events involved are independent. Recall that events A and B are independent if $P(A \mid B) = P(A)$ or $P(B \mid A) = P(B)$. Hence, using equations (4.11) and (4.12) for the special case of independent events, we obtain the following multiplication law.

MULTIPLICATION LAW FOR INDEPENDENT EVENTS

$$P(A \cap B) = P(A)P(B) \qquad\qquad (4.13)$$

To compute the probability of the intersection of two independent events, we simply multiply the corresponding probabilities. Note that the multiplication law for independent events provides another way to determine whether A and B are independent. That is, if $P(A \cap B) = P(A)P(B)$, then A and B are independent; if $P(A \cap B) \neq P(A)P(B)$, then A and B are dependent.

As an application of the multiplication law for independent events, consider the situation of a service station manager who knows from past experience that 80% of the customers use a credit card when they purchase gasoline. What is the probability that the next two customers purchasing gasoline will each use a credit card? If we let

A = the event that the first customer uses a credit card

B = the event that the second customer uses a credit card

then the event of interest is $A \cap B$. Given no other information, we can reasonably assume that A and B are independent events. Thus,

$$P(A \cap B) = P(A)P(B) = (.80)(.80) = .64$$

To summarize this section, we note that our interest in conditional probability is motivated by the fact that events are often related. In such cases, we say the events are dependent and the conditional probability formulas in equations (4.7) and (4.8) must be used to compute the event probabilities. If two events are not related, they are independent; in this case neither event's probability is affected by whether the other event occurred.

NOTES AND COMMENTS

Do not confuse the notion of mutually exclusive events with that of independent events. Two events with nonzero probabilities cannot be both mutually exclusive and independent. If one mutually exclusive event is known to occur, the other cannot occur; thus, the probability of the other event occurring is reduced to zero. They are therefore dependent.

Exercises

Methods

30. Suppose that we have two events, A and B, with $P(A) = .50$, $P(B) = .60$, and $P(A \cap B) = .40$.
    a.   Find $P(A \mid B)$.
    b.   Find $P(B \mid A)$.
    c.   Are A and B independent? Explain.

31. Assume that we have two events, A and B, that are mutually exclusive. Assume further that we know $P(A) = .30$ and $P(B) = .40$.
    a. What is $P(A \cap B)$?
    b. What is $P(A \mid B)$?
    c. A student in statistics argues that the concepts of mutually exclusive events and independent events are really the same, and that if events are mutually exclusive they must be independent. Do you agree with this statement? Use the probability information in this problem to justify your answer.
    d. What general conclusion would you make about mutually exclusive and independent events given the results of this problem?

Applications

32. Due to rising health insurance costs, 43 million people in the United States go without health insurance (*Time*, December 1, 2003). Sample data representative of the national health insurance coverage for individuals 18 years of age and older are shown here.

		Health Insurance	
		Yes	**No**
Age	**18 to 34**	750	170
	35 and over	950	130

    a. Develop a joint probability table for these data and use the table to answer the remaining questions.
    b. What do the marginal probabilities tell you about the age of the U.S. population?
    c. What is the probability that a randomly selected individual does not have health insurance coverage?
    d. If the individual is between the ages of 18 and 34, what is the probability that the individual does not have health insurance coverage?
    e. If the individual is age 35 or over, what is the probability that the individual does not have health insurance coverage?
    f. If the individual does not have health insurance, what is the probability that the individual is in the 18 to 34 age group?
    g. What does the probability information tell you about health insurance coverage in the United States?

33. In a survey of MBA students, the following data were obtained on students' first reason for application to the school in which they matriculated.

SELF test

		Reason for Application			
		School Quality	**School Cost or Convenience**	**Other**	**Total**
Enrollment Status	**Full Time**	421	393	76	890
	Part Time	400	593	46	1039
	Total	821	986	122	1929

    a. Develop a joint probability table for these data.
    b. Use the marginal probabilities of school quality, school cost or convenience, and other to comment on the most important reason for choosing a school.

c. If a student goes full time, what is the probability that school quality is the first reason for choosing a school?

d. If a student goes part time, what is the probability that school quality is the first reason for choosing a school?

e. Let A denote the event that a student is full time and let B denote the event that the student lists school quality as the first reason for applying. Are events A and B independent? Justify your answer.

34. The following table shows the probabilities of blood types in the general population (Hoxworth Blood Center, Cincinnati, Ohio, March 2003).

	A	B	AB	O
Rh+	.34	.09	.04	.38
Rh−	.06	.02	.01	.06

a. What is the probability a person will have type O blood?

b. What is the probability a person will be Rh−?

c. What is the probability a person will be Rh− given he or she has type O blood?

d. What is the probability a person will have type B blood given he or she is Rh+?

e. What is the probability a married couple will both be Rh−?

f. What is the probability a married couple will both have type AB blood?

35. The U.S. Bureau of Labor Statistics collected data on the occupations of workers 25 to 64 years old. The following table shows the number of male and female workers (in thousands) in each occupation category (*Statistical Abstract of the United States: 2002*).

Occupation	Male	Female
Managerial/Professional	19079	19021
Tech./Sales/Administrative	11079	19315
Service	4977	7947
Precision Production	11682	1138
Operators/Fabricators/Labor	10576	3482
Farming/Forestry/Fishing	1838	514

a. Develop a joint probability table.

b. What is the probability of a female worker being a manager or professional?

c. What is the probability of a male worker being in precision production?

d. Is occupation independent of gender? Justify your answer with a probability calculation.

36. Reggie Miller of the Indiana Pacers is the National Basketball Association's best career free throw shooter, making 89% of his shots (*USA Today*, January 22, 2004). Assume that late in a basketball game, Reggie Miller is fouled and is awarded two shots.

a. What is the probability that he will make both shots?

b. What is the probability that he will make at least one shot?

c. What is the probability that he will miss both shots?

d. Late in a basketball game, a team often intentionally fouls an opposing player in order to stop the game clock. The usual strategy is to intentionally foul the other team's worst free throw shooter. Assume that the Indiana Pacers' center makes 58% of his free throw shots. Calculate the probabilities for the center as shown in parts (a), (b), and (c), and show that intentionally fouling the Indiana Pacers' center is a better strategy than intentionally fouling Reggie Miller.

37. A purchasing agent placed rush orders for a particular raw material with two different suppliers, *A* and *B*. If neither order arrives in four days, the production process must be shut down until at least one of the orders arrives. The probability that supplier *A* can deliver the material in four days is .55. The probability that supplier *B* can deliver the material in four days is .35.
    a. What is the probability that both suppliers will deliver the material in four days? Because two separate suppliers are involved, we are willing to assume independence.
    b. What is the probability that at least one supplier will deliver the material in four days?
    c. What is the probability that the production process will be shut down in four days because of a shortage of raw material (i.e., both orders are late)?

38. The Minneapolis Heart Institute Foundation conducted a study to determine the benefit of follow-up care for patients discharged from a hospital after treatment for a heart attack (*The Wall Street Journal*, November 11, 2002). Out of 2060 patients, 1070 did not return for follow-up treatment and 990 did. Within 24 months, 14 of the patients receiving follow-up treatment died, and 29 of the patients not receiving follow-up treatment died. Within 54 months, 20 of the patients receiving follow-up treatment died, and 49 of the patients not receiving follow-up treatment died.
    a. What is the probability of a patient dying within 24 months of being discharged after treatment for a heart attack?
    b. Using the data for 24 months after discharge, compute the conditional probabilities of dying for patients receiving and not receiving follow-up treatment.
    c. Is the probability of dying within 24 months of discharge independent of whether the person receives follow-up treatment? Explain.
    d. Using the data for 54 months after discharge, compute the conditional probabilities of dying for patients receiving and not receiving follow-up treatment.
    e. Would you recommend enrolling in a follow-up treatment program to a friend?

Bayes' Theorem

In the discussion of conditional probability, we indicated that revising probabilities when new information is obtained is an important phase of probability analysis. Often, we begin the analysis with initial or **prior probability** estimates for specific events of interest. Then, from sources such as a sample, a special report, or a product test, we obtain additional information about the events. Given this new information, we update the prior probability values by calculating revised probabilities, referred to as **posterior probabilities**. **Bayes' theorem** provides a means for making these probability calculations. The steps in this probability revision process are shown in Figure 4.9.

As an application of Bayes' theorem, consider a manufacturing firm that receives shipments of parts from two different suppliers. Let A_1 denote the event that a part is from supplier 1 and A_2 denote the event that a part is from supplier 2. Currently, 65% of the parts purchased by the company are from supplier 1 and the remaining 35% are from supplier 2. Hence, if a part is selected at random, we would assign the prior probabilities $P(A_1) = .65$ and $P(A_2) = .35$.

The quality of the purchased parts varies with the source of supply. Historical data suggest that the quality ratings of the two suppliers are as shown in Table 4.6. If we let *G*

FIGURE 4.9 PROBABILITY REVISION USING BAYES' THEOREM

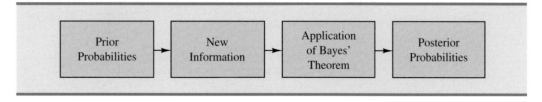

TABLE 4.6   HISTORICAL QUALITY LEVELS OF TWO SUPPLIERS

	Percentage Good Parts	Percentage Bad Parts
Supplier 1	98	2
Supplier 2	95	5

denote the event that a part is good and B denote the event that a part is bad, the information in Table 4.6 provides the following conditional probability values.

$$P(G \mid A_1) = .98 \quad P(B \mid A_1) = .02$$
$$P(G \mid A_2) = .95 \quad P(B \mid A_2) = .05$$

The tree diagram in Figure 4.10 depicts the process of the firm receiving a part from one of the two suppliers and then discovering that the part is good or bad as a two-step experiment. We see that four experimental outcomes are possible; two correspond to the part being good and two correspond to the part being bad.

Each of the experimental outcomes is the intersection of two events, so we can use the multiplication rule to compute the probabilities. For instance,

$$P(A_1, G) = P(A_1 \cap G) = P(A_1)P(G \mid A_1)$$

The process of computing these joint probabilities can be depicted in what is called a probability tree (see Figure 4.11). From left to right through the tree, the probabilities for each branch at step 1 are prior probabilities and the probabilities for each branch at step 2 are conditional probabilities. To find the probabilities of each experimental outcome, we simply multiply the probabilities on the branches leading to the outcome. Each of these joint probabilities is shown in Figure 4.11 along with the known probabilities for each branch.

Suppose now that the parts from the two suppliers are used in the firm's manufacturing process and that a machine breaks down because it attempts to process a bad part. Given

FIGURE 4.10   TREE DIAGRAM FOR TWO-SUPPLIER EXAMPLE

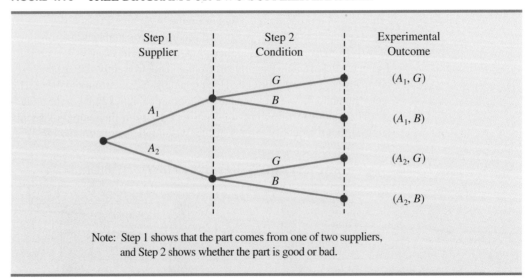

Note: Step 1 shows that the part comes from one of two suppliers, and Step 2 shows whether the part is good or bad.

FIGURE 4.11   PROBABILITY TREE FOR TWO-SUPPLIER EXAMPLE

the information that the part is bad, what is the probability that it came from supplier 1 and what is the probability that it came from supplier 2? With the information in the probability tree (Figure 4.11), Bayes' theorem can be used to answer these questions.

Letting B denote the event that the part is bad, we are looking for the posterior probabilities $P(A_1 \mid B)$ and $P(A_2 \mid B)$. From the law of conditional probability, we know that

$$P(A_1 \mid B) = \frac{P(A_1 \cap B)}{P(B)} \qquad (4.14)$$

Referring to the probability tree, we see that

$$P(A_1 \cap B) = P(A_1)P(B \mid A_1) \qquad (4.15)$$

To find $P(B)$, we note that event B can occur in only two ways: $(A_1 \cap B)$ and $(A_2 \cap B)$. Therefore, we have

$$\begin{aligned} P(B) &= P(A_1 \cap B) + P(A_2 \cap B) \\ &= P(A_1)P(B \mid A_1) + P(A_2)P(B \mid A_2) \end{aligned} \qquad (4.16)$$

Substituting from equations (4.15) and (4.16) into equation (4.14) and writing a similar result for $P(A_2 \mid B)$, we obtain Bayes' theorem for the case of two events.

The Reverend Thomas Bayes (1702–1761), a Presbyterian minister, is credited with the original work leading to the version of Bayes' theorem in use today.

BAYES' THEOREM (TWO-EVENT CASE)

$$P(A_1 \mid B) = \frac{P(A_1)P(B \mid A_1)}{P(A_1)P(B \mid A_1) + P(A_2)P(B \mid A_2)} \qquad (4.17)$$

$$P(A_2 \mid B) = \frac{P(A_2)P(B \mid A_2)}{P(A_1)P(B \mid A_1) + P(A_2)P(B \mid A_2)} \qquad (4.18)$$

Using equation (4.17) and the probability values provided in the example, we have

$$P(A_1 \mid B) = \frac{P(A_1)P(B \mid A_1)}{P(A_1)P(B \mid A_1) + P(A_2)P(B \mid A_2)}$$

$$= \frac{(.65)(.02)}{(.65)(.02) + (.35)(.05)} = \frac{.0130}{.0130 + .0175}$$

$$= \frac{.0130}{.0305} = .4262$$

In addition, using equation (4.18), we find $P(A_2 \mid B)$.

$$P(A_2 \mid B) = \frac{(.35)(.05)}{(.65)(.02) + (.35)(.05)}$$

$$= \frac{.0175}{.0130 + .0175} = \frac{.0175}{.0305} = .5738$$

Note that in this application we started with a probability of .65 that a part selected at random was from supplier 1. However, given information that the part is bad, the probability that the part is from supplier 1 drops to .4262. In fact, if the part is bad, it has better than a 50-50 chance that it came from supplier 2; that is, $P(A_2 \mid B) = .5738$.

Bayes' theorem is applicable when the events for which we want to compute posterior probabilities are mutually exclusive and their union is the entire sample space.* For the case of n mutually exclusive events $A_1, A_2, \ldots, A_n$, whose union is the entire sample space, Bayes' theorem can be used to compute any posterior probability $P(A_i \mid B)$ as shown here.

BAYES' THEOREM

$$P(A_i \mid B) = \frac{P(A_i)P(B \mid A_i)}{P(A_1)P(B \mid A_1) + P(A_2)P(B \mid A_2) + \cdots + P(A_n)P(B \mid A_n)} \qquad \textbf{(4.19)}$$

With prior probabilities $P(A_1), P(A_2), \ldots, P(A_n)$ and the appropriate conditional probabilities $P(B \mid A_1), P(B \mid A_2), \ldots, P(B \mid A_n)$, equation (4.19) can be used to compute the posterior probability of the events $A_1, A_2, \ldots, A_n$.

Tabular Approach

A tabular approach is helpful in conducting the Bayes' theorem calculations. Such an approach is shown in Table 4.7 for the two supplier example. The computations shown there are done in the following steps.

Step 1. Prepare the following three columns:

Column 1—The mutually exclusive events A_i for which posterior probabilities are desired

Column 2—The prior probabilities $P(A_i)$ for the events

Column 3—The conditional probabilities $P(B \mid A_i)$ of the new information B given each event

Step 2. In column 4, compute the joint probabilities $P(A_i \cap B)$ for each event and the new information B by using the multiplication law. These joint probabilities are

---

*If the union of events is the entire sample space, the events are said to be *collectively exhaustive*.

TABLE 4.7   TABULAR APPROACH TO BAYES' THEOREM CALCULATIONS FOR THE TWO-SUPPLIER EXAMPLE

(1) Events A_i	(2) Prior Probabilities $P(A_i)$	(3) Conditional Probabilities $P(B \mid A_i)$	(4) Joint Probabilities $P(A_i \cap B)$	(5) Posterior Probabilities $P(A_i \mid B)$
A_1	.65	.02	.0130	.0130/.0305 = .4262
A_2	.35	.05	.0175	.0175/.0305 = .5738
	1.00		$P(B) = .0305$	1.0000

found by multiplying the prior probabilities in column 2 by the corresponding conditional probabilities in column 3; that is, $P(A_i \cap B) = P(A_i)P(B \mid A_i)$.

Step 3. Sum the joint probabilities in column 4. The sum is the probability of the new information, $P(B)$. Thus we see in Table 4.7 that there is a .0130 probability that the part came from supplier 1 and is bad and a .0175 probability that the part came from supplier 2 and is bad. Because these are the only two ways in which a bad part can be obtained, the sum .0130 + .0175 shows an overall probability of .0305 of finding a bad part from the combined shipments of the two suppliers.

Step 4. In column 5, compute the posterior probabilities using the basic relationship of conditional probability.

$$P(A_i \mid B) = \frac{P(A_i \cap B)}{P(B)}$$

Note that the joint probabilities $P(A_i \cap B)$ are in column 4 and the probability $P(B)$ is the sum of column 4.

Using Excel to Compute Posterior Probabilities

The tabular approach to Bayes' theorem can be easily implemented within an Excel worksheet. In this subsection we show how the Bayes' theorem calculations shown in Table 4.7 can be made. Refer to Figure 4.12 as we describe the tasks involved. The formula worksheet is in the background; the value worksheet is in the foreground.

Enter Data: Labels are placed in rows 1 and 2 and the two mutually exclusive events are identified in cells A3:A4. The prior probabilities were entered into cells B3:B4 and the conditional probabilities were entered into cells C3:C4.

FIGURE 4.12   EXCEL WORKSHEET FOR COMPUTING POSTERIOR PROBABILITIES

	A	B	C	D	E	F
1		Prior	Conditional	Joint	Posterior	
2	Events	Probabilities	Probabilities	Probabilities	Probabilities	
3	A1	0.65	0.02	=B3*C3	=D3/$D$5	
4	A2	0.35	0.05	=B4*C4	=D4/$D$5	
5		=SUM(B3:B4)		=SUM(D3:D4)	=SUM(E3:E4)	
6						

	A	B	C	D	E	F
1		Prior	Conditional	Joint	Posterior	
2	Events	Probabilities	Probabilities	Probabilities	Probabilities	
3	A1	0.65	0.02	0.0130	0.4262	
4	A2	0.35	0.05	0.0175	0.5738	
5		1		0.0305	1.0000	
6						

Enter Functions and Formulas: The formulas in cells D3:D4 show that the joint probabilities are the product of the prior probabilities in column B and the conditional probabilities in column C. The results, shown in cells D3:D4 of the value worksheet, are the same as those shown in Table 4.7. The sum in cell D5 shows that the probability of finding a bad part is .0305. This probability is the denominator in Bayes' theorem. The formulas in cells E3:E4 provide the posterior probabilities. From the value worksheet we see that they are the same as the posterior probabilities in Table 4.7.

Note that the same worksheet could be used to find the posterior probabilities of the two suppliers given a good part is found. The prior probabilities in cells B3:B4 would not change. But we would replace the conditional probabilities in cells C3:C4 with the values .98 and .95, respectively. Doing so would provide $P(A_1 \mid G) = .6570$ and $P(A_2 \mid G) = .3430$ in cells E3:E4.

This worksheet can also be modified to handle Bayes' theorem calculations for more than two events. Just add a row for each additional event and move the sum row down.

NOTES AND COMMENTS

1. Bayes' theorem is used extensively in decision analysis. The prior probabilities are often subjective estimates provided by a decision maker. Sample information is obtained and posterior probabilities are computed for use in choosing the best decision.

2. An event and its complement are mutually exclusive, and their union is the entire sample space. Thus, Bayes' theorem is always applicable for computing posterior probabilities of an event and its complement.

Exercises

Methods

39. The prior probabilities for events A_1 and A_2 are $P(A_1) = .40$ and $P(A_2) = .60$. It is also known that $P(A_1 \cap A_2) = 0$. Suppose $P(B \mid A_1) = .20$ and $P(B \mid A_2) = .05$.
    a. Are A_1 and A_2 mutually exclusive? Explain.
    b. Compute $P(A_1 \cap B)$ and $P(A_2 \cap B)$.
    c. Compute $P(B)$.
    d. Use Bayes' theorem to compute $P(A_1 \mid B)$ and $P(A_2 \mid B)$.

40. The prior probabilities for events A_1, A_2, and A_3 are $P(A_1) = .20, P(A_2) = .50$, and $P(A_3) = .30$. The conditional probabilities of event B given A_1, A_2, and A_3 are $P(B \mid A_1) = .50$, $P(B \mid A_2) = .40$, and $P(B \mid A_3) = .30$.
    a. Compute $P(B \cap A_1), P(B \cap A_2)$, and $P(B \cap A_3)$.
    b. Use Bayes' theorem, equation (4.19), to compute the posterior probability $P(A_2 \mid B)$.
    c. Use the tabular approach to applying Bayes' theorem to compute $P(A_1 \mid B), P(A_2 \mid B)$, and $P(A_3 \mid B)$.

Applications

41. A consulting firm submitted a bid for a large research project. The firm's management initially felt they had a 50-50 chance of getting the project. However, the agency to which the bid was submitted subsequently requested additional information on the bid. Past experience indicates that for 75% of the successful bids and 40% of the unsuccessful bids the agency requested additional information.
    a. What is the prior probability of the bid being successful (i.e., prior to the request for additional information)?

b.   What is the conditional probability of a request for additional information given that the bid will ultimately be successful?

c.   Compute the posterior probability that the bid will be successful given a request for additional information.

42.   A local bank reviewed its credit card policy with the intention of recalling some of its credit cards. In the past approximately 5% of cardholders defaulted, leaving the bank unable to collect the outstanding balance. Hence, management established a prior probability of .05 that any particular cardholder will default. The bank also found that the probability of missing a monthly payment is .20 for customers who do not default. Of course, the probability of missing a monthly payment for those who default is 1.

a.   Given that a customer missed one or more monthly payments, compute the posterior probability that the customer will default.

b.   The bank would like to recall its card if the probability that a customer will default is greater than .20. Should the bank recall its card if the customer misses a monthly payment? Why or why not?

43.   Small cars get better gas mileage, but they are not as safe as bigger cars. Small cars accounted for 18% of the vehicles on the road, but accidents involving small cars led to 11,898 fatalities during a recent year (*Reader's Digest,* May 2000). Assume the probability a small car is involved in an accident is .18. The probability of an accident involving a small car leading to a fatality is .128 and the probability of an accident not involving a small car leading to a fatality is .05. Suppose you learn of an accident involving a fatality. What is the probability a small car was involved? Assume that the likelihood of getting into an accident is independent of car size.

44.   The American Council of Education reported that 47% of college freshmen earn a degree and graduate within five years (Associated Press, May 6, 2002). Assume that graduation records show women make up 50% of the students who graduated within five years, but only 45% of the students who did not graduate within five years. The students who had not graduated within five years either dropped out or were still working on their degrees.

a.   Let A_1 = the student graduated within five years
     A_2 = the student did not graduate within five years
     W = the student is a female student
     Using the given information, what are the values for $P(A_1)$, $P(A_2)$, $P(W \mid A_1)$, and $P(W \mid A_2)$?

b.   What is the probability that a female student will graduate within five years?

c.   What is the probability that a male student will graduate within five years?

d.   Given the preceding results, what are the percentage of women and the percentage of men in the entering freshman class?

45.   In an article about investment growth, *Money* magazine reported that drug stocks show powerful long-term trends and offer investors unparalleled potential for strong and steady gains. The federal Health Care Financing Administration supports this conclusion through its forecast that annual prescription drug expenditures will reach $366 billion by 2010, up from $117 billion in 2000. Many individuals age 65 and older rely heavily on prescription drugs. For this group, 82% take prescription drugs regularly, 55% take three or more prescriptions regularly, and 40% currently use five or more prescriptions. In contrast, 49% of people under age 65 take prescriptions regularly, with 37% taking three or more prescriptions regularly and 28% using five or more prescriptions (*Money,* September 2001). The U.S. Census Bureau reports that of the 281,421,906 people in the United States, 34,991,753 are age 65 years and older (U.S. Census Bureau, *Census 2000*).

a.   Compute the probability that a person in the United States is age 65 or older.

b.   Compute the probability that a person takes prescription drugs regularly.

c.   Compute the probability that a person is age 65 or older and takes five or more prescriptions.

d.   Given a person uses five or more prescriptions, compute the probability that the person is age 65 or older.

Summary

In this chapter we introduced basic probability concepts and illustrated how probability analysis can be used to provide helpful information for decision making. We described how probability can be interpreted as a numerical measure of the likelihood that an event will occur. In addition, we saw that the probability of an event can be computed either by summing the probabilities of the experimental outcomes (sample points) comprising the event or by using the relationships established by the addition, conditional probability, and multiplication laws of probability. For cases in which additional information is available, we showed how Bayes' theorem can be used to obtain revised or posterior probabilities.

Glossary

Probability A numerical measure of the likelihood that an event will occur.

Experiment A process that generates well-defined outcomes.

Sample space The set of all experimental outcomes.

Sample point An element of the sample space. A sample point represents an experimental outcome.

Tree diagram A graphical representation that helps in visualizing a multiple-step experiment.

Basic requirements for assigning probabilities Two requirements that restrict the manner in which probability assignments can be made: (1) for each experimental outcome E_i we must have $0 \leq P(E_i) \leq 1$; (2) considering all experimental outcomes, we must have $P(E_1) + P(E_2) + \cdots + P(E_n) = 1$.

Classical method A method of assigning probabilities that is appropriate when all the experimental outcomes are equally likely.

Relative frequency method A method of assigning probabilities that is appropriate when data are available to estimate the proportion of the time the experimental outcome will occur if the experiment is repeated a large number of times.

Subjective method A method of assigning probabilities on the basis of judgment.

Event A collection of sample points.

Complement of A The event consisting of all sample points that are not in A.

Venn diagram A graphical representation for showing symbolically the sample space and operations involving events in which the sample space is represented by a rectangle and events are represented as circles within the sample space.

Union of A and B The event containing all sample points belonging to A or B or both. The union is denoted $A \cup B$.

Intersection of A and B The event containing the sample points belonging to both A and B. The intersection is denoted $A \cap B$.

Addition law A probability law used to compute the probability of the union of two events. It is $P(A \cup B) = P(A) + P(B) - P(A \cap B)$. For mutually exclusive events, $P(A \cap B) = 0$; in this case the addition law reduces to $P(A \cup B) = P(A) + P(B)$.

Mutually exclusive events Events that have no sample points in common; that is, $A \cap B$ is empty and $P(A \cap B) = 0$.

Conditional probability The probability of an event given that another event already occurred. The conditional probability of A given B is $P(A \mid B) = P(A \cap B)/P(B)$.

Joint probability The probability of two events both occurring; that is, the probability of the intersection of two events.

Marginal probability The values in the margins of a joint probability table that provide the probabilities of each event separately.

Independent events Two events A and B where $P(A \mid B) = P(A)$ or $P(B \mid A) = P(B)$; that is, the events have no influence on each other.

Multiplication law A probability law used to compute the probability of the intersection of two events. It is $P(A \cap B) = P(B)P(A \mid B)$ or $P(A \cap B) = P(A)P(B \mid A)$. For independent events it reduces to $P(A \cap B) = P(A)P(B)$.

Prior probabilities Initial estimates of the probabilities of events.

Posterior probabilities Revised probabilities of events based on additional information.

Bayes' theorem A method used to compute posterior probabilities.

Key Formulas

Counting Rule for Combinations

$$C_n^N = \binom{N}{n} = \frac{N!}{n!(N-n)!} \tag{4.1}$$

Counting Rule for Permutations

$$P_n^N = n!\binom{N}{n} = \frac{N!}{(N-n)!} \tag{4.2}$$

Computing Probability Using the Complement

$$P(A) = 1 - P(A^c) \tag{4.5}$$

Addition Law

$$P(A \cup B) = P(A) + P(B) - P(A \cap B) \tag{4.6}$$

Conditional Probability

$$P(A \mid B) = \frac{P(A \cap B)}{P(B)} \tag{4.7}$$

$$P(B \mid A) = \frac{P(A \cap B)}{P(A)} \tag{4.8}$$

Multiplication Law

$$P(A \cap B) = P(B)P(A \mid B) \tag{4.11}$$

$$P(A \cap B) = P(A)P(B \mid A) \tag{4.12}$$

Multiplication Law for Independent Events

$$P(A \cap B) = P(A)P(B) \tag{4.13}$$

Bayes' Theorem

$$P(A_i \mid B) = \frac{P(A_i)P(B \mid A_i)}{P(A_1)P(B \mid A_1) + P(A_2)P(B \mid A_2) + \cdots + P(A_n)P(B \mid A_n)} \tag{4.19}$$

Supplementary Exercises

46. In a *BusinessWeek*/Harris Poll, 1035 adults were asked about their attitudes toward business (*BusinessWeek*, September 11, 2000). One question asked: "How would you rate large U.S. companies on making good products and competing in a global environment?" The responses were: excellent—18%, pretty good—50%, only fair—26%, poor—5%, and don't know/no answer—1%.
    a. What is the probability that a respondent rated U.S. companies pretty good or excellent?
    b. How many respondents rated U.S. companies poor?
    c. How many respondents did not know or did not answer?

47. A financial manager made two new investments—one in the oil industry and one in municipal bonds. After a one-year period, each of the investments will be classified as either successful or unsuccessful. Consider the making of the two investments as an experiment.
    a. How many sample points exist for this experiment?
    b. Show a tree diagram and list the sample points.
    c. Let O = the event that the oil industry investment is successful and M = the event that the municipal bond investment is successful. List the sample points in O and in M.
    d. List the sample points in the union of the events ($O \cup M$).
    e. List the sample points in the intersection of the events ($O \cap M$).
    f. Are events O and M mutually exclusive? Explain.

48. In early 2003, President Bush proposed eliminating the taxation of dividends to shareholders on the grounds that it was double taxation. Corporations pay taxes on the earnings that are later paid out in dividends. In a poll of 671 Americans, TechnoMetrica Market Intelligence found that 47% favored the proposal, 44% opposed it, and 9% were not sure (*Investor's Business Daily,* January 13, 2003). In looking at the responses across party lines the poll showed that 29% of Democrats were in favor, 64% of Republicans were in favor, and 48% of Independents were in favor.
    a. How many of those polled favored elimination of the tax on dividends?
    b. What is the conditional probability in favor of the proposal given the person polled is a Democrat?
    c. Is party affiliation independent of whether one is in favor of the proposal?
    d. If we assume people's responses were consistent with their own self-interest, which group do you believe will benefit most from passage of the proposal?

49. A study of 31,000 hospital admissions in New York State found that 4% of the admissions led to treatment-caused injuries. One-seventh of these treatment-caused injuries resulted in death, and one-fourth were caused by negligence. Malpractice claims were filed in one out of 7.5 cases involving negligence, and payments were made in one out of every two claims.
    a. What is the probability a person admitted to the hospital will suffer a treatment-caused injury due to negligence?
    b. What is the probability a person admitted to the hospital will die from a treatment-caused injury?
    c. In the case of a negligent treatment-caused injury, what is the probability a malpractice claim will be paid?

50. A telephone survey to determine viewer response to a new television show obtained the following data.

Rating	Frequency
Poor	4
Below average	8
Average	11
Above average	14
Excellent	13

a. What is the probability that a randomly selected viewer will rate the new show as average or better?
b. What is the probability that a randomly selected viewer will rate the new show below average or worse?

51. The following crosstabulation shows household income by educational level of the head of household (*Statistical Abstract of the United States: 2002*).

Education Level	Household Income ($1000s)					
	Under 25	25.0– 49.9	50.0– 74.9	75.0– 99.9	100 or more	Total
Not H.S. Graduate	9,285	4,093	1,589	541	354	15,862
H.S. Graduate	10,150	9,821	6,050	2,737	2,028	30,786
Some College	6,011	8,221	5,813	3,215	3,120	26,380
Bachelor's Degree	2,138	3,985	3,952	2,698	4,748	17,521
Beyond Bach. Deg.	813	1,497	1,815	1,589	3,765	9,479
Total	28,397	27,617	19,219	10,780	14,015	100,028

a. Develop a joint probability table.
b. What is the probability of a head of household not being a high school graduate?
c. What is the probability of a head of household having a bachelor's degree or more education?
d. What is the probability of a household headed by someone with a bachelor's degree earning $100,000 or more?
e. What is the probability of a household having income below $25,000?
f. What is the probability of a household headed by someone with a bachelor's degree earning less than $25,000?
g. Is household income independent of educational level?

52. A GMAC MBA new-matriculants survey provided the following data for 2018 students.

Age Group	Applied to More Than One School	
	Yes	No
23 and under	207	201
24–26	299	379
27–30	185	268
31–35	66	193
36 and over	51	169

a. For a randomly selected MBA student, prepare a joint probability table for the experiment consisting of observing the student's age and whether the student applied to one or more schools.
b. What is the probability that a randomly selected applicant is 23 or under?
c. What is the probability that a randomly selected applicant is older than 26?
d. What is the probability that a randomly selected applicant applied to more than one school?

53. Refer again to the data from the GMAC new-matriculants survey in exercise 52.
a. Given that a person applied to more than one school, what is the probability that the person is 24–26 years old?
b. Given that a person is in the 36-and-over age group, what is the probability that the person applied to more than one school?
c. What is the probability that a person is 24–26 years old or applied to more than one school?

d.   Suppose a person is known to have applied to only one school. What is the probability that the person is 31 or more years old?

e.   Is the number of schools applied to independent of age? Explain.

54. An IBD/TIPP poll conducted to learn about attitudes toward investment and retirement (*Investor's Business Daily,* May 5, 2000) asked male and female respondents how important they felt level of risk was in choosing a retirement investment. The following joint probability table was constructed from the data provided. "Important" means the respondent said level of risk was either important or very important.

	Male	Female	Total
Important	.22	.27	.49
Not Important	.28	.23	.51
Total	.50	.50	1.00

a.   What is the probability a survey respondent will say level of risk is important?

b.   What is the probability a male respondent will say level of risk is important?

c.   What is the probability a female respondent will say level of risk is important?

d.   Is the level of risk independent of the gender of the respondent? Why or why not?

e.   Do male and female attitudes toward risk differ?

55. A large consumer goods company ran a television advertisement for one of its soap products. On the basis of a survey that was conducted, probabilities were assigned to the following events.

$$B = \text{individual purchased the product}$$
$$S = \text{individual recalls seeing the advertisement}$$
$$B \cap S = \text{individual purchased the product and recalls seeing the advertisement}$$

The probabilities assigned were $P(B) = .20$, $P(S) = .40$, and $P(B \cap S) = .12$.

a.   What is the probability of an individual's purchasing the product given that the individual recalls seeing the advertisement? Does seeing the advertisement increase the probability that the individual will purchase the product? As a decision maker, would you recommend continuing the advertisement (assuming that the cost is reasonable)?

b.   Assume that individuals who do not purchase the company's soap product buy from its competitors. What would be your estimate of the company's market share? Would you expect that continuing the advertisement will increase the company's market share? Why or why not?

c.   The company also tested another advertisement and assigned it values of $P(S) = .30$ and $P(B \cap S) = .10$. What is $P(B \mid S)$ for this other advertisement? Which advertisement seems to have had the bigger effect on customer purchases?

56. Cooper Realty is a small real estate company located in Albany, New York, specializing primarily in residential listings. They recently became interested in determining the likelihood of one of their listings being sold within a certain number of days. An analysis of company sales of 800 homes in previous years produced the following data.

		Days Listed Until Sold			
		Under 30	31–90	Over 90	Total
	Under $150,000	50	40	10	100
Initial Asking Price	**$150,000–$199,999**	20	150	80	250
	$200,000–$250,000	20	280	100	400
	Over $250,000	10	30	10	50
	Total	100	500	200	800

a. If A is defined as the event that a home is listed for more than 90 days before being sold, estimate the probability of A.

b. If B is defined as the event that the initial asking price is under \$150,000, estimate the probability of B.

c. What is the probability of $A \cap B$?

d. Assuming that a contract was just signed to list a home with an initial asking price of less than \$150,000, what is the probability that the home will take Cooper Realty more than 90 days to sell?

e. Are events A and B independent?

57. A company studied the number of lost-time accidents occurring at its Brownsville, Texas, plant. Historical records show that 6% of the employees suffered lost-time accidents last year. Management believes that a special safety program will reduce such accidents to 5% during the current year. In addition, it estimates that 15% of employees who had lost-time accidents last year will experience a lost-time accident during the current year.

a. What percentage of the employees will experience lost-time accidents in both years?

b. What percentage of the employees will suffer at least one lost-time accident over the two-year period?

58. The Dallas IRS auditing staff, concerned with identifying potentially fraudulent tax returns, believes that the probability of finding a fraudulent return given that the return contains deductions for contributions exceeding the IRS standard is .20. Given that the deductions for contributions do not exceed the IRS standard, the probability of a fraudulent return decreases to .02. If 8% of all returns exceed the IRS standard for deductions due to contributions, what is the best estimate of the percentage of fraudulent returns?

59. An oil company purchased an option on land in Alaska. Preliminary geologic studies assigned the following prior probabilities.

$$P(\text{high-quality oil}) = .50$$
$$P(\text{medium-quality oil}) = .20$$
$$P(\text{no oil}) = .30$$

a. What is the probability of finding oil?

b. After 200 feet of drilling on the first well, a soil test is taken. The probabilities of finding the particular type of soil identified by the test follow.

$$P(\text{soil} \mid \text{high-quality oil}) = .20$$
$$P(\text{soil} \mid \text{medium-quality oil}) = .80$$
$$P(\text{soil} \mid \text{no oil}) = .20$$

How should the firm interpret the soil test? What are the revised probabilities, and what is the new probability of finding oil?

60. Companies that do business over the Internet can often obtain probability information about Web site visitors from previous Web sites visited. The article "Internet Marketing" (*Interfaces,* March/April 2001) described how clickstream data on Web sites visited could be used in conjunction with a Bayesian updating scheme to determine the gender of a Web site visitor. Par Fore created a Web site to market golf equipment and apparel. Management would like a certain offer to appear for female visitors and a different offer to appear for male visitors. From a sample of past Web site visits, management learned that 60% of the visitors to ParFore.com are male and 40% are female.

a. What is the prior probability that the next visitor to the Web site will be female?

b. Suppose you know that the current visitor to ParFore.com previously visited the Dillard's Web site, and that women are three times as likely to visit the Dillard's Web site as men. What is the revised probability that the current visitor to ParFore.com is female? Should you display the offer that appeals more to female visitors or the one that appeals more to male visitors?

Case Problem   # Hamilton County Judges

Hamilton County judges try thousands of cases each year. In an overwhelming majority of the cases disposed, the verdict stands as rendered. However, some cases are appealed, and of those appealed, some of the cases are reversed. Kristen DelGuzzi of *The Cincinnati Enquirer* conducted a study of cases handled by Hamilton County judges over a three-year period. Shown in Table 4.8 are the results for 182,908 cases handled (disposed) by 38 judges in Common Pleas Court, Domestic Relations Court, and Municipal Court. Two of the judges (Dinkelacker and Hogan) did not serve in the same court for the entire three-year period.

The purpose of the newspaper's study was to evaluate the performance of the judges. Appeals are often the result of mistakes made by judges, and the newspaper wanted to know which judges were doing a good job and which were making too many mistakes. You are called in to assist in the data analysis. Use your knowledge of probability and conditional probability to help with the ranking of the judges. You also may be able to analyze the likelihood of appeal and reversal for cases handled by different courts.

Managerial Report

Prepare a report with your rankings of the judges. Also, include an analysis of the likelihood of appeal and case reversal in the three courts. At a minimum, your report should include the following:

1. The probability of cases being appealed and reversed in the three different courts.
2. The probability of a case being appealed for each judge.
3. The probability of a case being reversed for each judge.
4. The probability of reversal given an appeal for each judge.
5. Rank the judges within each court. State the criteria you used and provide a rationale for your choice.

TABLE 4.8 TOTAL CASES DISPOSED, APPEALED, AND REVERSED IN HAMILTON COUNTY COURTS

Judge

Common Pleas Court

Judge	Total Cases Disposed	Appealed Cases	Reversed Cases
Fred Cartolano	3,037	137	12
Thomas Crush	3,372	119	10
Patrick Dinkelacker	1,258	44	8
Timothy Hogan	1,954	60	7
Robert Kraft	3,138	127	7
William Mathews	2,264	91	18
William Morrissey	3,032	121	22
Norbert Nadel	2,959	131	20
Arthur Ney, Jr.	3,219	125	14
Richard Niehaus	3,353	137	16
Thomas Nurre	3,000	121	6
John O'Connor	2,969	129	12
Robert Ruehlman	3,205	145	18
J. Howard Sundermann	955	60	10
Ann Marie Tracey	3,141	127	13
Ralph Winkler	3,089	88	6
Total	**43,945**	**1762**	**199**

Domestic Relations Court

Judge	Total Cases Disposed	Appealed Cases	Reversed Cases
Penelope Cunningham	2,729	7	1
Patrick Dinkelacker	6,001	19	4
Deborah Gaines	8,799	48	9
Ronald Panioto	12,970	32	3
Total	**30,499**	**106**	**17**

Municipal Court

Judge	Total Cases Disposed	Appealed Cases	Reversed Cases
Mike Allen	6,149	43	4
Nadine Allen	7,812	34	6
Timothy Black	7,954	41	6
David Davis	7,736	43	5
Leslie Isaiah Gaines	5,282	35	13
Karla Grady	5,253	6	0
Deidra Hair	2,532	5	0
Dennis Helmick	7,900	29	5
Timothy Hogan	2,308	13	2
James Patrick Kenney	2,798	6	1
Joseph Luebbers	4,698	25	8
William Mallory	8,277	38	9
Melba Marsh	8,219	34	7
Beth Mattingly	2,971	13	1
Albert Mestemaker	4,975	28	9
Mark Painter	2,239	7	3
Jack Rosen	7,790	41	13
Mark Schweikert	5,403	33	6
David Stockdale	5,371	22	4
John A. West	2,797	4	2
Total	**108,464**	**500**	**104**

CHAPTER 5

Discrete Probability Distributions

CONTENTS

CITIBANK*
LONG ISLAND CITY, NEW YORK

Citibank, a division of Citigroup, makes available a wide range of financial services, including checking and savings accounts, loans and mortgages, insurance, and investment services, within the framework of a unique strategy for delivering those services called Citibanking. Citibanking entails a consistent brand identity all over the world, consistent product offerings, and high-level customer service. Citibanking lets you manage your money anytime, anywhere, anyway you choose. Whether you need to save for the future or borrow for today, you can do it all at Citibank.

Citibanking's automatic teller machines (ATMs) located in Citicard Banking Centers (CBCs) let customers do all their banking in one place with the touch of a finger, 24 hours a day, 7 days a week. More than 150 different banking functions from deposits to managing investments can be performed with ease. Citibanking ATMs are so much more than just cash machines that customers today use them for 80% of their transactions.

Each Citibank CBC operates as a waiting line system with randomly arriving customers seeking service at one of the ATMs. If all ATMs are busy, the arriving customers wait in line. Periodic CBC capacity studies are used to analyze customer waiting times and to determine whether additional ATMs are needed.

Data collected by Citibank showed that customer arrivals were random and followed a probability distribution known as the Poisson distribution. Using the Poisson distribution, Citibank can compute probabilities for the number of customers arriving at a CBC during any time period and make decisions concerning the number of ATMs needed. For example, let x = the num-

A Citibank ATM in Manhattan. © PhotoDisc/Getty Images.

ber of customers arriving during a one-minute period. Assuming that a particular CBC has a mean arrival rate of two customers per minute, the following table shows the probabilities for the number of customers arriving during a one-minute period.

x	Probability
0	.1353
1	.2707
2	.2707
3	.1804
4	.0902
5 or more	.0527

Discrete probability distributions, such as the one used by Citibank, are the topic of this chapter. In addition to the Poisson distribution, you will learn about the binomial and hypergeometric distributions and how they can be used to provide helpful probability information.

---

*The authors are indebted to Ms. Stacey Karter, Citibank, for providing this Statistics in Practice.

In this chapter we continue the study of probability by introducing the concepts of random variables and probability distributions. The focus of this chapter is discrete probability distributions. Three special discrete probability distributions—the binomial, Poisson, and hypergeometric—are covered.

5.1 Random Variables

In Chapter 4 we defined the concept of an experiment and its associated experimental outcomes. A random variable provides a means for describing experimental outcomes using numerical values. Random variables must assume numerical values.

> **RANDOM VARIABLE**
>
> A **random variable** is a numerical description of the outcome of an experiment.

Random variables must assume numerical values.

In effect, a random variable associates a numerical value with each possible experimental outcome. The particular numerical value of the random variable depends on the outcome of the experiment. A random variable can be classified as being either *discrete* or *continuous* depending on the numerical values it assumes.

Discrete Random Variables

A random variable that may assume either a finite number of values or an infinite sequence of values such as 0, 1, 2, . . . is referred to as a **discrete random variable**. For example, consider the experiment of an accountant taking the certified public accountant (CPA) examination. The examination has four parts. We can define a random variable as $x =$ the number of parts of the CPA examination passed. It is a discrete random variable because it may assume the finite number of values 0, 1, 2, 3, or 4.

As another example of a discrete random variable, consider the experiment of cars arriving at a tollbooth. The random variable of interest is $x =$ the number of cars arriving during a one-day period. The possible values for x come from the sequence of integers 0, 1, 2, and so on. Hence, x is a discrete random variable assuming one of the values in this infinite sequence.

Although the outcomes of many experiments can naturally be described by numerical values, others cannot. For example, a survey question might ask an individual to recall the message in a recent television commercial. This experiment would have two possible outcomes: the individual cannot recall the message and the individual can recall the message. We can still describe these experimental outcomes numerically by defining the discrete random variable x as follows: let $x = 0$ if the individual cannot recall the message and $x = 1$ if the individual can recall the message. The numerical values for this random variable are arbitrary (we could use 5 and 10), but they are acceptable in terms of the definition of a random variable—namely, x is a random variable because it provides a numerical description of the outcome of the experiment.

Table 5.1 provides some additional examples of discrete random variables. Note that in each example the discrete random variable assumes a finite number of values or an infinite sequence of values such as 0, 1, 2, ... These types of discrete random variables are discussed in detail in this chapter.

TABLE 5.1   EXAMPLES OF DISCRETE RANDOM VARIABLES

Experiment	Random Variable (x)	Possible Values for the Random Variable
Contact five customers	Number of customers who place an order	0, 1, 2, 3, 4, 5
Inspect a shipment of 50 radios	Number of defective radios	0, 1, 2, $\cdots$, 49, 50
Operate a restaurant for one day	Number of customers	0, 1, 2, 3, $\cdots$
Sell an automobile	Gender of the customer	0 if male; 1 if female

Continuous Random Variables

A random variable that may assume any numerical value in an interval or collection of intervals is called a **continuous random variable**. Experimental outcomes based on measurement scales such as time, weight, distance, and temperature can be described by continuous random variables. For example, consider an experiment of monitoring incoming telephone calls to the claims office of a major insurance company. Suppose the random variable of interest is x = the time between consecutive incoming calls in minutes. This random variable may assume any value in the interval $x \geq 0$. Actually, an infinite number of values are possible for x, including values such as 1.26 minutes, 2.751 minutes, 4.3333 minutes, and so on. As another example, consider a 90-mile section of interstate highway I-75 north of Atlanta, Georgia. For an emergency ambulance service located in Atlanta, we might define the random variable as x = number of miles to the location of the next traffic accident along this section of I-75. In this case, x would be a continuous random variable assuming any value in the interval $0 \leq x \leq 90$. Additional examples of continuous random variables are listed in Table 5.2. Note that each example describes a random variable that may assume any value in an interval of values. Continuous random variables and their probability distributions will be the topic of Chapter 6.

TABLE 5.2 EXAMPLES OF CONTINUOUS RANDOM VARIABLES

Experiment	Random Variable (x)	Possible Values for the Random Variable
Operate a bank	Time between customer arrivals in minutes	$x \geq 0$
Fill a soft drink can (max = 12.1 ounces)	Number of ounces	$0 \leq x \leq 12.1$
Construct a new library	Percentage of project complete after six months	$0 \leq x \leq 100$
Test a new chemical process	Temperature when the desired reaction takes place (min 150° F; max 212° F)	$150 \leq x \leq 212$

NOTES AND COMMENTS

One way to determine whether a random variable is discrete or continuous is to think of the values of the random variable as points on a line segment. Choose two points representing values of the random variable. If the entire line segment between the two points also represents possible values for the random variable, then the random variable is continuous.

Exercises

Methods

1. Consider the experiment of tossing a coin twice.
    a. List the experimental outcomes.
    b. Define a random variable that represents the number of heads occurring on the two tosses.
    c. Show what value the random variable would assume for each of the experimental outcomes.
    d. Is this random variable discrete or continuous?

2. Consider the experiment of a worker assembling a product.
    a. Define a random variable that represents the time in minutes required to assemble the product.
    b. What values may the random variable assume?
    c. Is the random variable discrete or continuous?

Applications

3. Three students scheduled interviews for summer employment at the Brookwood Institute. In each case the interview results in either an offer for a position or no offer. Experimental outcomes are defined in terms of the results of the three interviews.
    a. List the experimental outcomes.
    b. Define a random variable that represents the number of offers made. Is the random variable continuous?
    c. Show the value of the random variable for each of the experimental outcomes.

4. Suppose we know home mortgage rates for 12 Florida lending institutions. Assume that the random variable of interest is the number of lending institutions in this group that offers a 30-year fixed rate of 8.5% or less. What values may this random variable assume?

5. To perform a certain type of blood analysis, lab technicians must perform two procedures. The first procedure requires either one or two separate steps, and the second procedure requires either one, two, or three steps.
    a. List the experimental outcomes associated with performing the blood analysis.
    b. If the random variable of interest is the total number of steps required to do the complete analysis (both procedures), show what value the random variable will assume for each of the experimental outcomes.

6. Listed is a series of experiments and associated random variables. In each case, identify the values that the random variable can assume and state whether the random variable is discrete or continuous.

Experiment	Random Variable (x)
a. Take a 20-question examination	Number of questions answered correctly
b. Observe cars arriving at a tollbooth for 1 hour	Number of cars arriving at tollbooth
c. Audit 50 tax returns	Number of returns containing errors
d. Observe an employee's work	Number of nonproductive hours in an eight-hour workday
e. Weigh a shipment of goods	Number of pounds

5.2 Discrete Probability Distributions

The **probability distribution** for a random variable describes how probabilities are distributed over the values of the random variable. For a discrete random variable x, the probability distribution is defined by a **probability function**, denoted by $f(x)$. The probability function provides the probability for each value of the random variable.

As an illustration of a discrete random variable and its probability distribution, consider the sales of automobiles at DiCarlo Motors in Saratoga, New York. Over the past 300 days of operation, sales data show 54 days with no automobiles sold, 117 days with 1 automobile sold, 72 days with 2 automobiles sold, 42 days with 3 automobiles sold, 12 days with 4 automobiles sold, and 3 days with 5 automobiles sold. Suppose we consider the experiment of selecting a day of operation at DiCarlo Motors and define the random variable of interest as x = the number of automobiles sold during a day. From historical data, we know

x is a discrete random variable that can assume the values 0, 1, 2, 3, 4, or 5. In probability function notation, $f(0)$ is the probability of 0 automobiles sold, $f(1)$ is the probability of 1 automobile sold, and so on. Because historical data show 54 of 300 days with 0 automobiles sold, we assign the value $54/300 = .18$ to $f(0)$, indicating that the probability of 0 automobiles being sold during a day is .18. Similarly, because 117 of 300 days had 1 automobile sold, we assign the value $117/300 = .39$ to $f(1)$, indicating that the probability of exactly 1 automobile being sold during a day is .39. Continuing in this way for the other values of the random variable, we compute the values for $f(2), f(3), f(4),$ and $f(5)$ as shown in Table 5.3, the probability distribution for the number of automobiles sold during a day at DiCarlo Motors.

A primary advantage of defining a random variable and its probability distribution is that once the probability distribution is known, it is relatively easy to determine the probability of a variety of events that may be of interest to a decision maker. For example, using the probability distribution for DiCarlo Motors as shown in Table 5.3, we see that the most probable number of automobiles sold during a day is 1 with a probability of $f(1) = .39$. In addition, there is an $f(3) + f(4) + f(5) = .14 + .04 + .01 = .19$ probability of selling three or more automobiles during a day. These probabilities, plus others the decision maker may ask about, provide information that can help the decision maker understand the process of selling automobiles at DiCarlo Motors.

In the development of a probability function for any discrete random variable, the following two conditions must be satisfied.

These conditions are the analogs to the two basic requirements for assigning probabilities to experimental outcomes presented in Chapter 4.

REQUIRED CONDITIONS FOR A DISCRETE PROBABILITY FUNCTION

$$f(x) \geq 0 \qquad \text{(5.1)}$$
$$\Sigma f(x) = 1 \qquad \text{(5.2)}$$

Table 5.3 shows that the probabilities for the random variable x satisfy equation (5.1); $f(x)$ is greater than or equal to 0 for all values of x. In addition, because the probabilities sum to 1, equation (5.2) is satisfied. Thus, the DiCarlo Motors probability function is a valid discrete probability function.

We can also present probability distributions graphically. In Figure 5.1 the values of the random variable x for DiCarlo Motors are shown on the horizontal axis and the probability associated with these values is shown on the vertical axis.

In addition to tables and graphs, a formula that gives the probability function, $f(x)$, for every value of x is often used to describe probability distributions. The simplest example of

TABLE 5.3   PROBABILITY DISTRIBUTION FOR THE NUMBER OF AUTOMOBILES SOLD DURING A DAY AT DICARLO MOTORS

x	$f(x)$
0	.18
1	.39
2	.24
3	.14
4	.04
5	.01
Total	1.00

FIGURE 5.1   GRAPHICAL REPRESENTATION OF THE PROBABILITY DISTRIBUTION
FOR THE NUMBER OF AUTOMOBILES SOLD DURING A DAY AT
DICARLO MOTORS

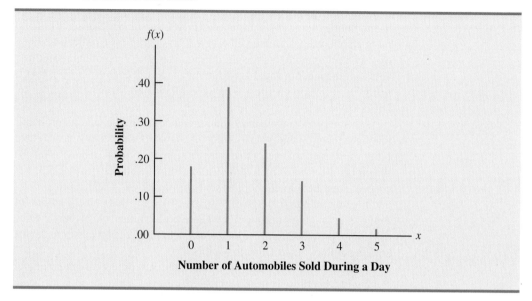

a discrete probability distribution given by a formula is the **discrete uniform probability distribution**. Its probability function is defined by equation (5.3).

DISCRETE UNIFORM PROBABILITY FUNCTION

$$f(x) = 1/n \qquad (5.3)$$

where

n = the number of values the random variable may assume

For example, suppose that for the experiment of rolling a die we define the random variable x to be the number of dots on the upward face. For this experiment, $n = 6$ values are possible for the random variable; $x = 1, 2, 3, 4, 5, 6$. Thus, the probability function for this discrete uniform random variable is

$$f(x) = 1/6 \qquad x = 1, 2, 3, 4, 5, 6$$

The possible values of the random variable and the associated probabilities are shown.

x	$f(x)$
1	1/6
2	1/6
3	1/6
4	1/6
5	1/6
6	1/6

As another example, consider the random variable x with the following discrete probability distribution.

x	$f(x)$
1	1/10
2	2/10
3	3/10
4	4/10

This probability distribution can be defined by the formula

$$f(x) = \frac{x}{10} \qquad \text{for } x = 1, 2, 3, \text{ or } 4$$

Evaluating $f(x)$ for a given value of the random variable will provide the associated probability. For example, using the preceding probability function, we see that $f(2) = 2/10$ provides the probability that the random variable assumes a value of 2.

The more widely used discrete probability distributions generally are specified by formulas. Three important cases are the binomial, Poisson, and hypergeometric distributions; these distributions are discussed later in the chapter.

Exercises

Methods

7.   The probability distribution for the random variable x follows.

x	$f(x)$
20	.20
25	.15
30	.25
35	.40

    a.   Is this probability distribution valid? Explain.
    b.   What is the probability that $x = 30$?
    c.   What is the probability that x is less than or equal to 25?
    d.   What is the probability that x is greater than 30?

Applications

8.   The following data were collected by counting the number of operating rooms in use at Tampa General Hospital over a 20-day period: On 3 of the days only one operating room was used, on 5 of the days two were used, on 8 of the days three were used, and on 4 days all four of the hospital's operating rooms were used.
    a.   Use the relative frequency approach to construct a probability distribution for the number of operating rooms in use on any given day.
    b.   Draw a graph of the probability distribution.
    c.   Show that your probability distribution satisfies the required conditions for a valid discrete probability distribution.

9. Nationally, 38% of fourth-graders cannot read an age-appropriate book. The following data show the number of children, by age, identified as learning disabled under special education. Most of these children have reading problems that should be identified and corrected before third grade. Current federal law prohibits most children from receiving extra help from special education programs until they fall behind by approximately two years' worth of learning, and that typically means third grade or later (*USA Today*, September 6, 2001).

Age	Number of Children
6	37,369
7	87,436
8	160,840
9	239,719
10	286,719
11	306,533
12	310,787
13	302,604
14	289,168

Suppose that we want to select a sample of children identified as learning disabled under special education for a program designed to improve reading ability. Let x be a random variable indicating the age of one randomly selected child.

a. Use the data to develop a probability distribution for x. Specify the values for the random variable and the corresponding values for the probability function $f(x)$.

b. Draw a graph of the probability distribution.

c. Show that the probability distribution satisfies equations (5.1) and (5.2).

10. Table 5.4 shows the percent frequency distributions of job satisfaction scores for a sample of information systems (IS) senior executives and IS middle managers. The scores range from a low of 1 (very dissatisfied) to a high of 5 (very satisfied).

TABLE 5.4 PERCENT FREQUENCY DISTRIBUTION OF JOB SATISFACTION SCORES FOR INFORMATION SYSTEMS EXECUTIVES AND MIDDLE MANAGERS

Job Satisfaction Score	IS Senior Executives (%)	IS Middle Managers (%)
1	5	4
2	9	10
3	3	12
4	42	46
5	41	28

a. Develop a probability distribution for the job satisfaction score of a senior executive.

b. Develop a probability distribution for the job satisfaction score of a middle manager.

c. What is the probability a senior executive will report a job satisfaction score of 4 or 5?

d. What is the probability a middle manager is very satisfied?

e. Compare the overall job satisfaction of senior executives and middle managers.

11. A technician services mailing machines at companies in the Phoenix area. Depending on the type of malfunction, the service call can take 1, 2, 3, or 4 hours. The different types of malfunctions occur at about the same frequency.

Thus, the properties of a binomial experiment are satisfied. The random variable of interest is x = the number of heads appearing in the five trials. In this case, x can assume the values of 0, 1, 2, 3, 4, or 5.

As another example, consider an insurance salesperson who visits 10 randomly selected families. The outcome associated with each visit is classified as a success if the family purchases an insurance policy and a failure if the family does not. From past experience, the salesperson knows the probability that a randomly selected family will purchase an insurance policy is .10. Checking the properties of a binomial experiment, we observe that:

1. The experiment consists of 10 identical trials; each trial involves contacting one family.
2. Two outcomes are possible on each trial: the family purchases a policy (success) or the family does not purchase a policy (failure).
3. The probabilities of a purchase and a nonpurchase are assumed to be the same for each sales call, with $p = .10$ and $1 - p = .90$.
4. The trials are independent because the families are randomly selected.

Because the four assumptions are satisfied, this example is a binomial experiment. The random variable of interest is the number of sales obtained in contacting the 10 families. In this case, x can assume the values of 0, 1, 2, 3, 4, 5, 6, 7, 8, 9, and 10.

Property 3 of the binomial experiment is called the *stationarity assumption* and is sometimes confused with property 4, independence of trials. To see how they differ, consider again the case of the salesperson calling on families to sell insurance policies. If, as the day wore on, the salesperson got tired and lost enthusiasm, the probability of success (selling a policy) might drop to .05, for example, by the tenth call. In such a case, property 3 (stationarity) would not be satisfied, and we would not have a binomial experiment. Even if property 4 held—that is, the purchase decisions of each family were made independently—it would not be a binomial experiment if property 3 was not satisfied.

In applications involving binomial experiments, a special mathematical formula, called the *binomial probability function,* can be used to compute the probability of x successes in the n trials. Using probability concepts introduced in Chapter 4, we will show in the context of an illustrative problem how the formula can be developed.

Martin Clothing Store Problem

Let us consider the purchase decisions of the next three customers who enter the Martin Clothing Store. On the basis of past experience, the store manager estimates the probability that any one customer will make a purchase is .30. What is the probability that two of the next three customers will make a purchase?

Using a tree diagram (Figure 5.4), we can see that the experiment of observing the three customers each making a purchase decision has eight possible outcomes. Using S to denote success (a purchase) and F to denote failure (no purchase), we are interested in experimental outcomes involving two successes in the three trials (purchase decisions). Next, let us verify that the experiment involving the sequence of three purchase decisions can be viewed as a binomial experiment. Checking the four requirements for a binomial experiment, we note that:

1. The experiment can be described as a sequence of three identical trials, one trial for each of the three customers who will enter the store.
2. Two outcomes—the customer makes a purchase (success) or the customer does not make a purchase (failure)—are possible for each trial.
3. The probability that the customer will make a purchase (.30) or will not make a purchase (.70) is assumed to be the same for all customers.
4. The purchase decision of each customer is independent of the decisions of the other customers.

FIGURE 5.4   TREE DIAGRAM FOR THE MARTIN CLOTHING STORE PROBLEM

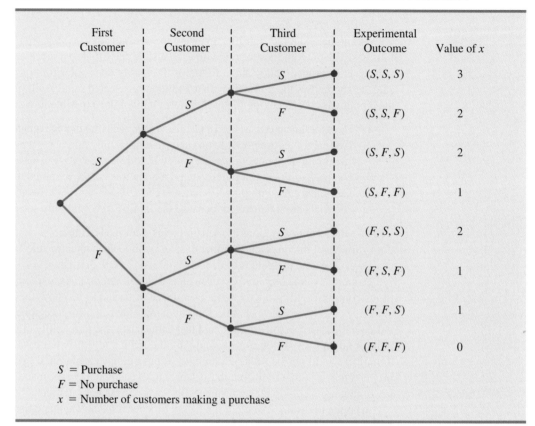

First Customer	Second Customer	Third Customer	Experimental Outcome	Value of x
		S	(S, S, S)	3
S	S	F	(S, S, F)	2
	F	S	(S, F, S)	2
		F	(S, F, F)	1
		S	(F, S, S)	2
F	S	F	(F, S, F)	1
	F	S	(F, F, S)	1
		F	(F, F, F)	0

S = Purchase
F = No purchase
x = Number of customers making a purchase

Hence, the properties of a binomial experiment are present.

The number of experimental outcomes resulting in exactly x successes in n trials can be computed using the following formula.*

> **NUMBER OF EXPERIMENTAL OUTCOMES PROVIDING EXACTLY x SUCCESSES IN n TRIALS**
>
> $$\binom{n}{x} = \frac{n!}{x!(n - x)!} \tag{5.6}$$
>
> where
>
> $$n! = n(n - 1)(n - 2) \cdots (2)(1)$$
>
> and, by definition,
>
> $$0! = 1$$

Now let us return to the Martin Clothing Store experiment involving three customer purchase decisions. Equation (5.6) can be used to determine the number of experimental

---

*This formula, introduced in Chapter 4, determines the number of combinations of n objects selected x at a time. For the binomial experiment, this combinatorial formula provides the number of experimental outcomes (sequences of n trials) resulting in x successes.

outcomes involving two purchases; that is, the number of ways of obtaining $x = 2$ successes in the $n = 3$ trials. From equation (5.6) we have

$$\binom{n}{x} = \binom{3}{2} = \frac{3!}{2!(3-2)!} = \frac{(3)(2)(1)}{(2)(1)(1)} = \frac{6}{2} = 3$$

Equation (5.6) shows that three of the experimental outcomes yield two successes. From Figure 5.4 we see these three outcomes are denoted by (S, S, F), (S, F, S), and (F, S, S).

Using equation (5.6) to determine how many experimental outcomes have three successes (purchases) in the three trials, we obtain

$$\binom{n}{x} = \binom{3}{3} = \frac{3!}{3!(3-3)!} = \frac{3!}{3!0!} = \frac{(3)(2)(1)}{3(2)(1)(1)} = \frac{6}{6} = 1$$

From Figure 5.4 we see that the one experimental outcome with three successes is identified by (S, S, S).

We know that equation (5.6) can be used to determine the number of experimental outcomes that result in x successes. If we are to determine the probability of x successes in n trials, however, we must also know the probability associated with each of these experimental outcomes. Because the trials of a binomial experiment are independent, we can simply multiply the probabilities associated with each trial outcome to find the probability of a particular sequence of successes and failures.

The probability of purchases by the first two customers and no purchase by the third customer, denoted (S, S, F), is given by

$$pp(1 - p)$$

With a .30 probability of a purchase on any one trial, the probability of a purchase on the first two trials and no purchase on the third is given by

$$(.30)(.30)(.70) = (.30)^2(.70) = .063$$

Two other experimental outcomes also result in two successes and one failure. The probabilities for all three experimental outcomes involving two successes follow.

| Trial Outcomes | | | | Probability of |
1st Customer	2nd Customer	3rd Customer	Experimental Outcome	Experimental Outcome
Purchase	Purchase	No purchase	(S, S, F)	$pp(1 - p) = p^2(1 - p)$ $= (.30)^2(.70) = .063$
Purchase	No purchase	Purchase	(S, F, S)	$p(1 - p)p = p^2(1 - p)$ $= (.30)^2(.70) = .063$
No purchase	Purchase	Purchase	(F, S, S)	$(1 - p)pp = p^2(1 - p)$ $= (.30)^2(.70) = .063$

Observe that all three experimental outcomes with two successes have exactly the same probability. This observation holds in general. In any binomial experiment, all sequences of trial outcomes yielding x successes in n trials have the *same probability* of occurrence. The probability of each sequence of trials yielding x successes in n trials follows.

$$\text{Probability of a particular sequence of trial outcomes} = p^x(1 - p)^{(n-x)} \tag{5.7}$$
with x successes in n trials

For the Martin Clothing Store, this formula shows that any experimental outcome with two successes has a probability of $p^2(1 - p)^{(3-2)} = p^2(1 - p)^1 = (.30)^2(.70)^1 = .063$.

Because equation (5.6) shows the number of outcomes in a binomial experiment with x successes and equation (5.7) gives the probability for each sequence involving x successes, we combine equations (5.6) and (5.7) to obtain the following **binomial probability function**.

BINOMIAL PROBABILITY FUNCTION

$$f(x) = \binom{n}{x} p^x (1 - p)^{(n-x)} \tag{5.8}$$

where

$$f(x) = \text{the probability of } x \text{ successes in } n \text{ trials}$$
$$n = \text{the number of trials}$$
$$\binom{n}{x} = \frac{n!}{x!(n - x)!}$$
$$p = \text{the probability of a success on any one trial}$$
$$1 - p = \text{the probability of a failure on any one trial}$$

In the Martin Clothing Store example, let us compute the probability that no customer makes a purchase, exactly one customer makes a purchase, exactly two customers make a purchase, and all three customers make a purchase. The calculations are summarized in Table 5.7, which gives the probability distribution of the number of customers making a purchase. Figure 5.5 is a graph of this probability distribution.

The binomial probability function can be applied to *any* binomial experiment. If we are satisfied that a situation demonstrates the properties of a binomial experiment and if we know the values of n and p, we can use equation (5.8) to compute the probability of x successes in the n trials.

TABLE 5.7   PROBABILITY DISTRIBUTION FOR THE NUMBER OF CUSTOMERS MAKING A PURCHASE

x	$f(x)$
0	$\dfrac{3!}{0!3!}(.30)^0(.70)^3 = .343$
1	$\dfrac{3!}{1!2!}(.30)^1(.70)^2 = .441$
2	$\dfrac{3!}{2!1!}(.30)^2(.70)^1 = .189$
3	$\dfrac{3!}{3!0!}(.30)^3(.70)^0 = \underline{.027}$
	1.000

FIGURE 5.5   GRAPHICAL REPRESENTATION OF THE PROBABILITY DISTRIBUTION
FOR THE NUMBER OF CUSTOMERS MAKING A PURCHASE

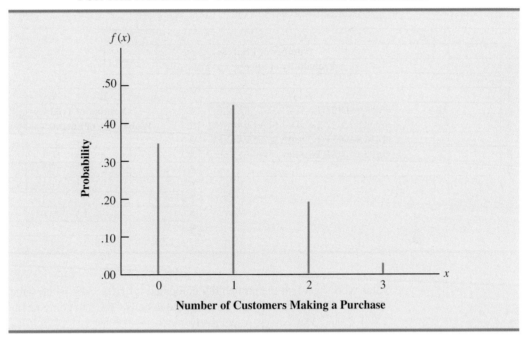

Number of Customers Making a Purchase

If we consider variations of the Martin experiment, such as 10 customers rather than three entering the store, the binomial probability function given by equation (5.8) is still applicable. Suppose we have a binomial experiment with $n = 10$, $x = 4$, and $p = .30$. The probability of making exactly four sales to 10 customers entering the store is

$$f(4) = \frac{10!}{4!6!} (.30)^4(.70)^6 = .2001$$

Using Excel to Compute Binomial Probabilities

For many probability functions that can be specified as formulas, Excel provides functions for computing probabilities and cumulative probabilities. In this section, we show how Excel's BINOMDIST function can be used to compute binomial probabilities and cumulative binomial probabilities. We begin by showing how to compute the binomial probabilities for the Martin Clothing Store example shown in Table 5.7. Refer to Figure 5.6 as we describe the tasks involved. The formula worksheet is in the background; the value worksheet is in the foreground.

Enter Data: In order to compute a binomial probability we must know the number of trials (n), the probability of success (p), and the value of the random variable (x). For the Martin Clothing Store example, the number of trials is 3; this value has been entered into cell D1. The probability of success is .3; this value has been entered into cell D2. Because we want to compute the probability for $x = 0$, 1, 2, and 3, these values were entered into cells B5:B8.

Enter Functions and Formulas: The BINOMDIST function has four inputs: the first is the value of x, the second is the value of n, the third is the value of p, and the fourth is FALSE or TRUE. We choose FALSE for the fourth input if a probability is desired and TRUE if a cumulative probability is desired. The formula =BINOMDIST(B5,$D$1,$D$2,FALSE) has been entered into cell C5 to compute the probability of 0 successes in 3 trials. Note in the

FIGURE 5.6   EXCEL WORKSHEET FOR COMPUTING BINOMIAL PROBABILITIES OF NUMBER OF CUSTOMERS MAKING A PURCHASE

	A	B	C	D	E
1			Number of Trials (*n*)	3	
2			Probability of Success (*p*)	0.3	
3					
4		*x*	*f*(*x*)		
5		0	=BINOMDIST(B5,$D$1,$D$2,FALSE)		
6		1	=BINOMDIST(B6,$D$1,$D$2,FALSE)		
7		2	=BINOMDIST(B7,$D$1,$D$2,FALSE)		
8		3	=BINOMDIST(B8,$D$1,$D$2,FALSE)		
9					

	A	B	C	D	E
1			Number of Trials (*n*)	3	
2			Probability of Success (*p*)	0.3	
3					
4			*x*	*f*(*x*)	
5			0	0.343	
6			1	0.441	
7			2	0.189	
8			3	0.027	
9					

value worksheet that the probability computed for $f(0)$, .343, is the same as that shown in Table 5.7. The formula in cell C5 is copied to cells C6:C8 to compute the probabilities for $x = 1$, 2, and 3 successes, respectively.

We can also compute cumulative probabilities using Excel's BINOMDIST function. To illustrate, let us consider the case of 10 customers entering the Martin Clothing Store and compute the probabilities and cumulative probabilities for the number of customers making a purchase. The cumulative probability for $x = 1$ is the probability of 1 or fewer purchases, the cumulative probability for $x = 2$ is the probability of 2 or fewer purchases, and so on. So, the cumulative probability for $x = 10$ is 1. Refer to Figure 5.7 as we describe the tasks involved in computing these cumulative probabilities. The formula worksheet is in the background; the value worksheet is in the foreground.

FIGURE 5.7   EXCEL WORKSHEET FOR COMPUTING PROBABILITIES AND CUMULATIVE PROBABILITIES FOR NUMBER OF PURCHASES WITH 10 CUSTOMERS

	A	B	C	D	E
1			Number of Trials (*n*)	10	
2			Probability of Success (*p*)	0.3	
3					
4		*x*	*f*(*x*)	Cum Prob	
5		0	=BINOMDIST(B5,$D$1,$D$2,FALSE)	=BINOMDIST(B5,$D$1,$D$2,TRUE)	
6		1	=BINOMDIST(B6,$D$1,$D$2,FALSE)	=BINOMDIST(B6,$D$1,$D$2,TRUE)	
7		2	=BINOMDIST(B7,$D$1,$D$2,FALSE)	=BINOMDIST(B7,$D$1,$D$2,TRUE)	
8		3	=BINOMDIST(B8,$D$1,$D$2,FALSE)	=BINOMDIST(B8,$D$1,$D$2,TRUE)	
9		4	=BINOMDIST(B9,$D$1,$D$2,FALSE)	=BINOMDIST(B9,$D$1,$D$2,TRUE)	
10		5	=BINOMDIST(B10,$D$1,$D$2,FALSE)	=BINOMDIST(B10,$D$1,$D$2,TRUE)	
11		6	=BINOMDIST(B11,$D$1,$D$2,FALSE)	=BINOMDIST(B11,$D$1,$D$2,TRUE)	
12		7	=BINOMDIST(B12,$D$1,$D$2,FALSE)	=BINOMDIST(B12,$D$1,$D$2,TRUE)	
13		8	=BINOMDIST(B13,$D$1,$D$2,FALSE)	=BINOMDIST(B13,$D$1,$D$2,TRUE)	
14		9	=BINOMDIST(B14,$D$1,$D$2,FALSE)	=BINOMDIST(B14,$D$1,$D$2,TRUE)	
15		10	=BINOMDIST(B15,$D$1,$D$2,FALSE)	=BINOMDIST(B15,$D$1,$D$2,TRUE)	
16					

	A	B	C	D	E
1			Number of Trials (*n*)	10	
2			Probability of Success (*p*)	0.3	
3					
4			*x*	*f*(*x*)	Cum Prob
5			0	0.0282	0.0282
6			1	0.1211	0.1493
7			2	0.2335	0.3828
8			3	0.2668	0.6496
9			4	0.2001	0.8497
10			5	0.1029	0.9527
11			6	0.0368	0.9894
12			7	0.0090	0.9984
13			8	0.0014	0.9999
14			9	0.0001	1.0000
15			10	0.0000	1.0000
16					

Enter Data: We entered the number of trials (10) into cell D1, the probability of success (.3) into cell D2, and the values for the random variable into cells B5:B15.

Enter Functions and Formulas: The binomial probabilities for each value of the random variable are computed in column C and the cumulative probabilities are computed in column D. We entered the formula =BINOMDIST(B5,$D$1,$D$2,FALSE) into cell C5 to compute the probability of 0 successes in 10 trials. Note that we used FALSE as the fourth input in the BINOMDIST function. The probability (.0282) is shown in cell C5 of the value worksheet. The formula in cell C5 is simply copied to cells C6:C15 to compute the remaining probabilities.

To compute the cumulative probabilities we start by entering the formula =BINOMDIST (B5,$D$1,$D$2,TRUE) into cell D5. Note that we used TRUE as the fourth input in the BINOMDIST function. The formula in cell D5 is then copied to cells D6:D15 to compute the remaining cumulative probabilities. In cell D5 of the value worksheet we see that the cumulative probability for $x = 0$ is the same as the probability for $x = 0$. Each of the remaining cumulative probabilities is the sum of the previous cumulative probability and the individual probability in column C. For instance, the cumulative probability for $x = 4$ is given by $.6496 + .2001 = .8497$. Note also that the cumulative probability for $x = 10$ is 1. The cumulative probability of $x = 9$ is also 1 because the probability of $x = 10$ is zero (to four decimal places of accuracy).

Expected Value and Variance for the Binomial Probability Distribution

In Section 5.3 we provided formulas for computing the expected value and variance of a discrete random variable. In the special case where the random variable has a binomial probability distribution with a known number of trials n and a known probability of success p, the general formulas for the expected value and variance can be simplified. The results follow.

EXPECTED VALUE AND VARIANCE FOR THE BINOMIAL PROBABILITY DISTRIBUTION

$$E(x) = \mu = np \tag{5.9}$$
$$\text{Var}(x) = \sigma^2 = np(1 - p) \tag{5.10}$$

For the Martin Clothing Store problem with three customers, we can use equation (5.9) to compute the expected number of customers who will make a purchase.

$$E(x) = np = 3(.30) = .9$$

Suppose that for the next month the Martin Clothing Store forecasts 1000 customers will enter the store. What is the expected number of customers who will make a purchase? The answer is $\mu = np = (1000)(.3) = 300$. Thus, to increase the expected number of purchases, Martin's must induce more customers to enter the store and/or somehow increase the probability that any individual customer will make a purchase after entering.

For the Martin Clothing Store problem with three customers, we see that the variance and standard deviation for the number of customers who will make a purchase are

The np chart and lot acceptance sampling are quality control procedures that are excellent examples of the use of the binomial distribution. These procedures are discussed in Chapter 14, Statistical Methods for Quality Control.

$$\sigma^2 = np(1 - p) = 3(.3)(.7) = .63$$
$$\sigma = \sqrt{.63} = .79$$

For the next 1000 customers entering the store, the variance and standard deviation for the number of customers who will make a purchase are

$$\sigma^2 = np(1 - p) = 1000(.3)(.7) = 210$$
$$\sigma = \sqrt{210} = 14.49$$

NOTES AND COMMENTS

Statisticians have developed tables that give probabilities and cumulative probabilities for a binomial random variable. These tables can be found in some statistics textbooks. With modern calculators and the capability of the BINOMDIST function in Microsoft Excel, such tables are unnecessary.

Exercises

Methods

25. Consider a binomial experiment with two trials and $p = .4$.
    a. Draw a tree diagram for this experiment (see Figure 5.4).
    b. Compute the probability of one success, $f(1)$.
    c. Compute $f(0)$.
    d. Compute $f(2)$.
    e. Compute the probability of at least one success.
    f. Compute the expected value, variance, and standard deviation.

26. Consider a binomial experiment with $n = 10$ and $p = .10$.
    a. Compute $f(0)$.
    b. Compute $f(2)$.
    c. Compute $P(x \leq 2)$.
    d. Compute $P(x \geq 1)$.
    e. Compute $E(x)$.
    f. Compute $\text{Var}(x)$ and σ.

27. Consider a binomial experiment with $n = 20$ and $p = .70$.
    a. Compute $f(12)$.
    b. Compute $f(16)$.
    c. Compute $P(x \geq 16)$.
    d. Compute $P(x \leq 15)$.
    e. Compute $E(x)$.
    f. Compute $\text{Var}(x)$ and σ.

Applications

28. A Harris Interactive survey for InterContinental Hotels & Resorts asked respondents, "When traveling internationally, do you generally venture out on your own to experience culture, or stick with your tour group and itineraries?" The survey found that 23% of the respondents stick with their tour group (*USA Today*, January 21, 2004).
    a. In a sample of six international travelers, what is the probability that two will stick with their tour group?
    b. In a sample of six international travelers, what is the probability that at least two will stick with their tour group?
    c. In a sample of 10 international travelers, what is the probability that none will stick with their tour group?

29. According to a *BusinessWeek*/Harris poll of 1035 adults, 40% of those surveyed agreed strongly with the proposition that business has too much power over American life (*Business-Week,* September 11, 2000). Assume this percentage is representative of the American population. In a sample of 20 individuals taken from a cross-section of the American population, what is the probability that at least five of these individuals will feel that business has too much power over American life?

SELF test

30. When a new machine is functioning properly, only 3% of the items produced are defective. Assume that we will randomly select two parts produced on the machine and that we are interested in the number of defective parts found.
    a. Describe the conditions under which this situation would be a binomial experiment.
    b. Draw a tree diagram similar to Figure 5.4 showing this problem as a two-trial experiment.
    c. How many experimental outcomes result in exactly one defect being found?
    d. Compute the probabilities associated with finding no defects, exactly one defect, and two defects.

31. Nine percent of undergraduate students carry credit card balances greater than $7000 (*Reader's Digest,* July 2002). Suppose 10 undergraduate students are selected randomly to be interviewed about credit card usage.
    a. Is the selection of 10 students a binomial experiment? Explain.
    b. What is the probability that two of the students will have a credit card balance greater than $7000?
    c. What is the probability that none will have a credit card balance greater than $7000?
    d. What is the probability that at least three will have a credit card balance greater than $7000?

32. Military radar and missile detection systems are designed to warn a country of an enemy attack. A reliability question is whether a detection system will be able to identify an attack and issue a warning. Assume that a particular detection system has a .90 probability of detecting a missile attack. Use the binomial probability distribution to answer the following questions.
    a. What is the probability that a single detection system will detect an attack?
    b. If two detection systems are installed in the same area and operate independently, what is the probability that at least one of the systems will detect the attack?
    c. If three systems are installed, what is the probability that at least one of the systems will detect the attack?
    d. Would you recommend that multiple detection systems be used? Explain.

33. Fifty percent of Americans believed the country was in a recession, even though technically the economy had not shown two straight quarters of negative growth (*BusinessWeek,* July 30, 2001). For a sample of 20 Americans, make the following calculations.
    a. Compute the probability that exactly 12 people believed the country was in a recession.
    b. Compute the probability that no more than five people believed the country was in a recession.
    c. How many people would you expect to say the country was in a recession?
    d. Compute the variance and standard deviation of the number of people who believed the country was in a recession.

34. Forty percent of business travelers carry either a cell phone or a laptop (*USA Today,* September 12, 2000). For a sample of 15 business travelers, make the following calculations.
    a. Compute the probability that three of the travelers carry a cell phone or laptop.
    b. Compute the probability that 12 of the travelers carry neither a cell phone nor a laptop.
    c. Compute the probability that at least three of the travelers carry a cell phone or a laptop.

35. A university found that 20% of its students withdraw without completing the introductory statistics course. Assume that 20 students registered for the course this semester.
    a. Compute the probability that two or fewer will withdraw.
    b. Compute the probability that exactly four will withdraw.
    c. Compute the probability that more than three will withdraw.
    d. Compute the expected number of withdrawals.

36. For the special case of a binomial random variable, we stated that the variance could be computed using the formula $\sigma^2 = np(1 - p)$. For the Martin Clothing Store problem with $n = 3$ and $p = .3$ we found $\sigma^2 = np(1 - p) = 3(.3)(.7) = .63$. Use the general definition of variance for a discrete random variable, equation (5.5), and the probabilities in Table 5.7 to verify that the variance is in fact .63.

37. Seventy-two percent of Americans have online access (*CNBC*, December 3, 2001). In a random sample of 30 people, what is the expected number of persons with online access? What are the variance and standard deviation?

(5.5) Poisson Probability Distribution

The Poisson probability distribution is often used to model random arrivals in waiting line situations.

In this section we consider a discrete random variable that is often useful in estimating the number of occurrences over a specified interval of time or space. For example, the random variable of interest might be the number of arrivals at a car wash in one hour, the number of repairs needed in 10 miles of highway, or the number of leaks in 100 miles of pipeline. If the following two properties are satisfied, the number of occurrences is a random variable described by the **Poisson probability distribution**.

PROPERTIES OF A POISSON EXPERIMENT

1. The probability of an occurrence is the same for any two intervals of equal length.
2. The occurrence or nonoccurrence in any interval is independent of the occurrence or nonoccurrence in any other interval.

The **Poisson probability function** is defined by equation (5.11).

Siméon Poisson taught mathematics at the Ecole Polytechnique in Paris from 1802 to 1808. In 1837, he published a work entitled, "Researches on the Probability of Criminal and Civil Verdicts," which includes a discussion of what later became known as the Poisson distribution.

POISSON PROBABILITY FUNCTION

$$f(x) = \frac{\mu^x e^{-\mu}}{x!}$$

(5.11)

where

$f(x)$ = the probability of x occurrences in an interval

μ = expected value or mean number of occurrences in an interval

$e = 2.71828$

Before we consider a specific example to see how the Poisson distribution can be applied, note that the number of occurrences, x, has no upper limit. It is a discrete random variable that may assume an infinite sequence of values ($x = 0, 1, 2, \ldots$).

An Example Involving Time Intervals

Bell Labs used the Poisson distribution to model the arrival of phone calls.

Suppose that we are interested in the number of arrivals at the drive-up teller window of a bank during a 15-minute period on weekday mornings. If we can assume that the probability of a car arriving is the same for any two time periods of equal length and that the arrival or nonarrival of a car in any time period is independent of the arrival or nonarrival in any other time period, the Poisson probability function is applicable. Suppose these assumptions are satisfied and an analysis of historical data shows that the average number of cars arriving in a 15-minute period of time is 10; in this case, the following probability function applies.

$$f(x) = \frac{10^x e^{-10}}{x!}$$

The random variable here is x = number of cars arriving in any 15-minute period.

If management wanted to know the probability of exactly five arrivals in 15 minutes, we would set $x = 5$ and thus obtain

$$\text{Probability of exactly} \atop \text{5 arrivals in 15 minutes} = f(5) = \frac{10^5 e^{-10}}{5!} = .0378$$

This probability was obtained by using a calculator to evaluate the probability function. Microsoft Excel also provides a function, called POISSON, for computing Poisson probabilities and cumulative probabilities. This function is easier to use when numerous probabilities and cumulative probabilities are desired. We show how to compute these probabilities with Excel at the end of this section.

In the preceding example, the mean of the Poisson distribution is $\mu = 10$ arrivals per 15-minute period. A property of the Poisson distribution is that the mean of the distribution and the variance of the distribution are *equal*. Thus, the variance for the number of arrivals during 15-minute periods is $\sigma^2 = 10$. The standard deviation is $\sigma = \sqrt{10} = 3.16$.

A property of the Poisson distribution is that the mean and variance are equal.

Our illustration involves a 15-minute period, but other time periods can be used. Suppose we want to compute the probability of one arrival in a 3-minute period. Because 10 is the expected number of arrivals in a 15-minute period, we see that $10/15 = 2/3$ is the expected number of arrivals in a 1-minute period and that $(2/3)(3 \text{ minutes}) = 2$ is the expected number of arrivals in a 3-minute period. Thus, the probability of x arrivals in a 3-minute time period with $\mu = 2$ is given by the following Poisson probability function.

$$f(x) = \frac{2^x e^{-2}}{x!}$$

The probability of one arrival in a 3-minute period is calculated as follows:

$$\text{Probability of exactly} \atop \text{1 arrival in 3 minutes} = f(1) = \frac{2^1 e^{-2}}{1!} = .2707$$

Earlier we computed the probability of five arrivals in a 15-minute period; it was .0378. Note that the probability of one arrival in a 3-minute period (.2707) is not the same. When computing a Poisson probability for a different time interval, we must first convert the mean arrival rate to the time period of interest and then compute the probability.

An Example Involving Length or Distance Intervals

Let us illustrate an application not involving time intervals in which the Poisson distribution is useful. Suppose we are concerned with the occurrence of major defects in a highway one month after resurfacing. We will assume that the probability of a defect is the same for any two highway intervals of equal length and that the occurrence or nonoccurrence of a defect in any one interval is independent of the occurrence or nonoccurrence of a defect in any other interval. Hence, the Poisson distribution can be applied.

Suppose we learn that major defects one month after resurfacing occur at the average rate of two per mile. Let us find the probability of no major defects in a particular 3-mile section of the highway. Because we are interested in an interval with a length of 3 miles, $\mu = (2 \text{ defects/mile})(3 \text{ miles}) = 6$ represents the expected number of major defects over the

3-mile section of highway. Using equation (5.11), the probability of no major defects is $f(0) = 6^0 e^{-6}/0! = .0025$. Thus, it is unlikely that no major defects will occur in the 3-mile section. In fact, this example indicates a $1 - .0025 = .9975$ probability of at least one major defect in the 3-mile highway section.

Using Excel to Compute Poisson Probabilities

The Excel function for computing Poisson probabilities and cumulative probabilities is called POISSON. It works in much the same way as the Excel function for computing binomial probabilities. Here we show how to use it to compute Poisson probabilities and cumulative probabilities. To illustrate, we use the example introduced earlier in this section; cars arrive at a bank drive-up teller window at the mean rate of 10 per 15-minute time interval. Refer to Figure 5.8 as we describe the tasks involved.

Enter Data: In order to compute a Poisson probability we must know the mean number of occurrences (μ) per time period and the number of occurrences for which we want to compute the probability (x). For the drive-up teller window example, the occurrences of interest are the arrivals of cars. The mean arrival rate is 10, which has been entered in cell D1. Earlier in this section, we computed the probability of 5 arrivals. But suppose we now want to compute the probability of zero up through 20 arrivals. To do so, we enter the values 0, 1, 2, ... , 20 into cells A4:A24.

Enter Functions and Formulas: The POISSON function has three inputs: the first is the value of x, the second is the value of μ, and the third is FALSE or TRUE. We choose FALSE

FIGURE 5.8 EXCEL WORKSHEET FOR COMPUTING POISSON PROBABILITIES

	A	B	C	D	E
1			Mean No. of Occurrences	10	
2					
3	No. of Arrivals (x)	Probability f(x)			
4	0	=POISSON(A4,$D$1,FALSE)			
5	1	=POISSON(A5,$D$1,FALSE)			
6	2	=POISSON(A6,$D$1,FALSE)			
7	3	=POISSON(A7,$D$1,FALSE)			
8	4	=POISSON(A8,$D$1,FALSE)			
9	5	=POISSON(A9,$D$1,FALSE)			
10	6	=POISSON(A10,$D$1,FALSE)			
11	7	=POISSON(A11,$D$1,FALSE)			
12	8	=POISSON(A12,$D$1,FALSE)			
13	9	=POISSON(A13,$D$1,FALSE)			
14	10	=POISSON(A14,$D$1,FALSE)			
15	11	=POISSON(A15,$D$1,FALSE)			
16	12	=POISSON(A16,$D$1,FALSE)			
17	13	=POISSON(A17,$D$1,FALSE)			
18	14	=POISSON(A18,$D$1,FALSE)			
19	15	=POISSON(A19,$D$1,FALSE)			
20	16	=POISSON(A20,$D$1,FALSE)			
21	17	=POISSON(A21,$D$1,FALSE)			
22	18	=POISSON(A22,$D$1,FALSE)			
23	19	=POISSON(A23,$D$1,FALSE)			
24	20	=POISSON(A24,$D$1,FALSE)			
25					

	A	B	C	D	E	F	G	H	I
1		Mean No. of Occurrences		10					
2									
3	No. of Arrivals (x)	Probability f(x)							
4	0	0.0000							
5	1	0.0005							
6	2	0.0023							
7	3	0.0076							
8	4	0.0189							
9	5	0.0378							
10	6	0.0631							
11	7	0.0901							
12	8	0.1126							
13	9	0.1251							
14	10	0.1251							
15	11	0.1137							
16	12	0.0948							
17	13	0.0729							
18	14	0.0521							
19	15	0.0347							
20	16	0.0217							
21	17	0.0128							
22	18	0.0071							
23	19	0.0037							
24	20	0.0019							
25									

Poisson Probabilities

for the third argument if a probability is desired. The formula =POISSON(A4, $D$1,FALSE) has been entered into cell B4 to compute the probability of 0 arrivals in a 15-minute period. The value worksheet in the foreground shows that the probability of 0 arrivals is 0.0000. The formula in cell B4 is copied to cells B5:B24 to compute the probabilities for 1 through 20 arrivals. Note, in cell B9 of the value worksheet, that the probability of 5 arrivals is .0378. This result is the same as we calculated earlier in the text.

Notice how easy it was to compute all the probabilities for 0 through 20 arrivals using the POISSON function. These calculations would take quite a bit of work using a calculator. We have also used Excel's Chart Wizard to develop a graph of the Poisson probability distribution of arrivals. See the value worksheet in Figure 5.8. This chart gives a nice graphical presentation of the probabilities for the various number of arrival possibilities in a 15-minute interval. We can quickly see that the most likely number of arrivals is 9 or 10 and that the probabilities fall off rather smoothly for smaller and larger values.

Let us now see how cumulative probabilities are generated using Excel's POISSON function. It is really a simple extension of what we have already done. We again use the example of arrivals at a drive-up teller window. Refer to Figure 5.9 as we describe the tasks involved.

FIGURE 5.9   EXCEL WORKSHEET FOR COMPUTING CUMULATIVE POISSON PROBABILITIES

	A	B	C	D	E
1			Mean No. of Occurrences	10	
2					
3	No. of Arrivals (x)	Cumulative Probability			
4	0	=POISSON(A4,$D$1,TRUE)			
5	1	=POISSON(A5,$D$1,TRUE)			
6	2	=POISSON(A6,$D$1,TRUE)			
7	3	=POISSON(A7,$D$1,TRUE)			
8	4	=POISSON(A8,$D$1,TRUE)			
9	5	=POISSON(A9,$D$1,TRUE)			
10	6	=POISSON(A10,$D$1,TRUE)			
11	7	=POISSON(A11,$D$1,TRUE)			
12	8	=POISSON(A12,$D$1,TRUE)			
13	9	=POISSON(A13,$D$1,TRUE)			
14	10	=POISSON(A14,$D$1,TRUE)			
15	11	=POISSON(A15,$D$1,TRUE)			
16	12	=POISSON(A16,$D$1,TRUE)			
17	13	=POISSON(A17,$D$1,TRUE)			
18	14	=POISSON(A18,$D$1,TRUE)			
19	15	=POISSON(A19,$D$1,TRUE)			
20	16	=POISSON(A20,$D$1,TRUE)			
21	17	=POISSON(A21,$D$1,TRUE)			
22	18	=POISSON(A22,$D$1,TRUE)			
23	19	=POISSON(A23,$D$1,TRUE)			
24	20	=POISSON(A24,$D$1,TRUE)			
25					

	A	B	C	D	E
1		Mean No. of Occurrences		10	
2					
3	No. of Arrivals (x)	Cumulative Probability			
4	0	0.0000			
5	1	0.0005			
6	2	0.0028			
7	3	0.0103			
8	4	0.0293			
9	5	0.0671			
10	6	0.1301			
11	7	0.2202			
12	8	0.3328			
13	9	0.4579			
14	10	0.5830			
15	11	0.6968			
16	12	0.7916			
17	13	0.8645			
18	14	0.9165			
19	15	0.9513			
20	16	0.9730			
21	17	0.9857			
22	18	0.9928			
23	19	0.9965			
24	20	0.9984			
25					

Enter Data: To compute cumulative Poisson probabilities we must provide the mean number of occurrences (μ) per time period and the values of x that we are interested in. The mean arrival rate (10) has been entered into cell D1. Suppose we want to compute the cumulative probabilities for a number of arrivals ranging from zero up through 20. To do so, we enter the values 0, 1, 2, . . . , 20 into cells A4:A24.

Enter Functions and Formulas: Refer to the formula worksheet in the background of Figure 5.8. The formulas we enter into cells B4:B24 of Figure 5.9 are the same as in Figure 5.8 with one exception. Instead of FALSE for the third argument we enter the word TRUE to obtain cumulative probabilities. After entering these formulas into cells B4:B24 of the worksheet in Figure 5.9 the cumulative probabilities shown were obtained.

Note, in Figure 5.9, that the probability of 5 or fewer arrivals is .0671 and that the probability of 4 or fewer arrivals is .0293. Thus, the probability of exactly 5 arrivals is the difference in these two numbers: $f(5) = .0671 - .0293 = .0378$. We computed this probability earlier in this section and in Figure 5.8. Using these cumulative probabilities it is easy to compute the probability that a random variable lies within a certain interval. For instance, suppose we wanted to know the probability of more than 5 and fewer than 16 arrivals. We would just find the cumulative probability of 15 arrivals and subtract from that the cumulative probability for 5 arrivals. Referring to Figure 5.9 to obtain the appropriate probabilities, we obtain $.9513 - .0671 = .8842$. With such a high probability, we could conclude that 6 to 15 cars will arrive in most 15-minute intervals. Using the cumulative probability for 20 arrivals, we can also conclude that the probability of more than 20 arrivals in a 15-minute period is $1 - .9984 = .0016$; thus, there is almost no chance of more than 20 cars arriving.

Exercises

Methods

38.   Consider a Poisson distribution with $\mu = 3$.
   a.   Write the appropriate Poisson probability function.
   b.   Compute $f(2)$.
   c.   Compute $f(1)$.
   d.   Compute $P(x \geq 2)$.

39.   Consider a Poisson distribution with a mean of two occurrences per time period.
   a.   Write the appropriate Poisson probability function.
   b.   What is the expected number of occurrences in three time periods?
   c.   Write the appropriate Poisson probability function to determine the probability of x occurrences in three time periods.
   d.   Compute the probability of two occurrences in one time period.
   e.   Compute the probability of six occurrences in three time periods.
   f.   Compute the probability of five occurrences in two time periods.

Applications

40.   Phone calls arrive at the rate of 48 per hour at the reservation desk for Regional Airways.
   a.   Compute the probability of receiving three calls in a five-minute interval of time.
   b.   Compute the probability of receiving exactly 10 calls in 15 minutes.

    c. Suppose no calls are currently on hold. If the agent takes five minutes to complete the current call, how many callers do you expect to be waiting by that time? What is the probability that none will be waiting?

    d. If no calls are currently being processed, what is the probability that the agent can take three minutes for personal time without being interrupted by a call?

41. During the period of time that a local university takes phone-in registrations, calls come in at the rate of one every two minutes.

    a. What is the expected number of calls in one hour?

    b. What is the probability of three calls in five minutes?

    c. What is the probability of no calls in a five-minute period?

42. More than 50 million guests stayed at bed and breakfasts (B&Bs) last year. The Web site for the Bed and Breakfast Inns of North America (http://www.cimarron.net), which averages approximately seven visitors per minute, enables many B&Bs to attract guests without waiting years to be mentioned in guidebooks (*Time,* September 2001).

    a. Compute the probability of no Web site visitors in a one-minute period.

    b. Compute the probability of two or more Web site visitors in a one-minute period.

    c. Compute the probability of one or more Web site visitors in a 30-second period.

    d. Compute the probability of five or more Web site visitors in a one-minute period.

43. Airline passengers arrive randomly and independently at the passenger-screening facility at a major international airport. The mean arrival rate is 10 passengers per minute.

    a. Compute the probability of no arrivals in a one-minute period.

    b. Compute the probability that three or fewer passengers arrive in a one-minute period.

    c. Compute the probability of no arrivals in a 15-second period.

    d. Compute the probability of at least one arrival in a 15-second period.

44. From 1990 through 1999, an average of approximately 26 aircraft accidents per year involved one or more passenger fatalities. Since 2000, the average decreased to 15 accidents per year (*The World Almanac and Book of Facts,* 2004). Assume that aircraft accidents continue to occur at the rate of 15 per year.

    a. Compute the mean number of aircraft accidents per month.

    b. Compute the probability of no accidents during a month.

    c. Compute the probability of exactly one accident during a month.

    d. Compute the probability of more than one accident during a month.

45. The National Safety Council reported that air bag–related fatalities dropped to 18 in the year 2000 (http://www.nsc.org).

    a. Compute the expected number of air bag–related fatalities per month.

    b. Compute the probability of no air bag–related fatalities in a month.

    c. Compute the probability of two or more air bag–related fatalities in a month.

Hypergeometric Probability Distribution

The **hypergeometric probability distribution** is closely related to the binomial distribution. The two probability distributions differ in two key ways. With the hypergeometric distribution, the trials are not independent; and the probability of success changes from trial to trial.

In the usual notation for the hypergeometric distribution, r denotes the number of elements in the population of size N labeled success, and $N - r$ denotes the number of elements in the population labeled failure. The **hypergeometric probability function** is used to compute the probability that in a random selection of n elements, selected without replacement, we obtain x elements labeled success and $n - x$ elements labeled failure. For this outcome to occur, we must obtain x successes from the r successes in the population and $n - x$ failures from the $N - r$ failures. The hypergeometric probability function provides $f(x)$, the probability of obtaining x successes in a sample of size n.

HYPERGEOMETRIC PROBABILITY FUNCTION

$$f(x) = \frac{\binom{r}{x}\binom{N-r}{n-x}}{\binom{N}{n}} \quad \text{for } 0 \leq x \leq r \tag{5.12}$$

where

$$f(x) = \text{probability of } x \text{ successes in } n \text{ trials}$$
$$n = \text{number of trials}$$
$$N = \text{number of elements in the population}$$
$$r = \text{number of elements in the population labeled success}$$

Note that $\binom{N}{n}$ represents the number of ways a sample of size n can be selected from a population of size N; $\binom{r}{x}$ represents the number of ways that x successes can be selected from a total of r successes in the population; and $\binom{N-r}{n-x}$ represents the number of ways that $n - x$ failures can be selected from a total of $N - r$ failures in the population.

To illustrate the computations involved in using equation (5.12), let us consider the following quality control application. Electric fuses produced by Ontario Electric are packaged in boxes of 12 units each. Suppose an inspector randomly selects 3 of the 12 fuses in a box for testing. If the box contains exactly 5 defective fuses, what is the probability that the inspector will find exactly 1 of the 3 fuses defective? In this application, $n = 3$ and $N = 12$. With $r = 5$ defective fuses in the box the probability of finding $x = 1$ defective fuse is

$$f(1) = \frac{\binom{5}{1}\binom{7}{2}}{\binom{12}{3}} = \frac{\left(\dfrac{5!}{1!4!}\right)\left(\dfrac{7!}{2!5!}\right)}{\left(\dfrac{12!}{3!9!}\right)} = \frac{(5)(21)}{220} = .4773$$

Now suppose that we wanted to know the probability of finding *at least* 1 defective fuse. The easiest way to answer this question is to first compute the probability that the inspector does not find any defective fuses. The probability of $x = 0$ is

$$f(0) = \frac{\binom{5}{0}\binom{7}{3}}{\binom{12}{3}} = \frac{\left(\dfrac{5!}{0!5!}\right)\left(\dfrac{7!}{3!4!}\right)}{\left(\dfrac{12!}{3!9!}\right)} = \frac{(1)(35)}{220} = .1591$$

Because the probability of zero defective fuses is $f(0) = .1591$, we conclude that the probability of finding at least 1 defective fuse is $1 - .1591 = .8409$. Thus, there is a reasonably high probability that the inspector will find at least 1 defective fuse.

The expected value and variance of a hypergeometric distribution are as follows.

$$E(x) = \mu = n\left(\frac{r}{N}\right) \tag{5.13}$$

$$\text{Var}(x) = \sigma^2 = n\left(\frac{r}{N}\right)\left(1 - \frac{r}{N}\right)\left(\frac{N-n}{N-1}\right) \tag{5.14}$$

In the preceding example $n = 3$, $r = 5$, and $N = 12$. Thus, the mean and variance for the number of defective fuses is

$$\mu = n\left(\frac{r}{N}\right) = 3\left(\frac{5}{12}\right) = 1.25$$

$$\sigma^2 = n\left(\frac{r}{N}\right)\left(1 - \frac{r}{N}\right)\left(\frac{N-n}{N-1}\right) = 3\left(\frac{5}{12}\right)\left(1 - \frac{5}{12}\right)\left(\frac{12-3}{12-1}\right) = .60$$

The standard deviation is $\sigma = \sqrt{.60} = .77$.

Using Excel to Compute Hypergeometric Probabilities

The Excel function for computing hypergeometric probabilities is called HYPGEOMDIST. It only computes probabilities, not cumulative probabilities. The HYPGEOMDIST function has four inputs: x, n, r, N. Its usage is similar to that of BINOMDIST for the binomial distribution and POISSON for the Poisson distribution, so we dispense with showing a worksheet figure and just show the usage of the formula. Let us reconsider the example of selecting 3 fuses for inspection from a fuse box containing 12 fuses, 5 of which are defective. We want to compute the probability that 1 of the 3 fuses selected is defective. In this case $x = 1$, $n = 3$, $r = 5$, and $N = 12$. So the appropriate formula to place in a cell of an Excel worksheet would be =HYPGEOMDIST(1,3,5,12). Placing this formula in a cell of an Excel worksheet provides a hypergeometric probability of .4773.

If we want to know the probability that none of the 3 fuses selected is defective, we have $x = 0$, $n = 3$, $r = 5$, and $N = 12$. So using the HYPGEOMDIST function to compute the probability of randomly selecting 3 fuses without any being defective we would enter the following formula into an Excel worksheet: =HYPGEOMDIST(0,3,5,12). The probability computed is .1591.

NOTES AND COMMENTS

Consider a hypergeometric distribution with n trials. Let $p = (r/N)$ denote the probability of a success on the first trial. If the population size is large, the term $(N - n)/(N - 1)$ in equation (5.14) approaches 1. As a result, the expected value and variance can be written $E(x) = np$ and $\text{Var}(x) = np(1 - p)$. Note that these expressions are the same as the expressions used to compute the expected value and variance of a binomial distribution, as in equations (5.9) and (5.10). When the population size is large, a hypergeometric distribution can be approximated by a binomial distribution with n trials and a probability of success $p = (r/N)$.

Exercises

Methods

46. Suppose $N = 10$ and $r = 3$. Compute the hypergeometric probabilities for the following values of n and x.
    a. $n = 4, x = 1$.
    b. $n = 2, x = 2$.
    c. $n = 2, x = 0$.
    d. $n = 4, x = 2$.

47. Suppose $N = 15$ and $r = 4$. What is the probability of $x = 3$ for $n = 10$?

Applications

48. In a survey conducted by the Gallup Organization, respondents were asked, "What is your favorite sport to watch?" Football and basketball ranked number one and two in terms of preference (http://www.gallup.com, January 3, 2004). Assume that in a group of 10 individuals, seven preferred football and three preferred basketball. A random sample of three of these individuals is selected.
    a.   What is the probability that exactly two preferred football?
    b.   What is the probability that the majority (either two or three) preferred football?

49. Blackjack, or twenty-one as it is frequently called, is a popular gambling game played in Las Vegas casinos. A player is dealt two cards. Face cards (jacks, queens, and kings) and tens have a point value of 10. Aces have a point value of 1 or 11. A 52-card deck contains 16 cards with a point value of 10 (jacks, queens, kings, and tens) and four aces.
    a.   What is the probability that both cards dealt are aces or 10-point cards?
    b.   What is the probability that both of the cards are aces?
    c.   What is the probability that both of the cards have a point value of 10?
    d.   A blackjack is a 10-point card and an ace for a value of 21. Use your answers to parts (a), (b), and (c) to determine the probability that a player is dealt blackjack. (*Hint:* Part (d) is not a hypergeometric problem. Develop your own logical relationship as to how the hypergeometric probabilities from parts (a), (b), and (c) can be combined to answer this question.)

50. Axline Computers manufactures personal computers at two plants, one in Texas and the other in Hawaii. The Texas plant has 40 employees; the Hawaii plant has 20. A random sample of 10 employees is to be asked to fill out a benefits questionnaire.
    a.   What is the probability that none of the employees in the sample work at the plant in Hawaii?
    b.   What is the probability that one of the employees in the sample works at the plant in Hawaii?
    c.   What is the probability that two or more of the employees in the sample work at the plant in Hawaii?
    d.   What is the probability that nine of the employees in the sample work at the plant in Texas?

51. The 2003 Zagat Restaurant Survey provides food, decor, and service ratings for some of the top restaurants across the United States. For 15 top-ranking restaurants located in Boston, the average price of a dinner, including one drink and tip, was $48.60. You are leaving for a business trip to Boston and will eat dinner at three of these restaurants. Your company will reimburse you for a maximum of $50 per dinner. Business associates familiar with these restaurants have told you that the meal cost at one-third of these restaurants will exceed $50. Suppose that you randomly select three of these restaurants for dinner.
    a.   What is the probability that none of the meals will exceed the cost covered by your company?
    b.   What is the probability that one of the meals will exceed the cost covered by your company?

c. What is the probability that two of the meals will exceed the cost covered by your company?

d. What is the probability that all three of the meals will exceed the cost covered by your company?

52. A shipment of 10 items has two defective and eight nondefective items. In the inspection of the shipment, a sample of items will be selected and tested. If a defective item is found, the shipment of 10 items will be rejected.

a. If a sample of three items is selected, what is the probability that the shipment will be rejected?

b. If a sample of four items is selected, what is the probability that the shipment will be rejected?

c. If a sample of five items is selected, what is the probability that the shipment will be rejected?

d. If management would like a .90 probability of rejecting a shipment with two defective and eight nondefective items, how large a sample would you recommend?

Summary

A random variable provides a numerical description of the outcome of an experiment. The probability distribution for a random variable describes how the probabilities are distributed over the values the random variable can assume. For any discrete random variable x, the probability distribution is defined by a probability function, denoted by $f(x)$, which provides the probability associated with each value of the random variable. Once the probability function is defined, we can compute the expected value, variance, and standard deviation for the random variable.

The binomial distribution can be used to determine the probability of x successes in n trials whenever the experiment has the following properties:

1. The experiment consists of a sequence of n identical trials.
2. Two outcomes are possible on each trial, one called success and the other failure.
3. The probability of a success p does not change from trial to trial. Consequently, the probability of failure, $1 - p$, does not change from trial to trial.
4. The trials are independent.

When the four properties hold, the binomial probability function can be used to determine the probability of obtaining x successes in n trials. Formulas were also presented for the mean and variance of the binomial distribution.

The Poisson distribution is used when it is desirable to determine the probability of obtaining x occurrences over an interval of time or space. The following assumptions are necessary for the Poisson distribution to be applicable.

1. The probability of an occurrence of the event is the same for any two intervals of equal length.
2. The occurrence or nonoccurrence of the event in any interval is independent of the occurrence or nonoccurrence of the event in any other interval.

A third discrete probability distribution, the hypergeometric, was introduced in Section 5.6. Like the binomial, it is used to compute the probability of x successes in n trials. But, in contrast to the binomial, the probability of success changes from trial to trial.

Glossary

Random variable A numerical description of the outcome of an experiment.
Discrete random variable A random variable that may assume either a finite number of values or an infinite sequence of values.

Continuous random variable A random variable that may assume any numerical value in an interval or collection of intervals.

Probability distribution A description of how the probabilities are distributed over the values of the random variable.

Probability function A function, denoted by $f(x)$, that provides the probability that x assumes a particular value for a discrete random variable.

Discrete uniform probability distribution A probability distribution for which each possible value of the random variable has the same probability.

Expected value A measure of the central location of a random variable.

Variance A measure of the variability, or dispersion, of a random variable.

Standard deviation The positive square root of the variance.

Binomial experiment An experiment having the four properties stated at the beginning of Section 5.4.

Binomial probability distribution A probability distribution showing the probability of x successes in n trials of a binomial experiment.

Binomial probability function The function used to compute binomial probabilities.

Poisson probability distribution A probability distribution showing the probability of x occurrences of an event over a specified interval of time or space.

Poisson probability function The function used to compute Poisson probabilities.

Hypergeometric probability distribution A probability distribution showing the probability of x successes in n trials from a population with r successes and $N - r$ failures.

Hypergeometric probability function The function used to compute hypergeometric probabilities.

Key Formulas

Discrete Uniform Probability Function

$$f(x) = 1/n \tag{5.3}$$

where

$$n = \text{the number of values the random variable may assume}$$

Expected Value of a Discrete Random Variable

$$E(x) = \mu = \Sigma x f(x) \tag{5.4}$$

Variance of a Discrete Random Variable

$$\text{Var}(x) = \sigma^2 = \Sigma(x - \mu)^2 f(x) \tag{5.5}$$

Number of Experimental Outcomes Providing Exactly x Successes in n Trials

$$\binom{n}{x} = \frac{n!}{x!(n - x)!} \tag{5.6}$$

Binomial Probability Function

$$f(x) = \binom{n}{x} p^x (1 - p)^{(n-x)} \tag{5.8}$$

Expected Value for the Binomial Distribution

$$E(x) = \mu = np \tag{5.9}$$

Variance for the Binomial Distribution

$$\text{Var}(x) = \sigma^2 = np(1 - p) \tag{5.10}$$

Poisson Probability Function

$$f(x) = \frac{\mu^x e^{-\mu}}{x!} \tag{5.11}$$

Hypergeometric Probability Function

$$f(x) = \frac{\binom{r}{x}\binom{N-r}{n-x}}{\binom{N}{n}} \quad \text{for } 0 \leq x \leq r \tag{5.12}$$

Expected Value for the Hypergeometric Distribution

$$E(x) = \mu = n\left(\frac{r}{N}\right) \tag{5.13}$$

Variance for the Hypergeometric Distribution

$$\text{Var}(x) = \sigma^2 = n\left(\frac{r}{N}\right)\left(1 - \frac{r}{N}\right)\left(\frac{N-n}{N-1}\right) \tag{5.14}$$

Supplementary Exercises

53. The *Barron's* Big Money Poll asked 131 investment managers across the United States about their short-term investment outlook (*Barron's,* October 28, 2002). Their responses showed 4% were very bullish, 39% were bullish, 29% were neutral, 21% were bearish, and 7% were very bearish. Let x be the random variable reflecting the level of optimism about the market. Set $x = 5$ for very bullish down through $x = 1$ for very bearish.
    a. Develop a probability distribution for the level of optimism of investment managers.
    b. Compute the expected value for the level of optimism.
    c. Compute the variance and standard deviation for the level of optimism.
    d. Comment on what your results imply about the level of optimism and its variability.

54. The American Association of Individual Investors publishes an annual guide to the top mutual funds (*The Individual Investor's Guide to the Top Mutual Funds,* 22e, American Association of Individual Investors, 2003). Table 5.8 contains their ratings of the total risk for 29 categories of mutual funds.

TABLE 5.8   RISK RATING FOR 29 CATEGORIES OF MUTUAL FUNDS

Total Risk	Number of Fund Categories
Low	7
Below Average	6
Average	3
Above Average	6
High	7

    a. Let $x = 1$ for low risk up through $x = 5$ for high risk, and develop a probability distribution for level of risk.

    b. What are the expected value and variance for total risk?

    c. It turns out that 11 of the fund categories were bond funds. For the bond funds, 7 categories were rated low and 4 were rated below average. Compare the total risk of the bond funds with the 18 categories of stock funds.

55. The budgeting process for a midwestern college resulted in expense forecasts for the coming year (in $ millions) of $9, $10, $11, $12, and $13. Because the actual expenses are unknown, the following respective probabilities are assigned: .3, .2, .25, .05, and .2.

    a. Show the probability distribution for the expense forecast.

    b. What is the expected value of the expense forecast for the coming year?

    c. What is the variance of the expense forecast for the coming year?

    d. If income projections for the year are estimated at $12 million, comment on the financial position of the college.

56. A survey conducted by the Bureau of Transportation Statistics (BTS) showed that the average commuter spends about 26 minutes on a one-way door-to-door trip from home to work. In addition, 5% of commuters reported a one-way commute of more than one hour (http://www.bts.gov, January 12, 2004).

    a. If 20 commuters are surveyed on a particular day, what is the probability that 3 will report a one-way commute of more than one hour?

    b. If 20 commuters are surveyed on a particular day, what is the probability that none will report a one-way commute of more than one hour?

    c. If a company has 2000 employees, what is the expected number of employees that have a one-way commute of more than one hour?

    d. If a company has 2000 employees, what is the variance and standard deviation of the number of employees that have a one-way commute of more than one hour?

57. A company is planning to interview Internet users to learn how its proposed Web site will be received by different age groups. According to the Census Bureau, 40% of individuals ages 18 to 54 and 12% of individuals age 55 and over use the Internet (*Statistical Abstract of the United States: 2000*).

    a. How many people from the 18–54 age group must be contacted to find an expected number of at least 10 Internet users?

    b. How many people from the age group 55 and over must be contacted to find an expected number of at least 10 Internet users?

    c. If you contact the number of 18- to 54-year-old people suggested in part (a), what is the standard deviation of the number who will be Internet users?

    d. If you contact the number of people age 55 and older suggested in part (b), what is the standard deviation of the number who will be Internet users?

58. Many companies use a quality control technique called acceptance sampling to monitor incoming shipments of parts, raw materials, and so on. In the electronics industry, component parts are commonly shipped from suppliers in large lots. Inspection of a sample of n components can be viewed as the n trials of a binomial experiment. The outcome for each component tested (trial) will be that the component is classified as good or defective. Reynolds Electronics accepts a lot from a particular supplier if the defective components in the lot do not exceed 1%. Suppose a random sample of five items from a recent shipment is tested.

    a. Assume that 1% of the shipment is defective. Compute the probability that no items in the sample are defective.

    b. Assume that 1% of the shipment is defective. Compute the probability that exactly one item in the sample is defective.

    c. What is the probability of observing one or more defective items in the sample if 1% of the shipment is defective?

    d. Would you feel comfortable accepting the shipment if one item was found to be defective? Why or why not?

59. The unemployment rate is 4.1% (*Barron's,* September 4, 2000). Assume that 100 employable people are selected randomly.
     a.   What is the expected number of people who are unemployed?
     b.   What are the variance and standard deviation of the number of people who are unemployed?

60. A poll conducted by Zogby International showed that of those Americans who said music plays a "very important" role in their lives, 30% said their local radio stations "always" play the kind of music they like (http://www.zogby.com, January 12, 2004). Suppose a sample of 800 people who say music plays an important role in their lives is taken.
     a.   How many would you expect to say that their local radio stations always play the kind of music they like?
     b.   What is the standard deviation of the number of respondents who think their local radio stations always play the kind of music they like?
     c.   What is the standard deviation of the number of respondents who do not think their local radio stations always play the kind of music they like?

61. Cars arrive at a car wash randomly and independently; the probability of an arrival is the same for any two time intervals of equal length. The mean arrival rate is 15 cars per hour. What is the probability that 20 or more cars will arrive during any given hour of operation?

62. A new automated production process averages 1.5 breakdowns per day. Because of the cost associated with a breakdown, management is concerned about the possibility of having three or more breakdowns during a day. Assume that breakdowns occur randomly, that the probability of a breakdown is the same for any two time intervals of equal length, and that breakdowns in one period are independent of breakdowns in other periods. What is the probability of having three or more breakdowns during a day?

63. A regional director responsible for business development in the state of Pennsylvania is concerned about the number of small business failures. If the mean number of small business failures per month is 10, what is the probability that exactly four small businesses will fail during a given month? Assume that the probability of a failure is the same for any two months and that the occurrence or nonoccurrence of a failure in any month is independent of failures in any other month.

64. Customer arrivals at a bank are random and independent; the probability of an arrival in any one-minute period is the same as the probability of an arrival in any other one-minute period. Answer the following questions, assuming a mean arrival rate of three customers per minute.
     a.   What is the probability of exactly three arrivals in a one-minute period?
     b.   What is the probability of at least three arrivals in a one-minute period?

65. A deck of playing cards contains 52 cards, four of which are aces. What is the probability that the deal of a five-card hand provides:
     a.   A pair of aces?
     b.   Exactly one ace?
     c.   No aces?
     d.   At least one ace?

66. Through the week ending September 16, 2001, Tiger Woods was the leading money winner on the PGA Tour, with total earnings of $5,517,777. Of the top 10 money winners, seven players used a Titleist brand golf ball (http://www.pgatour.com). Suppose that we randomly select two of the top 10 money winners.
     a.   What is the probability that exactly one uses a Titleist golf ball?
     b.   What is the probability that both use Titleist golf balls?
     c.   What is the probability that neither uses a Titleist golf ball?

CHAPTER 6

Continuous Probability Distributions

CONTENTS

STATISTICS *in* PRACTICE

PROCTER & GAMBLE*
CINCINNATI, OHIO

Procter & Gamble (P&G) produces and markets such products as detergents, disposable diapers, over-the-counter pharmaceuticals, dentifrices, bar soaps, mouthwashes, and paper towels. Worldwide, it has the leading brand in more categories than any other consumer products company.

As a leader in the application of statistical methods in decision making, P&G employs people with diverse academic backgrounds: engineering, statistics, operations research, and business. The major quantitative technologies for which these people provide support are probabilistic decision and risk analysis, advanced simulation, quality improvement, and quantitative methods (e.g., linear programming, regression analysis, probability analysis).

The Industrial Chemicals Division of P&G is a major supplier of fatty alcohols derived from natural substances such as coconut oil and from petroleum-based derivatives. The division wanted to know the economic risks and opportunities of expanding its fatty-alcohol production facilities, so it called in P&G's experts in probabilistic decision and risk analysis to help. After structuring and modeling the problem, they determined that the key to profitability was the cost difference between the petroleum- and coconut-based raw materials. Future costs were unknown, but the analysts were able to approximate them with the following continuous random variables.

x = the coconut oil price per pound of fatty alcohol

and

y = the petroleum raw material price per pound
of fatty alcohol

Because the key to profitability was the difference between these two random variables, a third random variable, $d = x - y$, was used in the analysis. Experts were interviewed to determine

Some of Procter & Gamble's many well-known products. © Joe Higgins/South-Western.

the probability distributions for x and y. In turn, this information was used to develop a probability distribution for the difference in prices d. This continuous probability distribution showed a .90 probability that the price difference would be $.0655 or less and a .50 probability that the price difference would be $.035 or less. In addition, there was only a .10 probability that the price difference would be $.0045 or less.[†]

The Industrial Chemicals Division thought that being able to quantify the impact of raw material price differences was key to reaching a consensus. The probabilities obtained were used in a sensitivity analysis of the raw material price difference. The analysis yielded sufficient insight to form the basis for a recommendation to management.

The use of continuous random variables and their probability distributions was helpful to P&G in analyzing the economic risks associated with its fatty-alcohol production. In this chapter, you will gain an understanding of continuous random variables and their probability distributions including one of the most important probability distributions in statistics, the normal distribution.

---

*The authors are indebted to Joel Kahn of Procter & Gamble for providing this Statistics in Practice.

[†]The price differences stated here have been modified to protect proprietary data.

In the preceding chapter we discussed discrete random variables and their probability distributions. In this chapter we turn to the study of continuous random variables. Specifically, we discuss three continuous probability distributions: the uniform, the normal, and the exponential.

A fundamental difference separates discrete and continuous random variables in terms of how probabilities are computed. For a discrete random variable, the probability function $f(x)$ provides the probability that the random variable assumes a particular value. With continuous random variables, the counterpart of the probability function is the **probability density function**, also denoted by $f(x)$. The difference is that the probability density function does not directly provide probabilities. However, the area under the graph of $f(x)$ corresponding to a given interval does provide the probability that the continuous random variable x assumes a value in that interval. So when we compute probabilities for continuous random variables we are computing the probability that the random variable assumes any value in an interval.

Because the area under the graph of $f(x)$ at any particular point is zero, one of the implications of the definition of probability for continuous random variables is that the probability of any particular value of the random variable is zero. In Section 6.1 we demonstrate these concepts for a continuous random variable that has a uniform distribution.

Much of the chapter is devoted to describing and showing applications of the normal distribution. The normal distribution is of major importance because of its wide applicability and its extensive use in statistical inference. The chapter closes with a discussion of the exponential distribution. The exponential distribution is useful in applications involving variables such as waiting times and service times.

6.1   Uniform Probability Distribution

Consider the random variable x representing the flight time of an airplane traveling from Chicago to New York. Suppose the flight time can be any value in the interval from 120 minutes to 140 minutes. Because the random variable x can assume any value in that interval, x is a continuous rather than a discrete random variable. Let us assume that sufficient actual flight data are available to conclude that the probability of a flight time within any 1-minute interval is the same as the probability of a flight time within any other 1-minute interval contained in the larger interval from 120 to 140 minutes. With every 1-minute interval being equally likely, the random variable x is said to have a **uniform probability distribution**. The probability density function, which defines the uniform distribution for the flight-time random variable, is

Whenever the probability is proportional to the length of the interval, the random variable is uniformly distributed.

$$f(x) = \begin{cases} 1/20 & \text{for } 120 \leq x \leq 140 \\ 0 & \text{elsewhere} \end{cases}$$

Figure 6.1 is a graph of this probability density function. In general, the uniform probability density function for a random variable x is defined by the following formula.

UNIFORM PROBABILITY DENSITY FUNCTION

$$f(x) = \begin{cases} \dfrac{1}{b - a} & \text{for } a \leq x \leq b \\ 0 & \text{elsewhere} \end{cases} \tag{6.1}$$

For the flight-time random variable, $a = 120$ and $b = 140$.

FIGURE 6.1   UNIFORM PROBABILITY DISTRIBUTION FOR FLIGHT TIME

As noted in the introduction, for a continuous random variable, we consider probability only in terms of the likelihood that a random variable assumes a value within a
specified interval. In the flight time example, an acceptable probability question is:
What is the probability that the flight time is between 120 and 130 minutes? That is, what
is $P(120 \leq x \leq 130)$? Because the flight time must be between 120 and 140 minutes
and because the probability is described as being uniform over this interval, we feel
comfortable saying $P(120 \leq x \leq 130) = .50$. In the following subsection we show that
this probability can be computed as the area under the graph of $f(x)$ from 120 to 130 (see
Figure 6.2).

Area as a Measure of Probability

Let us make an observation about the graph in Figure 6.2. Consider the area under the
graph of $f(x)$ in the interval from 120 to 130. The area is rectangular, and the area of a
rectangle is simply the width multiplied by the height. With the width of the interval equal
to $130 - 120 = 10$ and the height equal to the value of the probability density function
$f(x) = 1/20$, we have area = width $\times$ height = $10(1/20) = 10/20 = .50$.

FIGURE 6.2   AREA PROVIDES PROBABILITY OF A FLIGHT TIME BETWEEN 120
              AND 130 MINUTES

What observation can you make about the area under the graph of $f(x)$ and probability? They are identical! Indeed, this observation is valid for all continuous random variables. Once a probability density function $f(x)$ is identified, the probability that x takes a value between some lower value x_1 and some higher value x_2 can be found by computing the area under the graph of $f(x)$ over the interval from x_1 to x_2.

Given the uniform distribution for flight time and using the interpretation of area as probability, we can answer any number of probability questions about flight times. For example, what is the probability of a flight time between 128 and 136 minutes? The width of the interval is $136 - 128 = 8$. With the uniform height of $f(x) = 1/20$, we see that $P(128 \leq x \leq 136) = 8(1/20) = .40$.

Note that $P(120 \leq x \leq 140) = 20(1/20) = 1$; that is, the total area under the graph of $f(x)$ is equal to 1. This property holds for all continuous probability distributions and is the analog of the condition that the sum of the probabilities must equal 1 for a discrete probability function. For a continuous probability density function, we must also require that $f(x) \geq 0$ for all values of x. This requirement is the analog of the requirement that $f(x) \geq 0$ for discrete probability functions.

Two major differences stand out between the treatment of continuous random variables and the treatment of their discrete counterparts.

To see that the probability of any single point is 0, refer to Figure 6.2 and compute the probability of a single point, say, $x = 125$. $P(x = 125) = P(125 \leq x \leq 125) = 0(1/20) = 0$.

1. We no longer talk about the probability of the random variable assuming a particular value. Instead, we talk about the probability of the random variable assuming a value within some given interval.

2. The probability of a continuous random variable assuming a value within some given interval from x_1 to x_2 is defined to be the area under the graph of the probability density function between x_1 and x_2. Because a single point is an interval of zero width, this implies that the probability of a continuous random variable assuming any particular value exactly is zero. It also means that the probability of a continuous random variable assuming a value in any interval is the same whether or not the endpoints are included.

The calculation of the expected value and variance for a continuous random variable is analogous to that for a discrete random variable. However, because the computational procedure involves integral calculus, we leave the derivation of the appropriate formulas to more advanced texts.

For the uniform continuous probability distribution introduced in this section, the formulas for the expected value and variance are

$$E(x) = \frac{a + b}{2}$$

$$\mathrm{Var}(x) = \frac{(b - a)^2}{12}$$

In these formulas, a is the smallest value and b is the largest value that the random variable may assume.

Applying these formulas to the uniform distribution for flight times from Chicago to New York, we obtain

$$E(x) = \frac{(120 + 140)}{2} = 130$$

$$\mathrm{Var}(x) = \frac{(140 - 120)^2}{12} = 33.33$$

The standard deviation of flight times can be found by taking the square root of the variance. Thus, $\sigma = 5.77$ minutes.

NOTES AND COMMENTS

To see more clearly why the height of a probability density function is not a probability, think about a random variable with the following uniform probability distribution.

$$f(x) = \begin{cases} 2 & \text{for } 0 \le x \le .5 \\ 0 & \text{elsewhere} \end{cases}$$

The height of the probability density function, $f(x)$, is 2 for values of x between 0 and .5. However, we know probabilities can never be greater than 1. Thus, we see that $f(x)$ cannot be interpreted as the probability of x.

Exercises

Methods

1. The random variable x is known to be uniformly distributed between 1.0 and 1.5.
    a.   Show the graph of the probability density function.
    b.   Compute $P(x = 1.25)$.
    c.   Compute $P(1.0 \le x \le 1.25)$.
    d.   Compute $P(1.20 < x < 1.5)$.

2. The random variable x is known to be uniformly distributed between 10 and 20.
    a.   Show the graph of the probability density function.
    b.   Compute $P(x < 15)$.
    c.   Compute $P(12 \le x \le 18)$.
    d.   Compute $E(x)$.
    e.   Compute $\text{Var}(x)$.

Applications

3. Delta Airlines quotes a flight time of 2 hours, 5 minutes for its flights from Cincinnati to Tampa. Suppose we believe that actual flight times are uniformly distributed between 2 hours and 2 hours, 20 minutes.
    a.   Show the graph of the probability density function for flight time.
    b.   What is the probability that the flight will be no more than 5 minutes late?
    c.   What is the probability that the flight will be more than 10 minutes late?
    d.   What is the expected flight time?

4. Most computer languages include a function that can be used to generate random numbers. In Excel, the RAND function can be used to generate random numbers between 0 and 1. If we let x denote a random number generated using RAND, then x is a continuous random variable with the following probability density function.

$$f(x) = \begin{cases} 1 & \text{for } 0 \le x \le 1 \\ 0 & \text{elsewhere} \end{cases}$$

    a.   Graph the probability density function.
    b.   What is the probability of generating a random number between .25 and .75?
    c.   What is the probability of generating a random number with a value less than or equal to .30?
    d.   What is the probability of generating a random number with a value greater than .60?
    e.   Generate 50 random numbers by entering =RAND() into 50 cells of an Excel worksheet.
    f.   Compute the mean and standard deviation for the random numbers in part (e).

5. The driving distance for the top 100 golfers on the PGA tour is between 284.7 and 310.6 yards (*Golfweek,* March 29, 2003). Assume that the driving distance for these golfers is uniformly distributed over this interval.
   a. Give a mathematical expression for the probability density function of driving distance.
   b. What is the probability the driving distance for one of these golfers is less than 290 yards?
   c. What is the probability the driving distance for one of these golfers is at least 300 yards?
   d. What is the probability the driving distance for one of these golfers is between 290 and 305 yards?
   e. How many of these golfers drive the ball at least 290 yards?

6. The label on a bottle of liquid detergent shows the contents to be 12 ounces per bottle. The production operation fills the bottle uniformly according to the following probability density function.

$$f(x) = \begin{cases} 8 & \text{for } 11.975 \le x \le 12.100 \\ 0 & \text{elsewhere} \end{cases}$$

   a. What is the probability that a bottle will be filled with between 12 and 12.05 ounces?
   b. What is the probability that a bottle will be filled with 12.02 or more ounces?
   c. Quality control accepts a bottle that is filled to within .02 ounces of the number of ounces shown on the container label. What is the probability that a bottle of this liquid detergent will fail to meet the quality control standard?

7. Suppose we are interested in bidding on a piece of land and we know one other bidder is interested.* The seller announced that the highest bid in excess of $10,000 will be accepted. Assume that the competitor's bid x is a random variable that is uniformly distributed between $10,000 and $15,000.
   a. Suppose you bid $12,000. What is the probability that your bid will be accepted?
   b. Suppose you bid $14,000. What is the probability that your bid will be accepted?
   c. What amount should you bid to maximize the probability that you get the property?
   d. Suppose you know someone who is willing to pay you $16,000 for the property. Would you consider bidding less than the amount in part (c)? Why or why not?

6.2   Normal Probability Distribution

Abraham de Moivre, a French mathematician, published The Doctrine of Chances *in 1733. He derived the normal distribution.*

The most important probability distribution for describing a continuous random variable is the **normal probability distribution**. The normal distribution has been used in a wide variety of practical applications in which the random variables are heights and weights of people, test scores, scientific measurements, amounts of rainfall, and other similar values. It is also widely used in statistical inference, which is the major topic of the remainder of this book. In such applications, the normal distribution provides a description of the likely results obtained through sampling.

Normal Curve

The form, or shape, of the normal distribution is illustrated by the bell-shaped normal curve in Figure 6.3. The probability density function that defines the bell-shaped curve of the normal distribution follows.

---

*This exercise is based on a problem suggested to us by Professor Roger Myerson of Northwestern University.

FIGURE 6.3 BELL-SHAPED CURVE FOR THE NORMAL DISTRIBUTION

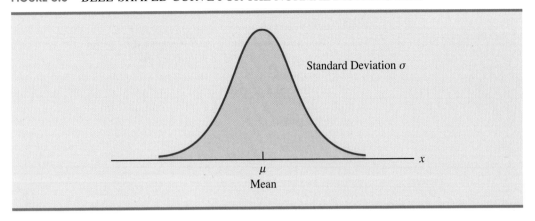

NORMAL PROBABILITY DENSITY FUNCTION

$$f(x) = \frac{1}{\sigma\sqrt{2\pi}} e^{-(x-\mu)^2/2\sigma^2} \qquad (6.2)$$

where

μ = mean
σ = standard deviation
π = 3.14159
e = 2.71828

We make several observations about the characteristics of the normal distribution.

The normal curve has two parameters, μ and σ. They determine the location and shape of the normal distribution.

1. The entire family of normal distributions is differentiated by two parameters: the mean μ and the standard deviation σ.
2. The highest point on the normal curve is at the mean, which is also the median and mode of the distribution.
3. The mean of the distribution can be any numerical value: negative, zero, or positive. Three normal distributions with the same standard deviation but three different means (-10, 0, and 20) are shown here.

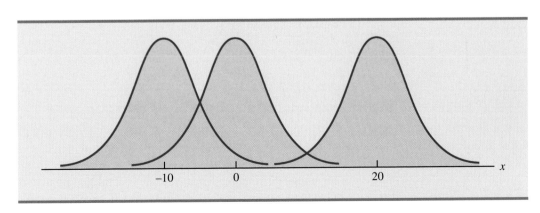

4. The normal distribution is symmetric, with the shape of the normal curve to the left of the mean a mirror image of the shape of the normal curve to the right of the mean. The tails of the normal curve extend to infinity in both directions and theoretically never touch the horizontal axis. Because it is symmetric, the normal distribution is not skewed; its skewness measure is zero.

5. The standard deviation determines how flat and wide the normal curve is. Larger values of the standard deviation result in wider, flatter curves, showing more variability in the data. Two normal distributions with the same mean but with different standard deviations are shown here.

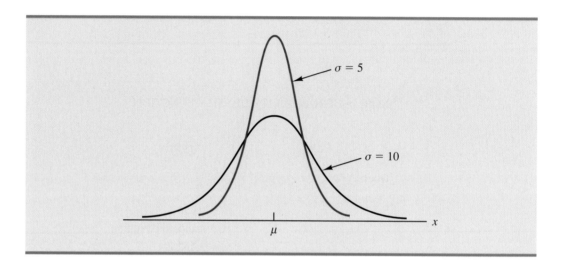

6. Probabilities for the normal random variable are given by areas under the normal curve. The total area under the curve for the normal distribution is 1. Because the distribution is symmetric, the area under the curve to the left of the mean is .50 and the area under the curve to the right of the mean is .50.

7. The percentage of values in some commonly used intervals are:

a. 68.3% of the values of a normal random variable are within plus or minus one standard deviation of its mean.

These percentages are the basis for the empirical rule introduced in Section 3.3.

b. 95.4% of the values of a normal random variable are within plus or minus two standard deviations of its mean.

c. 99.7% of the values of a normal random variable are within plus or minus three standard deviations of its mean.

Figure 6.4 shows properties (a), (b), and (c) graphically.

Standard Normal Probability Distribution

A random variable that has a normal distribution with a mean of zero and a standard deviation of one is said to have a **standard normal probability distribution**. The letter z is commonly used to designate this particular normal random variable. Figure 6.5 is the graph of the standard normal distribution. It has the same general appearance as other normal distributions, but with the special properties of $\mu = 0$ and $\sigma = 1$.

FIGURE 6.4 AREAS UNDER THE CURVE FOR ANY NORMAL DISTRIBUTION

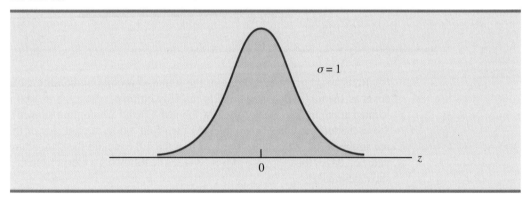

FIGURE 6.5 THE STANDARD NORMAL DISTRIBUTION

Because $\mu = 0$ and $\sigma = 1$, the formula for the standard normal probability density function is a simpler version of equation (6.2).

STANDARD NORMAL DENSITY FUNCTION

$$f(z) = \frac{1}{\sqrt{2\pi}} e^{-z^2/2} \qquad (6.3)$$

As with other continuous random variables, probability calculations with any normal distribution are made by computing areas under the graph of the probability density function. Thus, to find the probability that a normal random variable is within any specific interval, we must compute the area under the normal curve over that interval.

For the normal probability density function, the height of the normal curve varies and the mathematics required to compute the areas that represent probability are beyond the scope of this text.

For the standard normal distribution, areas under the normal curve have been computed and are available in tables that can be used to compute probabilities. Such a table appears on the two pages inside the front cover of the text. The table on the left-hand page contains areas, or cumulative probabilities, for z values less than or equal to the mean of zero. The table on the right-hand page contains areas, or cumulative probabilities, for z values greater than or equal to the mean of zero.

The three types of probabilities we need to compute include (1) the probability that the standard normal random variable z will be less than or equal to a given value; (2) the probability that z will be between two given values; and (3) the probability that z will be greater than or equal to a given value. To see how the cumulative probability table for the standard normal distribution can be used to compute these three types of probabilities, let us consider some examples.

Because the standard normal random variable is continuous, $P(z \leq 1.00) = P(z < 1.00)$.

We start by showing how to compute the probability that z is less than or equal to 1.00; that is, $P(z \leq 1.00)$. This cumulative probability is the area under the normal curve to the left of $z = 1.00$ in the following graph.

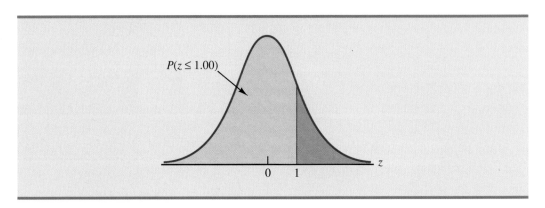

Refer to the right-hand page of the standard normal probability table inside the front cover of the text. The cumulative probability corresponding to $z = 1.00$ is the table value located at the intersection of the row labeled 1.0 and the column labeled .00. First we find 1.0 in the left column of the table and then find .00 in the top row of the table. By looking in the body of the table, we find that the 1.0 row and the .00 column intersect at the value of .8413; thus, $P(z \leq 1.00) = .8413$. The following excerpt from the probability table shows these steps.

z	.00	.01	.02
.			
.			
.			
.9	.8159	.8186	.8212
1.0	.8413	.8438	.8461
1.1	.8643	.8665	.8686
1.2	.8849	.8869	.8888
.			
.			
.			

$P(z \leq 1.00)$

To illustrate the second type of probability calculation we show how to compute the probability that z is in the interval between $-.50$ and 1.25; that is, $P(-.50 \leq z \leq 1.25)$. The following graph shows this area, or probability.

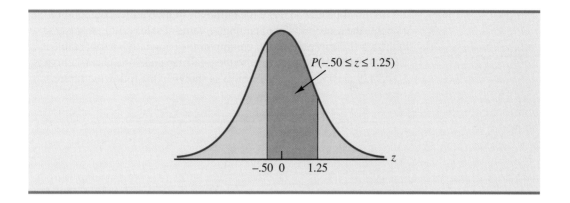

Three steps are required to compute this probability. First, we find the area under the normal curve to the left of $z = 1.25$. Second, we find the area under the normal curve to the left of $z = -.50$. Finally, we subtract the area to the left of $z = -.50$ from the area to the left of $z = 1.25$ to find $P(-.50 \le z \le 1.25)$.

To find the area under the normal curve to the left of $z = 1.25$, we first locate the 1.2 row in the standard normal probability table and then move across to the .05 column. Because the table value in the 1.2 row and the .05 column is .8944, $P(z \le 1.25) = .8944$. Similarly, to find the area under the curve to the left of $z = -.50$ we use the left-hand page of the table to locate the table value in the $-.5$ row and the .00 column; with a table value of .3085, $P(z \le -.50) = .3085$. Thus, $P(-.50 \le z \le 1.25) = P(z \le 1.25) - P(z \le -.50) = .8944 - .3085 = .5859$.

Let us consider another example of computing the probability that z is in the interval between two given values. Often it is of interest to compute the probability that a normal random variable assumes a value within a certain number of standard deviations of the mean. Suppose we want to compute the probability that the standard normal random variable is within one standard deviation of the mean; that is, $P(-1.00 \le z \le 1.00)$. To compute this probability we must find the area under the curve between -1.00 and 1.00. Earlier we found that $P(z \le 1.00) = .8413$. Referring again to the table inside the front cover of the book, we find that the area under the curve to the left of $z = -1.00$ is .1587, so $P(z \le -1.00) = .1587$. Therefore, $P(-1.00 \le z \le 1.00) = P(z \le 1.00) - P(z \le -1.00) = .8413 - .1587 = .6826$. This probability is shown graphically in the following figure.

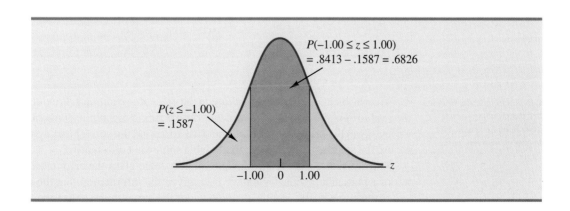

To illustrate how to make the third type of probability computation, suppose we want to compute the probability of obtaining a z value of at least 1.58; that is, $P(z \geq 1.58)$. The value in the $z = 1.5$ row and the .08 column of the cumulative normal table is .9429; thus, $P(z \leq 1.58) = .9429$. However, because the total area under the normal curve is 1, $P(z \geq 1.58) = 1 - .9429 = .0571$. This probability is shown in the following figure.

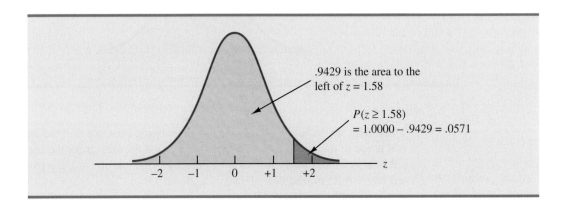

In the preceding illustrations, we showed how to compute probabilities given specified z values. In some situations, we are given a probability and are interested in working backward to find the corresponding z value. Suppose we want to find a z value such that the probability of obtaining a larger z value is .10. The following figure shows this situation graphically.

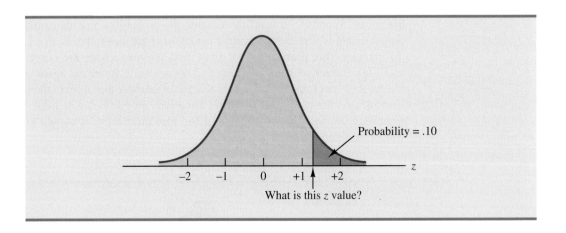

Given a probability, we can use the standard normal table in an inverse fashion to find the corresponding z value.

This problem is the inverse of those in the preceding examples. Previously, we specified the z value of interest and then found the corresponding probability, or area. In this example, we are given the probability, or area, and asked to find the corresponding z value. To do so, we use the standard normal probability table somewhat differently.

Recall that the standard normal probability table gives the area under the curve to the left of a particular z value. We have been given the information that the area in the upper tail of the curve is .10. Hence, the area under the curve to the left of the unknown z value must equal .9000. Scanning the body of the table, we find .8997 is the cumulative probability value closest to .9000. The section of the table providing this result follows.

z	.06	.07	.08	.09
.				
.				
.				
1.0	.8554	.8577	.8599	.8621
1.1	.8770	.8790	.8810	.8830
1.2	.8962	.8980	.8997	.9015
1.3	.9131	.9147	.9162	.9177
1.4	.9279	.9292	.9306	.9319
.				
.				
.				

Cumulative probability value
closest to .9000

Reading the z value from the left-most column and the top row of the table, we find that the corresponding z value is 1.28. Thus, an area of approximately .9000 (actually .8997) will be to the left of $z = 1.28$.* In terms of the question originally asked, there is an approximately .10 probability of a z value larger than 1.28.

Later we will show how Excel can be used to obtain these probabilities.

The examples illustrate that the table of cumulative probabilities for the standard normal probability distribution can be used to find probabilities associated with values of the standard normal random variable z. Two types of questions can be asked. The first type of question specifies a value, or values, for z and asks us to use the table to determine the corresponding areas or probabilities. The second type of question provides an area, or probability, and asks us to use the table to determine the corresponding z value. Thus, we need to be flexible in using the standard normal probability table to answer the desired probability question. In most cases, sketching a graph of the standard normal probability distribution and shading the appropriate area will help to visualize the situation and aid in determining the correct answer.

Computing Probabilities for Any Normal Probability Distribution

The reason for discussing the standard normal distribution so extensively is that probabilities for all normal distributions are computed by using the standard normal distribution. That is, when we have a normal distribution with any mean μ and any standard deviation σ, we answer probability questions about the distribution by first converting to the standard normal distribution. Then we can use the standard normal probability table and the appropriate z values to find the desired probabilities. The formula used to convert any normal random variable x with mean μ and standard deviation σ to the standard normal random variable z follows.

The formula for the standard normal random variable is similar to the formula we introduced in Chapter 3 for computing z-scores for a data set.

CONVERTING TO THE STANDARD NORMAL RANDOM VARIABLE

$$z = \frac{x - \mu}{\sigma}$$

(6.4)

*We could use interpolation in the body of the table to get a better approximation of the z value that corresponds to an area of .9000. Doing so to provide one more decimal place of accuracy would yield a z value of 1.282. However, in most practical situations, sufficient accuracy is obtained by simply using the table value closest to the desired probability.

A value of x equal to its mean μ results in $z = (\mu - \mu)/\sigma = 0$. Thus, we see that a value of x equal to its mean μ corresponds to $z = 0$. Now suppose that x is one standard deviation above its mean; that is, $x = \mu + \sigma$. Applying equation (6.4), we see that the corresponding z value is $z = [(\mu + \sigma) - \mu]/\sigma = \sigma/\sigma = 1$. Thus, an x value that is one standard deviation above its mean corresponds to $z = 1$. In other words, *we can interpret z as the number of standard deviations that the normal random variable x is from its mean μ.*

To see how this conversion enables us to compute probabilities for any normal distribution, suppose we have a normal distribution with $\mu = 10$ and $\sigma = 2$. What is the probability that the random variable x is between 10 and 14? Using equation (6.4), we see that at $x = 10$, $z = (x - \mu)/\sigma = (10 - 10)/2 = 0$ and that at $x = 14$, $z = (14 - 10)/2 = 4/2 = 2$. Thus, the answer to our question about the probability of x being between 10 and 14 is given by the equivalent probability that z is between 0 and 2 for the standard normal distribution. In other words, the probability that we are seeking is the probability that the random variable x is between its mean and two standard deviations above the mean. Using $z = 2.00$ and the standard normal probability table inside the front cover of the text, we see that $P(z \leq 2) = .9772$. Because $P(z \leq 0) = .5000$, we can compute $P(.00 \leq z \leq 2.00) = P(z \leq 2) - P(z \leq 0) = .9772 - .5000 = .4772$. Hence the probability that x is between 10 and 14 is .4772.

Grear Tire Company Problem

We turn now to an application of the normal probability distribution. Suppose the Grear Tire Company developed a new steel-belted radial tire to be sold through a national chain of discount stores. Because the tire is a new product, Grear's managers believe that the mileage guarantee offered with the tire will be an important factor in the acceptance of the product. Before finalizing the tire mileage guarantee policy, Grear's managers want probability information about x = number of miles the tires will last.

From actual road tests with the tires, Grear's engineering group estimated that the mean tire mileage is $\mu = 36{,}500$ miles and that the standard deviation is $\sigma = 5000$. In addition, the data collected indicate that a normal distribution is a reasonable assumption. What percentage of the tires can be expected to last more than 40,000 miles? In other words, what is the probability that the tire mileage, x, will exceed 40,000? This question can be answered by finding the area of the darkly shaded region in Figure 6.6.

FIGURE 6.6   GREAR TIRE COMPANY MILEAGE DISTRIBUTION

At $x = 40,000$, we have

$$z = \frac{x - \mu}{\sigma} = \frac{40,000 - 36,500}{5000} = \frac{3500}{5000} = .70$$

Refer now to the bottom of Figure 6.6. We see that a value of $x = 40,000$ on the Grear Tire normal distribution corresponds to a value of $z = .70$ on the standard normal distribution. Using the standard normal probability table, we see that the area under the standard normal curve to the left of $z = .70$ is .7580. Thus, $1.000 - .7580 = .2420$ is the probability that z will exceed .70 and hence x will exceed 40,000. We can conclude that about 24.2% of the tires will exceed 40,000 in mileage.

Let us now assume that Grear is considering a guarantee that will provide a discount on replacement tires if the original tires do not provide the guaranteed mileage. What should the guarantee mileage be if Grear wants no more than 10% of the tires to be eligible for the discount guarantee? This question is interpreted graphically in Figure 6.7.

According to Figure 6.7, the area under the curve to the left of the unknown guarantee mileage must be .10. So, we must first find the z-value that cuts off an area of .10 in the left tail of a standard normal distribution. Using the standard normal probability table, we see that $z = -1.28$ cuts off an area of approximately .10 in the lower tail. Hence, $z = -1.28$ is the value of the standard normal random variable corresponding to the desired mileage guarantee on the Grear Tire normal distribution. To find the value of x corresponding to $z = -1.28$, we have

The guarantee mileage we need to find is 1.28 standard deviations below the mean. Thus, $x = \mu - 1.28\sigma$.

$$z = \frac{x - \mu}{\sigma} = -1.28$$
$$x - \mu = -1.28\sigma$$
$$x = \mu - 1.28\sigma$$

With $\mu = 36,500$ and $\sigma = 5000$,

$$x = 36,500 - 1.28(5000) = 30,100$$

With the guarantee set at 30,000 miles, the actual percentage eligible for the guarantee will be 9.68%.

Thus, a guarantee of 30,100 miles will meet the requirement that approximately 10% of the tires will be eligible for the guarantee. Perhaps, with this information, the firm will set its tire mileage guarantee at 30,000 miles.

FIGURE 6.7 GREAR'S DISCOUNT GUARANTEE

Again, we see the important role that probability distributions play in providing decision-making information. Namely, once a probability distribution is established for a particular application, it can be used to obtain probability information about the problem. Probability does not make a decision recommendation directly, but it provides information that helps the decision maker better understand the risks and uncertainties associated with the problem. Ultimately, this information may assist the decision maker in reaching a good decision.

Using Excel to Compute Normal Probabilities

Excel provides two functions for computing probabilities and z values for a standard normal probability distribution: NORMSDIST and NORMSINV. The NORMSDIST function computes the cumulative probability given a z value, and the NORMSINV function computes the z value given a cumulative probability. Two similar functions, NORMDIST and NORMINV, are available for computing the cumulative probability and the x value for any normal distribution. We begin by showing how to use the NORMSDIST and NORMSINV functions.

The letter S that appears in the name of the NORMSDIST and NORMSINV functions reminds us that these functions relate to the standard normal probability distribution.

The NORMSDIST function provides the area under the standard normal curve to the left of a given z value; thus, it provides the same cumulative probability we would obtain if we used the standard normal probability table inside the front cover of the text. Using the NORMSDIST function is just like having Excel look up cumulative normal probabilities for you. The NORMSINV function is the inverse of the NORMSDIST function; it takes a cumulative probability as input and provides the z value corresponding to that cumulative probability.

Let's see how both of these functions work by computing the probabilities and z values obtained earlier in this section using the standard normal probability table. Refer to Figure 6.8 as we describe the tasks involved. The formula worksheet is in the background; the value worksheet is in the foreground.

Enter Data: No data are entered in the worksheet. We will simply enter the appropriate z values and probabilities directly into the formulas as needed.

Enter Functions and Formulas: The NORMSDIST function has one input: the z value for which we want to obtain the cumulative probability. To illustrate the use of the NORMSDIST function we compute the four probabilities shown in cells D3:D6 of Figure 6.8.

FIGURE 6.8   EXCEL WORKSHEET FOR COMPUTING PROBABILITIES AND z VALUES FOR THE STANDARD NORMAL DISTRIBUTION

	A	B	C	D		E				
1			Probabilities: Standard Normal Distribution							
2										
3			$P(z <= 1)$	=NORMSDIST(1)			A	B	C	D	E
4			$P(-.50 <= z <= 1.25)$	=NORMSDIST(1.25)-NORMSDIST(-0.5)		1	Probabilities: Standard Normal Distribution				
5			$P(-1.00 <= z <= 1.00)$	=NORMSDIST(1)-NORMSDIST(-1)		2					
6			$P(z >= 1.58)$	=1-NORMSDIST(1.58)		3			$P(z <= 1)$	0.8413	
7						4		$P(-.50 <= z <= 1.25)$		0.5858	
8						5		$P(-1.00 <= z <= 1.00)$		0.6827	
9			Finding z values Given Probabilities			6			$P(z >= 1.58)$	0.0571	
10						7					
11			z value with .10 in upper tail	=NORMSINV(0.9)		8					
12			z value with .025 in upper tail	=NORMSINV(0.975)		9		Finding z values Given Probabilities			
13			z value with .025 in lower tail	=NORMSINV(0.025)		10					
14						11		z value with .10 in upper tail		1.28	
						12		z value with .025 in upper tail		1.96	
						13		z value with .025 in lower tail		-1.96	
						14					

To compute the cumulative probability to the left of a given z value (area in lower tail), we simply evaluate NORMSDIST at the z value. For instance, to compute $P(z \leq 1)$ we entered the formula =NORMSDIST(1) into cell D3. The result, .8413, is the same as obtained using the standard normal probability table.

To compute the probability of z being in an interval we compute the value of NORMSDIST at the upper endpoint of the interval and subtract the value of NORMSDIST at the lower endpoint of the interval. For instance, to find $P(-.50 \leq z \leq 1.25)$, we enter the formula =NORMSDIST(1.25)−NORMSDIST(−.50) into cell D4. The interval probability in cell D5 is computed in a similar fashion.

The probability in cell D4, 0.5858, differs from what we computed earlier (.5859) due to rounding.

To compute the probability to the right of a given z value (upper tail area), we must subtract the cumulative probability represented by the area under the curve below the z value (lower tail area) from 1. For example, to compute $P(z \geq 1.58)$ we entered the formula =1-NORMSDIST(1.58) into cell D6.

To compute the z value corresponding to a given cumulative probability (lower tail area), we use the NORMSINV function. To find the z value corresponding to an upper tail probability of .10, we note that the corresponding lower tail area is .90 and enter the formula =NORMSINV(0.9) into cell D11. Actually, NORMSINV(0.9) gives us the z value providing a cumulative probability (lower tail area) of .9. But it is also the z value corresponding to an upper tail area of .10.

Two other z values are computed in Figure 6.8. These z values will be used extensively in succeeding chapters. To compute the z value corresponding to an upper tail probability of .025, we entered the formula =NORMSINV(0.975) into cell D12. To compute the z value corresponding to a lower tail probability of .025, we entered the formula =NORMSINV(0.025) into cell D13. We see that $z = 1.96$ corresponds to an upper tail probability of .025, and $z = -1.96$ corresponds to a lower tail probability of .025.

Let us now turn to the Excel functions for computing cumulative probabilities and x values for any normal distribution. The NORMDIST function provides the area under the normal curve to the left of a given value of the random variable x; thus it provides cumulative probabilities. The NORMINV function is the inverse of the NORMDIST function; it takes a cumulative probability as input and provides the value of x corresponding to that cumulative probability. The NORMDIST and NORMINV functions do the same thing for any normal distribution that the NORMSDIST and NORMSINV functions do for the standard normal distribution.

Let's see how both of these functions work by computing probabilities and x values for the Grear Tire Company example introduced earlier in this section. Recall that the lifetime of a Grear tire has a mean of 36,500 miles and a standard deviation of 5000 miles. Refer to Figure 6.9 as we describe the tasks involved. The formula worksheet is in the background; the value worksheet is in the foreground.

Enter Data: No data are entered in the worksheet. We simply enter the appropriate x values and probabilities directly into the formulas as needed.

Enter Functions and Formulas: The NORMDIST function has four inputs: (1) the x value we want to compute the cumulative probability for, (2) the mean, (3) the standard deviation, and (4) a value of TRUE or FALSE. For the fourth input, we enter TRUE if a cumulative probability is desired, and we enter FALSE if the height of the curve is desired. Because we will always be using NORMDIST to compute cumulative probabilities, we will always choose TRUE for the fourth input.

To compute the cumulative probability to the left of a given x value (lower tail area), we simply evaluate NORMDIST at the x value. For instance, to compute the probability that a Grear tire will last 20,000 miles or less, we entered the formula =NORMDIST(20000,36500,5000,TRUE) into cell D3. The value worksheet shows that this cumulative probability is .0005. So, we can conclude that almost all Grear tires will last at least 20,000 miles.

FIGURE 6.9 EXCEL WORKSHEET FOR COMPUTING PROBABILITIES AND x VALUES FOR THE NORMAL DISTRIBUTION

	A	B	C	D	E	F
1			Probabilities: Normal Distribution			
2						
3			$P(x <= 20000)$	=NORMDIST(20000,36500,5000,TRUE)		
4			$P(20000 <= x <= 40000)$	=NORMDIST(40000,36500,5000,TRUE)-NORMDIST(20000,36500,5000,TRUE)		
5			$P(x >= 40000)$	=1-NORMDIST(40000,36500,5000,TRUE)		
6						
7			Finding x values Given Probabilities			
8						
9			x value with .10 in lower tail	=NORMINV(0.1,36500,5000)		
10			x value with .025 in upper tail	=NORMINV(0.975,36500,5000)		
11						

	A	B	C	D	E	F
1	Probabilities: Normal Distribution					
2						
3			$P(x <= 20000)$	0.0005		
4			$P(20000 <= x <= 40000)$	0.7576		
5			$P(x >= 40000)$	0.2420		
6						
7	Finding x values Given Probabilities					
8						
9		x value with .10 in lower tail		30092.24		
10		x value with .025 in upper tail		46299.82		
11						

To compute the probability of x being in an interval we compute the value of NORMDIST at the upper endpoint of the interval and subtract the value of NORMDIST at the lower endpoint of the interval. The formula in cell D4 provides the probability that a tire's lifetime is between 20,000 and 40,000 miles, $P(20,000 \le x \le 40,000)$. In the value worksheet, we see that this probability is .7576.

To compute the probability to the right of a given x value (upper tail area), we must subtract the cumulative probability represented by the area under the curve below the x value (lower tail area) from 1. The formula in cell D5 computes the probability that a Grear tire will last for at least 40,000 miles. We see that this probability is .2420.

To compute the x value for a given cumulative probability, we use the NORMINV function. The NORMINV function has only three inputs. The first input is the cumulative probability; the second and third inputs are the mean and standard deviation. For instance, to compute the tire mileage corresponding to a lower tail area of .1 for Grear Tire, we enter the formula =NORMINV(0.1,36500,5000) into cell D9. From the value worksheet, we see that 10% of the Grear tires will last for 30,092.24 miles or less.

To compute the minimum tire mileage for the top 2.5% of Grear tires, we want to find the value of x corresponding to an area of .025 in the upper tail. This calculation is the same as finding the x value that provides a cumulative probability of .975. Thus we entered the formula =NORMINV(0.975,36500,5000) into cell D10 to compute this tire mileage. From the value worksheet, we see that 2.5% of the Grear tires will last at least 46,299.82 miles.

EXERCISES

Methods

8. Using Figure 6.4 as a guide, sketch a normal curve for a random variable x that has a mean of $\mu = 100$ and a standard deviation of $\sigma = 10$. Label the horizontal axis with values of 70, 80, 90, 100, 110, 120, and 130.

Exponential Probability Density Function

$$f(x) = \frac{1}{\mu} e^{-x/\mu} \qquad \text{for } x \geq 0, \mu > 0 \qquad \text{(6.5)}$$

Exponential Distribution: Cumulative Probabilities

$$P(x \leq x_0) = 1 - e^{-x_0/\mu} \qquad \text{(6.6)}$$

Supplementary Exercises

33. A business executive, transferred from Chicago to Atlanta, needs to sell her house in Chicago quickly. The executive's employer has offered to buy the house for $210,000, but the offer expires at the end of the week. The executive does not currently have a better offer, but can afford to leave the house on the market for another month. From conversations with her realtor, the executive believes the price she will get by leaving the house on the market for another month is uniformly distributed between $200,000 and $225,000.
     a. If she leaves the house on the market for another month, what is the mathematical expression for the probability density function of the sales price?
     b. If she leaves it on the market for another month, what is the probability she will get at least $215,000 for the house?
     c. If she leaves it on the market for another month, what is the probability she will get less than $210,000?
     d. Should the executive leave the house on the market for another month? Why or why not?

34. The U.S. Bureau of Labor Statistics reports that the average annual expenditure on food and drink for all families is $5700 (*Money,* December 2003). Assume that annual expenditure on food and drink is normally distributed and that the standard deviation is $1500.
     a. What is the range of expenditures of the 10% of families with the lowest annual spending on food and drink?
     b. What percentage of families spend more than $7000 annually on food and drink?
     c. What is the range of expenditures for the 5% of families with the highest annual spending on food and drink?

35. Motorola used the normal distribution to determine the probability of defects and the number of defects expected in a production process. Assume a production process produces items with a mean weight of 10 ounces. Calculate the probability of a defect and the expected number of defects for a 1000-unit production run in the following situations.
     a. The process standard deviation is .15, and the process control is set at plus or minus one standard deviation. Units with weights less than 9.85 or greater than 10.15 ounces will be classified as defects.
     b. Through process design improvements, the process standard deviation can be reduced to .05. Assume the process control remains the same, with weights less than 9.85 or greater than 10.15 ounces being classified as defects.
     c. What is the advantage of reducing process variation, thereby causing process control limits to be at a greater number of standard deviations from the mean?

36. The average annual amount American households spend for daily transportation is $6312 (*Money,* August 2001). Assume that the amount spent is normally distributed.
     a. Suppose you learn that 5% of American households spend less than $1000 for daily transportation. What is the standard deviation of the amount spent?
     b. What is the probability that a household spends between $4000 and $6000?
     c. What is the range of spending for the 3% of households with the highest daily transportation cost?

37.   *Condé Nast Traveler* publishes a Gold List of the top hotels all over the world. The Broadmoor Hotel in Colorado Springs contains 700 rooms and is on the 2004 Gold List (*Condé Nast Traveler,* January 2004). Suppose Broadmoor's marketing group forecasts a mean demand of 670 rooms for the coming weekend. Assume that demand for the upcoming weekend is normally distributed with a standard deviation of 30.

   a.   What is the probability all the hotel's room will be rented?

   b.   What is the probability 50 or more rooms will not be rented?

   c.   Would you recommend the hotel consider offering a promotion to increase demand? What considerations would be important?

38.   Ward Doering Auto Sales is considering offering a special service contract that will cover the total cost of any service work required on leased vehicles. From experience, the company manager estimates that yearly service costs are approximately normally distributed, with a mean of $150 and a standard deviation of $25.

   a.   If the company offers the service contract to customers for a yearly charge of $200, what is the probability that any one customer's service costs will exceed the contract price of $200?

   b.   What is Ward's expected profit per service contract?

39.   Is lack of sleep causing traffic fatalities? A study conducted under the auspices of the National Highway Traffic Safety Administration found that the average number of fatal crashes caused by drowsy drivers each year was 1550 (*Business Week,* January 26, 2004). Assume the annual number of fatal crashes per year is normally distributed with a standard deviation of 300.

   a.   What is the probability of fewer than 1000 fatal crashes in a year?

   b.   What is the probability the number of fatal crashes will be between 1000 and 2000 for a year?

   c.   For a year to be in the upper 5% with respect to the number of fatal crashes, how many fatal crashes would have to occur?

40.   Assume that the test scores from a college admissions test are normally distributed, with a mean of 450 and a standard deviation of 100.

   a.   What percentage of the people taking the test score between 400 and 500?

   b.   Suppose someone receives a score of 630. What percentage of the people taking the test score better? What percentage score worse?

   c.   If a particular university will not admit anyone scoring below 480, what percentage of the persons taking the test would be acceptable to the university?

41.   According to *Advertising Age,* the average base salary for women working as copywriters in advertising firms is higher than the average base salary for men. The average base salary for women is $67,000 and the average base salary for men is $65,500 (*Working Woman,* July/August 2000). Assume salaries are normally distributed and that the standard deviation is $7000 for both men and women.

   a.   What is the probability of a woman receiving a salary in excess of $75,000?

   b.   What is the probability of a man receiving a salary in excess of $75,000?

   c.   What is the probability of a woman receiving a salary below $50,000?

   d.   How much would a woman have to make to have a higher salary than 99% of her male counterparts?

42.   A machine fills containers with a particular product. The standard deviation of filling weights is known from past data to be .6 ounce. If only 2% of the containers hold less than 18 ounces, what is the mean filling weight for the machine? That is, what must μ equal? Assume the filling weights have a normal distribution.

43.   The time in minutes for which a student uses a computer terminal at the computer center of a major university follows an exponential probability distribution with a mean of 36 minutes. Assume a student arrives at the terminal just as another student is beginning to work on the terminal.

a. What is the probability that the wait for the second student will be 15 minutes or less?
b. What is the probability that the wait for the second student will be between 15 and 45 minutes?
c. What is the probability that the second student will have to wait an hour or more?

44. The Web site for the Bed and Breakfast Inns of North America (http://www.cimarron.net) gets approximately seven visitors per minute (*Time,* September 2001). Suppose the number of Web site visitors per minute follows a Poisson probability distribution.
a. What is the mean time between visits to the Web site?
b. Show the exponential probability density function for the time between Web site visits.
c. What is the probability no one will access the Web site in a 1-minute period?
d. What is the probability no one will access the Web site in a 12-second period?

45. The average travel time to work for New York City residents is 36.5 minutes (*Time Almanac,* 2001).
a. Assume the exponential probability distribution is applicable and show the probability density function for the travel time to work for a typical New Yorker.
b. What is the probability it will take a typical New Yorker between 20 and 40 minutes to travel to work?
c. What is the probability it will take a typical New Yorker more than 40 minutes to travel to work?

46. The time (in minutes) between telephone calls at an insurance claims office has the following exponential probability distribution.

$$f(x) = .50e^{-.50x} \qquad \text{for } x \geq 0$$

a. What is the mean time between telephone calls?
b. What is the probability of having 30 seconds or less between telephone calls?
c. What is the probability of having 1 minute or less between telephone calls?
d. What is the probability of having 5 or more minutes without a telephone call?

Case Problem   Specialty Toys

Specialty Toys, Inc., sells a variety of new and innovative children's toys. Management learned that the preholiday season is the best time to introduce a new toy, because many families use this time to look for new ideas for December holiday gifts. When Specialty discovers a new toy with good market potential, it chooses an October market entry date.

In order to get toys in its stores by October, Specialty places one-time orders with its manufacturers in June or July of each year. Demand for children's toys can be highly volatile. If a new toy catches on, a sense of shortage in the marketplace often increases the demand to high levels and large profits can be realized. However, new toys can also flop, leaving Specialty stuck with high levels of inventory that must be sold at reduced prices. The most important question the company faces is deciding how many units of a new toy should be purchased to meet anticipated sales demand. If too few are purchased, sales will be lost; if too many are purchased, profits will be reduced because of low prices realized in clearance sales.

For the coming season, Specialty plans to introduce a new product called Weather Teddy. This variation of a talking teddy bear is made by a company in Taiwan. When a child presses Teddy's hand, the bear begins to talk. A built-in barometer selects one of five responses that predict the weather conditions. The responses range from "It looks to be a very nice day! Have fun" to "I think it may rain today. Don't forget your umbrella." Tests with the product show that, even though it is not a perfect weather predictor, its predictions are surprisingly good. Several of Specialty's managers claimed Teddy gave predictions of the weather that were as good as many local television weather forecasters.

As with other products, Specialty faces the decision of how many Weather Teddy units to order for the coming holiday season. Members of the management team suggested order quantities of 15,000, 18,000, 24,000, or 28,000 units. The wide range of order quantities suggested indicates considerable disagreement concerning the market potential. The product management team asks you for an analysis of the stock-out probabilities for various order quantities, an estimate of the profit potential, and to help make an order quantity recommendation. Specialty expects to sell Weather Teddy for $24 based on a cost of $16 per unit. If inventory remains after the holiday season, Specialty will sell all surplus inventory for $5 per unit. After reviewing the sales history of similar products, Specialty's senior sales forecaster predicted an expected demand of 20,000 units with a 0.90 probability that demand would be between 10,000 units and 30,000 units.

Managerial Report

Prepare a managerial report that addresses the following issues and recommends an order quantity for the Weather Teddy product.

1. Use the sales forecaster's prediction to describe a normal probability distribution that can be used to approximate the demand distribution. Sketch the distribution and show its mean and standard deviation.
2. Compute the probability of a stock-out for the order quantities suggested by members of the management team.
3. Compute the projected profit for the order quantities suggested by the management team under three scenarios: worst case in which sales = 10,000 units, most likely case in which sales = 20,000 units, and best case in which sales = 30,000 units.
4. One of Specialty's managers felt that the profit potential was so great that the order quantity should have a 70% chance of meeting demand and only a 30% chance of any stock-outs. What quantity would be ordered under this policy, and what is the projected profit under the three sales scenarios?
5. Provide your own recommendation for an order quantity and note the associated profit projections. Provide a rationale for your recommendation.

CHAPTER 7

Sampling and Sampling Distributions

CONTENTS

MEADWESTVACO CORPORATION*
STAMFORD, CONNECTICUT

MeadWestvaco Corporation, a leading producer of packaging, coated and specialty papers, consumer and office products, and specialty chemicals, employs more than 30,000 people. It operates worldwide in 33 countries and serves customers located in approximately 100 countries. MeadWestvaco holds a leading position in paper production, with an annual capacity of 1.8 million tons. The company's products include textbook paper, glossy magazine paper, beverage packaging systems, and office products. MeadWestvaco's internal consulting group uses sampling to provide a variety of information that enables the company to obtain significant productivity benefits and remain competitive.

For example, MeadWestvaco maintains large woodland holdings, which supply the trees, or raw material, for many of the company's products. Managers need reliable and accurate information about the timberlands and forests to evaluate the company's ability to meet its future raw material needs. What is the present volume in the forests? What is the past growth of the forests? What is the projected future growth of the forests? With answers to these important questions MeadWestvaco's managers can develop plans for the future, including long-term planting and harvesting schedules for the trees.

How does MeadWestvaco obtain the information it needs about its vast forest holdings? Data collected from sample plots throughout the forests are the basis for learning about the population of trees owned by the company. To identify the sample plots, the timberland holdings are first divided into three sections based on location and types of tree. Using maps and random numbers, MeadWestvaco analysts identify random samples of ⅕- to ⅐-acre plots in each section of the

Random sampling of its forest holdings enables MeadWestvaco Corporation to meet future raw material needs. © Walter Hodges/Corbis.

forest. MeadWestvaco foresters collect data from these sample plots to learn about the forest population.

Foresters throughout the organization participate in the field data collection process. Periodically, two-person teams gather information on each tree in every sample plot. The sample data are entered into the company's continuous forest inventory (CFI) computer system. Reports from the CFI system include a number of frequency distribution summaries containing statistics on types of trees, present forest volume, past forest growth rates, and projected future forest growth and volume. Sampling and the associated statistical summaries of the sample data provide the reports essential for the effective management of MeadWestvaco's forests and timberlands.

In this chapter you will learn about simple random sampling and the sample selection process. In addition, you will learn how statistics such as the sample mean and sample proportion are used to estimate the population mean and population proportion. The important concept of a sampling distribution is also introduced.

*The authors are indebted to Dr. Edward P. Winkofsky for providing this Statistics in Practice.

In Chapter 1, we defined a *population* and a *sample*. The definitions are restated here.

1. A *population* is the set of all the elements of interest in a study.
2. A *sample* is a subset of the population.

Numerical characteristics of a population, such as the mean and standard deviation, are called **parameters**. A primary purpose of statistical inference is to develop estimates and test hypotheses about population parameters using information contained in a sample.

Let us begin by citing two situations in which samples provide estimates of population parameters.

1. A tire manufacturer developed a new tire designed to provide an increase in mileage over the firm's current line of tires. To estimate the mean number of miles provided by the new tires, the manufacturer selected a sample of 120 new tires for testing. The test results provided a sample mean of 36,500 miles. Hence, an estimate of the mean tire mileage for the population of new tires is 36,500 miles.
2. Members of a political party were considering supporting a particular candidate for election to the U.S. Senate, and party leaders wanted an estimate of the proportion of registered voters favoring the candidate. The time and cost associated with contacting every individual in the population of registered voters were prohibitive. Hence, a sample of 400 registered voters was selected and 160 of the 400 voters indicated a preference for the candidate. An estimate of the proportion of the population of registered voters favoring the candidate is 160/400 = .40.

These two examples illustrate some of the reasons why samples are used. Note that in the tire mileage example, collecting the data on tire life involves wearing out each tire tested. Clearly it is not feasible to test every tire in the population; a sample is the only realistic way to obtain the desired tire mileage data. In the example involving the election, contacting every registered voter in the population is theoretically possible, but the time and cost in doing so are prohibitive; thus, a sample of registered voters is preferred.

A sample mean provides an estimate of a population mean, and a sample proportion provides an estimate of a population proportion. With estimates such as these, some estimation error can be expected. This chapter provides the basis for determining how large that error might be.

It is important to realize that sample results provide only *estimates* of the values of the population characteristics. We do not expect the sample mean of 36,500 miles to exactly equal the mean mileage for all tires in the population, nor do we expect exactly .40, or 40%, of the population of registered voters to favor the candidate. The reason is simply that the sample contains only a portion of the population. With proper sampling methods, the sample results will provide "good" estimates of the population parameters. But how good can we expect the sample results to be? Fortunately, statistical procedures are available for answering this question.

In this chapter we show how simple random sampling can be used to select a sample from a population. We then show how data obtained from a simple random sample can be used to compute estimates of a population mean, a population standard deviation, and a population proportion. In addition, we introduce the important concept of a sampling distribution. As we show, knowledge of the appropriate sampling distribution is what enables us to make statements about how close the sample estimates are to the corresponding population parameters. The last section discusses some alternatives to simple random sampling that are often employed in practice.

7.1   The Electronics Associates Sampling Problem

The director of personnel for Electronics Associates, Inc. (EAI), has been assigned the task of developing a profile of the company's 2500 managers. The characteristics to be identified include the mean annual salary for the managers and the proportion of managers having completed the company's management training program.

Using the 2500 managers as the population for this study, we can find the annual salary and the training program status for each individual by referring to the firm's personnel records. The data file containing this information for all 2500 managers in the population is on the CD that accompanies the text.

EAI

Using the EAI data set and the formulas presented in Chapter 3, we compute the population mean and the population standard deviation for the annual salary data.

$$\text{Population mean: } \mu = \$51{,}800$$
$$\text{Population standard deviation: } \sigma = \$4000$$

The data for the training program status show that 1500 of the 2500 managers completed the training program. Letting p denote the proportion of the population that completed the training program, we see that $p = 1500/2500 = .60$. The population mean annual salary ($\mu = \$51,800$), the population standard deviation of annual salary ($\sigma = \$4000$), and the population proportion that completed the training program ($p = .60$) are parameters of the population of EAI managers.

Now, suppose that the necessary information on all the EAI managers was not readily available in the company's database. The question we now consider is how the firm's director of personnel can obtain estimates of the population parameters by using a sample of managers rather than all 2500 managers in the population. Suppose that a sample of 30 managers will be used. Clearly, the time and the cost of developing a profile would be substantially less for 30 managers than for the entire population. If the personnel director could be assured that a sample of 30 managers would provide adequate information about the population of 2500 managers, working with a sample would be preferable to working with the entire population. Let us explore the possibility of using a sample for the EAI study by first showing how to select a sample of 30 managers.

Often the cost of collecting information from a sample is substantially less than from a population, especially when personal interviews must be conducted to collect the information.

 ## 7.2 Simple Random Sampling

Several methods can be used to select a sample from a population; one of the most common is **simple random sampling**. The definition of a simple random sample and the process of selecting a simple random sample depend on whether the population is *finite* or *infinite*. Because the EAI sampling problem involves a finite population of 2500 managers, we first consider sampling from a finite population.

Sampling from a Finite Population

A simple random sample of size n from a finite population of size N is defined as follows.

> **SIMPLE RANDOM SAMPLE (FINITE POPULATION)**
>
> A simple random sample of size n from a finite population of size N is a sample selected such that each possible sample of size n has the same probability of being selected.

The random numbers generated using Excel's RAND function follow a uniform probability distribution between 0 and 1.

The procedures used to select a simple random sample from a finite population are based upon the use of random numbers. We can use Excel's RAND function to generate a random number between 0 and 1 by entering the formula =RAND() into any cell in a worksheet. The number generated is called a random number because the mathematical procedure used by the RAND function guarantees that every number between 0 and 1 has the same probability of being selected. Let us see how these random numbers can be used to select a simple random sample.

Our procedure for selecting a simple random sample of size n from a population of size N involves two steps.

Step 1. Assign a random number to each element of the population.
Step 2. Select the n elements corresponding to the n smallest random numbers.

Because each set of n elements in the population has the same probability of being assigned the n smallest random numbers, each set of n elements has the same probability of being selected for the sample. If we select the sample using this two-step procedure, every sample of size n has the same probability of being selected; thus, the sample selected satisfies the definition of a simple random sample.

TABLE 7.1   NATIONAL BASEBALL LEAGUE TEAMS

Arizona	Milwaukee
Atlanta	New York
Chicago	Philadelphia
Cincinnati	Pittsburgh
Colorado	San Diego
Florida	San Francisco
Houston	St. Louis
Los Angeles	Washington

Let us consider an example involving selecting a simple random sample of size $n = 5$ from a population of size $N = 16$. Table 7.1 contains a list of the 16 teams in the National Baseball League. Suppose we want to select a simple random sample of 5 teams to conduct in-depth interviews about how they manage their minor league franchises.

Step 1 of our simple random sampling procedure requires that we assign a random number to each of the 16 teams in the population. Figure 7.1 shows a worksheet used to generate a random number corresponding to each of the 16 teams in the population. The names of the baseball teams are in column A, and the random numbers generated are in column B. From the formula worksheet in the background we see that the formula =RAND( ) has been entered into cells B2:B17 to generate the random numbers between 0 and 1. From the value worksheet in the foreground we see that Arizona is assigned the random number .850862, Atlanta has been assigned the random number .706245, and so on.

FIGURE 7.1   WORKSHEET USED TO GENERATE A RANDOM NUMBER CORRESPONDING TO EACH TEAM

National League

	A	B	C
1	**Team**	**Random Numbers**	
2	Arizona	=RAND()	
3	Atlanta	=RAND()	
4	Chicago	=RAND()	
5	Cincinnati	=RAND()	
6	Colorado	=RAND()	
7	Florida	=RAND()	
8	Houston	=RAND()	
9	Los Angeles	=RAND()	
10	Milwaukee	=RAND()	
11	New York	=RAND()	
12	Philadelphia	=RAND()	
13	Pittsburgh	=RAND()	
14	San Diego	=RAND()	
15	San Francisco	=RAND()	
16	St. Louis	=RAND()	
17	Washington	=RAND()	
18			

	A	B	C
1	**Team**	**Random Numbers**	
2	Arizona	0.850862	
3	Atlanta	0.706245	
4	Chicago	0.724789	
5	Cincinnati	0.614784	
6	Colorado	0.553815	
7	Florida	0.857324	
8	Houston	0.179123	
9	Los Angeles	0.525636	
10	Milwaukee	0.471490	
11	New York	0.523103	
12	Philadelphia	0.851552	
13	Pittsburgh	0.806185	
14	San Diego	0.327713	
15	San Francisco	0.374168	
16	St. Louis	0.066942	
17	Washington	0.158452	
18			

The second step is to select the five teams corresponding to the five smallest random numbers as our sample. Looking through the random numbers in Figure 7.1, we see that the team corresponding to the smallest random number (.066942) is St. Louis, and that the four teams corresponding to the next four smallest random numbers are Washington, Houston, San Diego, and San Francisco. Thus, these five teams make up the simple random sample.

Searching through the list of random numbers in Figure 7.1 to find the five smallest random numbers is tedious, and it is easy to make mistakes. Excel's SORT procedure simplifies this step. We illustrate by sorting the list of baseball teams in Figure 7.1 to find the five teams corresponding to the five smallest random numbers. Refer to the foreground worksheet in Figure 7.1 as we describe the steps involved.

Step 1. Select cells A2:B17
Step 2. Select the **Data** menu
Step 3. Choose the **Sort** option
Step 4. When the Sort dialog box appears:
        Choose **Random Numbers** in the **Sort by** text box
        Choose **Ascending**
        Click **OK**

After completing these steps we obtain the worksheet shown in Figure 7.2.* The teams listed in rows 2–6 are the ones corresponding to the smallest five random numbers; they are our simple random sample. Note that the random numbers shown in Figure 7.2 are in ascending order, and that the teams are not in their original order. For instance, St. Louis is the

FIGURE 7.2   USING EXCEL'S SORT PROCEDURE TO SELECT A SIMPLE RANDOM SAMPLE OF FIVE TEAMS

	A	B	C
1	**Team**	**Random Numbers**	
2	St. Louis	0.066942	
3	Washington	0.158452	
4	Houston	0.179123	
5	San Diego	0.327713	
6	San Francisco	0.374168	
7	Milwaukee	0.471490	
8	New York	0.523103	
9	Los Angeles	0.525636	
10	Colorado	0.553815	
11	Cincinnati	0.614784	
12	Atlanta	0.706245	
13	Chicago	0.724789	
14	Pittsburgh	0.806185	
15	Arizona	0.850862	
16	Philadelphia	0.851552	
17	Florida	0.857324	
18			

*In order to show the random numbers from Figure 7.1 in ascending order in this worksheet, we turned off the automatic recalculation option prior to sorting for illustrative purposes. If the recalculation option were not turned off, a new set of random numbers would have been generated when the sort was completed. But the same five teams would be selected.

The Excel sort procedure for identifying the managers associated with the 30 smallest random numbers is especially valuable with such a large population.

last team listed in Figure 7.1, but it is the first team selected in the simple random sample. Washington, the second team in our sample, is the tenth team in the original list, and so on.

We now use this simple random sampling procedure to select a simple random sample of 30 EAI managers from the population of 2500 EAI managers. We begin by generating 2500 random numbers, one for each manager in the population. Then we select 30 managers corresponding to the 30 smallest random numbers as our sample. Refer to Figure 7.3 as we describe the steps involved.

FIGURE 7.3 USING EXCEL TO SELECT A SIMPLE RANDOM SAMPLE WITHOUT REPLACEMENT

	A	B	C	D	E	F	G	H
1	Manager	Annual Salary	Training Program	Random Numbers				
2	1	55769.50	No	0.613872				
3	2	50823.00	Yes	0.473204				
4	3	48408.20	No	0.549011				
5	4	49787.50	No	0.047482				
6	5	52801.60	Yes	0.531085				
7	6	51767.70	No	0.994296				
8	7	58346.60	Yes	0.189065				
9	8	46670.20	No	0.020714				
10	9	50246.80	Yes	0.647318				
11	10	51255.00	No	0.524341				
12	11	52546.60	No	0.764998				
13	12	49512.50	Yes	0.255244				
14	13	51753.00	Yes	0.010923				
15	14	53547.10	No	0.238003				
16	15	48052.20	No	0.635675				
17	16	44652.50	Yes	0.177294				
18	17	51764.90	Yes	0.415097				
19	18	45187.80	Yes	0.883440				
20	19	49867.50	Yes	0.476824				
21	20	53706.30	Yes	0.101065				
22	21	52039.50	Yes	0.775323				
23	22	52973.60	No	0.011729				
24	23	53372.50	No	0.762026				
25	24	54592.00	Yes	0.066344				
26	25	55738.10	Yes	0.776766				
27	26	52975.10	Yes	0.828493				
28	27	52386.20	Yes	0.841532				
29	28	51051.60	Yes	0.899427				
30	29	52095.60	Yes	0.486284				
31	30	44956.50	No	0.264628				

The formula in cells D2:D2501 is =RAND().

Note: Rows 32–2501 are not shown.

	A	B	C	D	E
1	Manager	Annual Salary	Training Program	Random Numbers	
2	812	49094.30	Yes	0.000193	
3	1411	53263.90	Yes	0.000484	
4	1795	49643.50	Yes	0.002641	
5	2095	49894.90	Yes	0.002763	
6	1235	47621.60	No	0.002940	
7	744	55924.00	Yes	0.002977	
8	470	49092.30	Yes	0.003182	
9	1606	51404.40	Yes	0.003448	
10	1744	50957.70	Yes	0.004203	
11	179	55109.70	Yes	0.005293	
12	1387	45922.60	Yes	0.005709	
13	1782	57268.40	No	0.005729	
14	1006	55688.80	Yes	0.005796	
15	278	51564.70	No	0.005966	
16	1850	56188.20	No	0.006250	
17	844	51766.00	Yes	0.006708	
18	2028	52541.30	No	0.007767	
19	1654	44980.00	Yes	0.008095	
20	444	51932.60	Yes	0.009686	
21	556	52973.00	Yes	0.009711	
22	2449	45120.90	Yes	0.010595	
23	13	51753.00	Yes	0.010923	
24	2187	54391.80	No	0.011364	
25	1633	50164.20	No	0.011603	
26	22	52973.60	No	0.011729	
27	1530	50241.30	No	0.013570	
28	820	52793.90	No	0.013669	
29	1258	50979.40	Yes	0.014042	
30	2349	55860.90	Yes	0.014532	
31	1698	57309.10	No	0.014539	

Enter Data: The first three columns of the worksheet in the background show the annual salary data and training program status for the first 30 managers in the population of 2500 EAI managers. (The complete worksheet contains all 2500 managers.)

Enter Functions and Formulas: In the background worksheet, the label **Random Numbers** has been entered into cell D1 and the formula =RAND() has been entered into cells D2:D2501 to generate a random number between 0 and 1 for each of the 2500 EAI managers. The random number generated for the first manager is 0.613872, the random number generated for the second manager is 0.473204, and so on.

Apply Tools: All that remains is to find the managers associated with the 30 smallest random numbers. To do so we sort the data in columns A through D into ascending order by the random numbers in column D.

     Step 1. Select cells A2:D2501
     Step 2. Select the **Data** menu
     Step 3. Choose the **Sort** option
     Step 4. When the Sort dialog box appears
                Choose **Random Numbers** in the **Sort by** text box
                Choose **Ascending**
                Click **OK**

After completing these steps we obtain the worksheet shown in the foreground of Figure 7.3. The managers listed in rows 2–31 are the ones corresponding to the smallest 30 random numbers that were generated. Hence, this group of 30 managers is a simple random sample. Note that the random numbers shown in the foreground of Figure 7.3 are in ascending order, and that the managers are not in their original order. For instance, manager 812 in the population is associated with the smallest random number and is the first element in the sample, and manager 13 in the population (see row 14 of the background worksheet) has been included as the 22nd observation in the sample (row 23 of the foreground worksheet).

Sampling from an Infinite Population

In practice, a population being studied is usually considered infinite if it involves an ongoing process that makes listing or counting every element in the population impossible.

In some situations, the population is either infinite or so large that for practical purposes it must be treated as infinite. For example, suppose that a fast-food restaurant would like to obtain a profile of its customers by selecting a simple random sample of customers and asking each customer to complete a short questionnaire. In such situations, the ongoing process of customer visits to the restaurant can be viewed as coming from an infinite population. The definition of a simple random sample from an infinite population follows.

SIMPLE RANDOM SAMPLE (INFINITE POPULATION)

A simple random sample from an infinite population is a sample selected such that the following conditions are satisfied.

     1. Each element selected comes from the population.
     2. Each element is selected independently.

For infinite populations, a sample selection procedure must be specially devised to select the items independently and thus avoid a selection bias that gives higher selection probabilities to certain types of elements.

For the example of selecting a simple random sample of customers at a fast-food restaurant, the first requirement is satisfied by any customer who comes into the restaurant. The second requirement is satisfied by selecting customers independently. The purpose of the second requirement is to prevent selection bias. Selection bias would occur if, for instance, five consecutive customers selected were all friends who arrived together. We might expect these customers to exhibit similar profiles. Selection bias can be avoided by ensuring that the selection of a particular customer does not influence the selection of any other customer. In other words, the customers must be selected independently.

McDonald's, the fast-food restaurant leader, implemented a simple random sampling procedure for just such a situation. The sampling procedure was based on the fact that some customers presented discount coupons. Whenever a customer presented a discount coupon, the next customer served was asked to complete a customer profile questionnaire. Because arriving customers presented discount coupons randomly, and independently, this sampling plan ensured that customers were selected independently. Thus, the two requirements for a simple random sample from an infinite population were satisfied.

Infinite populations are often associated with an ongoing process that operates continuously over time. For example, parts being manufactured on a production line, transactions occurring at a bank, telephone calls arriving at a technical support center, and customers entering stores may all be viewed as coming from an infinite population. In such cases, a creative sampling procedure ensures that no selection bias occurs and that the sample elements are selected independently.

NOTES AND COMMENTS

The number of different simple random samples of size n that can be selected from a finite population of size N is

$$\frac{N!}{n!(N - n)!}$$

In this formula, $N!$ and $n!$ are the factorial computations discussed in Chapter 4. For the EAI problem with $N = 2500$ and $n = 30$, this expression can be used to show that approximately 2.75×10^{69} different simple random samples of 30 EAI managers are possible.

Exercises

Methods

1. Consider a finite population with five elements labeled A, B, C, D, and E. Ten possible simple random samples of size 2 can be selected.
   a. List the 10 samples beginning with AB, AC, and so on.
   b. Using simple random sampling, what is the probability that each sample of size 2 is selected?
   c. Suppose we use Excel's RAND function to assign random numbers to the five elements: A (.7266), B (.0476), C (.2459), D (.0957), E (.9408). List the simple random sample of size 2 that will be selected by using these random numbers.

2. Assume a finite population has 10 elements. Number the elements from 1 to 10 and use the following 10 random numbers to select a sample of size 4.

   .7545   .0936   .0341   .3242   .1449   .9060   .2420   .9773   .5428   .0729

3. The American League consists of 14 baseball teams. Suppose a sample of 5 teams is to be selected to conduct player interviews. The following table lists the 14 teams and the random numbers assigned by Excel's RAND function. Use these random numbers to select a sample of size 5.

American League

Team	Random Number	Team	Random Number
New York	0.178624	Boston	0.290197
Baltimore	0.578370	Tampa Bay	0.867778
Toronto	0.965807	Minnesota	0.811810
Chicago	0.562178	Cleveland	0.960271
Detroit	0.253574	Kansas City	0.326836
Oakland	0.288287	Los Angeles	0.895267
Texas	0.500879	Seattle	0.839071

4. The 10 most active issues on the New York Stock Exchange on September 17, 2004, are listed here (*The Sun News,* September 18, 2004).

Nortel	General Electric	Lucent	Pfizer	Texas Instruments
Exxon/Mobil	Citigroup	Wal-Mart	EMC	Motorola

Exchange authorities decided to sample three of these companies to investigate trading practices. Select a simple random sample of three companies for this investigation.

EAI

5. In this section we used a two-step procedure to select a simple random sample of 30 EAI managers. Use this procedure to select a simple random sample of 50 EAI managers.

6. Indicate whether the following populations should be considered finite or infinite.
   a. All registered voters in the state of California
   b. All television sets that could be produced by the Allentown, Pennsylvania, plant of the TV-M Company
   c. All orders that could be processed by a mail-order firm
   d. All emergency telephone calls that could come into a local police station
   e. All components that Fibercon, Inc., produced on the second shift on May 17

7.3   Point Estimation

Now that we described how to select a simple random sample, let us return to the sample selected for the EAI problem. The simple random sample of 30 managers selected using Excel and the corresponding data on annual salary and management training program participation are as shown in Table 7.2. The notation x_1, x_2, and so on is used to denote the annual salary of the first manager in the sample, the annual salary of the second manager in the sample, and so on. Participation in the management training program is indicated by Yes in the management training program column.

To estimate the value of a population parameter, we compute a corresponding characteristic of the sample, referred to as a **sample statistic**. For example, to estimate the population mean μ and the population standard deviation σ for the annual salary of EAI managers, we use the data in Table 7.2 to calculate the corresponding sample statistics: the sample mean $\bar{x}$ and the sample standard deviation s. Using the formulas for a sample mean and a sample standard deviation presented in Chapter 3, the sample mean is

$$\bar{x} = \frac{\Sigma x_i}{n} = \frac{1{,}554{,}420}{30} = \$51{,}814$$

TABLE 7.2 ANNUAL SALARY AND TRAINING PROGRAM STATUS FOR A SIMPLE RANDOM SAMPLE OF 30 EAI MANAGERS

Annual Salary ($)	Management Training Program	Annual Salary ($)	Management Training Program
$x_1 = 49{,}094.30$	Yes	$x_{16} = 51{,}766.00$	Yes
$x_2 = 53{,}263.90$	Yes	$x_{17} = 52{,}541.30$	No
$x_3 = 49{,}643.50$	Yes	$x_{18} = 44{,}980.00$	Yes
$x_4 = 49{,}894.90$	Yes	$x_{19} = 51{,}932.60$	Yes
$x_5 = 47{,}621.60$	No	$x_{20} = 52{,}973.00$	Yes
$x_6 = 55{,}924.00$	Yes	$x_{21} = 45{,}120.90$	Yes
$x_7 = 49{,}092.30$	Yes	$x_{22} = 51{,}753.00$	Yes
$x_8 = 51{,}404.40$	Yes	$x_{23} = 54{,}391.80$	No
$x_9 = 50{,}957.70$	Yes	$x_{24} = 50{,}164.20$	No
$x_{10} = 55{,}109.70$	Yes	$x_{25} = 52{,}973.60$	No
$x_{11} = 45{,}922.60$	Yes	$x_{26} = 50{,}241.30$	No
$x_{12} = 57{,}268.40$	No	$x_{27} = 52{,}793.90$	No
$x_{13} = 55{,}688.80$	Yes	$x_{28} = 50{,}979.40$	Yes
$x_{14} = 51{,}564.70$	No	$x_{29} = 55{,}860.90$	Yes
$x_{15} = 56{,}188.20$	No	$x_{30} = 57{,}309.10$	No

and the sample standard deviation is

$$s = \sqrt{\frac{\Sigma(x_i - \bar{x})^2}{n - 1}} = \sqrt{\frac{325{,}009{,}260}{29}} = \$3348$$

To estimate p, the proportion of managers in the population who completed the management training program, we use the corresponding sample proportion $\bar{p}$. Let x denote the number of managers in the sample who completed the management training program. The data in Table 7.2 show that $x = 19$. Thus, with a sample size of $n = 30$, the sample proportion is

$$\bar{p} = \frac{x}{n} = \frac{19}{30} = .63$$

By making the preceding computations, we perform the statistical procedure called *point estimation.* We refer to the sample mean $\bar{x}$ as the **point estimator** of the population mean μ, the sample standard deviation s as the point estimator of the population standard deviation σ, and the sample proportion $\bar{p}$ as the point estimator of the population proportion p. The numerical value obtained for $\bar{x}$, s, or $\bar{p}$ is called the **point estimate**. Thus, for the simple random sample of 30 EAI managers shown in Table 7.2, $51,814 is the point estimate of μ, $3348 is the point estimate of σ, and .63 is the point estimate of p. Table 7.3 summarizes the sample results and compares the point estimates to the actual values of the population parameters.

As evident from Table 7.3, the point estimates differ somewhat from the corresponding population parameters. This difference is to be expected because a sample, and not the entire population, is being used to develop the point estimates. In the next chapter, we will show how to construct an interval estimate in order to provide information about how close the point estimate is to the population parameter.

TABLE 7.3   SUMMARY OF POINT ESTIMATES OBTAINED FROM A SIMPLE RANDOM SAMPLE OF 30 EAI MANAGERS

Population Parameter	Parameter Value	Point Estimator	Point Estimate
μ = Population mean annual salary	$51,800	$\bar{x}$ = Sample mean annual salary	$51,814
σ = Population standard deviation for annual salary	$4000	s = Sample standard deviation for annual salary	$3348
p = Population proportion having completed the management training program	.60	$\bar{p}$ = Sample proportion having completed the management training program	.63

NOTES AND COMMENTS

In our discussion of point estimators, we use $\bar{x}$ to denote a sample mean and $\bar{p}$ to denote a sample proportion. Our use of $\bar{p}$ is based on the fact that the sample proportion is also a *sample mean*. Suppose that in a sample of size n with data values $x_1, x_2, \ldots, x_n$, we let $x_i = 1$ when a characteristic of interest is present for the ith observation and $x_i = 0$ when the characteristic is not present. Then the sample pro-portion is computed by $\Sigma x_i/n$, which is the formula for a sample mean. We also like the consistency of using the bar over the letter to remind the reader that the sample proportion $\bar{p}$ estimates the population proportion just as the sample mean $\bar{x}$ es-timates the population mean. Some texts use $\hat{p}$ instead of $\bar{p}$ to denote the sample proportion.

Exercises

Methods

7. The following data are from a simple random sample.

    5   8   10   7   10   14

    a. What is the point estimate of the population mean?
    b. What is the point estimate of the population standard deviation?

8. A survey question for a sample of 150 individuals yielded 75 Yes responses, 55 No re-sponses, and 20 No Opinions.
    a. What is the point estimate of the proportion in the population who respond Yes?
    b. What is the point estimate of the proportion in the population who respond No?

Applications

9. A simple random sample of five months of sales data provided the following information:

Month	1	2	3	4	5
Units Sold	94	100	85	94	92

    a. Develop a point estimate of the population mean number of units sold per month.
    b. Develop a point estimate of the population standard deviation.

MutualFund

10. *BusinessWeek* published information on 283 equity mutual funds (*BusinessWeek*, January 26, 2004). A sample of 40 of those funds is contained in the data set MutualFund. Use the data set to answer the following questions.
    a. Develop a point estimate of the proportion of the *BusinessWeek* equity funds that are load funds.

b. Develop a point estimate of the proportion of funds that are classified as high risk.

c. Develop a point estimate of the proportion of funds that have a below-average risk rating.

11. *Appliance Magazine* provided estimates of the life expectancy of household appliances (*USA Today,* September 5, 2000). A simple random sample of 10 VCRs shows the following useful life in years.

6.5   8.0   6.2   7.4   7.0   8.4   9.5   4.6   5.0   7.4

a. Develop a point estimate of the population mean life expectancy for VCRs.

b. Develop a point estimate of the population standard deviation for life expectancy of VCRs.

12. A sample of 50 *Fortune* 500 companies (*Fortune,* April 14, 2003) showed 5 were based in New York, 6 in California, 2 in Minnesota, and 1 in Wisconsin.

a. Develop an estimate of the proportion of *Fortune* 500 companies based in New York.

b. Develop an estimate of the number of *Fortune* 500 companies based in Minnesota.

c. Develop an estimate of the proportion of *Fortune* 500 companies that are not based in these four states.

13. A Louis Harris poll used a survey of 1008 adults to learn about how people feel about the economy (*BusinessWeek,* August 7, 2000). Responses were as follows:

595 adults   The economy is growing.
332 adults   The economy is staying about the same.
 81 adults   The economy is shrinking.

Develop a point estimate of the following population parameters.

a. The proportion of all adults who feel the economy is growing

b. The proportion of all adults who feel the economy is staying about the same

c. The proportion of all adults who feel the economy is shrinking

14. In this section we showed how a simple random sample of 30 EAI managers can be used to develop point estimates of the population mean annual salary, the population standard deviation for annual salary, and the population proportion having completed the management training program.

EAI

a. Use Excel to select a simple random sample of 50 EAI managers.

b. Develop a point estimate of the population mean annual salary.

c. Develop a point estimate of the population standard deviation for annual salary.

d. Develop a point estimate of the population proportion having completed the management training program.

7.4 Introduction to Sampling Distributions

In the preceding section we said that the sample mean $\bar{x}$ is the point estimator of the population mean μ, and the sample proportion $\bar{p}$ is the point estimator of the population proportion p. For the simple random sample of 30 EAI managers shown in Table 7.2, the point estimate of μ is $\bar{x} = \$51,814$ and the point estimate of p is $\bar{p} = .63$. Suppose we select another simple random sample of 30 EAI managers and obtain the following point estimates:

Sample mean: $\bar{x} = \$52,670$
Sample proportion: $\bar{p} = .70$

Note that different values of $\bar{x}$ and $\bar{p}$ were obtained. Indeed, a second simple random sample of 30 EAI managers cannot be expected to provide the same point estimates as the first sample.

Now, suppose we repeat the process of selecting a simple random sample of 30 EAI managers over and over again, each time computing the values of $\bar{x}$ and $\bar{p}$. Table 7.4 contains a portion of the results obtained for 500 simple random samples, and Table 7.5 shows

TABLE 7.4 VALUES OF $\bar{x}$ AND $\bar{p}$ FROM 500 SIMPLE RANDOM SAMPLES OF 30 EAI MANAGERS

Sample Number	Sample Mean $(\bar{x})$	Sample Proportion $(\bar{p})$
1	51,814	.63
2	52,670	.70
3	51,780	.67
4	51,588	.53
.	.	.
.	.	.
.	.	.
500	51,752	.50

the frequency and relative frequency distributions for the 500 $\bar{x}$ values. Figure 7.4 shows the relative frequency histogram for the $\bar{x}$ values.

In Chapter 5 we defined a random variable as a numerical description of the outcome of an experiment. If we consider the process of selecting a simple random sample as an experiment, the sample mean $\bar{x}$ is a numerical description of the outcome of the experiment. Thus, the sample mean $\bar{x}$ is a random variable. As a result, just like other random variables, $\bar{x}$ has a mean or expected value, a standard deviation, and a probability distribution. Because the various possible values of $\bar{x}$ are the result of different simple random samples, the probability distribution of $\bar{x}$ is called the **sampling distribution** of $\bar{x}$. Knowledge of this sampling distribution and its properties will enable us to make probability statements about how close the sample mean $\bar{x}$ is to the population mean μ.

Let us return to Figure 7.4. We would need to enumerate every possible sample of 30 managers and compute each sample mean to completely determine the sampling distribution of $\bar{x}$. However, the histogram of 500 $\bar{x}$ values gives an approximation of this sampling distribution. From the approximation we observe the bell-shaped appearance of the distribution. We note that the largest concentration of the $\bar{x}$ values and the mean of the 500 $\bar{x}$ values are near the population mean $\mu = \$51,800$. We will describe the properties of the sampling distribution of $\bar{x}$ more fully in the next section.

The 500 values of the sample proportion $\bar{p}$ are summarized by the relative frequency histogram in Figure 7.5. As in the case of $\bar{x}$, $\bar{p}$ is a random variable. If every possible sample

TABLE 7.5 FREQUENCY DISTRIBUTION OF $\bar{x}$ FROM 500 SIMPLE RANDOM SAMPLES OF 30 EAI MANAGERS

Mean Annual Salary ($)	Frequency	Relative Frequency
49,500.00–49,999.99	2	.004
50,000.00–50,499.99	16	.032
50,500.00–50,999.99	52	.104
51,000.00–51,499.99	101	.202
51,500.00–51,999.99	133	.266
52,000.00–52,499.99	110	.220
52,500.00–52,999.99	54	.108
53,000.00–53,499.99	26	.052
53,500.00–53,999.99	6	.012
Totals	500	1.000

FIGURE 7.4 RELATIVE FREQUENCY HISTOGRAM OF $\bar{x}$ VALUES FROM 500 SIMPLE
RANDOM SAMPLES OF 30 EAI MANAGERS

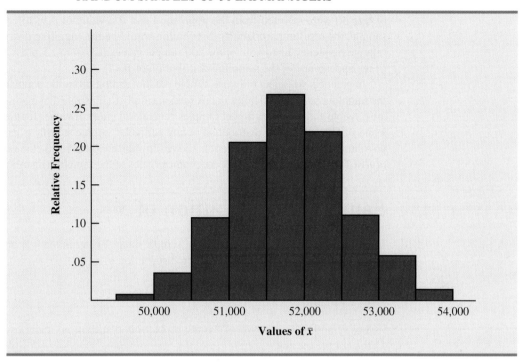

FIGURE 7.5 RELATIVE FREQUENCY HISTOGRAM OF $\bar{p}$ VALUES FROM 500 SIMPLE
RANDOM SAMPLES OF 30 EAI MANAGERS

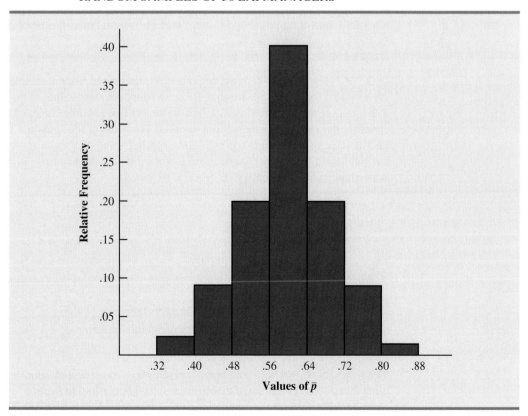

of size 30 were selected from the population and if a value of $\bar{p}$ were computed for each sample, the resulting probability distribution would be the sampling distribution of $\bar{p}$. The relative frequency histogram of the 500 sample values in Figure 7.5 provides a general idea of the appearance of the sampling distribution of $\bar{p}$.

In practice, we select only one simple random sample from the population. We repeated the sampling process 500 times in this section simply to illustrate that many different samples are possible and that the different samples generate a variety of values for the sample statistics $\bar{x}$ and $\bar{p}$. The probability distribution of any particular sample statistic is called the sampling distribution of the statistic. In Section 7.5 we show the characteristics of the sampling distribution of $\bar{x}$. In Section 7.6 we show the characteristics of the sampling distribution of $\bar{p}$.

7.5 Sampling Distribution of $\bar{x}$

In the previous section we said that the sample mean $\bar{x}$ is a random variable and its probability distribution is called the sampling distribution of $\bar{x}$.

> **SAMPLING DISTRIBUTION OF $\bar{x}$**
>
> The sampling distribution of $\bar{x}$ is the probability distribution of all possible values of the sample mean $\bar{x}$.

This section describes the properties of the sampling distribution of $\bar{x}$. Just as with other probability distributions we studied, the sampling distribution of $\bar{x}$ has an expected value or mean, a standard deviation, and a characteristic shape or form. Let us begin by considering the mean of all possible $\bar{x}$ values, which is referred to as the expected value of $\bar{x}$.

Expected Value of $\bar{x}$

In the EAI sampling problem we saw that different simple random samples result in a variety of values for the sample mean $\bar{x}$. Because many different values of the random variable $\bar{x}$ are possible, we are often interested in the mean of all possible values of $\bar{x}$ that can be generated by the various simple random samples. The mean of the $\bar{x}$ random variable is the expected value of $\bar{x}$. Let $E(\bar{x})$ represent the expected value of $\bar{x}$ and μ represent the mean of the population from which we are selecting a simple random sample. It can be shown that with simple random sampling, $E(\bar{x})$ and μ are equal.

The expected value of $\bar{x}$ equals the mean of the population from which the sample is selected.

> **EXPECTED VALUE OF $\bar{x}$**
>
> $$E(\bar{x}) = \mu \qquad (7.1)$$
>
> where
>
> $$E(\bar{x}) = \text{the expected value of } \bar{x}$$
> $$\mu = \text{the population mean}$$

This result shows that with simple random sampling, the expected value or mean of the sampling distribution of $\bar{x}$ is equal to the mean of the population. In Section 7.1 we saw that the mean annual salary for the population of EAI managers is $\mu = \$51,800$. Thus, according to equation (7.1), the mean of all possible sample means for the EAI study is also $51,800.

When the expected value of a point estimator equals the population parameter, we say the point estimator is **unbiased**. Thus, equation (7.1) shows that $\bar{x}$ is an unbiased estimator of the population mean μ.

Standard Deviation of $\bar{x}$

Let us define the standard deviation of the sampling distribution of $\bar{x}$. We will use the following notation.

$$\sigma_{\bar{x}} = \text{the standard deviation of } \bar{x}$$
$$\sigma = \text{the standard deviation of the population}$$
$$n = \text{the sample size}$$
$$N = \text{the population size}$$

It can be shown that with simple random sampling, the standard deviation of $\bar{x}$ depends on whether the population is finite or infinite. The two formulas for the standard deviation of $\bar{x}$ follow.

STANDARD DEVIATION OF $\bar{x}$

Finite Population   *Infinite Population*

$$\sigma_{\bar{x}} = \sqrt{\frac{N - n}{N - 1}}\left(\frac{\sigma}{\sqrt{n}}\right) \qquad\qquad \sigma_{\bar{x}} = \frac{\sigma}{\sqrt{n}} \qquad (7.2)$$

In comparing the two formulas shown above, we see that the factor $\sqrt{(N - n)/(N - 1)}$ is required for the finite population case but not for the infinite population case. This factor is commonly referred to as the **finite population correction factor**. In many practical sampling situations, we find that the population involved, although finite, is "large," whereas the sample size is relatively "small." In such cases the finite population correction factor $\sqrt{(N - n)/(N - 1)}$ is close to 1. As a result, the difference between the values of the standard deviation of $\bar{x}$ for the finite and infinite population cases becomes negligible. Then, $\sigma_{\bar{x}} = \sigma/\sqrt{n}$ becomes a good approximation to the standard deviation of $\bar{x}$ even though the population is finite. This observation leads to the following general guideline, or rule of thumb, for computing the standard deviation of $\bar{x}$.

USE THE FOLLOWING EXPRESSION TO COMPUTE THE STANDARD DEVIATION OF $\bar{x}$

$$\sigma_{\bar{x}} = \frac{\sigma}{\sqrt{n}} \qquad (7.3)$$

whenever

1. The population is infinite; or
2. The population is finite *and* the sample size is less than or equal to 5% of the population size; that is, $n/N \leq .05$.

Problem 17 shows that when $n/N \leq .05$, the finite population correction factor has little effect on the value of $\sigma_{\bar{x}}$.

In cases where $n/N > .05$, the finite population version of formula (7.2) should be used in the computation of $\sigma_{\bar{x}}$. Unless otherwise noted, throughout the text we will assume that the population size is "large," $n/N \leq .05$, and expression (7.3) can be used to compute $\sigma_{\bar{x}}$.

The term standard error *is used to refer to the standard deviation of a point estimator.*

Equation (7.3) shows that we need to know σ, the standard deviation of the population to compute $\sigma_{\bar{x}}$. To emphasize the difference between $\sigma_{\bar{x}}$ and σ, we refer to the standard deviation of $\bar{x}$, $\sigma_{\bar{x}}$, as the **standard error** of the mean. In general, the term *standard error* refers to the standard deviation of a point estimator. Later we will see that the value of the standard error of the mean is helpful in determining how far the sample mean may be from the population mean. Let us now return to the EAI example and compute the standard error of the mean associated with simple random samples of 30 EAI managers.

In Section 7.1 we saw that the standard deviation of annual salary for the population of 2500 EAI managers is $\sigma = 4000$. In this case, the population is finite, with $N = 2500$. However, with a sample size of 30, we have $n/N = 30/2500 = .012$. Because the sample size is less than 5% of the population size, we can ignore the finite population correction factor and use equation (7.3) to compute the standard error.

$$\sigma_{\bar{x}} = \frac{\sigma}{\sqrt{n}} = \frac{4000}{\sqrt{30}} = 730.3$$

Form of the Sampling Distribution of $\bar{x}$

The preceding results concerning the expected value and standard deviation for the sampling distribution of $\bar{x}$ are applicable for any population. The final step in identifying the characteristics of the sampling distribution of $\bar{x}$ is to determine the form or shape of the sampling distribution. We will consider two cases: (1) the population has a normal distribution; and (2) the population does not have a normal distribution.

Population Has a Normal Distribution In many situations it is reasonable to assume that the population from which we are selecting a simple random sample has a normal, or nearly normal, distribution. When the population has a normal distribution, the sampling distribution of $\bar{x}$ is normally distributed for any sample size.

Population Does Not Have a Normal Distribution When the population from which we are selecting a simple random sample does not have a normal distribution, the **central limit theorem** is helpful in identifying the shape of the sampling distribution of $\bar{x}$. A statement of the central limit theorem as it applies to the sampling distribution of $\bar{x}$ follows.

CENTRAL LIMIT THEOREM

In selecting simple random samples of size n from a population, the sampling distribution of the sample mean $\bar{x}$ can be approximated by a *normal distribution* as the sample size becomes large.

Figure 7.6 shows how the central limit theorem works for three different populations; each column refers to one of the populations. The top panel of the figure shows that none of the populations are normally distributed. Population I follows a uniform distribution. Population II is often called the rabbit-eared distribution. It is symmetric, but the more likely values fall in the tails of the distribution. Population III is shaped like the exponential distribution; it is skewed to the right.

The bottom three panels of Figure 7.6 show the shape of the sampling distribution for samples of size $n = 2$, $n = 5$, and $n = 30$. When the sample size is 2, we see that the shape of each sampling distribution is different from the shape of the corresponding population distribution. For samples of size 5, we see that the shape of the sampling distributions for Populations I and II already look similar to the shape of a normal distribution. Even though

FIGURE 7.6   ILLUSTRATION OF THE CENTRAL LIMIT THEOREM
FOR THREE POPULATIONS

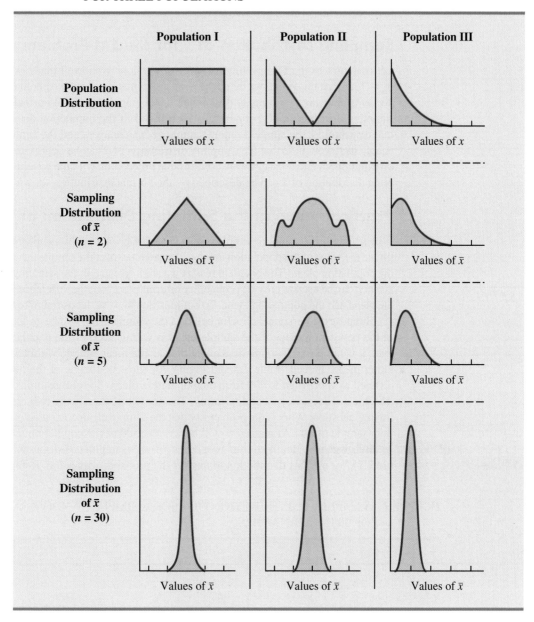

the shape of the sampling distribution for Population III begins to look similar to the shape of a normal distribution, some skewness to the right is still present. Finally, for samples of size 30, the shapes of each of the three sampling distributions are approximately normal.

From a practitioner standpoint, we often want to know how large the sample size needs to be before the central limit theorem applies and we can assume that the shape of the sampling distribution is approximately normal. Statistical researchers have investigated this question by studying the sampling distribution of $\bar{x}$ for a variety of populations and a variety of sample sizes. General statistical practice is to assume that, for most applications, the sampling distribution of $\bar{x}$ can be approximated by a normal distribution whenever the sample is size 30 or more. In cases where the population is highly skewed or outliers are present, samples of size 50 may be needed. Finally, if the population is discrete, the sample size needed for a normal approximation often depends on the population proportion. We say more about this issue when we discuss the sampling distribution of $\bar{p}$ in Section 7.6.

Sampling Distribution of $\bar{x}$ for the EAI Problem

Let us return to the EAI problem where we previously showed that $E(\bar{x}) = \$51,800$ and $\sigma_{\bar{x}} = 730.3$. At this point, we do not have any information about the population distribution; it may or may not be normally distributed. If the population has a normal distribution, the sampling distribution of $\bar{x}$ is normally distributed. If the population does not have a normal distribution, the simple random sample of 30 managers and the central limit theorem enable us to conclude that the sampling distribution of $\bar{x}$ can be approximated by a normal distribution. In either case, we are comfortable proceeding with the conclusion that the sampling distribution of $\bar{x}$ can be described by the normal distribution shown in Figure 7.7.

Practical Value of the Sampling Distribution of $\bar{x}$

Whenever a simple random sample is selected and the value of the sample mean is used to estimate the value of the population mean μ, we cannot expect the sample mean to exactly equal the population mean. The practical reason we are interested in the sampling distribution of $\bar{x}$ is that it can be used to provide probability information about the difference between the sample mean and the population mean. To demonstrate this use, let us return to the EAI problem.

Suppose the personnel director believes the sample mean will be an acceptable estimate of the population mean if the sample mean is within $500 of the population mean. However, it is not possible to guarantee that the sample mean will be within $500 of the population mean. Indeed, Table 7.5 and Figure 7.4 show that some of the 500 sample means differed by more than $2000 from the population mean. So we must think of the personnel director's request in probability terms: The personnel director is concerned with the following question: What is the probability that the sample mean computed using a simple random sample of 30 EAI managers will be within $500 of the population mean?

Because we identified the properties of the sampling distribution of $\bar{x}$ (see Figure 7.7), we use this distribution to answer the probability question. Refer to the sampling

FIGURE 7.7   SAMPLING DISTRIBUTION OF $\bar{x}$ FOR A SIMPLE RANDOM SAMPLE OF 30 EAI MANAGERS

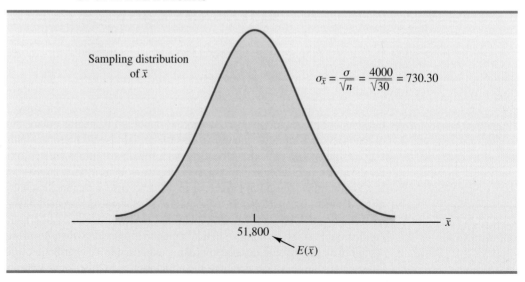

Sampling distribution of $\bar{x}$

$$\sigma_{\bar{x}} = \frac{\sigma}{\sqrt{n}} = \frac{4000}{\sqrt{30}} = 730.30$$

51,800

$E(\bar{x})$

FIGURE 7.8   PROBABILITY OF A SAMPLE MEAN BEING WITHIN $500
OF THE POPULATION MEAN FOR A SIMPLE RANDOM
SAMPLE OF 30 EAI MANAGERS

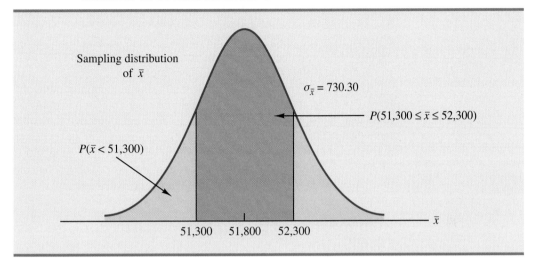

distribution of $\bar{x}$ shown again in Figure 7.8. With a population mean of $51,800, the personnel director wants to know the probability that $\bar{x}$ is between $51,300 and $52,300. This probability is given by the darkly shaded area of the sampling distribution shown in Figure 7.8. Because the sampling distribution is normally distributed, with mean 51,800 and standard error of the mean 730.3, we can use the standard normal probability table to find the area or probability.

We first calculate the z value at the upper endpoint of the interval (52,300) and use the table to find the area under the curve to the left of that point (left tail area). Then we compute the z value at the lower endpoint of the interval (51,300) and use the table to find the area under the curve to the left of that point (another left tail area). Subtracting the second tail area from the first gives us the desired probability.

At $\bar{x} = 52,300$, we have

$$z = \frac{52,300 - 51,800}{730.30} = .68$$

Referring to the standard normal probability table, we find a cumulative probability (area to the left of $z = .68$) of .7517.

At $\bar{x} = 51,300$, we have

$$z = \frac{51,300 - 51,800}{730.30} = -.68$$

The area under the curve to the left of $z = -.68$ is .2483. Therefore, $P(51,300 \leq \bar{x} \leq 52,300) = P(z \leq .68) - P(z < -.68) = .7517 - .2483 = .5034$.

The desired probability can also be computed using Excel's NORMDIST function. The advantage of using the NORMDIST function is that we do not have to make a separate computation of the z value. Evaluating the NORMDIST function at the upper endpoint of the interval provides the area under the curve to the left of 52,300. Entering the formula =NORMDIST(52300,51800,730.30,TRUE) into a cell of an Excel worksheet provides

Using Excel's NORMDIST function is easier and provides more accurate results than the tables.

.7532 for this cumulative probability. Evaluating the NORMDIST function at the lower endpoint of the interval provides the area under the curve to the left of 51,300. Entering the formula =NORMDIST(51300,51800,730.30,TRUE) into a cell of an Excel worksheet provides .2468 for this cumulative probability. The probability of $\bar{x}$ being in the interval from 51,300 to 52,300 is then given by .7532 − .2468 = .5064. We note that this result is slightly different from the probability obtained using the table, because in using the normal table we rounded to two decimal places of accuracy when computing the z value. The result obtained using NORMDIST is thus more accurate.

The sampling distribution of $\bar{x}$ can be used to provide probability information about how close the sample mean $\bar{x}$ is to the population mean μ.

The preceding computations show that a simple random sample of 30 EAI managers has a .5064 probability of providing a sample mean $\bar{x}$ that is within $500 of the population mean. Thus, there is a 1 − .5064 = .4936 probability that the sampling error will be more than $500. In other words, a simple random sample of 30 EAI managers has roughly a 50-50 chance of providing a sample mean within the allowable $500. Perhaps a larger sample size should be considered. Let us explore this possibility by considering the relationship between the sample size and the sampling distribution of $\bar{x}$.

Relationship Between Sample Size and the Sampling Distribution of $\bar{x}$

Suppose that in the EAI sampling problem we select a simple random sample of 100 EAI managers instead of the 30 originally considered. Intuitively, it would seem that with more data provided by the larger sample size, the sample mean based on $n = 100$ should provide a better estimate of the population mean than the sample mean based on $n = 30$. To see how much better, let us consider the relationship between the sample size and the sampling distribution of $\bar{x}$.

First note that $E(\bar{x}) = \mu$ regardless of the sample size. Thus, the mean of all possible values of $\bar{x}$ is equal to the population mean μ regardless of the sample size n. However, note that the standard error of the mean, $\sigma_{\bar{x}} = \sigma/\sqrt{n}$, is related to the square root of the sample size. Whenever the sample size is increased, the standard error of the mean $\sigma_{\bar{x}}$ is decreased. With $n = 30$, the standard error of the mean for the EAI problem is 730.30. However, with the increase in the sample size to $n = 100$, the standard error of the mean is decreased to

$$\sigma_{\bar{x}} = \frac{\sigma}{\sqrt{n}} = \frac{4000}{\sqrt{100}} = 400$$

The sampling distributions of $\bar{x}$ with $n = 30$ and $n = 100$ are shown in Figure 7.9. Because the sampling distribution with $n = 100$ provides a smaller standard error, the values of $\bar{x}$ vary less and tend to be grouped closer around the population mean than the values of $\bar{x}$ with $n = 30$.

We can use the sampling distribution of $\bar{x}$ for the case with $n = 100$ to compute the probability that a simple random sample of 100 EAI managers will provide a sample mean that is within $500 of the population mean. In this case the sampling distribution is normal with a mean of 51,800 and a standard deviation of 400 (see Figure 7.10). Again, we could compute the appropriate z values and use the standard normal probability distribution table to make this probability calculation. However, Excel's NORMDIST function is easier to use and provides more accurate results. Entering the formula =NORMDIST(52300,51800,400,TRUE) into a cell of an Excel worksheet provides the cumulative probability corresponding to $\bar{x} = 52,300$. The value provided by Excel is .8944. Entering the formula =NORMDIST (51300,51800,400,TRUE) into a cell of an Excel worksheet provides the cumulative proba-

FIGURE 7.9 COMPARISON OF THE SAMPLING DISTRIBUTIONS OF $\bar{x}$ FOR SIMPLE RANDOM SAMPLES OF $n = 30$ AND $n = 100$ EAI MANAGERS

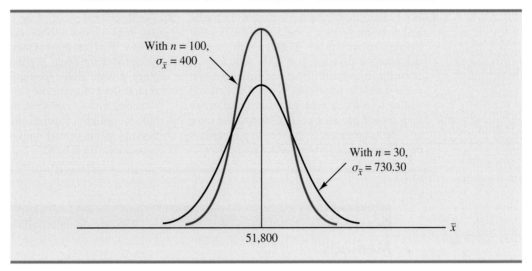

bility corresponding to $\bar{x} = 51,300$. The value provided by Excel is .1056. Thus, the probability of $\bar{x}$ being in the interval from 51,300 to 52,300 is given by $.8944 - .1056 = .7888$. By increasing the sample size from 30 to 100 EAI managers, we increase the probability that the sampling error will be \$500 or less; that is, the probability of obtaining a sample mean within \$500 of the population mean increases from .5064 to .7888.

The important point in this discussion is that as the sample size increases, the standard error of the mean decreases. As a result, a larger sample size will provide a higher probability that the sample mean falls within a specified distance of the population mean.

FIGURE 7.10 PROBABILITY OF A SAMPLE MEAN BEING WITHIN \$500 OF THE POPULATION MEAN FOR A SIMPLE RANDOM SAMPLE OF 100 EAI MANAGERS

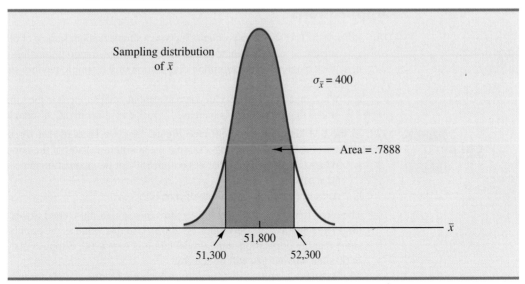

NOTES AND COMMENTS

1. In presenting the sampling distribution of $\bar{x}$ for the EAI problem, we took advantage of the fact that the population mean $\mu = 51{,}800$ and the population standard deviation $\sigma = 4000$ were known. However, usually the values of the population mean μ and the population standard deviation σ that are needed to determine the sampling distribution of $\bar{x}$ will be unknown. In Chapter 8 we show how the sample mean $\bar{x}$ and the sample standard deviation s are used when μ and σ are unknown.

2. The theoretical proof of the central limit theorem requires independent observations in the sample. This condition is met for infinite populations and for finite populations where sampling is done with replacement. Although the central limit theorem does not directly address sampling without replacement from finite populations, general statistical practice applies the findings of the central limit theorem when the population size is large.

EXERCISES

Methods

15. In a population with a mean of 200 and a standard deviation of 50, suppose a simple random sample of size 100 is selected and $\bar{x}$ is used to estimate μ.
    a. What is the probability that the sample mean will be within ± 5 of the population mean?
    b. What is the probability that the sample mean will be within ± 10 of the population mean?

16. Assume the population standard deviation is $\sigma = 25$. Compute the standard error of the mean, $\sigma_{\bar{x}}$, for sample sizes of 50, 100, 150, and 200. What can you say about the size of the standard error of the mean as the sample size is increased?

17. Suppose a simple random sample of size 50 is selected from a population with $\sigma = 10$. Find the value of the standard error of the mean in each of the following cases (use the finite population correction factor if appropriate).
    a. The population size is infinite.
    b. The population size is $N = 50{,}000$.
    c. The population size is $N = 5000$.
    d. The population size is $N = 500$.

Applications

18. Refer to the EAI sampling problem. Suppose a simple random sample of 60 managers is used.
    a. Sketch the sampling distribution of $\bar{x}$ when simple random samples of size 60 are used.
    b. What happens to the sampling distribution of $\bar{x}$ if simple random samples of size 120 are used?
    c. What general statement can you make about what happens to the sampling distribution of $\bar{x}$ as the sample size is increased? Does this generalization seem logical? Explain.

19. In the EAI sampling problem (see Figure 7.8), we showed that for $n = 30$, there was .5064 probability of obtaining a sample mean within $\pm\$500$ of the population mean.
    a. What is the probability that $\bar{x}$ is within $\$500$ of the population mean if a sample of size 60 is used?
    b. Answer part (a) for a sample of size 120.

20. The mean tuition cost at state universities throughout the United States is $\$4260$ per year (*St. Petersburg Times*, December 11, 2002). Use this value as the population mean and assume that the population standard deviation is $\sigma = \$900$. Suppose that a random sample of 50 state universities will be selected.
    a. Show the sampling distribution of $\bar{x}$ where $\bar{x}$ is the sample mean tuition cost for the 50 state universities.

b. What is the probability that the simple random sample will provide a sample mean within $250 of the population mean?

c. What is the probability that the simple random sample will provide a sample mean within $100 of the population mean?

21. The College Board American College Testing Program reported a population mean SAT score of $\mu = 1020$ (*The World Almanac 2003*). Assume that the population standard deviation is $\sigma = 100$.

   a. What is the probability that a random sample of 75 students will provide a sample mean SAT score within 10 of the population mean?

   b. What is the probability a random sample of 75 students will provide a sample mean SAT score within 20 of the population mean?

22. The mean annual starting salary for marketing majors is $34,000 (*Time,* May 8, 2000). Assume that for the population of graduates with a marketing major, the mean annual starting salary is $\mu = 34,000$, and the standard deviation is $\sigma = 2000$.

   a. What is the probability that a simple random sample of marketing majors will have a sample mean within ±$250 of the population mean for each of the following sample sizes: 30, 50, 100, 200, and 400?

   b. What is the advantage of a larger sample size when attempting to estimate the population mean?

23. *BusinessWeek* conducted a survey of graduates from 30 top MBA programs (*Business-Week,* September 22, 2003). On the basis of the survey, assume that the mean annual salary for male and female graduates 10 years after graduation is $168,000 and $117,000, respectively. Assume the standard deviation for the male graduates is $40,000, and for the female graduates it is $25,000.

   a. What is the probability that a simple random sample of 40 male graduates will provide a sample mean within $10,000 of the population mean, $168,000?

   b. What is the probability that a simple random sample of 40 female graduates will provide a sample mean within $10,000 of the population mean, $117,000?

   c. In which of the preceding two cases, part (a) or part (b), do we have a higher probability of obtaining a sample estimate within $10,000 of the population mean? Why?

   d. What is the probability that a simple random sample of 100 male graduates will provide a sample mean more than $4000 below the population mean?

24. The average annual cost of automobile insurance is $687 (*National Association of Insurance Commissioners,* January 2003). Use this value as the population mean and assume that the population standard deviation is $\sigma = \$230$. Consider a sample of 45 automobile insurance policies.

   a. Show the sampling distribution of $\bar{x}$ where $\bar{x}$ is the sample mean annual cost of automobile insurance.

   b. What is the probability that the sample mean is within $100 of the population mean?

   c. What is the probability that the sample mean is within $25 of the population mean?

   d. What sample size would you recommend if an insurance agency wanted the sample mean to estimate the population mean within ±$25?

25. *Money* magazine reported that the average price of a gallon of gasoline in the United States during the first quarter of 2001 was $1.46 (*Money,* August 2001). Assume the price reported by *Money* is the population mean, and the population standard deviation is $\sigma = \$.15$.

   a. What is the probability that the mean price for a sample of 30 gas stations is within $.03 of the population mean?

   b. What is the probability that the mean price for a sample of 50 gas stations is within $.03 of the population mean?

   c. What is the probability that the mean price for a sample of 100 gas stations is within $.03 of the population mean?

   d. Would you recommend a sample size of 30, 50, or 100 to have at least a .95 probability that the sample mean is within $.03 of the population mean?

26. To estimate the mean age for a population of 4000 employees, a simple random sample of 40 employees is selected.

   a. Would you use the finite population correction factor in calculating the standard error of the mean? Explain.

   b. If the population standard deviation is $\sigma = 8.2$ years, compute the standard error both with and without the finite population correction factor. What is the rationale for ignoring the finite population correction factor whenever $n/N \leq .05$?

   c. What is the probability that the sample mean age of the employees will be within ± 2 years of the population mean age?

7.6 Sampling Distribution of $\bar{p}$

The sample proportion $\bar{p}$ is the point estimator of the population proportion p. The formula for computing the sample proportion is

$$\bar{p} = \frac{x}{n}$$

where

   $x = $ the number of elements in the sample that possess the characteristic of interest

   $n = $ sample size

As noted in Section 7.4, the sample proportion $\bar{p}$ is a random variable and its probability distribution is called the sampling distribution of $\bar{p}$.

SAMPLING DISTRIBUTION OF $\bar{p}$

The sampling distribution of $\bar{p}$ is the probability distribution of all possible values of the sample proportion $\bar{p}$.

To determine how close the sample proportion $\bar{p}$ is to the population proportion p, we need to understand the properties of the sampling distribution of $\bar{p}$: the expected value of $\bar{p}$, the standard deviation of $\bar{p}$, and the shape or form of the sampling distribution of $\bar{p}$.

Expected Value of $\bar{p}$

The expected value of $\bar{p}$, the mean of all possible values of $\bar{p}$, is equal to the population proportion p.

EXPECTED VALUE OF $\bar{p}$

$$E(\bar{p}) = p \tag{7.4}$$

where

   $E(\bar{p}) = $ the expected value of $\bar{p}$

   $p = $ the population proportion

Because $E(\bar{p}) = p$, $\bar{p}$ is an unbiased estimator of p. Recall from Section 7.1 we noted that $p = .60$ for the EAI population, where p is the proportion of the population of managers who participated in the company's management training program. Thus, the expected value of $\bar{p}$ for the EAI sampling problem is .60.

Standard Deviation of $\bar{p}$

Just as we found for the standard deviation of $\bar{x}$, the standard deviation of $\bar{p}$ depends on whether the population is finite or infinite. The two formulas for computing the standard deviation of $\bar{p}$ follow.

STANDARD DEVIATION OF $\bar{p}$

Finite Population   *Infinite Population*

$$\sigma_{\bar{p}} = \sqrt{\frac{N-n}{N-1}}\sqrt{\frac{p(1-p)}{n}} \qquad \sigma_{\bar{p}} = \sqrt{\frac{p(1-p)}{n}} \qquad \text{(7.5)}$$

Comparing the two formulas in (7.5), we see that the only difference is the use of the finite population correction factor $\sqrt{(N-n)/(N-1)}$.

As was the case with the sample mean $\bar{x}$, the difference between the expressions for the finite population and the infinite population becomes negligible if the size of the finite population is large in comparison to the sample size. We follow the same rule of thumb that we recommended for the sample mean. That is, if the population is finite with $n/N \leq .05$, we will use $\sigma_{\bar{p}} = \sqrt{p(1-p)/n}$. However, if the population is finite with $n/N > .05$, the finite population correction factor should be used. Again, unless specifically noted, throughout the text we will assume that the population size is large in relation to the sample size and thus the finite population correction factor is unnecessary.

In Section 7.5 we used standard error of the mean to refer to the standard deviation of $\bar{x}$. We stated that in general the term *standard error* refers to the standard deviation of a point estimator. Thus, for proportions we use *standard error of the proportion* to refer to the standard deviation of $\bar{p}$. Let us now return to the EAI example and compute the standard error of the proportion associated with simple random samples of 30 EAI managers.

For the EAI study we know that the population proportion of managers who participated in the management training program is $p = .60$. With $n/N = 30/2500 = .012$, we can ignore the finite population correction factor when we compute the standard error of the proportion. For the simple random sample of 30 managers, $\sigma_{\bar{p}}$ is

$$\sigma_{\bar{p}} = \sqrt{\frac{p(1-p)}{n}} = \sqrt{\frac{.60(1-.60)}{30}} = .0894$$

Form of the Sampling Distribution of $\bar{p}$

Now that we know the mean and standard deviation of $\bar{p}$, we want to consider the form of the sampling distribution of $\bar{p}$. Applying the central limit theorem as it relates to $\bar{p}$ produces the following result.

The sampling distribution of $\bar{p}$ can be approximated by a normal probability distribution whenever the sample size is large.

These criteria are slightly different from the n ≥ 30 criteria we used for the large sample case for x̄. The reason is that small values of p or (1 − p) can cause the sampling distribution to be skewed even with n ≥ 30.

With $\bar{p}$, the sample size can be considered large whenever the following two conditions are satisfied.

$$np \geq 5$$
$$n(1 - p) \geq 5$$

In practical applications, when an estimate of a population proportion is desired, we find that sample sizes are almost always large enough to permit the use of a normal approximation for the sampling distribution of $\bar{p}$.

Recall that for the EAI sampling problem we know that the population proportion of managers who participated in the training program is $p = .60$. With a simple random sample of size 30, we have $np = 30(.60) = 18$ and $n(1 - p) = 30(.40) = 12$. Thus, the sampling distribution of $\bar{p}$ can be approximated by the normal distribution shown in Figure 7.11.

Practical Value of the Sampling Distribution of $\bar{p}$

The practical value of the sampling distribution of $\bar{p}$ is that it can be used to provide probability information about the difference between the sample proportion and the population proportion. For instance, suppose that in the EAI problem the personnel director wants to know the probability of obtaining a value of $\bar{p}$ that is within .05 of the population proportion of EAI managers who participated in the training program. That is, what is the probability of obtaining a sample with a sample proportion $\bar{p}$ between .55 and .65? The darkly shaded area in Figure 7.12 shows this probability. Using the fact that the sampling distribution of $\bar{p}$ can be approximated by a normal probability distribution with a mean of .60 and a standard error of $\sigma_{\bar{p}} = .0894$, we can use Excel's NORMDIST function to make this calculation. Entering the formula =NORMDIST(.65,.60,.0894,TRUE) into a cell of an Excel worksheet provides the cumulative probability corresponding to $\bar{p} = .65$. The value calculated by Excel is .7120. Entering the formula =NORMDIST(.55,.60,.0894,TRUE) into a cell of an Excel worksheet provides the cumulative probability corresponding to $\bar{p} = .55$. The value calculated by Excel is .2880. Thus, the probability of $\bar{p}$ being in the interval from .55 to .65 is given by .7120 − .2880 = .4240.

FIGURE 7.11   SAMPLING DISTRIBUTION OF $\bar{p}$ FOR THE PROPORTION OF EAI MANAGERS WHO PARTICIPATED IN THE MANAGEMENT TRAINING PROGRAM

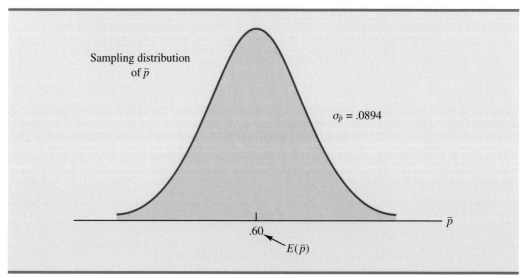

FIGURE 7.12 PROBABILITY OF OBTAINING $\bar{p}$ BETWEEN .55 AND .65

Sampling distribution
of $\bar{p}$

$\sigma_{\bar{p}} = .0894$

Area = .2880

Area = .4240 = .7120 − .2880

.55 .60 .65

$\bar{p}$

If we consider increasing the sample size to $n = 100$, the standard error of the proportion becomes

$$\sigma_{\bar{p}} = \sqrt{\frac{.60(1 - .60)}{100}} = .0490$$

With a sample size of 100 EAI managers, the probability of the sample proportion having a value within .05 of the population proportion can now be computed. Because the sampling distribution is approximately normal, with mean .60 and standard deviation .0490, we can use Excel's NORMDIST function to make this calculation. Entering the formula =NORMDIST(.65,.60,.0490,TRUE) into a cell of an Excel worksheet provides the cumulative probability corresponding to $\bar{p} = .65$. The value calculated by Excel is .8462. Entering the formula =NORMDIST(.55,.60,.0490,TRUE) into a cell of an Excel worksheet provides the cumulative probability corresponding to $\bar{p} = .55$. The value calculated by Excel is .1538. Thus, the probability of $\bar{p}$ being in the interval from .55 to .65 is given by .8462 − .1538 = .6924. Increasing the sample size increases the probability that the sampling error will be less than or equal to .05 by .2684 (from .4240 to .6924).

Exercises

Methods

27. A simple random sample of size 100 is selected from a population with $p = .40$.
    a. What is the expected value of $\bar{p}$?
    b. What is the standard error of $\bar{p}$?
    c. Show the sampling distribution of $\bar{p}$.
    d. What does the sampling distribution of $\bar{p}$ show?

28. A population proportion is .40. A simple random sample of size 200 will be taken and the sample proportion $\bar{p}$ will be used to estimate the population proportion.
    a. What is the probability that the sample proportion will be within ±.03 of the population proportion?
    b. What is the probability that the sample proportion will be within ±.05 of the population proportion?

29. Assume that the population proportion is .55. Compute the standard error of the proportion, $\sigma_{\bar{p}}$, for sample sizes of 100, 200, 500, and 1000. What can you say about the size of the standard error of the proportion as the sample size is increased?

30. The population proportion is .30. What is the probability that a sample proportion will be within $\pm.04$ of the population proportion for each of the following sample sizes?
  a. $n = 100$
  b. $n = 200$
  c. $n = 500$
  d. $n = 1000$
  e. What is the advantage of a larger sample size?

Applications

31. The president of Doerman Distributors, Inc., believes that 30% of the firm's orders come from first-time customers. A simple random sample of 100 orders will be used to estimate the proportion of first-time customers.
  a. Assume that the president is correct and $p = .30$. What is the sampling distribution of $\bar{p}$ for this study?
  b. What is the probability that the sample proportion $\bar{p}$ will be between .20 and .40?
  c. What is the probability that the sample proportion will be between .25 and .35?

32. *BusinessWeek* reported that 56% of the households in the United States have Internet access (*BusinessWeek,* May 21, 2001). Use a population proportion $p = .56$ and assume that a sample of 300 households will be selected.
  a. Show the sampling distribution of $\bar{p}$ where $\bar{p}$ is the sample proportion of households that have Internet access.
  b. What is the probability that the sample proportion will be within $\pm.03$ of the population proportion?
  c. Answer part (b) for sample sizes of 600 and 1000.

33. *Time*/CNN voter polls monitored public opinion for the presidential candidates during the 2000 presidential election campaign. One *Time*/CNN poll conducted by Yankelovich Partners, Inc., used a sample of 589 likely voters (*Time,* June 26, 2000). Assume the population proportion for a presidential candidate is $p = .50$. Let $\bar{p}$ be the sample proportion of likely voters favoring the presidential candidate.
  a. Show the sampling distribution of $\bar{p}$.
  b. What is the probability the *Time*/CNN poll will provide a sample proportion within $\pm.04$ of the population proportion?
  c. What is the probability the *Time*/CNN poll will provide a sample proportion within $\pm.03$ of the population proportion?
  d. What is the probability the *Time*/CNN poll will provide a sample proportion within $\pm.02$ of the population proportion?

34. Roper ASW conducted a survey to learn about American adults' attitudes toward money and happiness (*Money,* October 2003). Fifty-six percent of the respondents said they balance their checkbook at least once a month.
  a. Suppose a sample of 400 American adults were taken. Show the sampling distribution of the proportion of adults who balance their checkbook at least once a month.
  b. What is the probability that the sample proportion will be within $\pm.02$ of the population proportion?
  c. What is the probability that the sample proportion will be within $\pm.04$ of the population proportion?

35. The *Democrat and Chronicle* reported that 25% of the flights arriving at the San Diego airport during the first five months of 2001 were late (*Democrat and Chronicle,* July 23, 2001). Assume the population proportion is $p = .25$.

a.   Show the sampling distribution of $\bar{p}$, the proportion of late flights in a sample of 1000 flights.

b.   What is the probability that the sample proportion will be within $\pm.03$ of the population proportion if a sample of size 1000 is selected?

c.   Answer part (b) for a sample of 500 flights.

36.   The Grocery Manufacturers of America reported that 76% of consumers read the ingredients listed on a product's label. Assume the population proportion is $p = .76$ and a sample of 400 consumers is selected from the population.

a.   Show the sampling distribution of the sample proportion $\bar{p}$ where $\bar{p}$ is the proportion of the sampled consumers who read the ingredients listed on a product's label.

b.   What is the probability that the sample proportion will be within $\pm.03$ of the population proportion?

c.   Answer part (b) for a sample of 750 consumers.

37.   The Food Marketing Institute shows that 17% of households spend more than $100 per week on groceries. Assume the population proportion is $p = .17$ and a simple random sample of 800 households will be selected from the population.

a.   Show the sampling distribution of $\bar{p}$, the sample proportion of households spending more than $100 per week on groceries.

b.   What is the probability that the sample proportion will be within $\pm.02$ of the population proportion?

c.   Answer part (b) for a sample of 1600 households.

Sampling Methods

This section provides a brief introduction to sampling methods other than simple random sampling.

We described the simple random sampling procedure and discussed the properties of the sampling distributions of $\bar{x}$ and $\bar{p}$ when simple random sampling is used. However, simple random sampling is not the only sampling method available. Such methods as stratified random sampling, cluster sampling, and systematic sampling provide advantages over simple random sampling in some situations. In this section we briefly introduce these alternative sampling methods.

Stratified Random Sampling

In **stratified random sampling**, the elements in the population are first divided into groups called *strata,* such that each element in the population belongs to one and only one stratum. The basis for forming the strata, such as department, location, age, industry type, and so on, is at the discretion of the designer of the sample. However, the best results are obtained when the elements within each stratum are as much alike as possible. Figure 7.13 is a diagram of a population divided into *H* strata.

Stratified random sampling works best when the variance among elements in each stratum is relatively small.

After the strata are formed, a simple random sample is taken from each stratum. Formulas are available for combining the results for the individual stratum samples into one estimate of the population parameter of interest. The value of stratified random sampling depends on how homogeneous the elements are within the strata. If elements within strata are alike, the strata will have low variances. Thus relatively small sample sizes can be used to obtain good estimates of the strata characteristics. If strata are homogeneous, the stratified random sampling procedure provides results just as precise as those of simple random sampling by using a smaller total sample size.

Cluster Sampling

Cluster sampling works best when each cluster provides a small-scale representation of the population.

In **cluster sampling**, the elements in the population are first divided into separate groups called *clusters.* Each element of the population belongs to one and only one cluster (see Figure 7.14). A simple random sample of the clusters is then taken. All elements within each sampled cluster

FIGURE 7.13 DIAGRAM FOR STRATIFIED RANDOM SAMPLING

Population

Stratum 1   Stratum 2   . . .   Stratum H

form the sample. Cluster sampling tends to provide the best results when the elements within the clusters are not alike. In the ideal case, each cluster is a representative small-scale version of the entire population. The value of cluster sampling depends on how representative each cluster is of the entire population. If all clusters are alike in this regard, sampling a small number of clusters will provide good estimates of the population parameters.

One of the primary applications of cluster sampling is area sampling, where clusters are city blocks or other well-defined areas. Cluster sampling generally requires a larger total sample size than either simple random sampling or stratified random sampling. However, it can result in cost savings because of the fact that when an interviewer is sent to a sampled cluster (e.g., a city-block location), many sample observations can be obtained in a relatively short time. Hence, a larger sample size may be obtainable with a significantly lower total cost.

Systematic Sampling

In some sampling situations, especially those with large populations, it is time-consuming to select a simple random sample by first finding a random number and then counting or searching through the list of the population until the corresponding element is found. An alternative to simple random sampling is **systematic sampling**. For example, if a sample size of 50 is desired from a population containing 5000 elements, we will sample one element for every 5000/50 = 100 elements in the population. A systematic sample for this case involves selecting randomly one of the first 100 elements from the population list. Other sample elements are identified by starting with the first sampled element and then selecting every 100th element that follows in the population list. In effect, the sample of 50 is identified by moving systematically through the population and identifying every 100th element after the first randomly selected element. The sample of 50 usually will be easier to

FIGURE 7.14 DIAGRAM FOR CLUSTER SAMPLING

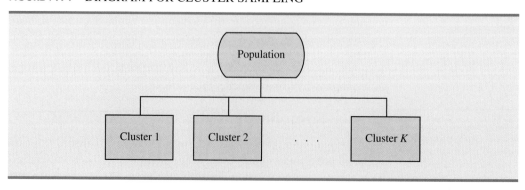

Population

Cluster 1   Cluster 2   . . .   Cluster K

identify in this way than it would be if simple random sampling were used. Because the first element selected is a random choice, a systematic sample is usually assumed to have the properties of a simple random sample. This assumption is especially applicable when the list of elements in the population is a random ordering of the elements.

Convenience Sampling

The sampling methods discussed thus far are referred to as *probability sampling* techniques. Elements selected from the population have a known probability of being included in the sample. The advantage of probability sampling is that the sampling distribution of the appropriate sample statistic generally can be identified. Formulas such as the ones for simple random sampling presented in this chapter can be used to determine the properties of the sampling distribution. Then the sampling distribution can be used to make probability statements about the error associated with the sample results.

Convenience sampling is a *nonprobability sampling* technique. As the name implies, the sample is identified primarily by convenience. Elements are included in the sample without prespecified or known probabilities of being selected. For example, a professor conducting research at a university may use student volunteers to constitute a sample simply because they are readily available and will participate as subjects for little or no cost. Similarly, an inspector may sample a shipment of oranges by selecting oranges haphazardly from among several crates. Labeling each orange and using a probability method of sampling would be impractical. Samples such as wildlife captures and volunteer panels for consumer research are also convenience samples.

Convenience samples have the advantage of relatively easy sample selection and data collection; however, it is impossible to evaluate the "goodness" of the sample in terms of its representativeness of the population. A convenience sample may provide good results or it may not; no statistically justified procedure allows a probability analysis and inference about the quality of the sample results. Sometimes researchers apply statistical methods designed for probability samples to a convenience sample, arguing that the convenience sample can be treated as though it were a probability sample. However, this argument cannot be supported, and we should be cautious in interpreting the results of convenience samples that are used to make inferences about populations.

Judgment Sampling

One additional nonprobability sampling technique is **judgment sampling**. In this approach, the person most knowledgeable on the subject of the study selects elements of the population that he or she feels are most representative of the population. Often this method is a relatively easy way of selecting a sample. For example, a reporter may sample two or three senators, judging that those senators reflect the general opinion of all senators. However, the quality of the sample results depends on the judgment of the person selecting the sample. Again, great caution is warranted in drawing conclusions based on judgment samples used to make inferences about populations.

NOTES AND COMMENTS

We recommend using probability sampling methods: simple random sampling, stratified random sampling, cluster sampling, or systematic sampling. For these methods, formulas are available for evaluating the "goodness" of the sample results in terms of the closeness of the results to the population parameters being estimated. An evaluation of the goodness cannot be made with convenience or judgment sampling. Thus, great care should be used in interpreting the results based on nonprobability sampling methods.

Summary

In this chapter we presented the concepts of simple random sampling and sampling distributions. We demonstrated how a simple random sample can be selected and how the data collected for the sample can be used to develop point estimates of population parameters. Because different simple random samples provide different values for the point estimators, point estimators such as $\bar{x}$ and $\bar{p}$ are random variables. The probability distribution of such a random variable is called a sampling distribution. In particular, we described the sampling distributions of the sample mean $\bar{x}$ and the sample proportion $\bar{p}$.

In considering the characteristics of the sampling distributions of $\bar{x}$ and $\bar{p}$, we stated that $E(\bar{x}) = \mu$ and $E(\bar{p}) = p$. Thus, the sample statistics $\bar{x}$ and $\bar{p}$ provide unbiased estimators of the population parameters μ and p. After developing the standard error formulas for these estimators, we described the conditions necessary for the sampling distributions of $\bar{x}$ and $\bar{p}$ to follow a normal distribution. Other sampling methods, including stratified random sampling, cluster sampling, systematic sampling, convenience sampling, and judgment sampling, were discussed.

Glossary

Parameter A numerical characteristic of a population, such as a population mean μ, a population standard deviation σ, a population proportion p, and so on.

Simple random sample Finite population: a sample selected such that each possible sample of size n has the same probability of being selected. Infinite population: a sample selected such that each element comes from the same population and the elements are selected independently.

Sample statistic A sample characteristic, such as a sample mean $\bar{x}$, a sample standard deviation s, a sample proportion $\bar{p}$, and so on. The value of the sample statistic is used to estimate the value of the corresponding population parameter.

Point estimator The sample statistic, such as $\bar{x}$, s, or $\bar{p}$, that provides the point estimate of the population parameter.

Point estimate The value of a point estimator used in a particular instance as an estimate of a population parameter.

Sampling distribution A probability distribution consisting of all possible values of a sample statistic.

Unbiased A property of a point estimator that is present when the expected value of the point estimator is equal to the population parameter it estimates.

Finite population correction factor The term $\sqrt{(N-n)/(N-1)}$ that is used in the formulas for $\sigma_{\bar{x}}$ and $\sigma_{\bar{p}}$ whenever a finite population, rather than an infinite population, is being sampled. The generally accepted rule of thumb is to ignore the finite population correction factor whenever $n/N \leq .05$.

Standard error The standard deviation of a point estimator.

Central limit theorem A theorem that enables one to use the normal probability distribution to approximate the sampling distribution of $\bar{x}$ whenever the sample size is large.

Stratified random sampling A probability sampling method in which the population is first divided into strata and a simple random sample is then taken from each stratum.

Cluster sampling A probability sampling method in which the population is first divided into clusters and then a simple random sample of the clusters is taken.

Systematic sampling A probability sampling method in which we randomly select one of the first k elements and then select every kth element thereafter.

Convenience sampling A nonprobability method of sampling whereby elements are selected for the sample on the basis of convenience.

Judgment sampling A nonprobability method of sampling whereby elements are selected for the sample based on the judgment of the person doing the study.

Key Formulas

Expected Value of $\bar{x}$

$$E(\bar{x}) = \mu \tag{7.1}$$

Standard Deviation of $\bar{x}$ (Standard Error)

Finite Population   *Infinite Population*

$$\sigma_{\bar{x}} = \sqrt{\frac{N-n}{N-1}}\left(\frac{\sigma}{\sqrt{n}}\right) \qquad \sigma_{\bar{x}} = \frac{\sigma}{\sqrt{n}} \tag{7.2}$$

Expected Value of $\bar{p}$

$$E(\bar{p}) = p \tag{7.4}$$

Standard Deviation of $\bar{p}$ (Standard Error)

Finite Population   *Infinite Population*

$$\sigma_{\bar{p}} = \sqrt{\frac{N-n}{N-1}}\sqrt{\frac{p(1-p)}{n}} \qquad \sigma_{\bar{p}} = \sqrt{\frac{p(1-p)}{n}} \tag{7.5}$$

Supplementary Exercises

Dining

38. Bob Miller, a food critic, wants to prepare an article on the quality of food at locally owned restaurants in Myrtle Beach, South Carolina. A list of 44 locally owned restaurants is contained in the data file named Dining that is on the CD accompanying the text (*Coastal Carolina Dining*, Fall 2004). Bob only has time to sample the food at five of these restaurants.
    a. In the data file the restaurants are listed in column A of an Excel worksheet. In column B we generated a random number for each of the restaurants in column A. Use these random numbers to select a simple random sample of five restaurants for Bob.
    b. Generate a new set of random numbers and use them to select a new simple random sample. Did you select the same restaurants?

39. Americans have become increasingly concerned about the rising cost of Medicare. In 1990, the average annual Medicare spending per enrollee was $3267; in 2003, the average annual Medicare spending per enrollee was $6883 (*Money*, Fall 2003). Suppose you hired a consulting firm to take a sample of fifty 2003 Medicare enrollees to further investigate the nature of expenditures. Assume the population standard deviation for 2003 was $2000.
    a. Show the sampling distribution of the mean amount of Medicare spending for a sample of fifty 2003 enrollees.
    b. What is the probability the sample mean will be within ±$300 of the population mean?
    c. What is the probability the sample mean will be greater than $7500? If the consulting firm tells you the sample mean for the Medicare enrollees they interviewed was $7500, would you question whether they followed correct simple random sampling procedures? Why or why not?

40. *BusinessWeek* surveyed MBA alumni 10 years after graduation (*BusinessWeek*, September 22, 2003). One finding was that alumni spend an average of $115.50 per week eating out socially. You have been asked to conduct a follow-up study by taking a sample of 40 of these MBA alumni. Assume the population standard deviation is $35.
    a. Show the sampling distribution of $\bar{x}$, the sample mean weekly expenditure for the 40 MBA alumni.
    b. What is the probability the sample mean will be within $10 of the population mean?
    c. Suppose you find a sample mean of $100. What is the probability of finding a sample mean of $100 or less? Would you consider this sample to be an unusually low spending group of alumni? Why or why not?

41. The mean television viewing time for Americans is 15 hours per week (*Money*, November 2003). Suppose a sample of 60 Americans is taken to further investigate viewing habits. Assume the population standard deviation for weekly viewing time is $\sigma = 4$ hours.
    a. What is the probability the sample mean will be within 1 hour of the population mean?
    b. What is the probability the sample mean will be within 45 minutes of the population mean?

42. The average annual salary for federal government employees in Indiana is $41,979 (*The World Almanac 2001*). Use this figure as the population mean and assume the population standard deviation is $\sigma = \$5000$. Suppose that a random sample of 50 federal government employees will be selected from the population.
    a. What is the value of the standard error of the mean?
    b. What is the probability that the sample mean will be more than $41,979?
    c. What is the probability the sample mean will be within $1000 of the population mean?
    d. How would the probability in part (c) change if the sample size were increased to 100?

43. Three firms carry inventories that differ in size. Firm A's inventory contains 2000 items, firm B's inventory contains 5000 items, and firm C's inventory contains 10,000 items. The population standard deviation for the cost of the items in each firm's inventory is $\sigma = 144$. A statistical consultant recommends that each firm take a sample of 50 items from its inventory to provide statistically valid estimates of the average cost per item. Managers of the small firm state that because it has the smallest population, it should be able to make the estimate from a much smaller sample than that required by the larger firms. However, the consultant states that to obtain the same standard error and thus the same precision in the sample results, all firms should use the same sample size regardless of population size.
    a. Using the finite population correction factor, compute the standard error for each of the three firms given a sample of size 50.
    b. What is the probability that for each firm the sample mean $\bar{x}$ will be within ± 25 of the population mean μ?

44. A researcher reports survey results by stating that the standard error of the mean is 20. The population standard deviation is 500.
    a. How large was the sample used in this survey?
    b. What is the probability that the point estimate was within ± 25 of the population mean?

45. A production process is checked periodically by a quality control inspector. The inspector selects simple random samples of 30 finished products and computes the sample mean product weights $\bar{x}$. If test results over a long period of time show that 5% of the $\bar{x}$ values are over 2.1 pounds and 5% are under 1.9 pounds, what are the mean and the standard deviation for the population of products produced with this process?

46. As of June 13, 2001, 30.5% of individual investors were bullish on the stock market short term (*AAII Journal*, July 2001). Answer the following questions assuming a sample of 200 individual investors is used.
    a. Show the sampling distribution of $\bar{p}$, the sample proportion of individual investors who are bullish on the market short term.

    b.   What is the probability that the sample proportion will be within $\pm.04$ of the population proportion?

    c.   What is the probability that the sample proportion will be within $\pm.02$ of the population proportion?

47.   A market research firm conducts telephone surveys with a 40% historical response rate. What is the probability that in a new sample of 400 telephone numbers, at least 150 individuals will cooperate and respond to the questions? In other words, what is the probability that the sample proportion will be at least 150/400 = .375?

48.   According to ORC International, 71% of Internet users connect their computers to the Internet by normal telephone lines (*USA Today,* January 18, 2000). Assume a population proportion $p = .71$.

    a.   What is the probability that a sample proportion from a simple random sample of 350 Internet users will be within $\pm.05$ of the population proportion?

    b.   What is the probability that a sample proportion from a simple random sample of 350 Internet users will be .75 or greater?

49.   The proportion of individuals insured by the All-Driver Automobile Insurance Company who received at least one traffic ticket during a five-year period is .15.

    a.   Show the sampling distribution of $\bar{p}$ if a random sample of 150 insured individuals is used to estimate the proportion having received at least one ticket.

    b.   What is the probability that the sample proportion will be within $\pm.03$ of the population proportion?

50.   Lori Jeffrey is a successful sales representative for a major publisher of college textbooks. Historically, Lori obtains a book adoption on 25% of her sales calls. Viewing her sales calls for one month as a sample of all possible sales calls, assume that a statistical analysis of the data yields a standard error of the proportion of .0625.

    a.   How large was the sample used in this analysis? That is, how many sales calls did Lori make during the month?

    b.   Let $\bar{p}$ indicate the sample proportion of book adoptions obtained during the month. Show the sampling distribution of $\bar{p}$.

    c.   Using the sampling distribution of $\bar{p}$, compute the probability that Lori will obtain book adoptions on 30% or more of her sales calls during a one-month period.

CHAPTER 8

Interval Estimation

CONTENTS

FOOD LION*
SALISBURY, NORTH CAROLINA

Founded in 1957 as Food Town, Food Lion is one of the largest supermarket chains in the United States with 1200 stores in 11 Southeastern and Mid-Atlantic states. The company sells more than 24,000 different products and offers nationally and regionally advertised brand-name merchandise, as well as a growing number of high-quality private label products manufactured especially for Food Lion. The company maintains its low price leadership and quality assurance through operating efficiencies such as standard store formats, innovative warehouse design, energy-efficient facilities, and data synchronization with suppliers. Food Lion looks to a future of continued innovation, growth, price leadership, and service to its customers.

Being in an inventory-intense business, Food Lion made the decision to adopt the LIFO (last-in, first-out) method of inventory valuation. This method matches current costs against current revenues, which minimizes the effect of radical price changes on profit and loss results. In addition, the LIFO method reduces net income thereby reducing income taxes during periods of inflation.

Food Lion establishes a LIFO index for each of seven inventory pools: Grocery, Paper/Household, Pet Supplies, Health & Beauty Aids, Dairy, Cigarette/Tobacco, and Beer/Wine. For example, a LIFO index of 1.008 for the Grocery pool would indicate that the company's grocery inventory value at current costs reflects a 0.8% increase due to inflation over the most recent one-year period.

A LIFO index for each inventory pool requires that the year-end inventory count for each product be valued at the current year-end cost and at the preceding year-end cost. To avoid excessive time and expense associated with counting the inventory

*The authors are indebted to Keith Cunningham, Tax Director, and Bobby Harkey, Staff Tax Accountant, at Food Lion for providing this Statistics in Practice.

The Food Lion store in the Cambridge Shopping Center, Charlotte, North Carolina. © Courtesy of Food Lion.

in all 1200 store locations, Food Lion selects a random sample of 50 stores. Year-end physical inventories are taken in each of the sample stores. The current-year and preceding-year costs for each item are then used to construct the required LIFO indexes for each inventory pool.

For a recent year, the sample estimate of the LIFO index for the Health & Beauty Aids inventory pool was 1.015. Using a 95% confidence level, Food Lion computed a margin of error of .006 for the sample estimate. Thus, the interval from 1.009 to 1.021 provided a 95% confidence interval estimate of the population LIFO index. This level of precision was judged to be very good.

In this chapter you will learn how to compute the margin of error associated with sample estimates. You will also learn how to use this information to construct and interpret interval estimates of a population mean and a population proportion.

In Chapter 7, we stated that a point estimator is a sample statistic used to estimate a population parameter. For instance, the sample mean $\bar{x}$ is a point estimator of the population mean μ and the sample proportion $\bar{p}$ is a point estimator of the population proportion p. Because a point estimator cannot be expected to provide the exact value of the population parameter, an **interval estimate** is often computed by adding and subtracting a value, called the **margin of error**, to the point estimate. The general form of an interval estimate is as follows:

$$\text{Point estimate} \pm \text{Margin of error}$$

The purpose of an interval estimate is to provide information about how close the point estimate, provided by the sample, is to the value of the population parameter.

In this chapter we show how to compute interval estimates of a population mean μ and a population proportion p. The general form of an interval estimate of a population mean is

$$\bar{x} \pm \text{Margin of error}$$

Similarly, the general form of an interval estimate of a population proportion is

$$\bar{p} \pm \text{Margin of error}$$

The sampling distributions of $\bar{x}$ and $\bar{p}$ play key roles in computing these interval estimates.

Population Mean: σ Known

In order to develop an interval estimate of a population mean, either the population standard deviation σ or the sample standard deviation s must be used to compute the margin of error. In most applications σ is not known, and s is used to compute the margin of error. In some applications, however, large amounts of relevant historical data are available and can be used to estimate the population standard deviation prior to sampling. Also, in quality control applications where a process is assumed to be operating correctly, or "in control," it is appropriate to treat the population standard deviation as known. We refer to such cases as the **σ known** case. In this section we introduce an example in which it is reasonable to treat σ as known and show how to construct an interval estimate for this case.

Each week Lloyd's Department Store selects a simple random sample of 100 customers in order to learn about the amount spent per shopping trip. With x representing the amount spent per shopping trip, the sample mean $\bar{x}$ provides a point estimate of μ, the mean amount spent per shopping trip for the population of all Lloyd's customers. Lloyd's has been using the weekly survey for several years. Based on the historical data, Lloyd's now assumes a known value of $\sigma = \$20$ for the population standard deviation. The historical data also indicate that the population follows a normal distribution.

Lloyd's

During the most recent week, Lloyd's surveyed 100 customers ($n = 100$) and obtained a sample mean of $\bar{x} = \$82$. The sample mean amount spent provides a point estimate of the population mean amount spent per shopping trip, μ. In the discussion that follows, we show how to compute the margin of error for this estimate and develop an interval estimate of the population mean.

Margin of Error and the Interval Estimate

In Chapter 7 we showed that the sampling distribution of $\bar{x}$ can be used to compute the probability that $\bar{x}$ will be within a given distance of μ. In the Lloyd's example, the historical data show that the population of amounts spent is normally distributed with a standard deviation of $\sigma = 20$. So, using what we learned in Chapter 7, we can conclude that the sampling distribution of $\bar{x}$ follows a normal distribution with an unknown mean μ, and a known standard error of $\sigma_{\bar{x}} = \sigma/\sqrt{n} = 20/\sqrt{100} = 2$. This sampling distribution is shown in Figure 8.1.*

---

*We use the fact that the population of amounts spent has a normal distribution to conclude that the sampling distribution of $\bar{x}$ has a normal distribution. If the population did not have a normal distribution, we could rely on the central limit theorem and the large sample size of $n = 100$ to conclude that the sampling distribution of $\bar{x}$ is approximately normal. In either case, the sampling distribution of $\bar{x}$ would appear as shown in Figure 8.1.

**FIGURE 8.1   SAMPLING DISTRIBUTION OF THE SAMPLE MEAN AMOUNT
SPENT FROM SIMPLE RANDOM SAMPLES OF 100 CUSTOMERS**

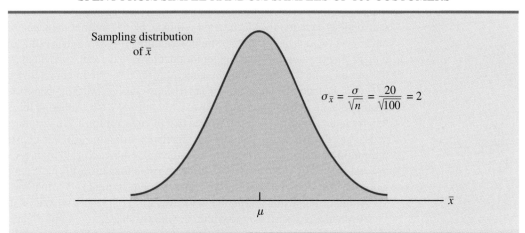

Because the sampling distribution shows how values of $\bar{x}$ are distributed around the population mean μ, the sampling distribution of $\bar{x}$ provides information about the possible differences between $\bar{x}$ and μ.

Using the standard normal probability table, we find that 95% of the values of any normally distributed random variable are within ± 1.96 standard deviations of the mean. Thus, when the sampling distribution of $\bar{x}$ is normally distributed, 95% of the $\bar{x}$ values must be within $\pm 1.96\sigma_{\bar{x}}$ of the mean μ. In the Lloyd's example we know that the sampling distribution of $\bar{x}$ is normally distributed with a standard error of $\sigma_{\bar{x}} = 2$. Because $\pm 1.96\sigma_{\bar{x}} = 1.96(2) = 3.92$, we can conclude that 95% of all $\bar{x}$ values obtained using a sample size of $n = 100$ will be within ± 3.92 of the population mean μ. See Figure 8.2.

**FIGURE 8.2   SAMPLING DISTRIBUTION OF $\bar{x}$ SHOWING THE LOCATION OF SAMPLE
MEANS THAT ARE WITHIN 3.92 OF μ**

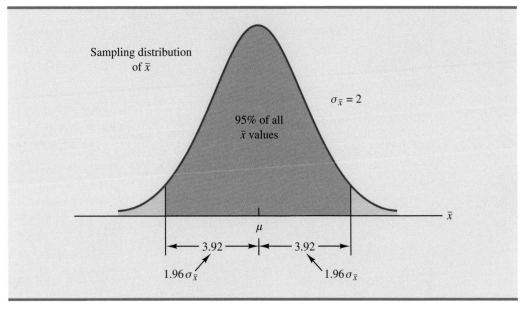

In the introduction to this chapter we said that the general form of an interval estimate of the population mean μ is $\bar{x} \pm$ margin of error. For the Lloyd's example, suppose we set the margin of error equal to 3.92 and compute the interval estimate of μ using $\bar{x} \pm 3.92$. To provide an interpretation for this interval estimate, let us consider the values of $\bar{x}$ that could be obtained if we took three *different* simple random samples, each consisting of 100 Lloyd's customers. The first sample mean might turn out to have the value shown as $\bar{x}_1$ in Figure 8.3. In this case, Figure 8.3 shows that the interval formed by subtracting 3.92 from $\bar{x}_1$ and adding 3.92 to $\bar{x}_1$ includes the population mean μ. Now consider what happens if the second sample mean turns out to have the value shown as $\bar{x}_2$ in Figure 8.3. Although this sample mean differs from the first sample mean, we see that the interval formed by subtracting 3.92 from $\bar{x}_2$ and adding 3.92 to $\bar{x}_2$ also includes the population mean μ. However, consider what happens if the third sample mean turns out to have the value shown as $\bar{x}_3$ in Figure 8.3. In this case, the interval formed by subtracting 3.92 from $\bar{x}_3$ and adding 3.92 to $\bar{x}_3$ does not include the population mean μ. Because $\bar{x}_3$ falls in the upper tail of the sampling distribution and is farther than 3.92 from μ, subtracting and adding 3.92 to $\bar{x}_3$ forms an interval that does not include μ.

Any sample mean $\bar{x}$ that is within the darkly shaded region of Figure 8.3 will provide an interval that contains the population mean μ. Because 95% of all possible sample means are in the darkly shaded region, 95% of all intervals formed by subtracting 3.92 from $\bar{x}$ and adding 3.92 to $\bar{x}$ will include the population mean μ.

Recall that during the most recent week, the quality assurance team at Lloyd's surveyed 100 customers and obtained a sample mean amount spent of $\bar{x} = 82$. Using $\bar{x} \pm 3.92$ to construct the interval estimate, we obtain 82 ± 3.92. Thus, the specific interval estimate of

FIGURE 8.3   INTERVALS FORMED FROM SELECTED SAMPLE MEANS
AT LOCATIONS $\bar{x}_1$, $\bar{x}_2$, AND $\bar{x}_3$

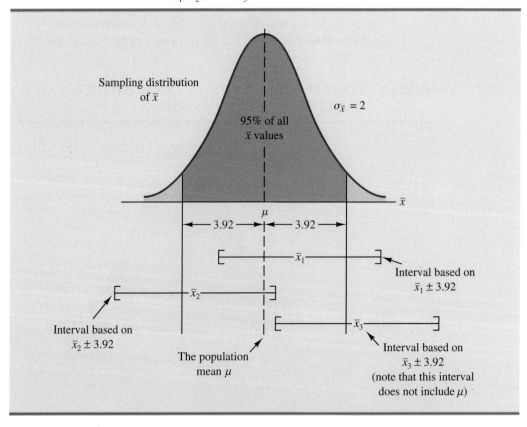

This discussion provides insight as to why the interval is called a 95% confidence interval.

μ based on the data from the most recent week is $82 - 3.92 = 78.08$ to $82 + 3.92 = 85.92$. Because 95% of all the intervals constructed using $\bar{x} \pm 3.92$ will contain the population mean, we say that we are 95% confident that the interval 78.08 to 85.92 includes the population mean μ. We say that this interval has been established at the 95% **confidence level**. The value .95 is referred to as the **confidence coefficient**, and the interval 78.08 to 85.92 is called the 95% **confidence interval**.

Another term sometimes associated with an interval estimate is the **level of significance**. The level of significance associated with an interval estimate is denoted by the Greek letter α. The level of significance and the confidence coefficient are related as follows:

$$\alpha = \text{Level of Significance} = 1 - \text{Confidence Coefficient}$$

The level of significance is also referred to as the significance level.

The level of significance is the probability that the interval estimation procedure will generate an interval that does not contain μ. For example, the level of significance corresponding to a .95 confidence coefficient is $\alpha = 1 - .95 = .05$. In Lloyd's case, the level of significance ($\alpha = .05$) is the probability of drawing a sample, computing the sample mean, and finding that $\bar{x}$ lies in one of the tails of the sampling distribution (see $\bar{x}_3$ in Figure 8.3). When the sample mean happens to fall in the tail of the sampling distribution (and it will 5% of the time), the confidence interval generated will not contain μ.

With the margin of error given by $z_{\alpha/2}(\sigma/\sqrt{n})$, the general form of an interval estimate of a population mean for the σ known case follows.

INTERVAL ESTIMATE OF A POPULATION MEAN: σ KNOWN

$$\bar{x} \pm z_{\alpha/2} \frac{\sigma}{\sqrt{n}} \tag{8.1}$$

where $(1 - \alpha)$ is the confidence coefficient and $z_{\alpha/2}$ is the z value providing an area of $\alpha/2$ in the upper tail of the standard normal probability distribution.

Let us use expression (8.1) to construct a 95% confidence interval for the Lloyd's example. For a 95% confidence interval, the confidence coefficient is $(1 - \alpha) = .95$ and thus, $\alpha = .05$. Using the tables of areas for the standard normal distribution, an area of $\alpha/2 = .05/2 = .025$ in the upper tail provides $z_{.025} = 1.96$. With the Lloyd's sample mean $\bar{x} = 82$, $\sigma = 20$, and a sample size $n = 100$, we obtain

$$82 \pm 1.96 \frac{20}{\sqrt{100}}$$

$$82 \pm 3.92$$

Thus, using expression (8.1), the margin of error is 3.92 and the 95% confidence interval is $82 - 3.92 = 78.08$ to $82 + 3.92 = 85.92$.

Although a 95% confidence level is frequently used, other confidence levels such as 90% and 99% may be considered. Values of $z_{\alpha/2}$ for the most commonly used confidence levels are shown in Table 8.1. Using these values and expression (8.1), the 90% confidence interval for the Lloyd's example is

$$82 \pm 1.645 \frac{20}{\sqrt{100}}$$

$$82 \pm 3.29$$

TABLE 8.1 VALUES OF $z_{\alpha/2}$ FOR THE MOST COMMONLY USED CONFIDENCE LEVELS

Confidence Level	α	$\alpha/2$	$z_{\alpha/2}$
90%	.10	.05	1.645
95%	.05	.025	1.960
99%	.01	.005	2.576

Thus, at 90% confidence, the margin of error is 3.29 and the confidence interval is $82 - 3.29 = 78.71$ to $82 + 3.29 = 85.29$. Similarly, the 99% confidence interval is

$$82 \pm 2.576 \frac{20}{\sqrt{100}}$$

$$82 \pm 5.15$$

Thus, at 99% confidence, the margin of error is 5.15 and the confidence interval is $82 - 5.15 = 76.85$ to $82 + 5.15 = 87.15$.

Comparing the results for the 90%, 95%, and 99% confidence levels, we see that in order to have a higher degree of confidence, the margin of error and thus the width of the confidence interval must be larger.

Using Excel

We will use the Lloyd's Department Store data to illustrate how Excel can be used to construct an interval estimate of the population mean for the σ known case. Refer to Figure 8.4 as we describe the tasks involved. The formula worksheet is in the background; the value worksheet appears in the foreground.

Enter Data: A label and the sales data are entered into cells A1:A101.

Enter Functions and Formulas: The sample size and sample mean are computed in cells D4:D5 using Excel's COUNT and AVERAGE functions, respectively. The value worksheet shows that the sample size is 100 and the sample mean is 82. The value of the known population standard deviation (20) is entered into cell D7 and the desired confidence coefficient (.95) is entered into cell D8. The level of significance is computed in cell D9 by entering the formula $=1-D8$; the value worksheet shows that the level of significance associated with a confidence coefficient of .95 is .05. The margin of error is computed in cell D11 using Excel's CONFIDENCE function. The CONFIDENCE function has three inputs: the level of significance (cell D9); the population standard deviation (cell D7); and the sample size (cell D4). Thus, to compute the margin of error associated with a 95% confidence interval, the following formula is entered into cell D11:

$$=\text{CONFIDENCE(D9,D7,D4)}$$

The resulting value of 3.92 is the margin of error associated with the interval estimate of the population mean amount spent per week.

Cells D13:D15 provide the point estimate and the lower and upper limits for the confidence interval. Because the point estimate is just the sample mean, the formula $=D5$ is entered into cell D13. To compute the lower limit of the 95% confidence interval, $\bar{x} - $ (margin of error), we enter the formula $=D13-D11$ into cell D14. To compute the upper limit of the 95% confidence interval, $\bar{x} + $ (margin of error), we enter the formula $=D13+D11$ into cell D15. The value worksheet shows a lower limit of 78.08 and an upper limit of 85.92. In other words, the 95% confidence interval for the population mean is from 78.08 to 85.92.

The reason the number of degrees of freedom associated with the t value in expression (8.2) is $n - 1$ concerns the use of s as an estimate of the population standard deviation σ. The expression for the sample standard deviation is

$$s = \sqrt{\frac{\Sigma(x_i - \bar{x})^2}{n - 1}}$$

Degrees of freedom refer to the number of independent pieces of information that go into the computation of $\Sigma(x_i - \bar{x})^2$. The n pieces of information involved in computing $\Sigma(x_i - \bar{x})^2$ are as follows: $x_1 - \bar{x}, x_2 - \bar{x}, \ldots, x_n - \bar{x}$. In Section 3.2 we indicated that $\Sigma(x_i - \bar{x}) = 0$ for any data set. Thus, only $n - 1$ of the $x_i - \bar{x}$ values are independent; that is, if we know $n - 1$ of the values, the remaining value can be determined exactly by using the condition that the sum of the $x_i - \bar{x}$ values must be 0. Thus, $n - 1$ is the number of degrees of freedom associated with $\Sigma(x_i - \bar{x})^2$ and hence the number of degrees of freedom for the t distribution in expression (8.2).

To illustrate the interval estimation procedure for the σ unknown case, we will consider a study designed to estimate the mean credit card debt for the population of households in a certain city. A sample of $n = 85$ households provided the credit card balances shown in Table 8.3. For this situation, no previous estimate of the population standard deviation σ is available. Thus, the sample data must be used to estimate both the population mean and the population standard deviation. Using the data in Table 8.3, we compute the sample mean $\bar{x} = \$5900$ and the sample standard deviation $s = \$3058$. With 95% confidence and $n - 1 = 84$ degrees of freedom, Table 2 in Appendix B provides $t_{.025} = 1.989$. We can now use expression (8.2) to compute an interval estimate of the population mean.

$$5900 \pm 1.989 \frac{3058}{\sqrt{85}}$$

$$5900 \pm 660$$

The point estimate of the population mean is \$5900, the margin of error is \$660, and the 95% confidence interval is $5900 - 660 = \$5240$ to $5900 + 660 = \$6560$. Thus, we are 95% confident that the population mean credit card balance for all households is between \$5240 and \$6560.

TABLE 8.3   CREDIT CARD BALANCES FOR A SAMPLE OF 85 HOUSEHOLDS

Balance

9619	5994	3344	7888	7581	9980
5364	4652	13627	3091	12545	8718
8348	5376	968	943	7959	8452
7348	5998	4714	8762	2563	4935
381	7530	4334	1407	6787	5938
2998	3678	4911	6644	5071	5266
1686	3581	1920	7644	9536	10658
1962	5625	3780	11169	4459	3910
4920	5619	3478	7979	8047	7503
5047	9032	6185	3258	8083	1582
6921	13236	1141	8660	2153	
5759	4447	7577	7511	8003	
8047	609	4667	14442	6795	
3924	414	5219	4447	5915	
3470	7636	6416	6550	7164	

Using Excel

We will use the credit card balances in Table 8.3 to illustrate how Excel can be used to construct an interval estimate of the population mean for the σ unknown case. We start by summarizing the date using Excel's Descriptive Statistics tool described in Chapter 3. Refer to Figure 8.7 as we describe the tasks involved. The formula worksheet is in the background; the value worksheet is in the foreground.

Enter Data: A label and the credit card balances are entered into cells A1:A86.

Apply Analysis Tools: The following steps describe how to use Excel's Descriptive Statistics tool for these data:

Step 1. Select the **Tools** menu
Step 2. Choose the **Data Analysis** option
Step 3. Choose **Descriptive Statistics** from the list of Analysis Tools
Step 4. When the Descriptive Statistics dialog box appears:
      Enter A1:A86 in the **Input Range** box
      Select **Grouped By Columns**
      Select **Labels in First Row**
      Select **Output Range**
         Enter C1 in the **Output Range** box
      Select **Summary Statistics**
      Select **Confidence Level for Mean**
         Enter 95 in the **Confidence Level for Mean** box
      Click **OK**

FIGURE 8.7   EXCEL WORKSHEET: 95% CONFIDENCE INTERVAL FOR CREDIT CARD BALANCES

	A	B	C	D	E
1	Balance		*Balance*		
2	9619				
3	5364		Mean	5900	
4	8348		Standard Error	331.6867	
5	7348		Median	5759	
6	381		Mode	8047	
7	2998		Standard Deviation	3058	
8	1686		Sample Variance	9351364	
9	1962		Kurtosis	0.2327	
10	4920		Skewness	0.4076	
11	5047		Range	14061	
12	6921		Minimum	381	
13	5759		Maximum	14442	
14	8047		Sum	501500	
15	3924		Count	85	
16	3470		Confidence Level(95.0%)	660	
17	5994				
18	4652		**Point Estimate**	=D3	
19	5376		**Lower Limit**	=D18-D16	
20	5998		**Upper Limit**	=D18+D16	
85	7503				
86	1582				
87					

Note: Rows 21–84 are hidden.

	A	B	C	D	E	F
1	Balance		*Balance*			
2	9619					
3	5364		Mean	5900		**Point Estimate**
4	8348		Standard Error	331.6867		
5	7348		Median	5759		
6	381		Mode	8047		
7	2998		Standard Deviation	3058		
8	1686		Sample Variance	9351364		
9	1962		Kurtosis	0.2327		
10	4920		Skewness	0.4076		
11	5047		Range	14061		
12	6921		Minimum	381		
13	5759		Maximum	14442		
14	8047		Sum	501500		
15	3924		Count	85		
16	3470		Confidence Level(95.0%)	660		**Margin of Error**
17	5994					
18	4652		**Point Estimate**	5900		
19	5376		**Lower Limit**	5240		
20	5998		**Upper Limit**	6560		
85	7503					
86	1582					
87						

The sample mean ($\bar{x}$) is in cell D3. The margin of error, labeled "Confidence Level(95.0%)," appears in cell D16. The value worksheet shows $\bar{x} = 5900$ and a margin of error equal to 660.

Enter Functions and Formulas: Cells D18:D20 provide the point estimate and the lower and upper limits for the confidence interval. Because the point estimate is just the sample mean, the formula =D3 is entered into cell D18. To compute the lower limit of the 95% confidence interval, $\bar{x}$ − (margin of error), we enter the formula =D18-D16 into cell D19. To compute the upper limit of the 95% confidence interval, $\bar{x}$ + (margin of error), we enter the formula =D18+D16 into cell D20. The value worksheet shows a lower limit of 5240 and an upper limit of 6560. In other words, the 95% confidence interval for the population mean is from 5240 to 6560.

Practical Advice

If the population follows a normal distribution, the confidence interval provided by expression (8.2) is exact and can be used for any sample size. If the population does not follow a normal distribution, the confidence interval provided by expression (8.2) will be approximate. In this case, the quality of the approximation depends on both the distribution of the population and the sample size.

Larger sample sizes are needed if the distribution of the population is highly skewed or includes outliers.

In most applications, a sample size of $n \geq 30$ is adequate when using expression (8.2) to develop an interval estimate of a population mean. However, if the population distribution is highly skewed or contains outliers, most statisticians would recommend increasing the sample size to 50 or more. If the population is not normally distributed but is roughly symmetric, sample sizes as small as 15 can be expected to provide good approximate confidence intervals. With smaller sample sizes, expression (8.2) should only be used if the analyst believes, or is willing to assume, that the population distribution is at least approximately normal.

Using a Small Sample

In the following example we develop an interval estimate for a population mean when the sample size is small. As we already noted, an understanding of the distribution of the population becomes a factor in deciding whether the interval estimation procedure provides acceptable results.

Scheer Industries is considering a new computer-assisted program to train maintenance employees to do machine repairs. In order to fully evaluate the program, the director of manufacturing requested an estimate of the population mean time required for maintenance employees to complete the computer-assisted training.

A sample of 20 employees is selected, with each employee in the sample completing the training program. Data on the training time in days for the 20 employees are shown in Table 8.4. A histogram of the sample data appears in Figure 8.8. What can we say about the distribution of the population based on this histogram? First, the sample data do not support

TABLE 8.4   TRAINING TIME IN DAYS FOR A SAMPLE OF 20 SCHEER INDUSTRIES EMPLOYEES

CD file

Scheer

52	59	54	42
44	50	42	48
55	54	60	55
44	62	62	57
45	46	43	56

FIGURE 8.8 HISTOGRAM OF TRAINING TIMES FOR THE SCHEER INDUSTRIES SAMPLE

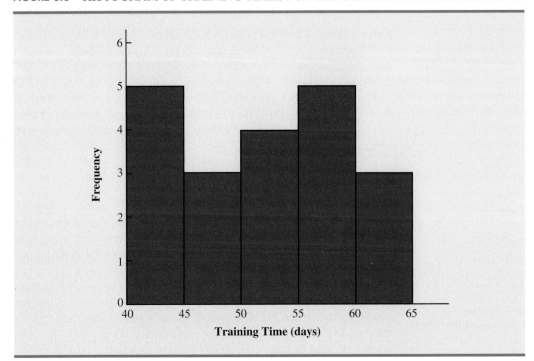

the conclusion that the distribution of the population is normal, yet we do not see any evidence of skewness or outliers. Therefore, using the guidelines in the previous subsection, we conclude that an interval estimate based on the t distribution appears acceptable for the sample of 20 employees.

We continue by computing the sample mean and sample standard deviation as follows.

$$\bar{x} = \frac{\Sigma x_i}{n} = \frac{1030}{20} = 51.5 \text{ days}$$

$$s = \sqrt{\frac{\Sigma(x_i - \bar{x})^2}{n - 1}} = \sqrt{\frac{889}{20 - 1}} = 6.84 \text{ days}$$

For a 95% confidence interval, we use Table 8.2 and $n - 1 = 19$ degrees of freedom to obtain $t_{.025} = 2.093$. Expression (8.2) provides the interval estimate of the population mean.

$$51.5 \pm 2.093\left(\frac{6.84}{\sqrt{20}}\right)$$

$$51.5 \pm 3.2$$

The point estimate of the population mean is 51.5 days. The margin of error is 3.2 days and the 95% confidence interval is $51.5 - 3.2 = 48.3$ days to $51.5 + 3.2 = 54.7$ days.

Using a histogram of the sample data to learn about the distribution of a population is not always conclusive, but in many cases it provides the only information available. The histogram, along with judgment on the part of the analyst, can often be used to decide whether expression (8.2) can be used to develop the interval estimate.

FIGURE 8.9 SUMMARY OF INTERVAL ESTIMATION PROCEDURES
FOR A POPULATION MEAN

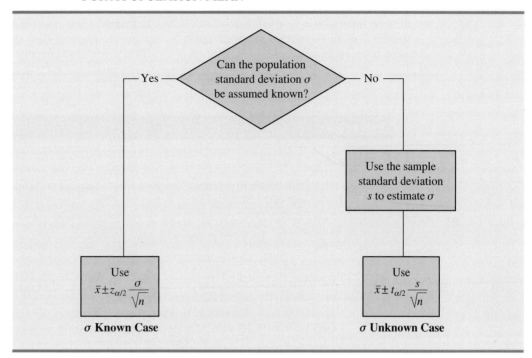

Summary of Interval Estimation Procedures

We provided two approaches to developing an interval estimate of a population mean. For the σ known case, σ and the standard normal distribution are used in expression (8.1) to compute the margin of error and to develop the interval estimate. For the σ unknown case, the sample standard deviation s and the t distribution are used in expression (8.2) to compute the margin of error and to develop the interval estimate.

A summary of the interval estimation procedures for the two cases is shown in Figure 8.9. In most applications, a sample size of $n \geq 30$ is adequate. If the population has a normal or approximately normal distribution, however, smaller sample sizes may be used. For the σ unknown case a sample size of $n \geq 50$ is recommended if the population distribution is believed to be highly skewed or has outliers.

NOTES AND COMMENTS

1. When σ is known, the margin of error, $z_{\alpha/2}(\sigma/\sqrt{n})$, is fixed and is the same for all samples of size n. When σ is unknown, the margin of error, $t_{\alpha/2}(s/\sqrt{n})$, varies from sample to sample. This variation occurs because s varies from sample to sample. A large value for s provides a larger margin of error, while a small value for s provides a smaller margin of error.

2. What happens to confidence interval estimates when the population is skewed? Con-

sider a population that is skewed to the right with large data values stretching the distribution to the right. When such skewness exists, the sample mean $\bar{x}$ and the sample standard deviation s are positively correlated. Larger values of s tend to be associated with larger values of $\bar{x}$. Thus, when $\bar{x}$ is larger than the population mean, s tends to be larger than σ. This skewness causes the margin of error, $t_{\alpha/2}(s/\sqrt{n})$, to be larger than it would be with

(continued)

σ known. The confidence interval with the larger margin of error tends to include the population mean μ more often than it would if the true value of σ were used. But when $\bar{x}$ is smaller than the population mean, the correlation between $\bar{x}$ and s causes the margin of error to be small. In this case, the confidence interval with the smaller margin of error tends to miss the population mean more than it would if we knew σ and used it. For this reason, we recommend using larger sample sizes with highly skewed population distributions.

Exercises

Methods

11. For a t distribution with 16 degrees of freedom, find the area, or probability, in each region.
    a. To the right of 2.120
    b. To the left of 1.337
    c. To the left of -1.746
    d. To the right of 2.583
    e. Between -2.120 and 2.120
    f. Between -1.746 and 1.746

12. Find the t value(s) for each of the following cases.
    a. Upper tail area of .025 with 12 degrees of freedom
    b. Lower tail area of .05 with 50 degrees of freedom
    c. Upper tail area of .01 with 30 degrees of freedom
    d. Where 90% of the area falls between these two t values with 25 degrees of freedom
    e. Where 95% of the area falls between these two t values with 45 degrees of freedom (See Table 2 of Appendix B for a more extensive t table.)

13. The following sample data are from a normal population: 10, 8, 12, 15, 13, 11, 6, 5.
    a. What is the point estimate of the population mean?
    b. What is the point estimate of the population standard deviation?
    c. With 95% confidence, what is the margin of error for the estimation of the population mean?
    d. What is the 95% confidence interval for the population mean?

14. A simple random sample with $n = 54$ provided a sample mean of 22.5 and a sample standard deviation of 4.4. (See Table 2 of Appendix B for a more extensive t table.)
    a. Develop a 90% confidence interval for the population mean.
    b. Develop a 95% confidence interval for the population mean.
    c. Develop a 99% confidence interval for the population mean.
    d. What happens to the margin of error and the confidence interval as the confidence level is increased?

Applications

15. Sales personnel for Skillings Distributors submit weekly reports listing the customer contacts made during the week. A sample of 65 weekly reports showed a sample mean of 19.5 customer contacts per week. The sample standard deviation was 5.2. Provide 90% and 95% confidence intervals for the population mean number of weekly customer contacts for the sales personnel.

16. The mean number of hours of flying time for pilots at Continental Airlines is 49 hours per month (*The Wall Street Journal*, February 25, 2003). Assume that this mean was based on actual flying times for a sample of 100 Continental pilots and that the sample standard deviation was 8.5 hours.

a.   At 95% confidence, what is the margin of error?
b.   What is the 95% confidence interval estimate of the population mean flying time for the pilots?
c.   The mean number of hours of flying time for pilots at United Airlines is 36 hours per month. Use your results from part (b) to discuss differences between the flying times for the pilots at the two airlines. *The Wall Street Journal* reported United Airlines as having the highest labor cost among all airlines. Does the information in this exercise provide insight as to why United Airlines might expect higher labor costs?

17. The International Air Transport Association surveys business travelers to develop quality ratings for transatlantic gateway airports. The maximum possible rating is 10. Suppose a simple random sample of 50 business travelers is selected and each traveler is asked to provide a rating for the Miami International Airport. The ratings obtained from the sample of 50 business travelers follow.

Miami

6	4	6	8	7	7	6	3	3	8	10	4	8
7	8	7	5	9	5	8	4	3	8	5	5	4
4	4	8	4	5	6	2	5	9	9	8	4	8
9	9	5	9	7	8	3	10	8	9	6		

Develop a 95% confidence interval estimate of the population mean rating for Miami.

18. Thirty fast-food restaurants including Wendy's, McDonald's, and Burger King were visited during the summer of 2000 (*The Cincinnati Enquirer,* July 9, 2000). During each visit, the customer went to the drive-through and ordered a basic meal such as a "combo" meal or a sandwich, fries, and shake. The time between pulling up to the menu board and receiving the filled order was recorded. The times in minutes for the 30 visits are as follows:

FastFood

0.9	1.0	1.2	2.2	1.9	3.6	2.8	5.2	1.8	2.1
6.8	1.3	3.0	4.5	2.8	2.3	2.7	5.7	4.8	3.5
2.6	3.3	5.0	4.0	7.2	9.1	2.8	3.6	7.3	9.0

a.   Provide a point estimate of the population mean drive-through time at fast-food restaurants.
b.   At 95% confidence, what is the margin of error?
c.   What is the 95% confidence interval estimate of the population mean?
d.   Discuss skewness that may be present in this population. What suggestion would you make for a repeat of this study?

19. A National Retail Foundation survey found households intended to spend an average of $649 during the December holiday season (*The Wall Street Journal,* December 2, 2002). Assume that the survey included 600 households and that the sample standard deviation was $175.
a.   With 95% confidence, what is the margin of error?
b.   What is the 95% confidence interval estimate of the population mean?
c.   The prior year, the population mean expenditure per household was $632. Discuss the change in holiday season expenditures over the one-year period.

20. The American Association of Advertising Agencies records data on nonprogram minutes on half-hour, prime-time television shows. Representative data in minutes for a sample of 20 prime-time shows on major networks at 8:30 P.M. follow.

TVtime

6.0	6.6	5.8
7.0	6.3	6.2
7.2	5.7	6.4
7.0	6.5	6.2
6.0	6.5	7.2
7.3	7.6	6.8
6.0	6.2	

Assume a normal population and provide a point estimate and a 95% confidence interval for the mean number of nonprogram minutes on half-hour, prime-time television shows at 8:30 P.M.

21. Complaints about rising prescription drug prices caused the U.S. Congress to consider laws that would force pharmaceutical companies to offer prescription discounts to senior citizens without drug benefits. The House Government Reform Committee provided data on the prescription cost for some of the most widely used drugs (*Newsweek,* May 8, 2000). Assume the following data show a sample of the prescription cost in dollars for Zocor, a drug used to lower cholesterol.

110	112	115	99	100	98	104	126

Given a normal population, what is the 95% confidence interval estimate of the population mean cost for a prescription of Zocor?

22. The first few weeks of 2004 were good for the stock market. A sample of 25 large open-end funds showed the following year-to-date returns through January 16, 2004 (*Barron's,* January 19, 2004).

OpenEndFunds

7.0	3.2	1.4	5.4	8.5
2.5	2.5	1.9	5.4	1.6
1.0	2.1	8.5	4.3	6.2
1.5	1.2	2.7	3.8	2.0
1.2	2.6	4.0	2.6	0.6

a. What is the point estimate of the population mean year-to-date return for large open-end funds?
b. Given that the population has a normal distribution, develop a 95% confidence interval for the population mean year-to-date return for open-end funds.

(8.3) Determining the Sample Size

In providing practical advice in the two preceding sections, we commented on the role of the sample size in providing approximate confidence intervals when the population is not normally distributed. In this section, we focus on another aspect of the sample size issue. We describe how to choose a sample size large enough to provide a desired margin of error. To see how this is done, we return to the σ known case presented in Section 8.1. Using expression (8.1), the interval estimate is

If a desired margin of error is selected prior to sampling, the procedures in this section can be used to determine the sample size necessary to satisfy the margin of error requirement.

$$\bar{x} \pm z_{\alpha/2} \frac{\sigma}{\sqrt{n}}$$

The quantity $z_{\alpha/2}(\sigma/\sqrt{n})$ is the margin of error. Thus, we see that $z_{\alpha/2}$, the population standard deviation σ, and the sample size n combine to determine the margin of error. Once we select a confidence coefficient $1 - \alpha$, $z_{\alpha/2}$ can be determined. Then, if we have a value for σ, we can determine the sample size n needed to provide any desired margin of error. Development of the formula used to compute the required sample size n follows.

Let E = the desired margin of error:

$$E = z_{\alpha/2} \frac{\sigma}{\sqrt{n}}$$

Solving for $\sqrt{n}$, we have

$$\sqrt{n} = \frac{z_{\alpha/2}\sigma}{E}$$

Squaring both sides of this equation, we obtain the following expression for the sample size.

Equation (8.3) can be used to provide a sample size recommendation. However, judgment on the part of the analyst should be used to determine whether the final sample size should be adjusted upward.

SAMPLE SIZE FOR AN INTERVAL ESTIMATE OF A POPULATION MEAN

$$n = \frac{(z_{\alpha/2})^2 \sigma^2}{E^2} \qquad (8.3)$$

This sample size provides the desired margin of error at the chosen confidence level.

In equation (8.3) E is the margin of error that the user is willing to accept, and the value of $z_{\alpha/2}$ follows directly from the confidence level to be used in developing the interval estimate. Although user preference must be considered, 95% confidence is the most frequently chosen value ($z_{.025} = 1.96$).

Finally, use of equation (8.3) requires a value for the population standard deviation σ. However, even if σ is unknown, we can use equation (8.3) provided we have a preliminary or *planning value* for σ. In practice, one of the following procedures can be chosen.

A planning value for the population standard deviation σ must be specified before the sample size can be determined. Three methods of obtaining a planning value for σ are discussed here.

1. Use the estimate of the population standard deviation computed from data of previous studies as the planning value for σ.
2. Use a pilot study to select a preliminary sample. The sample standard deviation from the preliminary sample can be used as the planning value for σ.
3. Use judgment or a "best guess" for the value of σ. For example, we might begin by estimating the largest and smallest data values in the population. The difference between the largest and smallest values provides an estimate of the range for the data. Finally, the range divided by 4 is often suggested as a rough approximation of the standard deviation and thus an acceptable planning value for σ.

Let us demonstrate the use of equation (8.3) to determine the sample size by considering the following example. A previous study that investigated the cost of renting automobiles in the United States found a mean cost of approximately \$55 per day for renting a midsize automobile. Suppose that the organization that conducted this study would like to conduct a new study in order to estimate the population mean daily rental cost for a midsize automobile in the United States. In designing the new study, the project director specifies that the population mean daily rental cost be estimated with a margin of error of \$2 and a 95% level of confidence.

The project director specified a desired margin of error of $E = 2$, and the 95% level of confidence indicates $z_{.025} = 1.96$. Thus, we only need a planning value for the population standard deviation σ in order to compute the required sample size. At this point, an analyst reviewed the sample data from the previous study and found that the sample standard deviation for the daily rental cost was \$9.65. Using 9.65 as the planning value for σ, we obtain

Equation (8.3) provides the minimum sample size needed to satisfy the desired margin of error requirement. If the computed sample size is not an integer, rounding up to the next integer value will provide a margin of error slightly smaller than required.

$$n = \frac{(z_{\alpha/2})^2 \sigma^2}{E^2} = \frac{(1.96)^2 (9.65)^2}{2^2} = 89.43$$

Thus, the sample size for the new study needs to be at least 89.43 midsize automobile rentals in order to satisfy the project director's \$2 margin-of-error requirement. In cases where the computed n is not an integer, we round up to the next integer value; hence, the recommended sample size is 90 midsize automobile rentals.

Exercises

Methods

23. How large a sample should be selected to provide a 95% confidence interval with a margin of error of 10? Assume that the population standard deviation is 40.

24. The range for a set of data is estimated to be 36.
    a. What is the planning value for the population standard deviation?
    b. At 95% confidence, how large a sample would provide a margin of error of 3?
    c. At 95% confidence, how large a sample would provide a margin of error of 2?

Applications

25. Refer to the Scheer Industries example in Section 8.2. Use 6.84 days as a planning value for the population standard deviation.
    a. Assuming 95% confidence, what sample size would be required to obtain a margin of error of 1.5 days?
    b. If the precision statement was made with 90% confidence, what sample size would be required to obtain a margin of error of 2 days?

26. *Bride's* magazine reported that the mean cost of a wedding is $19,000 (*USA Today*, April 17, 2000). Assume that the population standard deviation is $9400. *Bride's* plans to use an annual survey to monitor the cost of a wedding. Use 95% confidence.
    a. What is the recommended sample size if the desired margin of error is $1000?
    b. What is the recommended sample size if the desired margin of error is $500?
    c. What is the recommended sample size if the desired margin of error is $200?

27. Annual starting salaries for college graduates with degrees in business administration are generally expected to be between $30,000 and $45,000. Assume that a 95% confidence interval estimate of the population mean annual starting salary is desired. What is the planning value for the population standard deviation? How large a sample should be taken if the desired margin of error is
    a. $500?
    b. $200?
    c. $100?
    d. Would you recommend trying to obtain the $100 margin of error? Explain.

28. Smith Travel Research provides information on the one-night cost of hotel rooms throughout the United States (*USA Today*, July 8, 2002). Use $2 as the desired margin of error and $22.50 as the planning value for the population standard deviation to find the sample size recommended in (a), (b), and (c).
    a. A 90% confidence interval estimate of the population mean cost of hotel rooms
    b. A 95% confidence interval estimate of the population mean cost of hotel rooms
    c. A 99% confidence interval estimate of the population mean cost of hotel rooms
    d. When the desired margin of error is fixed, what happens to the sample size as the confidence level is increased? Would you recommend a 99% confidence level be used by Smith Travel Research? Discuss.

29. The travel-to-work time for residents of the 15 largest cities in the United States is reported in the *2003 Information Please Almanac*. Suppose that a preliminary simple random sample of residents of San Francisco is used to develop a planning value of 6.25 minutes for the population standard deviation.
    a. If we want to estimate the population mean travel-to-work time for San Francisco residents with a margin of error of 2 minutes, what sample size should be used? Assume 95% confidence.
    b. If we want to estimate the population mean travel-to-work time for San Francisco residents with a margin of error of 1 minute, what sample size should be used? Assume 95% confidence.

30. During the first quarter of 2003, the price/earnings (P/E) ratio for stocks listed on the New York Stock Exchange generally ranged from 5 to 60 (*The Wall Street Journal,* March 7, 2003). Assume that we want to estimate the population mean P/E ratio for all stocks listed on the exchange. How many stocks should be included in the sample if we want a margin of error of 3? Use 95% confidence.

(8.4) Population Proportion

In the introduction to this chapter we said that the general form of an interval estimate of a population proportion p is

$$\bar{p} \pm \text{Margin of error}$$

The sampling distribution of $\bar{p}$ plays a key role in computing the margin of error for this interval estimate.

In Chapter 7 we said that the sampling distribution of $\bar{p}$ can be approximated by a normal distribution whenever $np \geq 5$ and $n(1 - p) \geq 5$. Figure 8.10 shows the normal approximation of the sampling distribution of $\bar{p}$. The mean of the sampling distribution of $\bar{p}$ is the population proportion p, and the standard error of $\bar{p}$ is

$$\sigma_{\bar{p}} = \sqrt{\frac{p(1 - p)}{n}} \tag{8.4}$$

Because the sampling distribution of $\bar{p}$ is normally distributed, if we choose $z_{\alpha/2}\sigma_{\bar{p}}$ as the margin of error in an interval estimate of a population proportion, we know that $100(1 - \alpha)\%$ of the intervals generated will contain the true population proportion. Unfortunately, $\sigma_{\bar{p}}$ cannot be used directly in the computation of the margin of error because p will not be known; p is what we are trying to estimate. So, $\bar{p}$ is substituted for p and the margin of error for an interval estimate of a population proportion is given by

$$\text{Margin of error} = z_{\alpha/2}\sqrt{\frac{\bar{p}(1 - \bar{p})}{n}} \tag{8.5}$$

FIGURE 8.10 NORMAL APPROXIMATION OF THE SAMPLING DISTRIBUTION OF $\bar{p}$

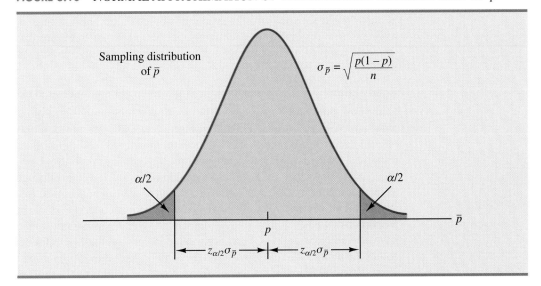

With this margin of error, the general expression for an interval estimate of a population proportion is as follows.

When developing confidence intervals for proportions, the quantity $z_{\alpha/2}\sqrt{\bar{p}(1 - \bar{p})/n}$ provides the margin of error.

INTERVAL ESTIMATE OF A POPULATION PROPORTION

$$\bar{p} \pm z_{\alpha/2} \sqrt{\frac{\bar{p}(1 - \bar{p})}{n}} \tag{8.6}$$

where $1 - \alpha$ is the confidence coefficient and $z_{\alpha/2}$ is the z value providing an area of $\alpha/2$ in the upper tail of the standard normal distribution.

TeeTimes

The following example illustrates the computation of the margin of error and interval estimate for a population proportion. A national survey of 900 women golfers was conducted to learn how women golfers view their treatment at golf courses in the United States. The survey found that 396 of the women golfers were satisfied with the availability of tee times. Thus, the point estimate of the proportion of the population of women golfers who are satisfied with the availability of tee times is $396/900 = .44$. Using expression (8.6) and a 95% confidence level,

$$\bar{p} \pm z_{\alpha/2} \sqrt{\frac{\bar{p}(1 - \bar{p})}{n}}$$

$$.44 \pm 1.96 \sqrt{\frac{.44(1 - .44)}{900}}$$

$$.44 \pm .0324$$

Thus, the margin of error is .0324 and the 95% confidence interval estimate of the population proportion is .4076 to .4724. Using percentages, the survey results enable us to state with 95% confidence that between 40.76% and 47.24% of all women golfers are satisfied with the availability of tee times.

Using Excel

Excel can be used to construct an interval estimate of the population proportion of women golfers who are satisfied with the availability of tee times. The responses in the survey were recorded as a Yes or No for each woman surveyed. Refer to Figure 8.11 as we describe the tasks involved in constructing a 95% confidence interval. The formula worksheet is in the background; the value worksheet is in the foreground.

Enter Data: The Yes-No data for the 900 women golfers are entered into cells A2:A901.

Enter Functions and Formulas: The descriptive statistics we need and the response of interest are provided in cells D3:D6. Because Excel's COUNT function only works with numerical data, we used the COUNTA function in cell D3 to compute the sample size. The response for which we want to develop an interval estimate, Yes or No, is entered into cell D4. Figure 8.11 shows that Yes has been entered into cell D4, indicating that we want to develop an interval estimate of the population proportion of women golfers who are satisfied with the availability of tee times. If we had wanted to develop an interval estimate of the population proportion of women golfers who are not satisfied with the availability of tee times, we would have entered No in cell D4. With Yes entered in cell D4, the COUNTIF function in cell D5 counts the number of Yes responses in the sample. The sample proportion is then computed in cell D6 by dividing the number of Yes responses in cell D5 by the sample size in cell D3.

FIGURE 8.11 EXCEL WORKSHEET: 95% CONFIDENCE INTERVAL FOR SURVEY OF WOMEN GOLFERS

	A	B	C	D	E
1	Response		Interval Estimate of a Population Proportion		
2	Yes				
3	No		Sample Size	=COUNTA(A2:A901)	
4	Yes		Response of Interest	Yes	
5	Yes		Count for Response	=COUNTIF(A2:A901,D4)	
6	No		Sample Proportion	=D5/D3	
7	No				
8	No		Confidence Coefficient	0.95	
9	Yes		Level of Significance (alpha)	=1-D8	
10	Yes		z Value	=NORMSINV(1-D9/2)	
11	Yes				
12	No		Standard Error	=SQRT(D6*(1-D6)/D3)	
13	No		Margin of Error	=D10*D12	
14	Yes				
15	No		Point Estimate	=D6	
16	No		Lower Limit	=D15-D13	
17	Yes		Upper Limit	=D15+D13	
18	No				
900	Yes				
901	Yes				
902					

CD file

TeeTimes

Note: Rows 19 to 899 are hidden.

	A	B	C	D	E	F	G
1	Response		Interval Estimate of a Population Proportion				
2	Yes						
3	No		Sample Size	900		Enter Yes as the	
4	Yes		Response of Interest	Yes		Response of Interest	
5	Yes		Count for Response	396			
6	No		Sample Proportion	0.44			
7	No						
8	No		Confidence Coefficient	0.95			
9	Yes		Level of Significance	0.05			
10	Yes		z Value	1.96			
11	Yes						
12	No		Standard Error	0.0165			
13	No		Margin of Error	0.0324			
14	Yes						
15	No		Point Estimate	0.44			
16	No		Lower Limit	0.4076			
17	Yes		Upper Limit	0.4724			
18	No						
900	Yes						
901	Yes						
902							

Cells D8:D10 are used to compute the appropriate z value. The confidence coefficient (0.95) is entered into cell D8 and the level of significance (α) is computed in cell D9 by entering the formula =1-D8. The z value corresponding to an upper tail area of $\alpha/2$ is computed by entering the formula =NORMSINV(1-D9/2) into cell D10. The value worksheet shows that $z_{.025} = 1.96$.

Cells D12:D13 provide the estimate of the standard error and the margin of error. In cell D12, we entered the formula =SQRT(D6*(1-D6)/D3) to compute the estimate of the standard error using the sample proportion and the sample size as inputs. The formula =D10*D12 is entered into cell D13 to compute the margin of error.

     Cells D15:D17 provide the point estimate and the lower and upper limits for a confidence interval. The point estimate in cell D15 is the sample proportion. The lower and upper limits in cells D16 and D17 are obtained by subtracting and adding the margin of error to the point estimate. We note that the 95% confidence interval for the proportion of women golfers who are satisfied with the availability of tee times is .4076 to .4724.

A Template for Other Problems The worksheet in Figure 8.11 can be used as a template for developing confidence intervals about a population proportion p. To use this worksheet for another problem of this type, we must first enter the new problem data in column A. The response of interest would then be typed in cell D4 and the ranges for the formulas in cells D3 and D5 would be revised to correspond to the new data. After doing so, the point estimate and a 95% confidence interval will be displayed in cells D15:D17. If a confidence interval with a different confidence coefficient is desired, we simply change the value in cell D8.

Determining the Sample Size

Let us consider the question of how large the sample size should be to obtain an estimate of a population proportion at a specified level of precision. The rationale for the sample size determination in developing interval estimates of p is similar to the rationale used in Section 8.3 to determine the sample size for estimating a population mean.

     Previously in this section we said that the margin of error associated with an interval estimate of a population proportion is $z_{\alpha/2}\sqrt{\bar{p}(1-\bar{p})/n}$. The margin of error is based on the value of $z_{\alpha/2}$, the sample proportion $\bar{p}$, and the sample size n. Larger sample sizes provide a smaller margin of error and better precision.

     Let E denote the desired margin of error.

$$E = z_{\alpha/2}\sqrt{\frac{\bar{p}(1-\bar{p})}{n}}$$

Solving this equation for n provides a formula for the sample size that will provide a margin of error of size E.

$$n = \frac{(z_{\alpha/2})^2\bar{p}(1-\bar{p})}{E^2}$$

Note, however, that we cannot use this formula to compute the sample size that will provide the desired margin of error because $\bar{p}$ will not be known until after we select the sample. What we need, then, is a planning value for $\bar{p}$ that can be used to make the computation. Using p^* to denote the planning value for $\bar{p}$, the following formula can be used to compute the sample size that will provide a margin of error of size E.

SAMPLE SIZE FOR AN INTERVAL ESTIMATE OF A POPULATION PROPORTION

$$n = \frac{(z_{\alpha/2})^2 p^*(1-p^*)}{E^2} \tag{8.7}$$

In practice, the planning value $p*$ can be chosen by one of the following procedures.

1. Use the sample proportion from a previous sample of the same or similar units.
2. Use a pilot study to select a preliminary sample. The sample proportion from this sample can be used as the planning value, $p*$.
3. Use judgment or a "best guess" for the value of $p*$.
4. If none of the preceding alternatives apply, use a planning value of $p* = .50$.

Let us return to the survey of women golfers and assume that the company is interested in conducting a new survey to estimate the current proportion of the population of women golfers who are satisfied with the availability of tee times. How large should the sample be if the survey director wants to estimate the population proportion with a margin of error of .025 at 95% confidence? With $E = .025$ and $z_{\alpha/2} = 1.96$, we need a planning value $p*$ to answer the sample size question. Using the previous survey result of $\bar{p} = .44$ as the planning value $p*$, equation (8.7) shows that

$$n = \frac{(z_{\alpha/2})^2 p*(1 - p*)}{E^2} = \frac{(1.96)^2(.44)(1 - .44)}{(.025)^2} = 1514.5$$

Thus, the sample size must be at least 1514.5 women golfers to satisfy the margin of error requirement. Rounding up to the next integer value indicates that a sample of 1515 women golfers is recommended to satisfy the margin of error requirement.

The fourth alternative suggested for selecting a planning value $p*$ is to use $p* = .50$. This value of $p*$ is frequently used when no other information is available. To understand why, note that the numerator of equation (8.7) shows that the sample size is proportional to the quantity $p*(1 - p*)$. A larger value for the quantity $p*(1 - p*)$ will result in a larger sample size. Table 8.5 gives some possible values of $p*(1 - p*)$. Note that the largest value of $p*(1 - p*)$ occurs when $p* = .50$. Thus, in case of any uncertainty about an appropriate planning value, we know that $p* = .50$ will provide the largest sample size recommendation. In effect, we play it safe by recommending the largest possible sample size. If the sample proportion turns out to be different from the .50 planning value, the margin of error will be smaller than anticipated. Thus, in using $p* = .50$, we guarantee that the sample size will be sufficient to obtain the desired margin of error.

In the survey of women golfers example, a planning value of $p* = .50$ would have provided the sample size

$$n = \frac{(z_{\alpha/2})^2 p*(1 - p*)}{E^2} = \frac{(1.96)^2(.50)(1 - .50)}{(.025)^2} = 1536.6$$

Thus, a slightly larger sample size of 1537 women golfers would be recommended.

TABLE 8.5   SOME POSSIBLE VALUES FOR $p*(1 - p*)$

$p*$	$p*(1 - p*)$	
.10	$(.10)(.90) = .09$	
.30	$(.30)(.70) = .21$	
.40	$(.40)(.60) = .24$	
.50	$(.50)(.50) = .25$	← Largest value for $p*(1 - p*)$
.60	$(.60)(.40) = .24$	
.70	$(.70)(.30) = .21$	
.90	$(.90)(.10) = .09$	

NOTES AND COMMENTS

The desired margin of error for estimating a population proportion is almost always .10 or less. In national public opinion polls conducted by organizations such as Gallup and Harris, a .03 or .04 margin of error is common. With such margins of error, equation (8.7) will almost always provide a sample size that is large enough to satisfy the requirements of $np \geq 5$ and $n(1 - p) \geq 5$ for using a normal distribution as an approximation for the sampling distribution of $\bar{p}$.

Exercises

Methods

31. A simple random sample of 400 individuals provides 100 Yes responses.
    a. What is the point estimate of the proportion of the population that would provide Yes responses?
    b. What is your estimate of the standard error of $\bar{p}$, $\sigma_{\bar{p}}$?
    c. Compute the 95% confidence interval for the population proportion.

32. A simple random sample of 800 elements generates a sample proportion $\bar{p} = .70$.
    a. Provide a 90% confidence interval for the population proportion.
    b. Provide a 95% confidence interval for the population proportion.

33. In a survey, the planning value for the population proportion is $p^* = .35$. How large a sample should be taken to provide a 95% confidence interval with a margin of error of .05?

34. At 95% confidence, how large a sample should be taken to obtain a margin of error of .03 for the estimation of a population proportion? Assume that past data are not available for developing a planning value for p^*.

Applications

35. A survey of 611 office workers investigated telephone answering practices, including how often each office worker was able to answer incoming telephone calls and how often incoming telephone calls went directly to voice mail (*USA Today*, April 21, 2002). A total of 281 office workers indicated that they never need voice mail and are able to take every telephone call.
    a. What is the point estimate of the proportion of the population of office workers who are able to take every telephone call?
    b. At 90% confidence, what is the margin of error?
    c. What is the 90% confidence interval for the proportion of the population of office workers who are able to take every telephone call?

36. A survey by the Society for Human Resource Management asked 346 job seekers why employees change jobs so frequently (*The Wall Street Journal*, March 28, 2000). The answer selected most (152 times) was "higher compensation elsewhere."
    a. What is the point estimate of the proportion of job seekers who would select "higher compensation elsewhere" as the reason for changing jobs?
    b. What is the 95% confidence interval estimate of the population proportion?

JobSatisfaction

37. Towers Perrin, a New York human resources consulting firm, conducted a survey of 1100 employees at medium-sized and large companies to determine how dissatisfied employees were with their jobs (*The Wall Street Journal*, January 29, 2003). The data are shown in the file named Job Satisfaction. A response of Yes indicates that the employee strongly dislikes the current work experience.
    a. What is the point estimate of the proportion of the population of employees who strongly dislike the current work experience?
    b. At 95% confidence, what is the margin of error?

c. What is the 95% confidence interval for the proportion of the population of employees who strongly dislike the current work experience?

d. Towers Perrin estimates that it costs employers one-third of an hourly employee's annual salary to find a successor and as much as 1.5 times the annual salary to find a successor for a highly compensated employee. What message did this survey send to employers?

38. Audience profile data collected at the ESPN SportsZone Web site showed that 26% of the users were women (*USA Today*, January 21, 1998). Assume that this percentage was based on a sample of 400 users.
   a. At 95% confidence, what is the margin of error associated with the estimated proportion of users who are women?
   b. What is the 95% confidence interval for the population proportion of ESPN SportsZone Web site users who are women?
   c. How large a sample should be taken if the desired margin of error is .03?

39. An Employee Benefit Research Institute survey explored the reasons small business employers offer a retirement plan to their employees (*USA Today*, April 4, 2000). The reason "competitive advantage in recruitment/retention" was anticipated 33% of the time.
   a. What sample size is recommended if a survey goal is to estimate the proportion of small business employers who offer a retirement plan primarily for "competitive advantage in recruitment/retention" with a margin of error of .03? Use 95% confidence.
   b. Repeat part (a) using 99% confidence.

40. The professional baseball home run record of 61 home runs in a season was held for 37 years by Roger Maris of the New York Yankees. However, between 1998 and 2001, three players—Mark McGwire, Sammy Sosa, and Barry Bonds—broke the standard set by Maris with Bonds holding the current record of 73 home runs in a single season. With the long-standing home run record being broken and with many other new offensive records being set, suspicion arose that baseball players might be using illegal muscle-building drugs called steroids. A *USA Today*/CNN/Gallup poll found that 86% of baseball fans think professional baseball players should be tested for steroids (*USA Today*, July 8, 2002). If 650 baseball fans were included in the sample, compute the margin of error and the 95% confidence interval for the population proportion of baseball fans who think professional baseball players should be tested for steroids.

41. An American Express retail survey found that 16% of U.S. consumers used the Internet to buy gifts during the holiday season (*USA Today*, January 18, 2000). If 1285 customers participated in the survey, what is the margin of error and what is the interval estimate of the population proportion of customers using the Internet to buy gifts? Use 95% confidence.

42. A poll for the presidential campaign sampled 491 potential voters in June. A primary purpose of the poll was to obtain an estimate of the proportion of potential voters who favor each candidate. Assume a planning value of $p^* = .50$ and a 95% confidence level.
   a. For $p^* = .50$, what was the planned margin of error for the June poll?
   b. Closer to the November election, better precision and smaller margins of error are desired. Assume the following margins of error are requested for surveys to be conducted during the presidential campaign. Compute the recommended sample size for each survey.

Survey	Margin of Error
September	.04
October	.03
Early November	.02
Pre-Election Day	.01

43. A Phoenix Wealth Management/Harris Interactive survey of 1500 individuals with net worth of $1 million or more provided a variety of statistics on wealthy people (*Business-Week,* September 22, 2003). The previous three-year period had been bad for the stock market, which motivated some of the questions asked.

    a. The survey reported that 53% of the respondents lost 25% or more of their portfolio value over the past three years. Develop a 95% confidence interval for the proportion of wealthy people who lost 25% or more of their portfolio value over the past three years.

    b. The survey reported that 31% of the respondents feel they have to save more for retirement to make up for what they lost. Develop a 95% confidence interval for the population proportion.

    c. Five percent of the respondents gave $25,000 or more to charity over the previous year. Develop a 95% confidence interval for the proportion who gave $25,000 or more to charity.

    d. Compare the margin of error for the interval estimates in parts (a), (b), and (c). How is the margin of error related to $\bar{p}$? When the same sample is being used to estimate a variety of proportions, which of the proportions should be used to choose the planning value p^*? Why do you think $p^* = .50$ is often used in these cases?

Summary

In this chapter we presented methods for developing interval estimates of a population mean and a population proportion. A point estimator may or may not provide a good estimate of a population parameter. The use of an interval estimate provides a measure of the precision of an estimate. Both the interval estimate of the population mean and the population proportion are of the form: point estimate ± margin of error.

We presented interval estimates for a population mean for two cases. In the σ known case, historical data or other information is used to develop an estimate of σ prior to taking a sample. Analysis of new sample data then proceeds based on the assumption that σ is known. In the σ unknown case, the sample data are used to estimate both the population mean and the population standard deviation. The final choice of which interval estimation procedure to use depends upon the analyst's understanding of which method provides the best estimate of σ.

In the σ known case, the interval estimation procedure is based on the assumed value of σ and the use of the standard normal distribution. In the σ unknown case, the interval estimation procedure uses the sample standard deviation s and the t distribution. In both cases the quality of the interval estimates obtained depends on the distribution of the population and the sample size. If the population is normally distributed the interval estimates will be exact in both cases, even for small sample sizes. If the population is not normally distributed, the interval estimates obtained will be approximate. Larger sample sizes will provide better approximations, but the more highly skewed the population is, the larger the sample size needs to be to obtain a good approximation. Practical advice about the sample size necessary to obtain good approximations was included in Sections 8.1 and 8.2. In most cases a sample of size 30 or more will provide good approximate confidence intervals.

The general form of the interval estimate for a population proportion is $\bar{p}$ ± margin of error. In practice the sample sizes used for interval estimates of a population proportion are generally large. Thus, the interval estimation procedure is based on the standard normal distribution.

Often a desired margin of error is specified prior to developing a sampling plan. We showed how to choose a sample size large enough to provide the desired precision.

Glossary

Interval estimate An estimate of a population parameter that provides an interval believed to contain the value of the parameter. For the interval estimates in this chapter, it has the form: point estimate ± margin of error.

Margin of error The ± value added to and subtracted from a point estimate in order to develop an interval estimate of a population parameter.

σ known The case when historical data or other information provides a good value for the population standard deviation prior to taking a sample. The interval estimation procedure uses this known value of σ in computing the margin of error.

Confidence level The confidence associated with an interval estimate. For example, if an interval estimation procedure provides intervals such that 95% of the intervals formed using the procedure will include the population parameter, the interval estimate is said to be constructed at the 95% confidence level.

Confidence coefficient The confidence level expressed as a decimal value. For example, .95 is the confidence coefficient for a 95% confidence level.

Confidence interval Another name for an interval estimate.

Level of significance The probability that the interval estimation procedure will generate an interval that does not contain μ.

σ unknown The more common case when no good basis exists for estimating the population standard deviation prior to taking the sample. The interval estimation procedure uses the sample standard deviation s in computing the margin of error.

t distribution A family of probability distributions that can be used to develop an interval estimate of a population mean whenever the population standard deviation σ is unknown and is estimated by the sample standard deviation s.

Degrees of freedom A parameter of the t distribution. When the t distribution is used in the computation of an interval estimate of a population mean, the appropriate t distribution has $n - 1$ degrees of freedom, where n is the size of the simple random sample.

Key Formulas

Interval Estimate of a Population Mean: σ Known

$$\bar{x} \pm z_{\alpha/2} \frac{\sigma}{\sqrt{n}} \tag{8.1}$$

Interval Estimate of a Population Mean: σ Unknown

$$\bar{x} \pm t_{\alpha/2} \frac{s}{\sqrt{n}} \tag{8.2}$$

Sample Size for an Interval Estimate of a Population Mean

$$n = \frac{(z_{\alpha/2})^2 \sigma^2}{E^2} \tag{8.3}$$

Interval Estimate of a Population Proportion

$$\bar{p} \pm z_{\alpha/2} \sqrt{\frac{\bar{p}(1 - \bar{p})}{n}} \tag{8.6}$$

Sample Size for an Interval Estimate of a Population Proportion

$$n = \frac{(z_{\alpha/2})^2 p^*(1 - p^*)}{E^2} \tag{8.7}$$

Supplementary Exercises

44. A survey of first-time home buyers found that the mean of annual household income was $50,000 (http://CNBC.com, July 11, 2000). Assume the survey used a sample of 400 first-time home buyers and assume that the population standard deviation is $20,500.
    a. At 95% confidence, what is the margin of error for this study?
    b. What is the 95% confidence interval for the population mean annual household income for first-time home buyers?

45. A survey conducted by the American Automobile Association showed that a family of four spends an average of $215.60 per day while on vacation. Suppose a sample of 64 families of four vacationing at Niagara Falls resulted in a sample mean of $252.45 per day and a sample standard deviation of $74.50.
    a. Develop a 95% confidence interval estimate of the mean amount spent per day by a family of four visiting Niagara Falls.
    b. Based on the confidence interval from part (a), does it appear that the population mean amount spent per day by families visiting Niagara Falls differs from the mean reported by the American Automobile Association? Explain.

46. The motion picture *Harry Potter and the Sorcerer's Stone* shattered the box office debut record previously held by *The Lost World: Jurassic Park* (*The Wall Street Journal,* November 19, 2001). A sample of 100 movie theaters showed that the mean three-day weekend gross was $25,467 per theater. The sample standard deviation was $4980.
    a. What is the margin of error for this study? Use 95% confidence.
    b. What is the 95% confidence interval estimate for the population mean weekend gross per theater?
    c. *The Lost World* took in $72.1 million in its first three-day weekend. *Harry Potter and the Sorcerer's Stone* was shown in 3672 theaters. What is an estimate of the total *Harry Potter and the Sorcerer's Stone* took in during its first three-day weekend?
    d. An Associated Press article claimed *Harry Potter* "shattered" the box office debut record held by *The Lost World*. Do your results agree with this claim?

47. Many stock market observers say that when the P/E ratio for stocks gets over 20 the market is overvalued. The P/E ratio is the stock price divided by the most recent 12 months of earnings. Suppose you are interested in seeing whether the current market is overvalued and would also like to know the proportion of companies that pay dividends. A random sample of 30 companies listed on the New York Stock Exchange (NYSE) is provided (*Barron's,* January 19, 2004).

NYSEStocks

Company	Dividend	P/E Ratio	Company	Dividend	P/E Ratio
Albertsons	Yes	14	NY Times A	Yes	25
BRE Prop	Yes	18	Omnicare	Yes	25
CityNtl	Yes	16	PallCp	Yes	23
DelMonte	No	21	PubSvcEnt	Yes	11
EnrgzHldg	No	20	SensientTch	Yes	11
Ford Motor	Yes	22	SmtProp	Yes	12
Gildan A	No	12	TJX Cos	Yes	21
HudsnUtdBcp	Yes	13	Thomson	Yes	30
IBM	Yes	22	USB Hldg	Yes	12
JeffPilot	Yes	16	US Restr	Yes	26
KingswayFin	No	6	Varian Med	No	41
Libbey	Yes	13	Visx	No	72
MasoniteIntl	No	15	Waste Mgt	No	23
Motorola	Yes	68	Wiley A	Yes	21
Ntl City	Yes	10	Yum Brands	No	18

a. What is a point estimate of the P/E ratio for the population of stocks listed on the New York Stock Exchange? Develop a 95% confidence interval.

b. Based on your answer to part (a), do you believe that the market is overvalued?

c. What is a point estimate of the proportion of companies on the NYSE that pay dividends? Is the sample size large enough to justify using the normal distribution to construct a confidence interval for this proportion? Why or why not?

Flights

48. US Airways conducted a number of studies that indicated a substantial savings could be obtained by encouraging Dividend Miles frequent flyer customers to redeem miles and schedule award flights online (*US Airways Attaché,* February 2003). One study collected data on the amount of time required to redeem miles and schedule an award flight over the telephone. A sample showing the time in minutes required for each of 150 award flights scheduled by telephone is contained in the data set Flights. Use Excel to help answer the following questions.

a. What is the sample mean number of minutes required to schedule an award flight by telephone?

b. What is the 95% confidence interval for the population mean time to schedule an award flight by telephone?

c. Assume a telephone ticket agent works 7.5 hours per day. How many award flights can one ticket agent be expected to handle a day?

d. Discuss why this information supported US Airways' plans to use an online system to reduce costs.

ActTemps

49. A survey by Accountemps asked a sample of 200 executives to provide data on the number of minutes per day office workers waste trying to locate mislabeled, misfiled, or misplaced items. Data consistent with this survey are contained in the data set ActTemps.

a. Use ActTemps to develop a point estimate of the number of minutes per day office workers waste trying to locate mislabeled, misfiled, or misplaced items.

b. What is the sample standard deviation?

c. What is the 95% confidence interval for the mean number of minutes wasted per day?

50. Mileage tests are conducted for a particular model of automobile. If a 98% confidence interval with a margin of error of 1 mile per gallon is desired, how many automobiles should be used in the test? Assume that preliminary mileage tests indicate the standard deviation is 2.6 miles per gallon.

51. In developing patient appointment schedules, a medical center wants to estimate the mean time that a staff member spends with each patient. How large a sample should be taken if the desired margin of error is two minutes at a 95% level of confidence? How large a sample should be taken for a 99% level of confidence? Use a planning value for the population standard deviation of eight minutes.

52. Annual salary plus bonus data for chief executive officers are presented in the *BusinessWeek* Annual Pay Survey. A preliminary sample showed that the standard deviation is $675 with data provided in thousands of dollars. How many chief executive officers should be in a sample if we want to estimate the population mean annual salary plus bonus with a margin of error of $100,000? (*Note:* The desired margin of error would be $E = 100$ if the data are in thousands of dollars.) Use 95% confidence.

53. The National Center for Education Statistics reported that 47% of college students work to pay for tuition and living expenses. Assume that a sample of 450 college students was used in the study.

a. Provide a 95% confidence interval for the population proportion of college students who work to pay for tuition and living expenses.

b. Provide a 99% confidence interval for the population proportion of college students who work to pay for tuition and living expenses.

c. What happens to the margin of error as the confidence is increased from 95% to 99%?

54. A *USA Today*/CNN/Gallup survey of 369 working parents found 200 who said they spend too little time with their children because of work commitments.
    a. What is the point estimate of the proportion of the population of working parents who feel they spend too little time with their children because of work commitments?
    b. At 95% confidence, what is the margin of error?
    c. What is the 95% confidence interval estimate of the population proportion of working parents who feel they spend too little time with their children because of work commitments?

55. Which would be hardest for you to give up: Your computer or your television? In a recent survey of 1677 U.S. Internet users, 74% of the young tech elite (average age of 22) say their computer would be very hard to give up (*PC Magazine,* February 3, 2004). Only 48% say their television would be very hard to give up.
    a. Develop a 95% confidence interval for the proportion of the young tech elite that would find it very hard to give up their computer.
    b. Develop a 99% confidence interval for the proportion of the young tech elite that would find it very hard to give up their television.
    c. In which case, part (a) or part (b), is the margin of error larger? Explain why.

56. A Roper Starch survey asked employees ages 18 to 29 whether they would prefer better health insurance or a raise in salary (*USA Today,* September 5, 2000). Answer the following questions assuming 340 of 500 employees said they would prefer better health insurance over a raise.
    a. What is the point estimate of the proportion of employees ages 18 to 29 who would prefer better health insurance?
    b. What is the 95% confidence interval estimate of the population proportion?

57. The *2003 Statistical Abstract of the United States* reported the percentage of people 18 years of age and older who smoke. Suppose that a study designed to collect new data on smokers and nonsmokers uses a preliminary estimate of the proportion who smoke of .30.
    a. How large a sample should be taken to estimate the proportion of smokers in the population with a margin of error of .02? Use 95% confidence.
    b. Assume that the study uses your sample size recommendation in part (a) and finds 520 smokers. What is the point estimate of the proportion of smokers in the population?
    c. What is the 95% confidence interval for the proportion of smokers in the population?

58. A well-known bank credit card firm wishes to estimate the proportion of credit card holders who carry a nonzero balance at the end of the month and incur an interest charge. Assume that the desired margin of error is .03 at 98% confidence.
    a. How large a sample should be selected if it is anticipated that roughly 70% of the firm's card holders carry a nonzero balance at the end of the month?
    b. How large a sample should be selected if no planning value for the proportion could be specified?

59. In a survey, 200 people were asked to identify their major source of news information; 110 stated that their major source was television news.
    a. Construct a 95% confidence interval for the proportion of people in the population who consider television their major source of news information.
    b. How large a sample would be necessary to estimate the population proportion with a margin of error of .05 at 95% confidence?

60. Although airline schedules and cost are important factors for business travelers when choosing an airline carrier, a *USA Today* survey found that business travelers list an airline's frequent flyer program as the most important factor. From a sample of $n = 1993$ business travelers who responded to the survey, 618 listed a frequent flyer program as the most important factor.
    a. What is the point estimate of the proportion of the population of business travelers who believe a frequent flyer program is the most important factor when choosing an airline carrier?

b. Develop a 95% confidence interval estimate of the population proportion.
c. How large a sample would be required to report the margin of error of .01 at 95% confidence? Would you recommend that *USA Today* attempt to provide this degree of precision? Why or why not?

Case Problem 1 Bock Investment Services

The goal of Bock Investment Services (BIS) is to be the leading money market advisory service in South Carolina. To provide better service for its present clients and to attract new clients, BIS developed a weekly newsletter. BIS is considering adding a new feature to the newsletter that will report the results of a weekly telephone survey of fund managers. To investigate the feasibility of offering this service, and to determine what type of information to include in the newsletter, BIS selected a simple random sample of 45 money market funds. A portion of the data obtained is shown in Table 8.6, which reports fund assets and yields for the past 7 and 30 days. Before calling the money market fund managers to obtain additional data, BIS decided to do some preliminary analysis of the data already collected.

Managerial Report

1. Use appropriate descriptive statistics to summarize the data on assets and yields for the money market funds.
2. Develop a 95% confidence interval estimate of the mean assets, mean 7-day yield, and mean 30-day yield for the population of money market funds. Provide a managerial interpretation of each interval estimate.
3. Discuss the implication of your findings in terms of how BIS could use this type of information in preparing its weekly newsletter.
4. What other information would you recommend that BIS gather to provide the most useful information to its clients?

Case Problem 2 Gulf Real Estate Properties

Gulf Real Estate Properties, Inc., is a real estate firm located in southwestern Florida. The company, which advertises itself as "expert in the real estate market," monitors condominium sales by collecting data on location, list price, sale price, and number of days it takes to sell each unit. Each condominium is classified as *Gulf View* if it is located directly on the Gulf of Mexico or *No Gulf View* if it is located on the bay or a golf course, near but not on the Gulf. Sample data from the Multiple Listing Service in Naples, Florida, provided recent sales data for 40 Gulf View condominiums and 18 No Gulf View condominiums.* Prices are in thousands of dollars. The data are shown in Table 8.7.

Managerial Report

1. Use appropriate descriptive statistics to summarize each of the three variables for the 40 Gulf View condominiums.
2. Use appropriate descriptive statistics to summarize each of the three variables for the 18 No Gulf View condominiums.
3. Compare your summary results. Discuss any specific statistical results that would help a real estate agent understand the condominium market.

---

*Data based on condominium sales reported in the Naples MLS (Coldwell Banker, June 2000).

TABLE 8.6   DATA FOR BOCK INVESTMENT SERVICES

Bock

Money Market Fund	Assets ($ millions)	7-Day Yield (%)	30-Day Yield (%)
Amcore	103.9	4.10	4.08
Alger	156.7	4.79	4.73
Arch MM/Trust	496.5	4.17	4.13
BT Instit Treas	197.8	4.37	4.32
Benchmark Div	2755.4	4.54	4.47
Bradford	707.6	3.88	3.83
Capital Cash	1.7	4.29	4.22
Cash Mgt Trust	2707.8	4.14	4.04
Composite	122.8	4.03	3.91
Cowen Standby	694.7	4.25	4.19
Cortland	217.3	3.57	3.51
Declaration	38.4	2.67	2.61
Dreyfus	4832.8	4.01	3.89
Elfun	81.7	4.51	4.41
FFB Cash	506.2	4.17	4.11
Federated Master	738.7	4.41	4.34
Fidelity Cash	13272.8	4.51	4.42
Flex-fund	172.8	4.60	4.48
Fortis	105.6	3.87	3.85
Franklin Money	996.8	3.97	3.92
Freedom Cash	1079.0	4.07	4.01
Galaxy Money	801.4	4.11	3.96
Government Cash	409.4	3.83	3.82
Hanover Cash	794.3	4.32	4.23
Heritage Cash	1008.3	4.08	4.00
Infinity/Alpha	53.6	3.99	3.91
John Hancock	226.4	3.93	3.87
Landmark Funds	481.3	4.28	4.26
Liquid Cash	388.9	4.61	4.64
MarketWatch	10.6	4.13	4.05
Merrill Lynch Money	27005.6	4.24	4.18
NCC Funds	113.4	4.22	4.20
Nationwide	517.3	4.22	4.14
Overland	291.5	4.26	4.17
Pierpont Money	1991.7	4.50	4.40
Portico Money	161.6	4.28	4.20
Prudential MoneyMart	6835.1	4.20	4.16
Reserve Primary	1408.8	3.91	3.86
Schwab Money	10531.0	4.16	4.07
Smith Barney Cash	2947.6	4.16	4.12
Stagecoach	1502.2	4.18	4.13
Strong Money	470.2	4.37	4.29
Transamerica Cash	175.5	4.20	4.19
United Cash	323.7	3.96	3.89
Woodward Money	1330.0	4.24	4.21

Source: Barron's, October 3, 1994.

TABLE 8.7   SALES DATA FOR GULF REAL ESTATE PROPERTIES

Gulf View Condominiums			No Gulf View Condominiums		
List Price	Sale Price	Days to Sell	List Price	Sale Price	Days to Sell
495.0	475.0	130	217.0	217.0	182
379.0	350.0	71	148.0	135.5	338
529.0	519.0	85	186.5	179.0	122
552.5	534.5	95	239.0	230.0	150
334.9	334.9	119	279.0	267.5	169
550.0	505.0	92	215.0	214.0	58
169.9	165.0	197	279.0	259.0	110
210.0	210.0	56	179.9	176.5	130
975.0	945.0	73	149.9	144.9	149
314.0	314.0	126	235.0	230.0	114
315.0	305.0	88	199.8	192.0	120
885.0	800.0	282	210.0	195.0	61
975.0	975.0	100	226.0	212.0	146
469.0	445.0	56	149.9	146.5	137
329.0	305.0	49	160.0	160.0	281
365.0	330.0	48	322.0	292.5	63
332.0	312.0	88	187.5	179.0	48
520.0	495.0	161	247.0	227.0	52
425.0	405.0	149			
675.0	669.0	142			
409.0	400.0	28			
649.0	649.0	29			
319.0	305.0	140			
425.0	410.0	85			
359.0	340.0	107			
469.0	449.0	72			
895.0	875.0	129			
439.0	430.0	160			
435.0	400.0	206			
235.0	227.0	91			
638.0	618.0	100			
629.0	600.0	97			
329.0	309.0	114			
595.0	555.0	45			
339.0	315.0	150			
215.0	200.0	48			
395.0	375.0	135			
449.0	425.0	53			
499.0	465.0	86			
439.0	428.5	158			

GulfProp

4. Develop a 95% confidence interval estimate of the population mean sales price and population mean number of days to sell for Gulf View condominiums. Interpret your results.

5. Develop a 95% confidence interval estimate of the population mean sales price and population mean number of days to sell for No Gulf View condominiums. Interpret your results.

6. Assume the branch manager requested estimates of the mean selling price of Gulf View condominiums with a margin of error of $40,000 and the mean selling price of No Gulf View condominiums with a margin of error of $15,000. Using 95% confidence, how large should the sample sizes be?

7. Gulf Real Estate Properties just signed contracts for two new listings: a Gulf View condominium with a list price of $589,000 and a No Gulf View condominium with a list price of $285,000. What is your estimate of the final selling price and number of days required to sell each of these units?

Case Problem 3   Metropolitan Research, Inc.

Metropolitan Research, Inc., a consumer research organization, conducts surveys designed to evaluate a wide variety of products and services available to consumers. In one particular study, Metropolitan looked at consumer satisfaction with the performance of automobiles produced by a major Detroit manufacturer. A questionnaire sent to owners of one of the manufacturer's full-sized cars revealed several complaints about early transmission problems. To learn more about the transmission failures, Metropolitan used a sample of actual transmission repairs provided by a transmission repair firm in the Detroit area. The following data show the actual number of miles driven for 50 vehicles at the time of transmission failure.

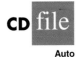

85,092	32,609	59,465	77,437	32,534	64,090	32,464	59,902
39,323	89,641	94,219	116,803	92,857	63,436	65,605	85,861
64,342	61,978	67,998	59,817	101,769	95,774	121,352	69,568
74,276	66,998	40,001	72,069	25,066	77,098	69,922	35,662
74,425	67,202	118,444	53,500	79,294	64,544	86,813	116,269
37,831	89,341	73,341	85,288	138,114	53,402	85,586	82,256
77,539	88,798						

Managerial Report

1. Use appropriate descriptive statistics to summarize the transmission failure data.

2. Develop a 95% confidence interval for the mean number of miles driven until transmission failure for the population of automobiles with transmission failure. Provide a managerial interpretation of the interval estimate.

3. Discuss the implication of your statistical finding in terms of the belief that some owners of the automobiles experienced early transmission failures.

4. How many repair records should be sampled if the research firm wants the population mean number of miles driven until transmission failure to be estimated with a margin of error of 5000 miles? Use 95% confidence.

5. What other information would you like to gather to evaluate the transmission failure problem more fully?

CHAPTER 9

Hypothesis Tests

CONTENTS

STATISTICS *in* PRACTICE

JOHN MORRELL & COMPANY*
CINCINNATI, OHIO

John Morrell & Company, which began in England in 1827, is considered the oldest continuously operating meat manufacturer in the United States. It is a wholly owned and independently managed subsidiary of Smithfield Foods, Smithfield, Virginia. John Morrell & Company offers an extensive product line of processed meats and fresh pork to consumers under 13 regional brands including John Morrell, E-Z-Cut, Tobin's First Prize, Dinner Bell, Hunter, Kretschmar, Rath, Rodeo, Shenson, Farmers Hickory Brand, Iowa Quality, and Peyton's. Each regional brand enjoys high brand recognition and loyalty among consumers.

Market research at Morrell provides management with up-to-date information on the company's various products and how the products compare with competing brands of similar products. A recent study investigated consumer preference for Morrell's Convenient Cuisine Beef Pot Roast compared to similar beef products from two major competitors. In the three-product comparison test, a sample of consumers was used to indicate how the products rated in terms of taste, appearance, aroma, and overall preference.

One research question concerned whether Morrell's Convenient Cuisine Beef Pot Roast was the preferred choice of more than 50% of the consumer population. Letting p indicate the population proportion preferring Morrell's product, the hypothesis test for the research question is as follows:

$$H_0: p \leq .50$$
$$H_a: p > .50$$

The null hypothesis H_0 indicates the preference for Morrell's product is less than or equal to 50%. If the sample data support

---

*The authors are indebted to Marty Butler, Vice President of Marketing, John Morrell, for providing this Statistics in Practice.

Convenient Cuisine fully cooked entrees allow consumers to heat and serve in the same microwaveable tray. © Courtesy of John Morrell's Convenient Cuisine products.

port rejecting H_0 in favor of the alternate hypothesis H_a, Morrell will draw the research conclusion that in a three-product comparison, their product is preferred by more than 50% of the consumer population.

In an independent taste test study using a sample of 224 consumers in Cincinnati, Milwaukee, and Los Angeles, 150 consumers selected the Morrell Convenient Cuisine Beef Pot Roast as the preferred product. Using statistical hypothesis testing procedures, the null hypothesis H_0 was rejected. The study provided statistical evidence supporting H_a and the conclusion that the Morrell product is preferred by more than 50% of the consumer population.

The point estimate of the population proportion was $\bar{p} = 150/224 = .67$. Thus, the sample data provided support for a food magazine advertisement showing that in a three-product taste comparison, Morrell's Convenient Cuisine Beef Pot Roast was "preferred 2 to 1 over the competition."

In this chapter we will discuss how to formulate hypotheses and how to conduct tests like the one used by Morrell. Through the analysis of sample data, we will be able to determine whether a hypothesis should or should not be rejected.

In Chapters 7 and 8 we showed how a sample could be used to develop point and interval estimates of population parameters. In this chapter we continue the discussion of statistical inference by showing how hypothesis testing can be used to determine whether a statement about the value of a population parameter should or should not be rejected.

In hypothesis testing we begin by making a tentative assumption about a population parameter. This tentative assumption is called the **null hypothesis** and is denoted by H_0. We then define another hypothesis, called the **alternative hypothesis**, which is the opposite of what is stated in the null hypothesis. The alternative hypothesis is denoted by H_a.

The hypothesis testing procedure uses data from a sample to test the two competing statements indicated by H_0 and H_a.

This chapter shows how hypothesis tests can be conducted about a population mean and a population proportion. We begin by providing examples that illustrate approaches to developing null and alternative hypotheses.

(9.1) Developing Null and Alternative Hypotheses

Learning to formulate hypotheses correctly will take practice. Expect some initial confusion over the proper choice for H_0 and H_a. The examples in this section show a variety of forms for H_0 and H_a depending upon the application.

In some applications it may not be obvious how the null and alternative hypotheses should be formulated. Care must be taken to structure the hypotheses appropriately so that the hypothesis testing conclusion provides the information the researcher or decision maker wants. Guidelines for establishing the null and alternative hypotheses are given for three types of situations in which hypothesis testing procedures are commonly employed.

Testing Research Hypotheses

Consider a particular automobile model that currently attains an average fuel efficiency of 24 miles per gallon. A product research group developed a new fuel injection system specifically designed to increase the miles-per-gallon rating. To evaluate the new system, several will be manufactured, installed in automobiles, and subjected to research-controlled driving tests. Here the product research group is looking for evidence to conclude that the new system *increases* the mean miles-per-gallon rating. In this case, the research hypothesis is that the new fuel injection system will provide a mean miles-per-gallon rating exceeding 24; that is, $\mu > 24$. As a general guideline, a research hypothesis should be stated as the *alternative hypothesis*. Hence, the appropriate null and alternative hypotheses for the study are

$$H_0: \mu \leq 24$$
$$H_a: \mu > 24$$

The conclusion that the research hypothesis is true is made if the sample data contradict the null hypothesis.

If the sample results indicate that H_0 cannot be rejected, researchers cannot conclude that the new fuel injection system is better. Perhaps more research and subsequent testing should be conducted. However, if the sample results indicate that H_0 can be rejected, researchers can make the inference that $H_a: \mu > 24$ is true. With this conclusion, the researchers gain the statistical support necessary to state that the new system increases the mean number of miles per gallon. Production with the new system should be considered.

In research studies such as these, the null and alternative hypotheses should be formulated so that the rejection of H_0 supports the research conclusion. The research hypothesis therefore should be expressed as the alternative hypothesis.

Testing the Validity of a Claim

As an illustration of testing the validity of a claim, consider the situation of a manufacturer of soft drinks who states that two-liter containers of its products contain an average of at least 67.6 fluid ounces. A sample of two-liter containers will be selected, and the contents will be measured to test the manufacturer's claim. In this type of hypothesis testing situation, we generally assume that the manufacturer's claim is true unless the sample evidence is contradictory. Using this approach for the soft drink example, we would state the null and alternative hypotheses as follows.

$$H_0: \mu \geq 67.6$$
$$H_a: \mu < 67.6$$

If the sample results indicate H_0 cannot be rejected, the manufacturer's claim will not be challenged. However, if the sample results indicate H_0 can be rejected, the inference will be made that H_a: $\mu < 67.6$ is true. With this conclusion, statistical evidence indicates that the manufacturer's claim is incorrect and that the soft drink containers are being filled with a mean less than the claimed 67.6 ounces. Appropriate action against the manufacturer may be considered.

A manufacturer's claim is usually given the benefit of the doubt and stated as the null hypothesis. The conclusion that the claim is false can be made if the null hypothesis is rejected.

In situations involving testing the validity of a claim, the null hypothesis is generally based on the assumption that the claim is true. The alternative hypothesis is then formulated so that rejection of H_0 will provide statistical evidence that the stated assumption is incorrect. Action to correct the claim should be considered whenever H_0 is rejected.

Testing in Decision-Making Situations

In testing research hypotheses or testing the validity of a claim, action is taken if H_0 is rejected. In some instances, however, action must be taken both when H_0 cannot be rejected and when H_0 can be rejected. In general, this type of situation occurs when a decision maker must choose between two courses of action, one associated with the null hypothesis and another associated with the alternative hypothesis. For example, on the basis of a sample of parts from a shipment just received, a quality control inspector must decide whether to accept the shipment or to return the shipment to the supplier because it does not meet specifications. Assume that specifications for a particular part require a mean length of 2 inches per part. If the mean length is greater or less than the 2-inch standard, the parts will cause quality problems in the assembly operation. In this case, the null and alternative hypotheses would be formulated as follows.

$$H_0: \mu = 2$$
$$H_a: \mu \neq 2$$

If the sample results indicate H_0 cannot be rejected, the quality control inspector will have no reason to doubt that the shipment meets specifications, and the shipment will be accepted. However, if the sample results indicate H_0 should be rejected, the conclusion will be that the parts do not meet specifications. In this case, the quality control inspector will have sufficient evidence to return the shipment to the supplier. Thus, we see that for these types of situations, action is taken both when H_0 cannot be rejected and when H_0 can be rejected.

Summary of Forms for Null and Alternative Hypotheses

The hypothesis tests in this chapter involve two population parameters: the population mean and the population proportion. Depending on the situation, hypothesis tests about a population parameter may take one of three forms: two use inequalities in the null hypothesis; the third uses an equality in the null hypothesis. For hypothesis tests involving a population mean, we let μ_0 denote the hypothesized value and we must choose one of the following three forms for the hypothesis test.

The three possible forms for hypothesis tests about a population mean are shown here. Note that the equality always appears in the null hypothesis H_0.

$$H_0: \mu \geq \mu_0 \qquad H_0: \mu \leq \mu_0 \qquad H_0: \mu = \mu_0$$
$$H_a: \mu < \mu_0 \qquad H_a: \mu > \mu_0 \qquad H_a: \mu \neq \mu_0$$

For reasons that will be clear later, the first two forms are called one-tailed tests. The third form is called a two-tailed test.

In many situations, the choice of H_0 and H_a is not obvious and judgment is necessary to select the proper form. However, as the preceding forms show, the equality part of the expression (either $\geq$, $\leq$, or $=$) *always* appears in the null hypothesis. In selecting the proper form of H_0 and H_a, keep in mind that the alternative hypothesis is often what the test is attempting to establish. Hence, asking whether the user is looking for evidence to support $\mu < \mu_0$, $\mu > \mu_0$, or $\mu \neq \mu_0$ will help determine H_a. The following exercises are designed to provide practice in choosing the proper form for a hypothesis test involving a population mean.

Exercises

1. The manager of the Danvers-Hilton Resort Hotel stated that the mean guest bill for a weekend is $600 or less. A member of the hotel's accounting staff noticed that the total charges for guest bills have been increasing in recent months. The accountant will use a sample of weekend guest bills to test the manager's claim.
    a.   Which form of the hypotheses should be used to test the manager's claim? Explain.

    $$H_0: \mu \geq 600 \qquad H_0: \mu \leq 600 \qquad H_0: \mu = 600$$
    $$H_a: \mu < 600 \qquad H_a: \mu > 600 \qquad H_a: \mu \neq 600$$

    b.   What conclusion is appropriate when H_0 cannot be rejected?
    c.   What conclusion is appropriate when H_0 can be rejected?

2. The manager of an automobile dealership is considering a new bonus plan designed to increase sales volume. Currently, the mean sales volume is 14 automobiles per month. The manager wants to conduct a research study to see whether the new bonus plan increases sales volume. To collect data on the plan, a sample of sales personnel will be allowed to sell under the new bonus plan for a one-month period.
    a.   Develop the null and alternative hypotheses most appropriate for this research situation.
    b.   Comment on the conclusion when H_0 cannot be rejected.
    c.   Comment on the conclusion when H_0 can be rejected.

3. A production line operation is designed to fill cartons with laundry detergent to a mean weight of 32 ounces. A sample of cartons is periodically selected and weighed to determine whether underfilling or overfilling is occurring. If the sample data lead to a conclusion of underfilling or overfilling, the production line will be shut down and adjusted to obtain proper filling.
    a.   Formulate the null and alternative hypotheses that will help in deciding whether to shut down and adjust the production line.
    b.   Comment on the conclusion and the decision when H_0 cannot be rejected.
    c.   Comment on the conclusion and the decision when H_0 can be rejected.

4. Because of high production-changeover time and costs, a director of manufacturing must convince management that a proposed manufacturing method reduces costs before the new method can be implemented. The current production method operates with a mean cost of $220 per hour. A research study will measure the cost of the new method over a sample production period.
    a.   Develop the null and alternative hypotheses most appropriate for this study.
    b.   Comment on the conclusion when H_0 cannot be rejected.
    c.   Comment on the conclusion when H_0 can be rejected.

9.2 Type I and Type II Errors

The null and alternative hypotheses are competing statements about the population. Either the null hypothesis H_0 is true or the alternative hypothesis H_a is true, but not both. Ideally the hypothesis testing procedure should lead to the acceptance of H_0 when H_0 is true and the

TABLE 9.1   ERRORS AND CORRECT CONCLUSIONS IN HYPOTHESIS TESTING

		Population Condition	
		H_0 True	H_a True
Conclusion	**Accept H_0**	Correct Conclusion	Type II Error
	Reject H_0	Type I Error	Correct Conclusion

rejection of H_0 when H_a is true. Unfortunately, the correct conclusions are not always possible. Because hypothesis tests are based on sample information, we must allow for the possibility of errors. Table 9.1 illustrates the two kinds of errors that can be made in hypothesis testing.

The first row of Table 9.1 shows what can happen if the conclusion is to accept H_0. If H_0 is true, this conclusion is correct. However, if H_a is true, we make a **Type II error**; that is, we accept H_0 when it is false. The second row of Table 9.1 shows what can happen if the conclusion is to reject H_0. If H_0 is true, we make a **Type I error**; that is, we reject H_0 when it is true. However, if H_a is true, rejecting H_0 is correct.

Recall the hypothesis testing illustration discussed in Section 9.1 in which an automobile product research group developed a new fuel injection system designed to increase the miles-per-gallon rating of a particular automobile. With the current model obtaining an average of 24 miles per gallon, the hypothesis test was formulated as follows.

$$H_0: \mu \leq 24$$
$$H_a: \mu > 24$$

The alternative hypothesis, $H_a: \mu > 24$, indicates that the researchers are looking for sample evidence to support the conclusion that the population mean miles per gallon with the new fuel injection system is greater than 24.

In this application, the Type I error of rejecting H_0 when it is true corresponds to the researchers claiming that the new system improves the miles-per-gallon rating ($\mu > 24$) when in fact the new system is not any better than the current system. In contrast, the Type II error of accepting H_0 when it is false corresponds to the researchers concluding that the new system is not any better than the current system ($\mu \leq 24$) when in fact the new system improves miles-per-gallon performance.

For the miles-per-gallon rating hypothesis test, the null hypothesis is $H_0: \mu \leq 24$. Suppose the null hypothesis is true as an equality; that is, $\mu = 24$. The probability of making a Type I error when the null hypothesis is true as an equality is called the **level of significance**. Thus, for the miles-per-gallon rating hypothesis test, the level of significance is the probability of rejecting $H_0: \mu \leq 24$ when $\mu = 24$. Because of the importance of this concept, we now restate the definition of level of significance.

LEVEL OF SIGNIFICANCE

The level of significance is the probability of making a Type I error when the null hypothesis is true as an equality.

The Greek symbol α (alpha) is used to denote the level of significance, and common choices for α are .05 and .01.

In practice, the person conducting the hypothesis test specifies the level of significance. By selecting α, that person is controlling the probability of making a Type I error. If the cost of making a Type I error is high, small values of α are preferred. If the cost of making a Type I error is not too high, larger values of α are typically used. Applications of hypothesis testing that only control for the Type I error are often called *significance tests*. Most applications of hypothesis testing are of this type.

Although most applications of hypothesis testing control for the probability of making a Type I error, they do not always control for the probability of making a Type II error.* Because of the uncertainty associated with making a Type II error when conducting significance tests, statisticians often recommend that we use the statement "do not reject H_0" instead of "accept H_0." Using the statement "do not reject H_0" carries the recommendation to withhold both judgment and action. In effect, by not directly accepting H_0, the statistician avoids the risk of making a Type II error. Whenever the probability of making a Type II error has not been determined and controlled, we will not make the statement "accept H_0." In such cases, only two conclusions are possible: *do not reject H_0* or *reject H_0*.

If the sample data are consistent with the null hypothesis H_0, we will follow the practice of concluding "do not reject H_0."

Exercises

5.   Nielsen reported that young men in the United States watch 56.2 minutes of prime-time TV daily (*The Wall Street Journal Europe,* November 18, 2003). A researcher believes that young men in Germany spend more time watching prime-time TV. A sample of German young men will be selected by the researcher and the time they spend watching TV in one day will be recorded. The sample results will be used to test the following null and alternative hypotheses.

$$H_0: \ \mu \leq 56.2$$
$$H_a: \ \mu > 56.2$$

   a.   What is the Type I error in this situation? What are the consequences of making this error?
   b.   What is the Type II error in this situation? What are the consequences of making this error?

6.   The label on a 3-quart container of orange juice claims that the orange juice contains an average of 1 gram of fat or less. Answer the following questions for a hypothesis test that could be used to test the claim on the label.
   a.   Develop the appropriate null and alternative hypotheses.
   b.   What is the Type I error in this situation? What are the consequences of making this error?
   c.   What is the Type II error in this situation? What are the consequences of making this error?

7.   Carpetland salespersons average $8000 per week in sales. Steve Contois, the firm's vice president, proposes a compensation plan with new selling incentives. Steve hopes that the results of a trial selling period will enable him to conclude that the compensation plan increases the average sales per salesperson.
   a.   Develop the appropriate null and alternative hypotheses.
   b.   What is the Type I error in this situation? What are the consequences of making this error?
   c.   What is the Type II error in this situation? What are the consequences of making this error?

---

*More advanced texts describe procedures for determining and controlling the probability of making a Type II error. See, for example, Anderson, D. R., D. J. Sweeney, and T. A. Williams, *Statistics for Business and Economics,* 9th ed. (Cincinnati: South-Western, 2005).

8. Suppose a new production method will be implemented if a hypothesis test supports the conclusion that the new method reduces the mean operating cost per hour.
   a. State the appropriate null and alternative hypotheses if the mean cost for the current production method is $220 per hour.
   b. What is the Type I error in this situation? What are the consequences of making this error?
   c. What is the Type II error in this situation? What are the consequences of making this error?

9.3 Population Mean: σ Known

In Chapter 8 we said that the σ known case corresponds to applications in which historical data or other information is available that enables us to obtain a good estimate of the population standard deviation prior to sampling. In such cases the population standard deviation can, for all practical purposes, be considered known. In this section we show how to conduct a hypothesis test about a population mean for the σ known case.

The methods presented in this section are exact if the sample is selected from a population that is normally distributed. In cases where it is not reasonable to assume the population is normally distributed, these methods are still applicable if the sample size is large enough. We provide some practical advice concerning the population distribution and the sample size at the end of the section.

One-Tailed Test

One-tailed tests about a population mean take one of the following two forms.

Lower Tail Test	Upper Tail Test
$H_0: \mu \geq \mu_0$	$H_0: \mu \leq \mu_0$
$H_a: \mu < \mu_0$	$H_a: \mu > \mu_0$

Let us consider an example involving a lower tail test.

The Federal Trade Commission (FTC) periodically conducts statistical studies designed to test the claims that manufacturers make about their products. For example, the label on a large can of Hilltop Coffee states that the can contains 3 pounds of coffee. The FTC knows that Hilltop's production process cannot place exactly 3 pounds of coffee in each can, even if the mean filling weight for the population of all cans filled is 3 pounds per can. However, as long as the population mean filling weight is at least 3 pounds per can, the rights of consumers will be protected. Thus, the FTC interprets the label information on a large can of coffee as a claim by Hilltop that the population mean filling weight is at least 3 pounds per can. We will show how the FTC can check Hilltop's claim by conducting a lower tail hypothesis test.

The first step is to develop the null and alternative hypotheses for the test. If the population mean filling weight is at least 3 pounds per can, Hilltop's claim is correct. This result establishes the null hypothesis for the test. However, if the population mean filling weight is less than 3 pounds per can, Hilltop's claim is incorrect. This result establishes the alternative hypothesis. With μ denoting the population mean filling weight, the null and alternative hypotheses are as follows:

$$H_0: \mu \geq 3$$
$$H_a: \mu < 3$$

Note that the hypothesized value of the population mean is $\mu_0 = 3$.

If the sample data indicate that H_0 cannot be rejected, the statistical evidence does not support the conclusion that a label violation has occurred. Hence, no action should be taken against Hilltop. However, if the sample data indicate H_0 can be rejected, we will conclude that the alternative hypothesis, H_a: $\mu < 3$, is true. In this case a conclusion of underfilling and a charge of a label violation against Hilltop would be justified.

Suppose a sample of 36 cans of coffee is selected and the sample mean $\bar{x}$ is computed as an estimate of the population mean μ. If the value of the sample mean $\bar{x}$ is less than 3 pounds, the sample results will cast doubt on the null hypothesis. What we want to know is how much less than 3 pounds must $\bar{x}$ be before we would be willing to declare the difference significant and risk making a Type I error by falsely accusing Hilltop of a label violation. A key factor in addressing this issue is the value the decision maker selects for the level of significance.

As noted in the preceding section, the level of significance, denoted by α, is the probability of making a Type I error by rejecting H_0 when the null hypothesis is true as an equality. The decision maker must specify the level of significance. If the cost of making a Type I error is high, a small value should be chosen for the level of significance. If the cost is not high, a larger value is more appropriate. In the Hilltop Coffee study, the director of the FTC's testing program made the following statement: "If the company is meeting its weight specifications at $\mu = 3$, I do not want to take action against them. But, I am willing to risk a 1% chance of making such an error." From the director's statement, we set the level of significance for the hypothesis test at $\alpha = .01$. Thus, we must design the hypothesis test so that the probability of making a Type I error when $\mu = 3$ is .01.

For the Hilltop Coffee study, by developing the null and alternative hypotheses and specifying the level of significance for the test, we carry out the first two steps required in conducting every hypothesis test. We are now ready to perform the third step of hypothesis testing: collect the sample data and compute the value of what is called a test statistic.

Test Statistic For the Hilltop Coffee study, previous FTC tests show that the population standard deviation can be assumed known with a value of $\sigma = .18$. In addition, these tests also show that the population of filling weights can be assumed to have a normal distribution. From the study of sampling distributions in Chapter 7 we know that if the population from which we are sampling is normally distributed, the sampling distribution of $\bar{x}$ will also be normally distributed. Thus, for the Hilltop Coffee study, the sampling distribution of $\bar{x}$ is normally distributed. With a known value of $\sigma = .18$ and a sample size of $n = 36$, Figure 9.1 shows the sampling distribution of $\bar{x}$ when the null hypothesis is true as an equality; that is, when $\mu = \mu_0 = 3$.* Note that the standard error of $\bar{x}$ is given by $\sigma_{\bar{x}} = \sigma/\sqrt{n} = .18/\sqrt{36} = .03$.

The standard error of $\bar{x}$ is the standard deviation of the sampling distribution of $\bar{x}$.

FIGURE 9.1   SAMPLING DISTRIBUTION OF $\bar{x}$ FOR THE HILLTOP COFFEE STUDY WHEN THE NULL HYPOTHESIS IS TRUE AS AN EQUALITY ($\mu = 3$)

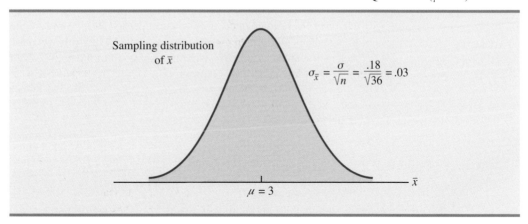

*In constructing sampling distributions for hypothesis tests, it is assumed that H_0 is satisfied as an equality.

Because the sampling distribution of $\bar{x}$ is normally distributed, the sampling distribution of

$$z = \frac{\bar{x} - \mu_0}{\sigma_{\bar{x}}} = \frac{\bar{x} - 3}{.03}$$

is a standard normal distribution. A value of $z = -1$ means that the value of $\bar{x}$ is one standard error below the hypothesized value of the mean, a value of $z = -2$ means that the value of $\bar{x}$ is two standard errors below the hypothesized value of the mean, and so on. We can use the standard normal probability table to find the lower tail probability corresponding to any z value. For instance, the lower tail area at $z = -3.00$ is .0013. Hence, the probability of obtaining a value of z that is three or more standard errors below the mean is .0013. As a result, the probability of obtaining a value of $\bar{x}$ that is 3 or more standard errors below the hypothesized population mean $\mu_0 = 3$ is also .0013. Such a result is unlikely if the null hypothesis is true.

For hypothesis tests about a population mean in the σ known case, we use the standard normal random variable z as a **test statistic** to determine whether $\bar{x}$ deviates from the hypothesized value of μ enough to justify rejecting the null hypothesis. With $\sigma_{\bar{x}} = \sigma/\sqrt{n}$, the test statistic used in the σ known case is as follows.

TEST STATISTIC FOR HYPOTHESIS TESTS ABOUT A POPULATION MEAN: σ KNOWN

$$z = \frac{\bar{x} - \mu_0}{\sigma/\sqrt{n}} \tag{9.1}$$

The key question for a lower tail test is: How small must the test statistic z be before we choose to reject the null hypothesis? Two approaches can be used to answer this question.

The first approach uses the value of the test statistic z to compute a probability called a **p-value**. The p-value measures the support (or lack of support) provided by the sample for the null hypothesis and is the basis for determining whether the null hypothesis should be rejected given the level of significance. The second approach requires that we first determine a value for the test statistic called the **critical value**. For a lower tail test, the critical value serves as a benchmark for determining whether the value of the test statistic is small enough to reject the null hypothesis. We begin with the p-value approach.

p-value Approach   In practice, the p-value approach has become the preferred method of determining whether the null hypothesis can be rejected, especially when using computer software packages such as Excel. To begin our discussion of the use of p-values in hypothesis testing, we now provide a formal definition for a p-value.

---

p-VALUE

The p-value is a probability, computed using the test statistic, that measures the support (or lack of support) provided by the sample for the null hypothesis.

Because a p-value is a probability, it ranges from 0 to 1. In general, the larger the p-value, the more support the test statistic provides for the null hypothesis. On the other hand, a small p-value indicates a sample test statistic that is unusual given the assumption that H_0 is true.

Small p-values lead to rejection of H_0, whereas large p-values indicate the null hypothesis should not be rejected.

Two steps are required to use the p-value approach. First, we must use the value of the test statistic to compute the p-value. The method used to compute a p-value depends on whether the test is a lower tail, an upper tail, or a two-tailed test. For a lower tail test, the p-value is the probability of obtaining a value for the test statistic as small as or smaller than that provided by the sample. Thus, to compute the p-value for the lower tail test in the σ known case, we must find the area under the standard normal curve to the left of the test statistic. After computing the p-value, we must then decide whether it is small enough to reject the null hypothesis; as we will show, this decision involves comparing the p-value to the level of significance.

CD file

Coffee

Let us now illustrate the p-value approach by computing the p-value for the Hilltop Coffee lower tail test. Suppose the sample of 36 Hilltop coffee cans provides a sample mean of $\bar{x} = 2.92$ pounds. Is $\bar{x} = 2.92$ small enough to cause us to reject H_0? Because this is a lower tail test, the p-value is the area under the standard normal curve to the left of the test statistic. Using $\bar{x} = 2.92$, $\sigma = .18$, and $n = 36$, we compute the value of the test statistic z.

$$z = \frac{\bar{x} - \mu_0}{\sigma/\sqrt{n}} = \frac{2.92 - 3}{.18/\sqrt{36}} = -2.67$$

Thus, the p-value is the probability that the test statistic z is less than or equal to -2.67 (the area under the standard normal curve to the left of the test statistic).

Using the standard normal probability table, we find that the lower tail area at $z = -2.67$ is .0038. Figure 9.2 shows that $\bar{x} = 2.92$ corresponds to $z = -2.67$ and a p-value = .0038. This p-value indicates a small probability of obtaining a sample mean of $\bar{x} = 2.92$ (and a test statistic of -2.67) or smaller when sampling from a population with $\mu = 3$. This p-value does not provide much support for the null hypothesis, but is it small enough to cause us to reject H_0? The answer depends upon the level of significance for the test.

As noted previously, the director of the FTC's testing program selected a value of .01 for the level of significance. The selection of $\alpha = .01$ means that the director is willing to accept a probability of .01 of rejecting the null hypothesis when it is true as an equality ($\mu_0 = 3$). The sample of 36 coffee cans in the Hilltop Coffee study resulted in a p-value = .0038, which means that the probability of obtaining a value of $\bar{x} = 2.92$ or less when the null hypothesis is true as an equality is .0038. Because .0038 is less than or equal to $\alpha = .01$, we reject H_0. Therefore, we find sufficient statistical evidence to reject the null hypothesis at the .01 level of significance.

We can now state the general rule for determining whether the null hypothesis can be rejected when using the p-value approach. For a level of significance α, the rejection rule using the p-value approach is as follows:

REJECTION RULE USING p-VALUE

Reject H_0 if p-value $\leq \alpha$

In the Hilltop Coffee test, the p-value of .0038 resulted in the rejection of the null hypothesis. Although the basis for making the rejection decision involves a comparison of the p-value to the level of significance specified by the FTC director, the observed p-value of .0038 means that we would reject H_0 for any value of $\alpha \geq .0038$. For this reason, the p-value is also called the *observed level of significance*.

Excel's NORMDIST function makes it easy to compute p-values.

Excel's NORMSDIST function can also be used to compute the p-value for the Hilltop Coffee study. Entering the function =NORMSDIST(-2.67) into any cell of an Excel worksheet provides the cumulative probability (lower tail area) corresponding to $z = -2.67$. The

FIGURE 9.2 *p*-VALUE FOR THE HILLTOP COFFEE STUDY WHEN $\bar{x} = 2.92$ AND $z = -2.67$

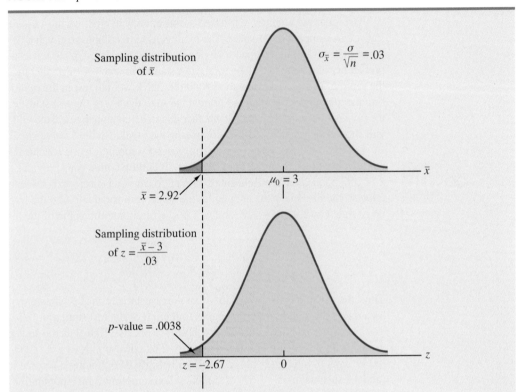

result obtained is .0038, which is the same *p*-value we obtained using the standard normal probability table.

Different decision makers may express different opinions concerning the cost of making a Type I error and may choose a different level of significance. By providing the *p*-value as part of the hypothesis testing results, another decision maker can compare the reported *p*-value to his or her own level of significance and possibly make a different decision with respect to rejecting H_0.

Critical Value Approach For a lower tail test, the critical value is the value of the test statistic that corresponds to an area of α (the level of significance) in the lower tail of the sampling distribution of the test statistic. In other words, the critical value is the largest value of the test statistic that will result in the rejection of the null hypothesis. Let us return to the Hilltop Coffee example and see how this approach works.

In the σ known case, the sampling distribution for the test statistic z is a standard normal distribution. Therefore, the critical value is the value of the test statistic that corresponds to an area of $\alpha = .01$ in the lower tail of a standard normal distribution. Using the standard normal probability table, we find that $z = -2.33$ provides an area of .01 in the lower tail (see Figure 9.3). Thus, if the sample results in a value of the test statistic that is less than or equal to -2.33, the corresponding *p*-value will be less than or equal to .01; in this case, we should reject the null hypothesis. Hence, for the Hilltop Coffee study the critical value rejection rule for a level of significance of .01 is

$$\text{Reject } H_0 \text{ if } z \leq -2.33$$

FIGURE 9.3   CRITICAL VALUE = -2.33 FOR THE HILLTOP COFFEE HYPOTHESIS TEST

In the Hilltop Coffee example, $\bar{x} = 2.92$ and the test statistic is $z = -2.67$. Because $z = -2.67 < -2.33$, we can reject H_0 and conclude that Hilltop Coffee is underfilling cans.

We can generalize the rejection rule for the critical value approach to handle any level of significance. The rejection rule for a lower tail test follows.

REJECTION RULE FOR A LOWER TAIL TEST: CRITICAL VALUE APPROACH

$$\text{Reject } H_0 \text{ if } z \leq -z_\alpha$$

where $-z_\alpha$ is the critical value; that is, the z value that provides an area of α in the lower tail of the standard normal distribution.

The p-value approach to hypothesis testing and the critical value approach will always lead to the same rejection decision; that is, whenever the p-value is less than or equal to α, the value of the test statistic will be less than or equal to the critical value. The advantage of the p-value approach is that the p-value tells us *how* significant the results are (the observed level of significance). If we use the critical value approach, we only know that the results are significant at the stated level of significance.

At the beginning of this section, we said that one-tailed tests about a population mean take one of the following two forms:

Lower Tail Test	**Upper Tail Test**
$H_0\text{: } \mu \geq \mu_0$	$H_0\text{: } \mu \leq \mu_0$
$H_a\text{: } \mu < \mu_0$	$H_a\text{: } \mu > \mu_0$

We used the Hilltop Coffee study to illustrate how to conduct a lower tail test. We can use the same general approach to conduct an upper tail test. The test statistic z is still computed using equation (9.1). But, for an upper tail test, the p-value is the probability of obtaining a value for the test statistic as large as or larger than that provided by the sample. Thus, to compute the p-value for the upper tail test in the σ known case, we must find the area under the standard normal curve to the right of the test statistic. Using the critical value approach causes us to reject the null hypothesis if the value of the test statistic is greater than or equal to the critical value z_α; in other words, we reject H_0 if $z \geq z_\alpha$.

Two-Tailed Test

In hypothesis testing, the general form for a **two-tailed test** about a population mean is as follows:

$$H_0: \mu = \mu_0$$
$$H_a: \mu \neq \mu_0$$

In this subsection we show how to conduct a two-tailed test about a population mean for the σ known case. As an illustration, we consider the hypothesis testing situation facing MaxFlight, Inc.

The U.S. Golf Association (USGA) establishes rules that manufacturers of golf equipment must meet if their products are to be acceptable for use in USGA events. MaxFlight uses a high-technology manufacturing process to produce golf balls with a mean driving distance of 295 yards. Sometimes, however, the process gets out of adjustment and produces golf balls with a mean driving distance different from 295 yards. When the mean distance falls below 295 yards, the company worries about losing sales because the golf balls do not provide as much distance as advertised. When the mean distance passes 295 yards, MaxFlight's golf balls may be rejected by the USGA for exceeding the overall distance standard concerning carry and roll.

MaxFlight's quality control program involves taking periodic samples of 50 golf balls to monitor the manufacturing process. For each sample, a hypothesis test is conducted to determine whether the process has fallen out of adjustment. Let us develop the null and alternative hypotheses. We begin by assuming that the process is functioning correctly; that is, the golf balls being produced have a mean distance of 295 yards. This assumption establishes the null hypothesis. The alternative hypothesis is that the mean distance is not equal to 295 yards. With a hypothesized value of $\mu_0 = 295$, the null and alternative hypotheses for the MaxFlight hypothesis test are as follows:

$$H_0: \mu = 295$$
$$H_a: \mu \neq 295$$

If the sample mean $\bar{x}$ is significantly less than 295 yards or significantly greater than 295 yards, we will reject H_0. In this case, corrective action will be taken to adjust the manufacturing process. On the other hand, if $\bar{x}$ does not deviate from the hypothesized mean $\mu_0 = 295$ by a significant amount, H_0 will not be rejected and no action will be taken to adjust the manufacturing process.

The quality control team selected $\alpha = .05$ as the level of significance for the test. Data from previous tests conducted when the process was known to be in adjustment show that the population standard deviation can be assumed known with a value of $\sigma = 12$. Thus, with a sample size of $n = 50$, the standard error of $\bar{x}$ is

$$\sigma_{\bar{x}} = \frac{\sigma}{\sqrt{n}} = \frac{12}{\sqrt{50}} = 1.7$$

Because the sample size is large, the central limit theorem (see Chapter 7) allows us to conclude that the sampling distribution of $\bar{x}$ can be approximated by a normal distribution. Figure 9.4 shows the sampling distribution of $\bar{x}$ for the MaxFlight hypothesis test with a hypothesized population mean of $\mu_0 = 295$.

Suppose that a sample of 50 golf balls is selected and that the sample mean is $\bar{x} = 297.6$ yards. This sample mean provides support for the conclusion that the population mean is larger than 295 yards. Is this value of $\bar{x}$ enough larger than 295 to cause us to reject H_0 at the .05 level of significance? In the previous section we described two approaches that can be used to answer this question: the p-value approach and the critical value approach.

CD file

GolfTest

FIGURE 9.4 SAMPLING DISTRIBUTION OF $\bar{x}$ FOR THE MAXFLIGHT HYPOTHESIS TEST

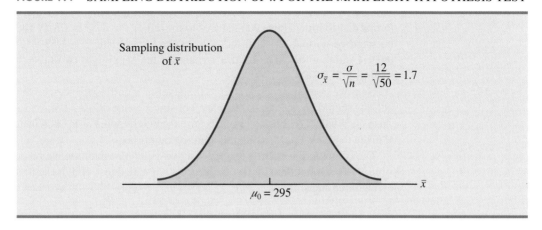

Sampling distribution of $\bar{x}$

$$\sigma_{\bar{x}} = \frac{\sigma}{\sqrt{n}} = \frac{12}{\sqrt{50}} = 1.7$$

$\mu_0 = 295$

p-value Approach Recall that the *p*-value is a probability, computed using the test statistic, that measures the support (or lack of support) provided by the sample for the null hypothesis. For a two-tailed test, values of the test statistic in *either* tail show a lack of support for the null hypothesis. For a two-tailed test, the *p*-value is the probability of obtaining a value for the test statistic *as unlikely as or more unlikely than* that provided by the sample. Let us see how the *p*-value is computed for the MaxFlight hypothesis test.

First we compute the value of the test statistic. For the σ known case, the test statistic *z* is a standard normal random variable. Using equation (9.1) with $\bar{x} = 297.6$, the value of the test statistic is

$$z = \frac{\bar{x} - \mu_0}{\sigma/\sqrt{n}} = \frac{297.6 - 295}{12/\sqrt{50}} = 1.53$$

Now to compute the *p*-value we must find the probability of obtaining a value for the test statistic *at least as unlikely as z* = 1.53. Clearly all values of $z \geq 1.53$ are *at least as unlikely*. But, because this is a two-tailed test, values of $z \leq -1.53$ are also *at least as unlikely as* the value of the test statistic provided by the sample. Referring to Figure 9.5, we see that the two-tailed *p*-value in this case is given by $P(z \leq -1.53) + P(z \geq 1.53)$. Because the

FIGURE 9.5 *p*-VALUE FOR THE MAXFLIGHT HYPOTHESIS TEST

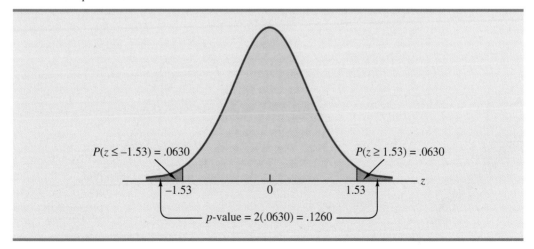

$P(z \leq -1.53) = .0630$ $P(z \geq 1.53) = .0630$

-1.53 0   1.53 z

p-value = 2(.0630) = .1260

normal curve is symmetric, we can compute this probability by finding the area under the standard normal curve to the right of $z = 1.53$ and doubling it. The table for the standard normal distribution shows that the area to the left of $z = 1.53$ is .9370. Thus, the area under the standard normal curve to the right of the test statistic $z = 1.53$ is $1.0000 - .9370 = .0630$. Doubling this, we find the p-value for the MaxFlight two-tailed hypothesis test is p-value $= 2(.0630) = .1260$.

Next we compare the p-value to the level of significance to see whether the null hypothesis should be rejected. With a level of significance of $\alpha = .05$, we do not reject H_0 because the p-value $= .1260 > .05$. Because the null hypothesis is not rejected, no action will be taken to adjust the MaxFlight manufacturing process.

The computation of the p-value for a two-tailed test may seem a bit confusing as compared to the computation of the p-value for a one-tailed test. But, it can be simplified by following three steps.

COMPUTATION OF p-VALUE FOR A TWO-TAILED TEST

1. Compute the value of the test statistic z.
2. If the value of the test statistic is in the upper tail ($z > 0$), find the area under the standard normal curve to the right of z. If the value of the test statistic is in the lower tail ($z < 0$), find the area under the standard normal curve to the left of z.
3. Double the tail area, or probability, obtained in step 2 to obtain the p-value.

Critical Value Approach Before leaving this section, let us see how the test statistic z can be compared to a critical value to make the hypothesis testing decision for a two-tailed test. Figure 9.6 shows that the critical values for the test will occur in both the lower and upper tails of the standard normal distribution. With a level of significance of $\alpha = .05$, the area in each tail beyond the critical values is $\alpha/2 = .05/2 = .025$. Using the standard normal probability table, we find the critical values for the test statistic are $-z_{.025} = -1.96$ and $z_{.025} = 1.96$. Thus, using the critical value approach, the two-tailed rejection rule is

$$\text{Reject } H_0 \text{ if } z \leq -1.96 \text{ or if } z \geq 1.96$$

Because the value of the test statistic for the MaxFlight study is $z = 1.53$, the statistical evidence will not permit us to reject the null hypothesis at the .05 level of significance.

FIGURE 9.6 CRITICAL VALUES FOR THE MAXFLIGHT HYPOTHESIS TEST

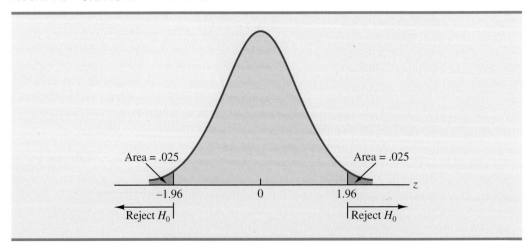

Using Excel

Excel can be used to conduct one-tailed and two-tailed hypothesis tests about a population mean for the σ known case using the p-value approach. Recall that the method used to compute a p-value depends upon whether the test is lower tail, upper tail, or two-tailed. Therefore, in the Excel procedure we describe we will use the sample results to compute three p-values: p-value (Lower Tail); p-value (Upper Tail); and p-value (Two Tail). The user can then choose α and draw a conclusion using whichever p-value is appropriate for the type of hypothesis test being conducted. We will illustrate using the MaxFlight two-tailed hypothesis test. Refer to Figure 9.7 as we describe the tasks involved. The formula worksheet is in the background; the value worksheet is in the foreground.

FIGURE 9.7   EXCEL WORKSHEET: HYPOTHESIS TEST FOR THE σ KNOWN CASE

	A	B	C	D	E
1	Yards		Hypothesis Test about a Population Mean:		
2	303		σ Known Case		
3	282				
4	289		Sample Size	=COUNT(A2:A51)	
5	298		Sample Mean	=AVERAGE(A2:A51)	
6	283				
7	317		Population Standard Deviation	12	
8	297		Hypothesized Value	295	
9	308				
10	317		Standard Error	=D7/SQRT(D4)	
11	293		Test Statistic z	=(D5-D8)/D10	
12	284				
13	290		p-value (Lower Tail)	=NORMSDIST(D11)	
14	304		p-value (Upper Tail)	=1-D13	
15	290		p-value (Two Tail)	=2*(MIN(D13,D14))	
16	311				
50	301				
51	292				
52					

	A	B	C	D	E
1	Yards		Hypothesis Test about a Population Mean:		
2	303		σ Known Case		
3	282				
4	289		Sample Size	50	
5	298		Sample Mean	297.6	
6	283				
7	317		Population Standard Deviation	12	
8	297		Hypothesized Value	295	
9	308				
10	317		Standard Error	1.6971	
11	293		Test Statistic z	1.5321	
12	284				
13	290		p-value (Lower Tail)	0.9372	
14	304		p-value (Upper Tail)	0.0628	
15	290		p-value (Two Tail)	0.1255	
16	311				
50	301				
51	292				
52					

CD file

GolfTest

Note: Rows 17–49 are hidden.

Enter Data: A label and the distance data for the sample of 50 golf balls are entered into cells A1:A51.

Enter Functions and Formulas: The descriptive statistics needed are provided in cells D4 and D5. Excel's COUNT and AVERAGE functions compute the sample size and the sample mean, respectively. The value of the known population standard deviation (12) is entered into cell D7, and the hypothesized value of the population mean (295) is entered into cell D8.

The standard error is obtained in cell D10 by entering the formula D7/SQRT(D4). The formula =(D5-D8)/D10 entered into cell D11 computes the test statistic $z(1.5321)$. To compute the p-value for a lower tail test, we enter the formula =NORMSDIST(D11) into cell D13. The p-value for an upper tail test is then computed in cell D14 as 1 minus the p-value for the lower tail test. Finally, the p-value for a two-tailed test is computed in cell D15 as 2 times the minimum of the 2 one-tailed p-values. The value worksheet shows that p-value (Lower Tail) = 0.9372, p-value (Upper Tail) = 0.0628, and p-value (Two Tail) = 0.1255.

The development of the worksheet is now complete. For the two-tailed MaxFlight problem we cannot reject $H_0 : \mu = 295$ using $\alpha = .05$ because the p-value (Two Tail) = 0.1255 is greater than α. Thus, the quality control manager has no reason to doubt that the manufacturing process is producing golf balls with a population mean distance of 295 yards.

A Template for Other Problems   The worksheet in Figure 9.7 can be used as a template for conducting any one-tailed and two-tailed hypothesis tests for the σ known case. Just enter the appropriate data in column A, adjust the ranges for the formulas in cells D4 and D5, enter the population standard deviation in cell D7, and enter the hypothesized value in cell D8. The standard error, the test statistic, and the three p-values will then appear. Depending on the form of the hypothesis test (lower tail, upper tail, or two-tailed), we can then choose the appropriate p-value to make the rejection decision.

We can further simplify the use of Figure 9.7 as a template for other problems by eliminating the need to enter new data ranges in cells D4 and D5. To do so we rewrite the cell formulas as follows:

Cell D4: =COUNT(A:A)
Cell D5: =AVERAGE(A:A)

The GolfTest data set includes a worksheet titled Template that uses the A:A method for entering the data ranges.

With the A:A method of specifying data ranges, Excel's COUNT function will count the number of numeric values in column A and Excel's AVERAGE function will compute the average of the numeric values in column A. Thus, to solve a new problem it is only necessary to enter the new data in column A, enter the value of the known population standard deviation in cell D7, and enter the hypothesized value of the population mean in cell D8.

The worksheet can also be used as a template for text exercises in which n, $\bar{x}$, and σ are given. Just ignore the data in column A and enter the values for n, $\bar{x}$, and σ into cells D4, D5, and D7, respectively. Then enter the appropriate hypothesized value for the population mean into cell D8. The p-values corresponding to lower tail, upper tail, and two-tailed hypothesis tests will then appear in cells D13:D15.

Summary and Practical Advice

We presented examples of a lower tail test and a two-tailed test about a population mean. Based upon these examples, we can now summarize the hypothesis testing procedures about a population mean for the σ known case as shown in Table 9.2. Note that μ_0 is the hypothesized value of the population mean.

TABLE 9.2 SUMMARY OF HYPOTHESIS TESTS ABOUT A POPULATION MEAN: σ KNOWN CASE

	Lower Tail Test	**Upper Tail Test**	**Two-Tailed Test**
Hypotheses	$H_0: \mu \geq \mu_0$ $H_a: \mu < \mu_0$	$H_0: \mu \leq \mu_0$ $H_a: \mu > \mu_0$	$H_0: \mu = \mu_0$ $H_a: \mu \neq \mu_0$
Test Statistic	$z = \dfrac{\bar{x} - \mu_0}{\sigma/\sqrt{n}}$	$z = \dfrac{\bar{x} - \mu_0}{\sigma/\sqrt{n}}$	$z = \dfrac{\bar{x} - \mu_0}{\sigma/\sqrt{n}}$
Rejection Rule: *p*-**Value Approach**	Reject H_0 if *p*-value $\leq \alpha$	Reject H_0 if *p*-value $\leq \alpha$	Reject H_0 if *p*-value $\leq \alpha$
Rejection Rule: **Critical Value** **Approach**	Reject H_0 if $z \leq -z_\alpha$	Reject H_0 if $z \geq z_\alpha$	Reject H_0 if $z \leq -z_{\alpha/2}$ or if $z \geq z_{\alpha/2}$

The hypothesis testing steps followed in the two examples presented in this section are common to every hypothesis test.

STEPS OF HYPOTHESIS TESTING

Step 1. Develop the null and alternative hypotheses.
Step 2. Specify the level of significance.
Step 3. Collect the sample data and compute the value of the test statistic.

p-Value Approach

Step 4. Use the value of the test statistic to compute the *p*-value.
Step 5. Reject H_0 if the *p*-value $\leq \alpha$.

Critical Value Approach

Step 4. Use the level of significance to determine the critical value and the rejection rule.
Step 5. Use the value of the test statistic and the rejection rule to determine whether to reject H_0.

Practical advice about the sample size for hypothesis tests is similar to the advice we provided about the sample size for interval estimation in Chapter 8. In most applications, a sample size of $n \geq 30$ is adequate when using the hypothesis testing procedure described in this section. In cases where the sample size is less than 30, the distribution of the population from which we are sampling becomes an important consideration. If the population is normally distributed, the hypothesis testing procedure that we described is exact and can be used for any sample size. If the population is not normally distributed but is at least roughly symmetric, sample sizes as small as 15 can be expected to provide acceptable results. With smaller sample sizes, the hypothesis testing procedure presented in this section should only be used if the analyst believes, or is willing to assume, that the population is at least approximately normally distributed.

Relationship Between Interval Estimation and Hypothesis Testing

We close this section by discussing the relationship between interval estimation and hypothesis testing. In Chapter 8 we showed how to develop a confidence interval estimate of a population mean. For the σ known case, the confidence interval estimate of a population mean corresponding to a $1 - \alpha$ confidence coefficient is given by

$$\bar{x} \pm z_{\alpha/2} \frac{\sigma}{\sqrt{n}} \tag{9.2}$$

Conducting a hypothesis test requires us first to develop the hypotheses about the value of a population parameter. In the case of the population mean, the two-tailed test takes the form

$$H_0: \mu = \mu_0$$
$$H_a: \mu \neq \mu_0$$

where μ_0 is the hypothesized value for the population mean. Using the two-tailed critical value approach, we do not reject H_0 for values of the sample mean $\bar{x}$ that are within $-z_{\alpha/2}$ and $+z_{\alpha/2}$ standard errors of μ_0. Thus, the do-not-reject region for the sample mean $\bar{x}$ in a two-tailed hypothesis test with a level of significance of α is given by

$$\mu_0 \pm z_{\alpha/2} \frac{\sigma}{\sqrt{n}} \tag{9.3}$$

A close look at expressions (9.2) and (9.3) provides insight about the relationship between the estimation and hypothesis testing approaches to statistical inference. Note in particular that both procedures require the computation of the values $z_{\alpha/2}$ and $\sigma/\sqrt{n}$. Focusing on α, we see that a confidence coefficient of $(1 - \alpha)$ for interval estimation corresponds to a level of significance of α in hypothesis testing. For example, a 95% confidence interval corresponds to a .05 level of significance for hypothesis testing. Furthermore, expressions (9.2) and (9.3) show that, because $z_{\alpha/2}(\sigma/\sqrt{n})$ is the plus or minus value for both expressions, if $\bar{x}$ is in the do-not-reject region defined by expression (9.3), the hypothesized value μ_0 will be in the confidence interval defined by expression (9.2). Conversely, if the hypothesized value μ_0 is in the confidence interval defined by expression (9.2), the sample mean $\bar{x}$ will be in the do-not-reject region for the hypothesis $H_0: \mu = \mu_0$ as defined by expression (9.3). These observations lead to the following procedure for using a confidence interval to conduct a two-tailed hypothesis test.

A CONFIDENCE INTERVAL APPROACH TO TESTING A HYPOTHESIS OF THE FORM

$$H_0: \mu = \mu_0$$
$$H_a: \mu \neq \mu_0$$

1. Select a simple random sample from the population and use the value of the sample mean $\bar{x}$ to develop the confidence interval for the population mean μ.

$$\bar{x} \pm z_{\alpha/2} \frac{\sigma}{\sqrt{n}}$$

For a two-tailed hypothesis test, the null hypothesis can be rejected if the confidence interval does not include μ_0.

2. If the confidence interval contains the hypothesized value μ_0, do not reject H_0. Otherwise, reject H_0.

TABLE 9.3   SUMMARY OF HYPOTHESIS TESTS ABOUT A POPULATION MEAN: σ UNKNOWN CASE

	Lower Tail Test	Upper Tail Test	Two-Tailed Test
Hypotheses	$H_0{:}\ \mu \geq \mu_0$ $H_a{:}\ \mu < \mu_0$	$H_0{:}\ \mu \leq \mu_0$ $H_a{:}\ \mu > \mu_0$	$H_0{:}\ \mu = \mu_0$ $H_a{:}\ \mu \neq \mu_0$
Test Statistic	$t = \dfrac{\bar{x} - \mu_0}{s/\sqrt{n}}$	$t = \dfrac{\bar{x} - \mu_0}{s/\sqrt{n}}$	$t = \dfrac{\bar{x} - \mu_0}{s/\sqrt{n}}$
Rejection Rule: *p*-**Value Approach**	Reject H_0 if p-value $\leq \alpha$	Reject H_0 if p-value $\leq \alpha$	Reject H_0 if p-value $\leq \alpha$
Rejection Rule: **Critical Value** **Approach**	Reject H_0 if $t \leq -t_\alpha$	Reject H_0 if $t \geq t_\alpha$	Reject H_0 if $t \leq -t_{\alpha/2}$ or if $t \geq t_{\alpha/2}$

lation is normally distributed, the hypothesis tests described in this section provide exact results for any sample size. When the population is not normally distributed, the procedures are approximations. Nonetheless, we find that sample sizes greater than 30 will provide good results in almost all cases. If the population is approximately normal, small sample sizes (e.g., $n < 15$) can provide acceptable results. In situations where the population cannot be approximated by a normal distribution, sample sizes of $n \geq 15$ will provide acceptable results as long as the population is not highly skewed and does not contain outliers. If the population is highly skewed or contains outliers, samples sizes approaching 50 are recommended.

Exercises

Methods

23. Consider the following hypothesis test:

$$H_0{:}\ \mu \leq 12$$
$$H_a{:}\ \mu > 12$$

A sample of 25 provided a sample mean $\bar{x} = 14$ and a sample standard deviation $s = 4.32$.
    a. Compute the value of the test statistic.
    b. What does the t distribution table (Table 2 in Appendix B) tell you about the p-value?
    c. At $\alpha = .05$, what is your conclusion?
    d. What is the rejection rule using the critical value? What is your conclusion?

24. Consider the following hypothesis test:

$$H_0{:}\ \mu = 18$$
$$H_a{:}\ \mu \neq 18$$

A sample of 48 provided a sample mean $\bar{x} = 17$ and a sample standard deviation $s = 4.5$.
    a. Compute the value of the test statistic.
    b. What does the t distribution table (Table 2 in Appendix B) tell you about the p-value?
    c. At $\alpha = .05$, what is your conclusion?
    d. What is the rejection rule using the critical value? What is your conclusion?

25. Consider the following hypothesis test:

$$H_0: \mu \geq 45$$
$$H_a: \mu < 45$$

A sample of 36 is used. Identify the *p*-value and state your conclusion for each of the following sample results. Use $\alpha = .01$.
   a. $\bar{x} = 44$ and $s = 5.2$
   b. $\bar{x} = 43$ and $s = 4.6$
   c. $\bar{x} = 46$ and $s = 5.0$

26. Consider the following hypothesis test:

$$H_0: \mu = 100$$
$$H_a: \mu \neq 100$$

A sample of 65 is used. Identify the *p*-value and state your conclusion for each of the following sample results. Use $\alpha = .05$.
   a. $\bar{x} = 103$ and $s = 11.5$
   b. $\bar{x} = 96.5$ and $s = 11.0$
   c. $\bar{x} = 102$ and $s = 10.5$

Applications

27. The Employment and Training Administration reported the U.S. mean unemployment insurance benefit of $238 per week (*The World Almanac 2003*). A researcher in the state of Virginia anticipated that sample data would show evidence that the mean weekly unemployment insurance benefit in Virginia was below the national level.
   a. Develop appropriate hypotheses such that rejection of H_0 will support the researcher's contention.
   b. For a sample of 100 individuals, the sample mean weekly unemployment insurance benefit was $231 with a sample standard deviation of $80. What is the *p*-value?
   c. At $\alpha = .05$, what is your conclusion?
   d. Repeat the preceding hypothesis test using the critical value approach.

28. The National Association of Professional Baseball Leagues, Inc., reported that attendance for 176 minor league baseball teams reached an all-time high during the 2001 season (*New York Times,* July 28, 2002). On a per-game basis, the mean attendance for minor league baseball was 3530 people per game. Midway through the 2002 season, the president of the association asked for an attendance report that would hopefully show that the mean attendance for 2002 was exceeding the 2001 level.
   a. Formulate hypotheses that could be used determine whether the mean attendance per game in 2002 was greater than the previous year's level.
   b. Assume that a sample of 92 minor league baseball games played during the first half of the 2002 season showed a mean attendance of 3740 people per game with a sample standard deviation of 810. What is the *p*-value?
   c. At $\alpha = .01$, what is your conclusion?

Diamonds

29. The cost of a one-carat VS2 clarity, H color diamond from Diamond Source USA is $5600 (http://www.diasource.com, March 2003). A midwestern jeweler makes calls to contacts in the diamond district of New York City to see whether the mean price of diamonds there differs from $5600.
   a. Formulate hypotheses that can be used to determine whether the mean price in New York City differs from $5600.
   b. A sample of 25 New York City contacts provided the prices shown in the CD file named Diamonds. What is the *p*-value?

  b.   What is the p-value?
  c.   Use $\alpha = .05$. What is your conclusion?

50. The College Board reported that the average number of freshman class applications to public colleges and universities is 6000 (*USA Today*, December 26, 2002). During a recent application/enrollment period, a sample of 32 colleges and universities showed that the sample mean number of freshman class applications was 5812 with a sample standard deviation of 1140. Do the data indicate a change in the mean number of applications? Use $\alpha = .05$.

51. An extensive study of the cost of health care in the United States presented data showing that the mean spending per Medicare enrollee in 2003 was $6883 (*Money*, Fall 2003). To investigate differences across the country, a researcher took a sample of 40 Medicare enrollees in Indianapolis. For the Indianapolis sample, the mean 2003 Medicare spending was $5980 and the standard deviation was $2518.
  a.   State the hypotheses that should be used if we would like to determine whether the mean annual Medicare spending in Indianapolis is lower than the national mean.
  b.   Use the preceding sample results to compute the test statistic and the p-value.
  c.   Use $\alpha = .05$. What is your conclusion?
  d.   Repeat the hypothesis test using the critical value approach.

52. The Chamber of Commerce of a Florida Gulf Coast community advertises that area residential property is available at a mean cost of $125,000 or less per lot. Suppose a sample of 32 properties provided a sample mean of $130,000 per lot and a sample standard deviation of $12,500. Using a .05 level of significance, test the validity of the advertising claim.

53. The population mean earnings per share for financial services corporations including American Express, E*TRADE Group, Goldman Sachs, and Merrill Lynch was $3 (*BusinessWeek*, August 14, 2000). In 2001, a sample of 10 financial services corporations provided the following earnings per share data:

    1.92   2.16   3.63   3.16   4.02   3.14   2.20   2.34   3.05   2.38

  a.   Formulate the null and alternative hypotheses that can be used to determine whether the population mean earnings per share in 2001 differ from the $3 reported in 2000.
  b.   Compute the sample mean.
  c.   Compute the sample standard deviation.
  d.   What is the p-value?
  e.   Use $\alpha = .05$. What is your conclusion?

54. A study by the Centers for Disease Control (CDC) found that 23.3% of adults are smokers and that roughly 70% of those who do smoke indicate that they want to quit (Associated Press, July 26, 2002). CDC reported that, of people who smoked at some point in their lives, 50% have been able to kick the habit. Part of the study suggested that the success rate for quitting rose by education level. Assume that a sample of 100 college graduates who smoked at some point in their lives showed that 64 had been able to successfully stop smoking.
  a.   State the hypotheses that can be used to determine whether the population of college graduates has a success rate higher than the overall population when it comes to breaking the smoking habit.
  b.   Given the sample data, what is the proportion of college graduates who, having smoked at some point in their lives, were able to stop smoking?
  c.   What is the p-value? At $\alpha = .01$, what is your hypothesis testing conclusion?

55. An airline promotion to business travelers is based on the assumption that two-thirds of business travelers use a laptop computer on overnight business trips.
  a.   State the hypotheses that can be used to test the assumption.
  b.   What is the sample proportion from an American Express–sponsored survey that found 355 of 546 business travelers use a laptop computer on overnight business trips?
  c.   What is the p-value?
  d.   Use $\alpha = .05$. What is your conclusion?

56. Shell Oil office workers were asked which work schedule appealed most: working five 8-hour days a week or working four 10-hour days a week (*USA Today*, September 11, 2000). Let $p =$ the proportion of the office worker population preferring the four-10-hour-days work week.
    a. State the hypotheses if Shell management is interested in statistical support that shows more than 50% of office workers prefer the four-10-hour-days work week.
    b. What is the sample proportion if a sample of 105 office workers showed 67 preferred the four-10-hour-days schedule?
    c. What is the *p*-value? Use $\alpha = .01$. What is your conclusion?

57. During the 2004 election year, new polling results were reported daily. In an IBD/TIPP poll of 910 adults, 503 respondents reported that they were optimistic about the national outlook, and President Bush's leadership index jumped 4.7 points to 55.3 (*Investor's Business Daily*, January 14, 2004).
    a. What is the sample proportion of respondents who are optimistic about the national outlook?
    b. A campaign manager wants to claim that this poll indicates that the majority of adults are optimistic about the national outlook. Construct a hypothesis test so that rejection of the null hypothesis will permit the conclusion that the proportion optimistic is greater than 50%.
    c. Use the polling data to compute the *p*-value for the hypothesis test in part (b). Explain to the manager what this *p*-value means about the level of significance of the results.

58. A radio station in Myrtle Beach announced that at least 90% of the hotels and motels would be full for the Memorial Day weekend. The station advised listeners to make reservations in advance if they planned to be in the resort over the weekend. On Saturday night a sample of 58 hotels and motels showed 49 with a no-vacancy sign and 9 with vacancies. What is your reaction to the radio station's claim after seeing the sample evidence? Use $\alpha = .05$ in making the statistical test. What is the *p*-value?

59. Environmental health indicators include air quality, water quality, and food quality. Twenty-five years ago, 47% of U.S. food samples contained pesticide residues (*U.S. News & World Report*, April 17, 2000). In a recent study, 44 of 125 food samples contained pesticide residues.
    a. State the hypotheses that can be used to show that the population proportion declined.
    b. What is the sample proportion?
    c. What is the *p*-value?
    d. Use $\alpha = .01$. What is your conclusion?

Case Problem 1 # Quality Associates, Inc.

Quality Associates, Inc., a consulting firm, advises its clients about sampling and statistical procedures that can be used to control their manufacturing processes. In one particular application, a client gave Quality Associates a sample of 800 observations taken during a time in which that client's process was operating satisfactorily. The sample standard deviation for these data was .21; hence, with so much data, the population standard deviation was assumed to be .21. Quality Associates then suggested that random samples of size 30 be taken periodically to monitor the process on an ongoing basis. By analyzing the new samples, the client could quickly learn whether the process was operating satisfactorily. When the process was not operating satisfactorily, corrective action could be taken to eliminate the problem. The design specification indicated the mean for the process should be 12. The hypothesis test suggested by Quality Associates follows.

$$H_0: \mu = 12$$
$$H_a: \mu \neq 12$$

Corrective action will be taken any time H_0 is rejected.

The following samples were collected at hourly intervals during the first day of operation of the new statistical process control procedure. These data are available in the data set Quality.

Quality

Sample 1	Sample 2	Sample 3	Sample 4
11.55	11.62	11.91	12.02
11.62	11.69	11.36	12.02
11.52	11.59	11.75	12.05
11.75	11.82	11.95	12.18
11.90	11.97	12.14	12.11
11.64	11.71	11.72	12.07
11.80	11.87	11.61	12.05
12.03	12.10	11.85	11.64
11.94	12.01	12.16	12.39
11.92	11.99	11.91	11.65
12.13	12.20	12.12	12.11
12.09	12.16	11.61	11.90
11.93	12.00	12.21	12.22
12.21	12.28	11.56	11.88
12.32	12.39	11.95	12.03
11.93	12.00	12.01	12.35
11.85	11.92	12.06	12.09
11.76	11.83	11.76	11.77
12.16	12.23	11.82	12.20
11.77	11.84	12.12	11.79
12.00	12.07	11.60	12.30
12.04	12.11	11.95	12.27
11.98	12.05	11.96	12.29
12.30	12.37	12.22	12.47
12.18	12.25	11.75	12.03
11.97	12.04	11.96	12.17
12.17	12.24	11.95	11.94
11.85	11.92	11.89	11.97
12.30	12.37	11.88	12.23
12.15	12.22	11.93	12.25

Managerial Report

1. Conduct a hypothesis test for each sample at the .01 level of significance and determine what action, if any, should be taken. Provide the test statistic and p-value for each test.
2. Compute the standard deviation for each of the four samples. Does the assumption of .21 for the population standard deviation appear reasonable?
3. Compute limits for the sample mean $\bar{x}$ around $\mu = 12$ such that, as long as a new sample mean is within those limits, the process will be considered to be operating satisfactorily. If $\bar{x}$ exceeds the upper limit or if $\bar{x}$ is below the lower limit, corrective action will be taken. These limits are referred to as upper and lower control limits for quality control purposes.
4. Discuss the implications of changing the level of significance to a larger value. What mistake or error could increase if the level of significance is increased?

Case Problem 2   # Unemployment Study

Each month the U.S. Bureau of Labor Statistics publishes a variety of unemployment statistics, including the number of individuals who are unemployed and the mean length of time the individuals have been unemployed. For November 1998, the Bureau of Labor Statistics reported that the national mean length of time of unemployment was 14.6 weeks.

The mayor of Philadelphia requested a study on the status of unemployment in the Philadelphia area. A sample of 50 unemployed residents of Philadelphia included data on their age and the number of weeks without a job. A portion of the data collected in November 1998 follows. The complete data set is available in the data file BLS.

BLS

Age	Weeks	Age	Weeks	Age	Weeks
56	22	22	11	25	12
35	19	48	6	25	1
22	7	48	22	59	33
57	37	25	5	49	26
40	18	40	20	33	13

Managerial Report

1. Use descriptive statistics to summarize the data.
2. Develop a 95% confidence interval estimate of the mean age of unemployed individuals in Philadelphia.
3. Conduct a hypothesis test to determine whether the mean duration of unemployment in Philadelphia is greater than the national mean duration of 14.6 weeks. Use a .01 level of significance. What is your conclusion?
4. Is there a relationship between the age of an unemployed individual and the number of weeks of unemployment? Explain.

CHAPTER 10

Comparisons Involving Means

CONTENTS

STATISTICS IN PRACTICE: FISONS
CORPORATION

FISONS CORPORATION
ROCHESTER, NEW YORK

Fisons Corporation, Rochester, New York, is a unit of Fisons Plc., UK. Fisons opened its U.S. operations in 1966.

Fisons Pharmaceutical Division uses extensive statistical procedures to test and develop new drugs. The testing process in the pharmaceutical industry usually consists of three stages: (1) preclinical testing, (2) testing for long-term usage and safety, and (3) clinical efficacy testing. At each successive stage, the chance that a drug will pass the rigorous tests decreases; however, the cost of further testing increases dramatically. Industry surveys indicate that on average the research and development for one new drug costs $250 million and takes 12 years. Hence, it is important to eliminate unsuccessful new drugs in the early stages of the testing process, as well as identify promising ones for further testing.

Statistics plays a major role in pharmaceutical research, where government regulations are stringent and rigorously enforced. In preclinical testing, a two- or three-population statistical study typically is used to determine whether a new drug should continue to be studied in the long-term usage and safety program. The populations may consist of the new drug, a control, and a standard drug. The preclinical testing process begins when a new drug is sent to the pharmacology group for evaluation of efficacy—the capacity of the drug to produce the desired effects. As part of the process, a statistician is asked to design an experiment that can be used to test the new drug. The design must specify the sample size and the statistical methods of analysis. In a two-population study, one sample is used to obtain data on the efficacy of the new drug (population 1) and a second sample is used to obtain data on the efficacy of a standard drug (population 2). Depending on the intended use, the new and standard drugs are tested in such disciplines as neurology, cardiology, and immunology. In most studies, the statistical method involves hypothesis testing for the difference between the means of the new drug population and the standard drug population. If a new drug

Statistical methods are used to test and develop new drugs. © Mark Richards/PhotoEdit.

lacks efficacy or produces undesirable effects in comparison with the standard drug, the new drug is rejected and withdrawn from further testing. Only new drugs that show promising comparisons with the standard drugs are forwarded to the long-term usage and safety testing program.

Further data collection and multipopulation studies are conducted in the long-term usage and safety testing program and in the clinical testing programs. The Food and Drug Administration (FDA) requires that statistical methods be defined prior to such testing to avoid data-related biases. In addition, to avoid human biases, some of the clinical trials are double or triple blind. That is, neither the subject nor the investigator knows what drug is administered to whom. If the new drug meets all requirements in relation to the standard drug, a new drug application (NDA) is filed with the FDA. The application is rigorously scrutinized by statisticians and scientists at the agency.

In this chapter you will learn how to construct interval estimates and conduct hypothesis tests about means with two or more populations. Techniques will be presented for analyzing independent random samples as well as matched samples.

In Chapters 8 and 9 we showed how to develop interval estimates and conduct hypothesis tests for situations involving a single population mean and a single population proportion. In this chapter we continue our discussion of statistical inference by showing how interval estimates and hypothesis tests can be developed for situations involving two or more populations. For example, we may want to develop an interval estimate of the difference between the mean starting salary for a population of men and the mean starting salary for a population of women standard normal distribution table, the area to the left of $z = 1.66$ is .9515. Thus, the area in the upper tail of the distribution is $1.0000 - .9515 = .0485$. Because this test is a two-tailed test, we must double the tail area: p-value $= 2(.0485) = .0970$. Following the usual rule to reject H_0 if p-value $\leq \alpha$, we see that the p-value of .0970 does not allow us to reject H_0 at the .05 level of significance. The sample results do not provide sufficient evidence to conclude that the training centers differ in quality.

In this chapter we will use the p-value approach to hypothesis testing as described in Chapter 9. However, if you prefer, the test statistic and the critical value rejection rule may be used. With $\alpha = .05$ and $z_{\alpha/2} = z_{.025} = 1.96$, the rejection rule employing the critical value approach would be reject H_0 if $z \leq -1.96$ or if $z \geq 1.96$. With $z = 1.66$, we reach the same do not reject H_0 conclusion.

In the preceding example, we demonstrated a two-tailed hypothesis test about the difference between two population means. Lower tail and upper tail tests can also be considered. These tests use the same test statistic as given in equation (10.5). The procedure for computing the p-value and the rejection rules for these one-tailed tests are the same as those presented in Chapter 9.

Using Excel to Conduct a Hypothesis Test

The Excel procedure used to conduct the hypothesis test to determine whether there is a significant difference in population means when σ_1 and σ_2 are assumed known is called *z-test: Two Sample for Means*. We illustrate using the sample data for exam scores at center A and at center B. With an assumed known standard deviation of 10 points at each center, the known variance of exam scores for each of the two populations is equal to $10^2 = 100$. Refer to the Excel worksheet shown in Figure 10.3 and the dialog box in Figure 10.4 as we describe the tasks involved.

Enter Data: Column A contains the examination score data for the simple random sample of 30 individuals trained at center A, and column B contains the examination score data for the simple random sample of 40 individuals trained at center B.

Apply Tools: The following steps will provide the information needed to conduct the hypothesis test to see whether there is a significant difference in test scores at the two centers.

Step 1. Select the **Tools** menu
Step 2. Choose **Data Analysis**
Step 3. Choose *z*-**Test: Two Sample for Means** from the list of Analysis Tools
Step 4. When the *z*-Test: Two Sample for Means dialog box appears (Figure 10.4):
Enter A1:A31 in the **Variable 1 Range** box
Enter B1:B41 in the **Variable 2 Range** box
Enter 0 in the **Hypothesized Mean Difference** box
Enter 100 in the **Variable 1 Variance (known)** box
Enter 100 in the **Variable 2 Variance (known)** box
Select **Labels**
Enter .05 in the **Alpha** box
Select **Output Range** and enter D4 in the box
Click **OK**

The value of the test statistic shown here (1.6562) and the p-value (.0977) differ slightly from those shown previously, because we rounded the test statistic to two places (1.66) in the text.

Descriptive statistics for the two samples are shown in cells E7:F9. The value of the test statistic, 1.6562, is shown in cell E11. The p-value for the test, labeled P(Z<=z) two-tail, is shown in cell E14. Because the p-value, 0.0977, is greater than the level of significance, $\alpha = .05$, we cannot conclude that the means for the two populations are different.

The z-test: Two Sample for Means can also be used to conduct one-tailed hypothesis tests. The only change required to make the hypothesis testing decision is that we need to use the p-value for a one-tailed test, labeled P(Z<=z) one-tail (see cell E12).

	A	B	C	D	E	F	G
1	**Center A**	**Center B**					
2	97	64					
3	95	85					
4	89	72		**z-Test: Two Sample for Means**			
5	79	64					
6	78	74			*Center A*	*Center B*	
7	87	93		**Mean**	82	78	
8	83	70		**Known Variance**	100	100	
9	94	79		**Observations**	30	40	
10	76	79		**Hypothesized Mean Difference**	0		
11	79	75		**z**	1.6562		
12	83	66		**P(Z<=z) one-tail**	0.0488		
13	84	83		**z Critical one-tail**	1.6449		
14	76	74		**P(Z<=z) two-tail**	0.0977		
15	82	70		**z Critical two-tail**	1.9600		
16	85	82					
17	85	82					
29	88	65					
30	60	78					
31	73	66					
32		84					
40		80					
41		76					
42							

Note: Rows 18–28 and 33–39 are hidden.

FIGURE 10.4   DIALOG BOX FOR EXCEL'S *z*-TEST: TWO SAMPLE FOR MEANS

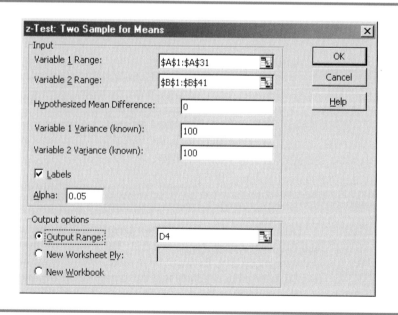

Practical Advice

In most applications of the interval estimation and hypothesis testing procedures presented in this section, random samples with $n_1 \geq 30$ and $n_2 \geq 30$ are adequate. In cases where either or both sample sizes are less than 30, the distributions of the populations become important considerations. In general, with smaller sample sizes, it is more important for the analyst to be satisfied that it is reasonable to assume that the distributions of the two populations are at least approximately normal.

Exercises

Methods

1. The following results are for two independent random samples taken from two populations.

Sample 1	Sample 2
$n_1 = 50$	$n_2 = 35$
$\bar{x}_1 = 13.6$	$\bar{x}_2 = 11.6$
$\sigma_1 = 2.2$	$\sigma_2 = 3.0$

   a. What is the point estimate of the difference between the two population means?
   b. Provide a 90% confidence interval for the difference between the two population means.
   c. Provide a 95% confidence interval for the difference between the two population means.

2. Consider the following hypothesis test.

$$H_0: \mu_1 - \mu_2 \leq 0$$
$$H_a: \mu_1 - \mu_2 > 0$$

The following results are for two independent samples taken from the two populations.

Sample 1	Sample 2
$n_1 = 40$	$n_2 = 50$
$\bar{x}_1 = 25.2$	$\bar{x}_2 = 22.8$
$\sigma_1 = 5.2$	$\sigma_2 = 6.0$

   a. What is the value of the test statistic?
   b. What is the p-value?
   c. With $\alpha = .05$, what is your hypothesis testing conclusion?

3. Consider the following hypothesis test.

$$H_0: \mu_1 - \mu_2 = 0$$
$$H_a: \mu_1 - \mu_2 \neq 0$$

The following results are for two independent samples taken from the two populations.

Sample 1	Sample 2
$n_1 = 80$	$n_2 = 70$
$\bar{x}_1 = 104$	$\bar{x}_2 = 106$
$\sigma_1 = 8.4$	$\sigma_2 = 7.6$

a. What is the value of the test statistic?
b. What is the p-value?
c. With $\alpha = .05$, what is your hypothesis testing conclusion?

Applications

4. Gasoline prices reached record high levels in 16 states during 2003 (*The Wall Street Journal,* March 7, 2003). Two of the affected states were California and Florida. The American Automobile Association reported a sample mean price of $2.04 per gallon in California and a sample mean price of $1.72 per gallon in Florida. Use a sample size of 40 for the California data and a sample size of 35 for the Florida data. Assume that prior studies indicating a population standard deviation of .10 in California and .08 in Florida are reasonable.
   a. What is a point estimate of the difference between the population mean prices per gallon in California and Florida?
   b. At 95% confidence, what is the margin of error?
   c. What is the 95% confidence interval estimate of the difference between the population mean prices per gallon in the two states?

5. A Cornell University study of wage differentials between men and women reported that one of the reasons wages for men are higher than wages for women is that men tend to have more years of work experience than women (*BusinessWeek,* August 28, 2000). Assume the following results were obtained for each group.

Men	Women
$n_1 = 100$	$n_2 = 85$
$\bar{x}_1 = 14.9$ years	$\bar{x}_2 = 10.3$ years
$\sigma_1 = 5.2$ years	$\sigma_2 = 3.8$ years

   a. What is the point estimate of the difference between the two population means?
   b. At 95% confidence, what is the margin of error?
   c. What is the 95% confidence interval estimate of the difference between the two population means?

Mortgage

6. The nation's 40,000 mortgage brokers are some of the most profitable small businesses in the United States. These low-profile companies find loans for companies in exchange for commissions. Mortgage Bankers Association of America provides data on the average size of loans handled by mortgage brokers (*The Wall Street Journal,* February 24, 2003). The CD file named Mortgage contains data from a sample of 250 loans made in 2001 and a sample of 270 loans made in 2002 that are consistent with these data. Based on historical loan data, the population standard deviations for loan amounts can be assumed known at $50,000 in 2001 and $55,000 in 2002. Do the sample data indicate an increase in the mean loan amount between 2001 and 2002? Use $\alpha = .05$.

7. During the 2003 season, Major League Baseball took steps to speed up the play of baseball games in order to maintain fan interest (*CNN Headline News,* September 30, 2003). The following results come from a sample of 60 games played during the summer of 2002

and a sample of 50 games played during the summer of 2003. The sample mean shows the mean duration of the games included in each sample.

2002 Season	2003 Season
$n_1 = 60$	$n_2 = 50$
$\bar{x}_1 = 2$ hours, 52 minutes	$\bar{x}_2 = 2$ hours, 46 minutes

a.   A research hypothesis was that the steps taken during the 2003 season would reduce the population mean duration of baseball games. Formulate the null and alternative hypotheses.

b.   What is the point estimate of the reduction in the mean duration of games during the 2003 season?

c.   Historical data indicate a population standard deviation of 12 minutes is a reasonable assumption for both years. Conduct the hypothesis test and report the p-value. At a .05 level of significance, what is your conclusion?

d.   Provide a 95% confidence interval estimate of the reduction in the mean duration of games during the 2003 season.

e.   What was the percentage reduction in the mean time of baseball games during the 2003 season? Should management be pleased with the results of the statistical analysis? Discuss. Should the length of baseball games continue to be an issue in future years? Explain.

8.   Arnold Palmer and Tiger Woods are two of the best golfers to ever play the game. To show how these two golfers would compare if both were playing at the top of their game, the following sample data provide the results of 18-hole scores during PGA tournament competition. Palmer's scores are from his 1960 season, while Woods' scores are from his 1999 season (*Golf Magazine,* February 2000).

Arnold Palmer	Tiger Woods
$n_1 = 112$	$n_2 = 84$
$\bar{x}_1 = 69.95$	$\bar{x}_2 = 69.56$

Use the sample results to test the hypothesis of no difference between the population mean 18-hole scores for the two golfers.

a.   Assume a population standard deviation of 2.5 for both golfers. What is the value of the test statistic?

b.   What is the p-value?

c.   At $\alpha = .01$, what is your conclusion?

Inferences About the Difference Between Two Population Means: σ_1 and σ_2 Unknown

In this section we extend the discussion of inferences about the difference between two population means to the case when the two population standard deviations, σ_1 and σ_2, are unknown. In this case, we will use the sample standard deviations, s_1 and s_2, to estimate the unknown population standard deviations. When we use the sample standard deviations, the interval estimation and hypothesis testing procedures will be based on the t distribution rather than the standard normal distribution.

Interval Estimation of $\mu_1 - \mu_2$

In the following example we show how to compute a margin of error and develop an interval estimate of the difference between two population means when σ_1 and σ_2 are unknown. Clearwater National Bank is conducting a study designed to identify differences between checking account practices by customers at two of its branch banks. A simple random sample of 28 checking accounts is selected from the Cherry Grove Branch and an independent simple random sample of 22 checking accounts is selected from the Beechmont Branch. The current checking account balance is recorded for each of the checking accounts. A summary of the account balances follows:

CheckAcct

	Cherry Grove	**Beechmont**
Sample Size	$n_1 = 28$	$n_2 = 22$
Sample Mean	$\bar{x}_1 = \$1025$	$\bar{x}_2 = \$910$
Sample Standard Deviation	$s_1 = \$150$	$s_2 = \$125$

Clearwater National Bank would like to estimate the difference between the mean checking account balance maintained by the population of Cherry Grove customers and the population of Beechmont customers. Let us develop the margin of error and an interval estimate of the difference between these two population means.

In Section 10.1, we provided the following interval estimate for the case when the population standard deviations, σ_1 and σ_2, are known.

$$\bar{x}_1 - \bar{x}_2 \pm z_{\alpha/2}\sqrt{\frac{\sigma_1^2}{n_1} + \frac{\sigma_2^2}{n_2}}$$

When σ_1 and σ_2 are estimated by s_1 and s_2, the t distribution is used to make inferences about the difference between two population means.

With σ_1 and σ_2 unknown, we will use the sample standard deviations s_1 and s_2 to estimate σ_1 and σ_2 and replace $z_{\alpha/2}$ with $t_{\alpha/2}$. As a result, the interval estimate of the difference between two population means is given by the following expression:

INTERVAL ESTIMATE OF THE DIFFERENCE BETWEEN TWO POPULATION
MEANS: σ_1 AND σ_2 UNKNOWN

$$\bar{x}_1 - \bar{x}_2 \pm t_{\alpha/2}\sqrt{\frac{s_1^2}{n_1} + \frac{s_2^2}{n_2}} \tag{10.6}$$

where $1 - \alpha$ is the confidence coefficient.

In this expression, the use of the t distribution is an approximation, but it provides excellent results and is relatively easy to use. The only difficulty that we encounter in using expression (10.6) is determining the appropriate degrees of freedom for $t_{\alpha/2}$. The formula used is as follows:

DEGREES OF FREEDOM: t DISTRIBUTION WITH TWO INDEPENDENT
RANDOM SAMPLES

The Excel worksheet in Figure 10.5 makes this computation easy.

$$df = \frac{\left(\dfrac{s_1^2}{n_1} + \dfrac{s_2^2}{n_2}\right)^2}{\dfrac{1}{n_1 - 1}\left(\dfrac{s_1^2}{n_1}\right)^2 + \dfrac{1}{n_2 - 1}\left(\dfrac{s_2^2}{n_2}\right)^2} \tag{10.7}$$

Let us return to the Clearwater National Bank example and show how to use expression (10.6) to provide a 95% confidence interval estimate of the difference between the population mean checking account balances at the two branch banks. The sample data show $n_1 = 28$, $\bar{x}_1 = \$1025$, and $s_1 = \$150$ for the Cherry Grove Branch, and $n_2 = 22$, $\bar{x}_2 = \$910$, and $s_2 = \$125$ for the Beechmont Branch. The calculation for degrees of freedom for $t_{\alpha/2}$ is as follows:

$$df = \frac{\left(\dfrac{s_1^2}{n_1} + \dfrac{s_2^2}{n_2}\right)^2}{\dfrac{1}{n_1 - 1}\left(\dfrac{s_1^2}{n_1}\right)^2 + \dfrac{1}{n_2 - 1}\left(\dfrac{s_2^2}{n_2}\right)^2} = \frac{\left(\dfrac{150^2}{28} + \dfrac{125^2}{22}\right)^2}{\dfrac{1}{28 - 1}\left(\dfrac{150^2}{28}\right)^2 + \dfrac{1}{22 - 1}\left(\dfrac{125^2}{22}\right)^2} = 47.8$$

We round the noninteger degrees of freedom *down* to 47 to provide a larger t value and a more conservative (wider) interval estimate. Using the t distribution table with 47 degrees of freedom, we find $t_{.025} = 2.012$. Using expression (10.6), we develop the 95% confidence interval estimate of the difference between the two population means as follows.

$$\bar{x}_1 - \bar{x}_2 \pm t_{.025}\sqrt{\frac{s_1^2}{n_1} + \frac{s_2^2}{n_2}}$$

$$1025 - 910 \pm 2.012\sqrt{\frac{150^2}{28} + \frac{125^2}{22}}$$

$$115 \pm 78$$

The point estimate of the difference between the population mean checking account balances at the two branches is $115 and the margin of error is $78. Thus the 95% confidence interval estimate of the difference between the two population means is $115 - 78 = \$37$ to $115 + 78 = \$193$.

This suggestion should help if you are using equation (10.7) to calculate the degrees of freedom by hand.

The computation of the degrees of freedom in equation (10.7) is cumbersome if you are doing the calculation by hand. However, note that the expressions s_1^2/n_1 and s_2^2/n_2 appear in both expression (10.6) and equation (10.7). These values only need to be computed once in order to evaluate both (10.6) and (10.7).

Using Excel to Construct a Confidence Interval

Excel's data analysis tools do not provide a procedure for developing interval estimates involving two population means. However, we can develop an Excel worksheet that can be used for a template to construct interval estimates. We will illustrate by constructing an interval estimate of the difference between the population means in the Clearwater National Bank study. Refer to Figure 10.5 as we describe the tasks involved. The formula worksheet is in the background; the value worksheet is in the foreground.

Enter Data: Column A contains the account balances for the simple random sample of 28 customers at the Cherry Grove Branch, and column B contains the account balances for the simple random sample of 22 customers at the Beechmont Branch.

Enter Functions and Formulas: The descriptive statistics needed are provided in cells E5:F7. Using the two sample standard deviations and the sample sizes, an estimate of the variance of the point estimator $\bar{x}_1 - \bar{x}_2$ is computed by entering the following formula into cell E9:

=E7^2/E5+F7^2/F5

An estimate of the standard error is then computed in cell E10 by taking the square root of the variance.

FIGURE 10.5   EXCEL WORKSHEET: CONSTRUCTING A 95% CONFIDENCE INTERVAL FOR CLEARWATER NATIONAL BANK

	A	B	C	D	E	F	G
1	Cherry Grove	Beechmont		Interval Estimate of Difference in Population Means:			
2	1263	997		σ_1 and σ_2 Unknown Case			
3	897	897					
4	849	912			Cherry Grove	Beechmont	
5	891	895		Sample Size	=COUNT(A2:A29)	=COUNT(B2:B23)	
6	964	785		Sample Mean	=AVERAGE(A2:A29)	=AVERAGE(B2:B23)	
7	810	751		Sample Standard Deviation	=STDEV(A2:A29)	=STDEV(B2:B23)	
8	877	882					
9	899	1110		Estimate of Variance	=E7^2/E5+F7^2/F5		
10	847	907		Standard Error	=SQRT(E9)		
11	1070	1226					
12	1252	762		Confidence Coefficient	0.95		
13	920	836		Level of Significance	=1-E12		
14	1256	1048		Degrees of Freedom	=E9^2/((1/(E5-1))*(E7^2/E5)^2+(1/(F5-1)*(F7^2/F5)^2))		
15	1196	774		t Value	=TINV(E13,E14)		
16	1150	807		Margin of Error	=E15*E10		
17	1024	972					
18	1016	980		Point Estimate of Difference	=E6-F6		
19	1126	877		Lower Limit	=E18-E16		
20	1289	943		Upper Limit	=E18+E16		
21	1220	993					
22	912	704					
23	1026	963					
24	786						
25	989						
26	1133						
27	990						
28	999						
29	1049						
30							

	A	B	C	D	E	F	G
1	Cherry Grove	Beechmont		Interval Estimate of Difference in Population Means:			
2	1263	997		σ_1 and σ_2 Unknown Case			
3	897	897					
4	849	912			Cherry Grove	Beechmont	
5	891	895		Sample Size	28	22	
6	964	785		Sample Mean	1025	910	
7	810	751		Sample Standard Deviation	150	125	
8	877	882					
9	899	1110		Estimate of Variance	1513.8550		
10	847	907		Standard Error	38.9083		
11	1070	1226					
12	1252	762		Confidence Coefficient	0.95		
13	920	836		Level of Significance	0.05		
14	1256	1048		Degrees of Freedom	47.8		
15	1196	774		t Value	2.012		
16	1150	807		Margin of Error	78		
17	1024	972					
18	1016	980		Point Estimate of Difference	115		
19	1126	877		Lower Limit	37		
20	1289	943		Upper Limit	193		
21	1220	993					
22	912	704					
23	1026	963					
24	786						
25	989						
26	1133						
27	990						
28	999						
29	1049						
30							

Cells E12:E16 are used to compute the appropriate t value and the margin of error. The confidence coefficient is entered into cell E12 (.95) and the corresponding level of significance is computed in cell E13 ($\alpha = .05$). In cell E14, we used formula (10.7) to compute the degrees of freedom (47.8). In cell E15, we used the TINV function to compute the t value needed for the interval estimate. The margin of error is computed in cell E16 by multiplying the t value by the standard error.

In cell E18 the difference in the sample means is used to compute the point estimate of the difference in the two population means (115). The lower limit of the confidence interval is computed in cell E19 (37) and the upper limit is computed in cell E20 (193);

thus, the 95% confidence interval estimate of the difference in the two population means is 37 to 193.

A Template for Other Problems This worksheet can be used as a template for developing interval estimates of the difference in population means when the population standard deviations are unknown. For another problem of this type, we must first enter the new problem data in columns A and B. The data ranges in cells E5:F7 must be modified in order to compute the sample means, sample sizes, and sample standard deviations for the new data. After doing so the point estimate and a 95% confidence interval will be displayed in cells E18:E20. If a confidence interval with a different confidence coefficient is desired, we simply change the value in cell E12.

We can further simplify the use of Figure 10.5 as a template for other problems by eliminating the need to enter new data ranges in cells E5:F7. We rewrite the cell formulas as follows:

Cell E5: =COUNT(A:A)
Cell F5: =COUNT(B:B)
Cell E6: =AVERAGE(A:A)
Cell F6: =AVERAGE(B:B)
Cell E7: =STDEV(A:A)
Cell F7: =STDEV(B:B)

The CheckAcct data set includes a worksheet titled Template that uses the A:A and B:B methods for entering the data ranges.

Using the A:A method of specifying data ranges in cells E5:F7, Excel's COUNT function will count the number of numeric values in column A, Excel's AVERAGE function will compute the average of the numeric values in column A, and Excel's STDEV function will compute the standard deviation of the numeric values in column A. Similarly, using the B:B method of specifying data ranges in cells F5:F7, Excel's COUNT function will count the number of numeric values in column B, Excel's AVERAGE function will compute the average of the numeric values in column B, and Excel's STDEV function will compute the standard deviation of the numeric values in column B. Thus, to solve a new problem it is only necessary to enter the new data into columns A and B.

This worksheet can also be used as a template for text exercises in which the sample sizes, sample means, and sample standard deviations are given. In this type of situation, no change in the data is necessary. We simply replace the values in cells E5:F7 with the given values of the sample sizes, sample means, and sample standard deviations. If something other than a 95% confidence interval is desired, the confidence coefficient in cell E12 must also be changed.

Hypothesis Tests About $\mu_1 - \mu_2$

Let us now consider hypothesis tests about the difference between the means of two populations when the population standard deviations σ_1 and σ_2 are unknown. Letting D_0 denote the hypothesized difference between μ_1 and μ_2, Section 10.1 showed that the test statistic used for the case where σ_1 and σ_2 are known is as follows.

$$z = \frac{(\bar{x}_1 - \bar{x}_2) - D_0}{\sqrt{\dfrac{\sigma_1^2}{n_1} + \dfrac{\sigma_2^2}{n_2}}}$$

The test statistic, z, follows the standard normal distribution.

When σ_1 and σ_2 are unknown, we use s_1 as an estimator of σ_1 and s_2 as an estimator of σ_2. Substituting these sample standard deviations for σ_1 and σ_2 provides the following test statistic when σ_1 and σ_2 are unknown.

TEST STATISTIC FOR HYPOTHESIS TESTS ABOUT $\mu_1 - \mu_2$: σ_1 AND σ_2 UNKNOWN

$$t = \frac{(\bar{x}_1 - \bar{x}_2) - D_0}{\sqrt{\dfrac{s_1^2}{n_1} + \dfrac{s_2^2}{n_2}}} \tag{10.8}$$

The degrees of freedom for t are given by equation (10.7).

Let us demonstrate the use of this test statistic in the following hypothesis testing example.

Consider a new computer software package developed to help systems analysts reduce the time required to design, develop, and implement an information system. To evaluate the benefits of the new software package, a random sample of 24 systems analysts is selected. Each analyst is given specifications for a hypothetical information system. Then 12 of the analysts are instructed to produce the information system by using current technology. The other 12 analysts are trained in the use of the new software package and then instructed to use it to produce the information system.

This study involves two populations: a population of systems analysts using the current technology and a population of systems analysts using the new software package. In terms of the time required to complete the information system design project, the population means are as follow.

μ_1 = the mean project completion time for systems analysts using the current technology

μ_2 = the mean project completion time for systems analysts using the new software package

The researcher in charge of the new software evaluation project hopes to show that the new software package will provide a shorter mean project completion time. Thus, the researcher is looking for evidence to conclude that μ_2 is less than μ_1; in this case, the difference between the two population means, $\mu_1 - \mu_2$, will be greater than zero. The research hypothesis $\mu_1 - \mu_2 > 0$ is stated as the alternative hypothesis. Thus, the hypothesis test becomes

$$H_0\colon \mu_1 - \mu_2 \leq 0$$
$$H_a\colon \mu_1 - \mu_2 > 0$$

We will use $\alpha = .05$ as the level of significance.

Suppose that the 24 analysts complete the study with the results shown in Table 10.1. Using the test statistic in equation (10.8), we have

$$t = \frac{(\bar{x}_1 - \bar{x}_2) - D_0}{\sqrt{\dfrac{s_1^2}{n_1} + \dfrac{s_2^2}{n_2}}} = \frac{(325 - 286) - 0}{\sqrt{\dfrac{40^2}{12} + \dfrac{44^2}{12}}} = 2.27$$

TABLE 10.1   COMPLETION TIME DATA AND SUMMARY STATISTICS FOR THE SOFTWARE TESTING STUDY

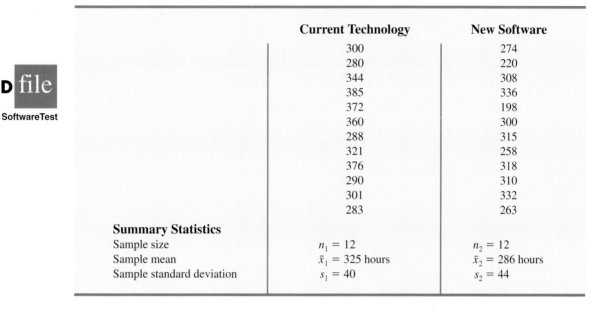

	Current Technology	New Software
	300	274
	280	220
	344	308
	385	336
	372	198
	360	300
	288	315
	321	258
	376	318
	290	310
	301	332
	283	263
Summary Statistics		
Sample size	$n_1 = 12$	$n_2 = 12$
Sample mean	$\bar{x}_1 = 325$ hours	$\bar{x}_2 = 286$ hours
Sample standard deviation	$s_1 = 40$	$s_2 = 44$

CD file

SoftwareTest

Computing the degrees of freedom using equation (10.7), we have

$$df = \frac{\left(\dfrac{s_1^2}{n_1} + \dfrac{s_2^2}{n_2}\right)^2}{\dfrac{1}{n_1 - 1}\left(\dfrac{s_1^2}{n_1}\right)^2 + \dfrac{1}{n_2 - 1}\left(\dfrac{s_2^2}{n_2}\right)^2} = \frac{\left(\dfrac{40^2}{12} + \dfrac{44^2}{12}\right)^2}{\dfrac{1}{12 - 1}\left(\dfrac{40^2}{12}\right)^2 + \dfrac{1}{12 - 1}\left(\dfrac{44^2}{12}\right)^2} = 21.8$$

Rounding down, we will use a t distribution with 21 degrees of freedom. This row of the t distribution table is as follows:

Area in Upper Tail	.20	.10	.05	.025	.01	.005
t Value (21 df)	.859	1.323	1.721	2.080	2.518	2.831

$t = 2.27$

Using the t distribution table, we can only determine a range for the p-value. Use of Excel shows the p-value = .0166.

With an upper tail test, the p-value is the area in the upper tail to the right of $t = 2.27$. From the preceding results, we see that the p-value is between .025 and .01. Thus, the p-value is less than $\alpha = .05$ and H_0 is rejected. The sample results enable the researcher to conclude that $\mu_1 - \mu_2 > 0$, or $\mu_2 < \mu_1$. Thus, the research study supports the conclusion that the new software package provides a smaller population mean completion time.

Using Excel to Conduct a Hypothesis Test

The Excel procedure used to conduct a hypothesis test to determine whether there is a significant difference in population means when the population standard deviations are unknown is called *t-test: Two-Sample Assuming Unequal Variances*. We illustrate this procedure using the sample data for the software evaluation study. Twelve systems analysts developed an information system using current technology, and 12 systems analysts developed an information system using a new software package. A one-tailed hypothesis test is to be conducted to see whether the mean completion time is shorter using the new software package.

Refer to the Excel worksheet shown in Figure 10.6 and the dialog box in Figure 10.7 as we describe the tasks involved.

Enter Data: Column A contains the completion time data for the simple random sample of 12 individuals using the current technology, and column B contains the completion time data for the simple random sample of 12 individuals using the new software.

Apply Tools: The following steps will provide the information needed to conduct the hypothesis test to see whether there is a significant difference in favor of the new software.

  Step 1. Select the **Tools** menu
  Step 2. Choose **Data Analysis**
  Step 3. Choose **t-Test: Two-Sample Assuming Unequal Variances** from the list of Analysis Tools
  Step 4. When the *t*-Test: Two-Sample Assuming Unequal Variances dialog box appears (see Figure 10.7):
        Enter A1:A13 in the **Variable 1 Range** box
        Enter B1:B13 in the **Variable 2 Range** box
        Enter 0 in the **Hypothesized Means Difference** box
        Select **Labels**
        Enter .05 in the **Alpha** box
        Select **Output Range** and enter D1 in the box
        Click **OK**

Descriptive statistics for the two samples are shown in cells E4:F6. The value of the test statistic, 2.2721, is shown in cell E9. The *p*-value for the test, labeled P(T<=t) one-tail, is shown in cell E10. Because the *p*-value, 0.0166, is less than the level of significance $\alpha =$ .05, we can conclude that the mean completion time for the population using the new software package is smaller.

The *t*-test: Two-Sample Assuming Unequal Variances can also be used to conduct two-tailed hypothesis tests. The only change required to make the hypothesis testing decision is that we need to use the *p*-value for a two-tailed test, labeled P(T<=t) two-tail (see cell E12).

FIGURE 10.6 USING EXCEL TO CONDUCT A HYPOTHESIS TEST ABOUT EQUALITY OF MEAN PROJECT COMPLETION TIMES

	A	B	C	D	E	F	G
1	Current	New		t-Test: Two-Sample Assuming Unequal Variances			
2	300	274					
3	280	220			*Current*	*New*	
4	344	308		**Mean**	325	286	
5	385	336		**Variance**	1599.6364	1935.8182	
6	372	198		**Observations**	12	12	
7	360	300		**Hypothesized Mean Difference**	0		
8	288	315		df	22		
9	321	258		t Stat	2.2721		
10	376	318		P(T<=t) one-tail	0.0166		
11	290	310		t Critical one-tail	1.7171		
12	301	332		P(T<=t) two-tail	0.0332		
13	283	263		t Critical two-tail	2.0739		
14							

FIGURE 10.7 DIALOG BOX FOR EXCEL'S t-TEST: TWO-SAMPLE ASSUMING UNEQUAL VARIANCES

Practical Advice

The interval estimation and hypothesis testing procedures presented in this section are robust and can be used with relatively small sample sizes. In most applications, sample sizes that are equal or nearly equal and result in a total sample size of $n_1 + n_2 \geq 20$ will provide very good results even if the populations are not normal. However, larger sample sizes are recommended if the distributions of the populations are highly skewed or contain outliers. Smaller sample sizes should only be used if the analyst is satisfied that the distributions of the populations are at least approximately normal.

NOTES AND COMMENTS

Another approach used to make inferences about the difference between two population means when σ_1 and σ_2 are unknown is based on the assumption that the two population standard deviations are *equal* ($\sigma_1 = \sigma_2 = \sigma$). Under this assumption, the two sample standard deviations are combined to provide the following *pooled sample variance:*

$$s_p^2 = \frac{(n_1 - 1)s_1^2 + (n_2 - 1)s_2^2}{n_1 + n_2 - 2}$$

The t test statistic becomes

$$t = \frac{(\bar{x}_1 - \bar{x}_2) - D_0}{s_p \sqrt{\dfrac{1}{n_1} + \dfrac{1}{n_2}}}$$

and has $n_1 + n_2 - 2$ degrees of freedom. At this point, the computation of the p-value and the interpretation of the sample results are identical to the procedures discussed earlier in this section.

A difficulty with this procedure is that the assumption that the two population standard deviations are equal is usually difficult to verify. Unequal population standard deviations are frequently encountered. Using the pooled procedure may not provide satisfactory results especially if the sample sizes n_1 and n_2 are quite different.

The t procedure that we presented in this section does not require the assumption of equal population standard deviations and can be applied whether the population standard deviations are equal or not. It is a more general procedure and is recommended for most applications.

Exercises

Methods

9. The following results are for independent random samples taken from two populations.

Sample 1	Sample 2
$n_1 = 20$	$n_2 = 30$
$\bar{x}_1 = 22.5$	$\bar{x}_2 = 20.1$
$s_1 = 2.5$	$s_2 = 4.8$

   a. What is the point estimate of the difference between the two population means?
   b. What is the degrees of freedom for the t distribution?
   c. At 95% confidence, what is the margin of error?
   d. What is the 95% confidence interval for the difference between the two popula-
      tion means?

10. Consider the following hypothesis test.

$$H_0: \mu_1 - \mu_2 = 0$$
$$H_a: \mu_1 - \mu_2 \neq 0$$

The following results are from independent samples taken from two populations.

Sample 1	Sample 2
$n_1 = 35$	$n_2 = 40$
$\bar{x}_1 = 13.6$	$\bar{x}_2 = 10.1$
$s_1 = 5.2$	$s_2 = 8.5$

   a. What is the value of the test statistic?
   b. What is the value of the degrees of freedom for the t distribution?
   c. What is the p-value?
   d. At $\alpha = .05$, what is your conclusion?

11. Consider the following data for two independent random samples taken from two normal
    populations.

Sample 1	10	7	13	7	9	8
Sample 2	8	7	8	4	6	9

   a. Compute the two sample means.
   b. Compute the two sample standard deviations.
   c. What is the point estimate of the difference between the two population means?
   d. What is the 90% confidence interval estimate of the difference between the two popu-
      lation means?

Applications

12. The U.S. Department of Transportation provides the number of miles that residents of the
    75 largest metropolitan areas travel per day in a car. Suppose that for a simple random
    sample of 50 Buffalo residents the mean is 22.5 miles a day and the standard deviation is
    8.4 miles a day, and for an independent simple random sample of 40 Boston residents the
    mean is 18.6 miles a day and the standard deviation is 7.4 miles a day.

a.   What is the point estimate of the difference between the mean number of miles that Buffalo residents travel per day and the mean number of miles that Boston residents travel per day?
b.   What is the 95% confidence interval for the difference between the two population means?

CD file

Cargo

13.   FedEx and United Parcel Service (UPS) are the world's two leading cargo carriers by volume and revenue (*The Wall Street Journal,* January 27, 2004). According to the Airports Council International, the Memphis International Airport (FedEx) and the Louisville International Airport (UPS) are two of the ten largest cargo airports in the world. The following random samples show the tons of cargo per day handled by these airports. Data are in thousands of tons.

Memphis

9.1	15.1	8.8	10.0	7.5	10.5
8.3	9.1	6.0	5.8	12.1	9.3

Louisville

4.7	5.0	4.2	3.3	5.5
2.2	4.1	2.6	3.4	7.0

a.   Compute the sample mean and sample standard deviation for each airport.
b.   What is the point estimate of the difference between the two population means? Interpret this value in terms of the higher-volume airport and a comparison of the volume difference between the two airports.
c.   Develop a 95% confidence interval of the difference between the daily population means for the two airports.

14.   Coastal areas of the United States including Cape Cod, the Outer Banks, the Carolinas, and the Gulf Coast had relatively high population growth rates during the 1990s. Data were collected on residents living in the coastal communities as well as on residents living in noncoastal areas throughout the United States (*USA Today,* July 21, 2000). Assume that the following sample results were obtained on the ages of individuals in the two populations:

Coastal Areas	**Noncoastal Areas**
$n_1 = 150$	$n_2 = 175$
$\bar{x}_1 = 39.3$ years	$\bar{x}_2 = 35.4$ years
$s_1 = 16.8$ years	$s_2 = 15.2$ years

Test the hypothesis of no difference between the two population means. Use $\alpha = .05$.
a.   Formulate the null and alternative hypotheses.
b.   What is the value of the test statistic?
c.   What is the *p*-value?
d.   What is your conclusion?

15.   Injuries to Major League Baseball players have been increasing in recent years. For the period 1992 to 2001, league expansion caused Major League Baseball rosters to increase 15%. However, the number of players being put on the disabled list due to injury increased 32% over the same period (*USA Today,* July 8, 2002). A research question addressed whether Major League Baseball players being put on the disabled list are on the list longer in 2001 than players put on the disabled list a decade earlier.

a. Using the population mean number of days a player is on the disabled list, formulate null and alternative hypotheses that can be used to test the research question.
b. Assume that the following data apply:

	2001 Season	1992 Season
Sample size	$n_1 = 45$	$n_2 = 38$
Sample mean	$\bar{x}_1 = 60$ days	$\bar{x}_2 = 51$ days
Sample standard deviation	$s_1 = 18$ days	$s_2 = 15$ days

What is the point estimate of the difference between population mean number of days on the disabled list for 2001 compared to 1992? What is the percentage increase in the number of days on the disabled list?

c. Use $\alpha = .01$. What is your conclusion about the number of days on the disabled list? What is the p-value?
d. Do these data suggest that Major League Baseball should be concerned about the situation?

SATVerbal

16. The College Board provided comparisons of Scholastic Aptitude Test (SAT) scores based on the highest level of education attained by the test taker's parents. A research hypothesis was that students whose parents had attained a higher level of education would on average score higher on the SAT. During 2003, the overall mean SAT verbal score was 507 (*The World Almanac 2004*). SAT verbal scores for independent samples of students follow. The first sample shows the SAT verbal test scores for students whose parents are college graduates with a bachelor's degree. The second sample shows the SAT verbal test scores for students whose parents are high school graduates but do not have a college degree.

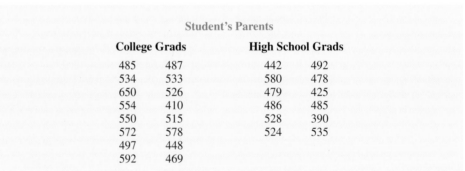

Student's Parents			
College Grads		High School Grads	
485	487	442	492
534	533	580	478
650	526	479	425
554	410	486	485
550	515	528	390
572	578	524	535
497	448		
592	469		

a. Formulate the hypotheses that can be used to determine whether the sample data support the hypothesis that students show a higher population mean verbal score on the SAT if their parents attained a higher level of education.
b. What is the point estimate of the difference between the means for the two populations?
c. Compute the p-value for the hypothesis test.
d. At $\alpha = .05$, what is your conclusion?

17. Periodically, Merrill Lynch customers are asked to evaluate Merrill Lynch financial consultants and services (2000 Merrill Lynch Client Satisfaction Survey). Higher ratings on the client satisfaction survey indicate better service with 7 the maximum service rating. Independent samples of service ratings for two financial consultants are summarized here. Consultant A has 10 years of experience, whereas consultant B has 1 year of experience. Use $\alpha = .05$ and test to see whether the consultant with more experience has the higher population mean service rating.

Consultant A	Consultant B
$n_1 = 16$	$n_2 = 10$
$\bar{x}_1 = 6.82$	$\bar{x}_2 = 6.25$
$s_1 = .64$	$s_2 = .75$

    a.   State the null and alternative hypotheses.
    b.   Compute the value of the test statistic.
    c.   What is the p-value?
    d.   What is your conclusion?

SAT

18. Educational test preparation companies provide tutoring, classroom learning, and practice tests in an effort to help students perform better on tests such as the Scholastic Aptitude Test (SAT). The test preparation companies claim that their courses will improve SAT score performances by an average of 120 points (*The Wall Street Journal,* January 23, 2003). A researcher is uncertain of this claim and believes that 120 points may be an overstatement in an effort to encourage students to take a test preparation course. In an evaluation study of one test preparation service, the researcher collects SAT score data for 35 students who took the test preparation course and 48 students who did not take the course. The CD file named SAT contains the scores for this study.

    a.   Formulate the hypotheses that can be used to test the researcher's belief that the improvement in SAT scores may be less than the stated average of 120 points.
    b.   Using $\alpha = .05$, what is your conclusion?
    c.   What is the point estimate of the improvement in the average SAT scores provided by the test preparation course? Provide a 95% confidence interval estimate of the improvement.
    d.   What advice would you have for the researcher after seeing the confidence interval?

(10.3) Inferences About the Difference Between Two Population Means: Matched Samples

Suppose employees at a manufacturing company can use two different methods to perform a production task. To maximize production output, the company wants to identify the method with the shorter population mean completion time. Let μ_1 denote the population mean completion time for production method 1 and μ_2 denote the population mean completion time for production method 2. With no preliminary indication of the preferred production method, we begin by tentatively assuming that the two production methods have the same population mean completion time. Thus, the null hypothesis is $H_0: \mu_1 - \mu_2 = 0$. If this hypothesis is rejected, we can conclude that the population mean completion times differ. In this case, the method providing the shorter mean completion time would be recommended. The null and alternative hypotheses are written as follows.

$$H_0: \mu_1 - \mu_2 = 0$$
$$H_a: \mu_1 - \mu_2 \neq 0$$

In choosing the sampling procedure that will be used to collect production time data and test the hypotheses, we consider two alternative designs. One is based on **independent samples** and the other is based on **matched samples**.

    1. *Independent sample design:* A simple random sample of workers is selected and each worker in the sample uses method 1. A second independent simple random sample of workers is selected and each worker in this sample uses method 2. The test of the difference between population means is based on the procedures in Section 10.2.

2. *Matched sample design:* One simple random sample of workers is selected. Each worker first uses one method and then uses the other method. The order of the two methods is assigned randomly to the workers, with some workers performing method 1 first and others performing method 2 first. Each worker provides a pair of data values, one value for method 1 and another value for method 2.

In the matched sample design the two production methods are tested under similar conditions (i.e., with the same workers); hence this design often leads to a smaller sampling error than the independent sample design. The primary reason is that in a matched sample design, variation between workers is eliminated because the same workers are used for both production methods.

Let us demonstrate the analysis of a matched sample design by assuming it is the method used to test the difference between population means for the two production methods. A random sample of six workers is used. The data on completion times for the six workers are given in Table 10.2. Note that each worker provides a pair of data values, one for each production method. Also note that the last column contains the difference in completion times d_i for each worker in the sample.

The key to the analysis of the matched sample design is to realize that we consider only the column of differences. Therefore, we have six data values (.6, −.2, .5, .3, .0, and .6) that will be used to analyze the difference between population means of the two production methods.

Let μ_d = the mean of the *difference* values for the population of workers. With this notation, the null and alternative hypotheses are rewritten as follows.

$$H_0\colon \mu_d = 0$$
$$H_a\colon \mu_d \neq 0$$

If H_0 is rejected, we can conclude that the population mean completion times differ.

The d notation is a reminder that the matched sample provides *difference* data. The sample mean and sample standard deviation for the six difference values in Table 10.2 follow.

Other than the use of the d notation, the formulas for the sample mean and sample standard deviation are the same ones used previously in the text.

$$\bar{d} = \frac{\Sigma d_i}{n} = \frac{1.8}{6} = .30$$

$$s_d = \sqrt{\frac{\Sigma(d_i - \bar{d})^2}{n - 1}} = \sqrt{\frac{.56}{5}} = .3347$$

With the small sample of $n = 6$ workers, we need to make the assumption that the population of differences has a normal distribution. This assumption is necessary so that we may

TABLE 10.2   TASK COMPLETION TIMES FOR A MATCHED SAMPLE DESIGN

Worker	Completion Time for Method 1 (minutes)	Completion Time for Method 2 (minutes)	Difference in Completion Times (d_i)
1	6.0	5.4	.6
2	5.0	5.2	−.2
3	7.0	6.5	.5
4	6.2	5.9	.3
5	6.0	6.0	.0
6	6.4	5.8	.6

It is not necessary to make the assumption that the population has a normal distribution if the sample size is large. Sample size guidelines for using the t distribution were presented in Chapters 8 and 9.

use the *t* distribution for hypothesis testing and interval estimation procedures. Based on this assumption, the following test statistic has a *t* distribution with $n - 1$ degrees of freedom.

TEST STATISTIC FOR HYPOTHESIS TESTS INVOLVING MATCHED SAMPLES

$$t = \frac{\bar{d} - \mu_d}{s_d/\sqrt{n}} \qquad (10.9)$$

Once the difference data are computed, the t distribution procedure for matched samples is the same as the one-population estimation and hypothesis testing procedures described in Chapters 8 and 9.

Let us use equation (10.9) to test the hypotheses $H_0: \mu_d = 0$ and $H_a: \mu_d \neq 0$, using $\alpha = .05$. Substituting the sample results $\bar{d} = .30$, $s_d = .3347$, and $n = 6$ into equation (10.9), we compute the value of the test statistic.

$$t = \frac{\bar{d} - \mu_d}{s_d/\sqrt{n}} = \frac{.30 - 0}{.3347/\sqrt{6}} = 2.20$$

Now let us compute the *p*-value for this two-tailed test. Because $t = 2.20 > 0$, the test statistic is in the upper tail of the *t* distribution. With $t = 2.20$, the area in the upper tail to the right of the test statistic can be found by using the *t* distribution table with degrees of freedom $= n - 1 = 6 - 1 = 5$. Information from the 5 degrees of freedom row of the *t* distribution table is as follows:

Area in Upper Tail	.20	.10	.05	.025	.01	.005
t Value (5 df)	0.920	1.476	2.015	2.571	3.365	4.032

$$t = 2.20$$

Thus, we see that the area in the upper tail is between .05 and .025. Because this test is a two-tailed test, we double these values to conclude that the *p*-value is between .10 and .05. This *p*-value is greater than $\alpha = .05$. Thus, the null hypothesis $H_0: \mu_d = 0$ is not rejected. Using Excel and the data in Table 10.2, we find the *p*-value $= .0795$.

We can also obtain an interval estimate of the difference between the two population means by using the single population methodology of Chapter 8. At 95% confidence, the calculation follows.

$$\bar{d} \pm t_{.025} \frac{s_d}{\sqrt{n}}$$

$$.3 \pm 2.571 \left(\frac{.3347}{\sqrt{6}} \right)$$

$$.3 \pm .35$$

Thus, the margin of error is .35 and the 95% confidence interval for the difference between the population means of the two production methods is $-.05$ minutes to .65 minutes.

Using Excel to Conduct a Hypothesis Test

Excel's t-Test: Paired Two Sample for Means tool can be used to conduct a hypothesis test about the difference between the population means when a matched sample design is used. We illustrate by conducting the hypothesis test involving the two production methods. Refer to the Excel worksheet shown in Figure 10.8 and the dialog box in Figure 10.9 as we describe the tasks involved.

FIGURE 10.8   USING EXCEL FOR A HYPOTHESIS TEST IN THE MATCHED SAMPLES STUDY

	A	B	C	D	E	F	G	H
1	Worker	Method 1	Method 2		t-Test: Paired Two Sample for Means			
2	1	6	5.4					
3	2	5	5.2			*Method 1*	*Method 2*	
4	3	7	6.5		**Mean**	6.1	5.8	
5	4	6.2	5.9		**Variance**	0.428	0.212	
6	5	6	6		**Observations**	6	6	
7	6	6.4	5.8		**Pearson Correlation**	0.8764		
8					**Hypothesized Mean Difference**	0		
9					**df**	5		
10					**t Stat**	2.196		
11					**P(T<=t) one-tail**	0.0398		
12					**t Critical one-tail**	2.015		
13					**P(T<=t) two-tail**	0.0795		
14					**t Critical two-tail**	2.571		
15								

Enter Data: Column A is used to identify each of the six workers who participated in the study. Column B contains the completion time data for each worker using method 1, and column C contains the completion time data for each worker using method 2.

Apply Tools: The following steps describe how to use Excel's t-Test: Paired Two Sample for Means tool to conduct the hypothesis test about the difference between the means of the two production methods

Step 1. Select the **Tools** menu
Step 2. Choose the **Data Analysis** option
Step 3. Choose **t-Test: Paired Two Sample for Means** from the list of Analysis Tools

FIGURE 10.9   DIALOG BOX FOR EXCEL'S t-TEST: PAIRED TWO SAMPLE FOR MEANS

Step 4. When the t-Test: Paired Two Sample for Means dialog box appears (see Figure 10.9):

Enter B1:B7 in the **Variable 1 Range** box
Enter C1:C7 in the **Variable 2 Range** box
Enter 0 in the **Hypothesized Mean Difference** box
Select **Labels**
Enter .05 in the **Alpha** box
Select **Output Range**
Enter E1 in the **Output Range** box (to identify the upper left corner of the section of the worksheet where the output will appear)
Click **OK**

The results are shown in cells E1:G14 of the worksheet shown in Figure 10.8. The *p*-value for the test, labeled P(T<= t) two-tail, is shown in cell F13. Because the *p*-value, 0.0795, is greater than the level of significance $\alpha = .05$, we cannot reject the null hypothesis that the mean completion times are equal.

The same procedure can also be used to conduct one-tailed hypothesis tests. The only change required to make the hypothesis testing decision is that we need to use the *p*-value for a one-tailed test, labeled P(T<= t) one-tail (see cell F11).

NOTES AND COMMENTS

1. In the example presented in this section, workers performed the production task with first one method and then the other method. This example illustrates a matched sample design in which each sampled element (worker) provides a pair of data values. It is also possible to use different but "similar" elements to provide the pair of data values. For example, a worker at one location could be matched with a similar worker at another location (similarity based on age, education, gender, experience, etc.). The pairs of workers would provide the difference data that could be used in the matched sample analysis.

2. A matched sample procedure for inferences about two population means generally provides better precision than the independent sample approach; therefore, it is the recommended design. However, in some applications the matching cannot be achieved, or perhaps the time and cost associated with matching are excessive. In such cases, the independent sample design should be used.

Exercises

Methods

19. Consider the following hypothesis test.

$$H_0: \mu_d \le 0$$
$$H_a: \mu_d > 0$$

The following data are from matched samples taken from two populations.

	Population	
Element	**1**	**2**
1	21	20
2	28	26
3	18	18
4	20	20
5	26	24

    a.   Compute the difference value for each element.
    b.   Compute $\bar{d}$.
    c.   Compute the standard deviation s_d.
    d.   Conduct a hypothesis test using $\alpha = .05$. What is your conclusion?

20.   The following data are from matched samples taken from two populations.

	Population	
Element	1	2
1	11	8
2	7	8
3	9	6
4	12	7
5	13	10
6	15	15
7	15	14

    a.   Compute the difference value for each element.
    b.   Compute $\bar{d}$.
    c.   Compute the standard deviation s_d.
    d.   What is the point estimate of the difference between the two population means?
    e.   Provide a 95% confidence interval for the difference between the two population means.

Applications

21.   A market research firm used a sample of individuals to rate the purchase potential of a particular product before and after the individuals saw a new television commercial about the product. The purchase potential ratings were based on a 0 to 10 scale, with higher values indicating a higher purchase potential. The null hypothesis stated that the mean rating "after" would be less than or equal to the mean rating "before." Rejection of this hypothesis would show that the commercial improved the mean purchase potential rating. Use $\alpha = .05$ and the following data to test the hypothesis and comment on the value of the commercial.

	Purchase Rating			Purchase Rating	
Individual	After	Before	Individual	After	Before
1	6	5	5	3	5
2	6	4	6	9	8
3	7	7	7	7	5
4	4	3	8	6	6

22.   A sample of 10 international telephone calls provided Sprint and WorldCom calling rates per minute for calls from the United States (*World Traveler*, July 2000).

Country	Sprint	WorldCom	Country	Sprint	WorldCom
Australia	.46	.26	France	.46	.26
Belgium	.69	.40	Germany	.46	.26
Brazil	.92	.53	Hong Kong	.92	.40
Colombia	.55	.53	Japan	.69	.40
Denmark	.50	.26	United Kingdom	.46	.26

    Provide a 95% confidence interval estimate of the difference between the two population means.

23. Bank of America's Consumer Spending Survey collected data on annual credit card charges in seven different categories of expenditures: transportation, groceries, dining out, household expenses, home furnishings, apparel, and entertainment (*U.S. Airways Attaché*, December 2003). Using data from a sample of 42 credit card accounts, assume that each account was used to identify the annual credit card charges for groceries (population 1) and the annual credit card charges for dining out (population 2). Using the difference data, the sample mean difference was $\bar{d} = \$850$, and the sample standard deviation was $s_d = \$1123$.

   a. Formulate the null and alternative hypotheses to test for no difference between the population mean credit card charges for groceries and the population mean credit card charges for dining out.

   b. Use a .05 level of significance. Can you conclude that the population means differ? What is the *p*-value?

   c. Which category, groceries or dining out, has a higher population mean annual credit card charge? What is the point estimate of the difference between the population means? What is the 95% confidence interval estimate of the difference between the population means?

24. Rental car gasoline prices per gallon were sampled at eight major airports. Data for Hertz and National car rental companies follow (*USA Today*, April 4, 2000).

Airport	Hertz	National	Airport	Hertz	National
Boston Logan	1.55	1.56	New York (JFK)	1.72	1.51
Chicago O'Hare	1.62	1.59	New York (LaGuardia)	1.67	1.50
Los Angeles	1.72	1.78	Orange County, CA	1.68	1.77
Miami	1.65	1.49	Washington (Dulles)	1.52	1.41

   Use $\alpha = .05$ to test the hypothesis of no difference between the population mean prices per gallon for the two companies.

25. In recent years, a growing array of entertainment options competes for consumer time. By 2004, cable television and radio surpassed broadcast television, recorded music, and the daily newspaper to become the two entertainment media with the greatest usage (*The Wall Street Journal*, January 26, 2004). Researchers used a sample of 15 individuals and collected data on the hours per week spent watching cable television and hours per week spent listening to the radio.

CD file
TVRadio

Individual	Television	Radio	Individual	Television	Radio
1	22	25	9	21	21
2	8	10	10	23	23
3	25	29	11	14	15
4	22	19	12	14	18
5	12	13	13	14	17
6	26	28	14	16	15
7	22	23	15	24	23
8	19	21			

   a. Use a .05 level of significance and test for a difference between the population mean usage for cable television and radio. What is the *p*-value?

   b. What is the sample mean number of hours per week spent watching cable television? What is the sample mean number of hours per week spent listening to radio? Which medium has the greater usage?

26. StreetInsider.com reported 2002 earnings per share data for a sample of major companies (February 12, 2003). Prior to 2002, financial analysts predicted the 2002 earnings per share for these same companies (*Barron's*, September 10, 2001). Use the following data to comment on differences between actual and estimated earnings per share.

Earnings

Company	Actual	Predicted
AT&T	1.29	0.38
American Express	2.01	2.31
Citigroup	2.59	3.43
Coca-Cola	1.60	1.78
DuPont	1.84	2.18
Exxon-Mobil	2.72	2.19
General Electric	1.51	1.71
Johnson & Johnson	2.28	2.18
McDonald's	0.77	1.55
Wal-Mart	1.81	1.74

a. Use $\alpha = .05$ and test for any difference between the population mean actual and population mean predicted earnings per share. What is the p-value? What is your conclusion?

b. What is the point estimate of the difference between the two means? Did the analysts tend to underestimate or overestimate the earnings?

c. At 95% confidence, what is the margin of error for the estimate in part (b)? What would you recommend based on this information?

10.4   Introduction to Analysis of Variance

National Computer Products, Inc. (NCP), manufactures printers and fax machines at plants located in Atlanta, Dallas, and Seattle. To measure how much employees at these plants know about the concept of total quality, a random sample of six employees was selected from each plant and given a quality awareness examination. The examination scores obtained for these 18 employees are listed in Table 10.3. The sample means, sample variances, and sample standard deviations for each group are also provided. Managers want to use these data to test the hypothesis that the mean examination score is the same for all three plants.

We will define population 1 as all employees at the Atlanta plant, population 2 as all employees at the Dallas plant, and population 3 as all employees at the Seattle plant. Let

$$\mu_1 = \text{mean examination score for population 1}$$
$$\mu_2 = \text{mean examination score for population 2}$$
$$\mu_3 = \text{mean examination score for population 3}$$

Although we will never know the actual values of μ_1, μ_2, and μ_3, we want to use the sample results to test the following hypotheses.

If H_0 is rejected, we cannot conclude that all population means are different. Rejecting H_0 means that at least two population means have different values.

$$H_0: \mu_1 = \mu_2 = \mu_3$$
$$H_a: \text{Not all population means are equal}$$

As we will demonstrate shortly, **analysis of variance** is a statistical procedure that can be used to determine whether the observed differences in the three sample means are large enough to reject H_0.

TABLE 10.3 EXAMINATION SCORES FOR 18 EMPLOYEES

Employee	Plant 1 Atlanta	Plant 2 Dallas	Plant 3 Seattle
1	85	71	59
2	75	75	64
3	82	73	62
4	76	74	69
5	71	69	75
6	85	82	67
Sample mean	79	74	66
Sample variance	34	20	32
Sample standard deviation	5.83	4.47	5.66

CD file

NCP

Analysis of variance can be used to analyze data obtained from both an observational study and an experimental study. In order to provide a common set of terminology for discussing the use of analysis of variance in both types of studies, we need to introduce the concepts of a response variable, a factor, and a treatment.

The two variables in the NCP example are plant location and score on the quality awareness examination. Because the objective is to determine whether the mean examination score is the same for plants located in Atlanta, Dallas, and Seattle, examination score is referred to as the dependent or *response variable* and plant location as the independent variable or *factor*. In general, the values of a factor selected for investigation are referred to as levels of the factor or *treatments*. Thus, in the NCP example the three treatments are Atlanta, Dallas, and Seattle. These three treatments define the populations of interest in the NCP example. For each treatment or population, the response variable is the examination score.

Assumptions for Analysis of Variance

Three assumptions are required to use analysis of variance.

If the sample sizes are equal, analysis of variance is not sensitive to departures from the assumption of normally distributed populations.

1. **For each population, the response variable is normally distributed.** Implication: In the NCP example, the examination scores (response variable) must be normally distributed at each plant.
2. **The variance of the response variable, denoted σ^2, is the same for all of the populations.** Implication: In the NCP example, the variance of examination scores must be the same for all three plants.
3. **The observations must be independent.** Implication: In the NCP example, the examination score for each employee must be independent of the examination score for any other employee.

A Conceptual Overview

If the means for the three populations are equal, we would expect the three sample means to be close together. In fact, the closer the three sample means are to one another, the more evidence we have for the conclusion that the population means are equal. Alternatively, the more the sample means differ, the more evidence we have for the conclusion that the population means are not equal. In other words, if the variability among the sample means is "small," it supports H_0; if the variability among the sample means is "large," it supports H_a.

If the null hypothesis, $H_0: \mu_1 = \mu_2 = \mu_3$, is true, we can use the variability among the sample means to develop an estimate of σ^2. First, note that if the assumptions for analysis of variance are satisfied, each sample will have come from the same normal distribution with mean μ and variance σ^2. Recall from Chapter 7 that the sampling distribution of the sample mean $\bar{x}$ for a simple random sample of size n from a normal population will be normally distributed with mean μ and variance σ^2/n. Figure 10.10 illustrates such a sampling distribution.

Thus, if the null hypothesis is true, we can think of each of the three sample means, $\bar{x}_1 = 79$, $\bar{x}_2 = 74$, and $\bar{x}_3 = 66$, from Table 10.3 as values drawn at random from the sampling distribution shown in Figure 10.10. In this case, the mean and variance of the three $\bar{x}$ values can be used to estimate the mean and variance of the sampling distribution. When the sample sizes are equal, as in the NCP example, the best estimate of the mean of the sampling distribution of $\bar{x}$ is the mean or average of the sample means. Thus, in the NCP example, an estimate of the mean of the sampling distribution of $\bar{x}$ is $(79 + 74 + 66)/3 = 73$. We refer to this estimate as the *overall sample mean*. An estimate of the variance of the sampling distribution of $\bar{x}$, $\sigma_{\bar{x}}^2$, is provided by the variance of the three sample means.

$$s_{\bar{x}}^2 = \frac{(79 - 73)^2 + (74 - 73)^2 + (66 - 73)^2}{3 - 1} = \frac{86}{2} = 43$$

Because $\sigma_{\bar{x}}^2 = \sigma^2/n$, solving for σ^2 gives

$$\sigma^2 = n\sigma_{\bar{x}}^2$$

Hence,

$$\text{Estimate of } \sigma^2 = n(\text{Estimate of } \sigma_{\bar{x}}^2) = ns_{\bar{x}}^2 = 6(43) = 258$$

The result, $ns_{\bar{x}}^2 = 258$, is referred to as the *between-treatments* estimate of σ^2.

The between-treatments estimate of σ^2 is based on the assumption that the null hypothesis is true. In this case, each sample comes from the same population, and there is only one sampling distribution of $\bar{x}$. To illustrate what happens when H_0 is false, suppose the population means all differ. Note that because the three samples are from normal popu-

FIGURE 10.10 SAMPLING DISTRIBUTION OF $\bar{x}$ GIVEN H_0 IS TRUE

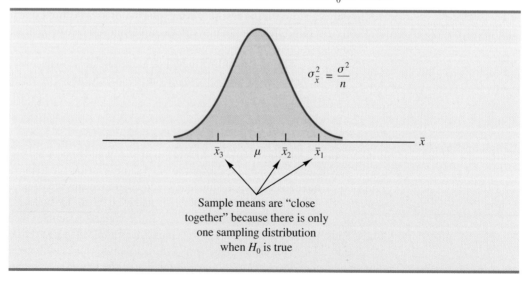

FIGURE 10.11 SAMPLING DISTRIBUTIONS OF $\bar{x}$ GIVEN H_0 IS FALSE

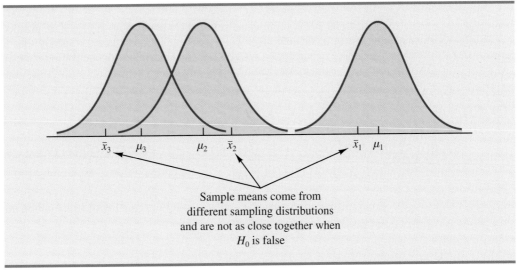

Sample means come from
different sampling distributions
and are not as close together when
H_0 is false

lations with different means, they will result in three different sampling distributions. Figure 10.11 shows that in this case, the sample means are not as close together as they were when H_0 was true. Thus, $\sigma_{\bar{x}}^2$ will be larger, causing the between-treatments estimate of σ^2 to be larger. In general, when the population means are not equal, the between-treatments estimate will overestimate the population variance σ^2.

The variation within each of the samples also has an effect on the conclusion we reach in analysis of variance. When a simple random sample is selected from each population, each of the sample variances provides an unbiased estimate of σ^2. Hence, we can combine or pool the individual estimates of σ^2 into one overall estimate. The estimate of σ^2 obtained in this way is called the *pooled* or *within-treatments* estimate of σ^2. Because each sample variance provides an estimate of σ^2 based only on the variation within each sample, the within-treatments estimate of σ^2 is not affected by whether the population means are equal. When the sample sizes are equal, the within-treatments estimate of σ^2 can be obtained by computing the average of the individual sample variances. For the NCP example we obtain

$$\text{Within-treatments estimate of } \sigma^2 = \frac{34 + 20 + 32}{3} = \frac{86}{3} = 28.67$$

In the NCP example, the between-treatments estimate of σ^2 (258) is much larger than the within-treatments estimate of σ^2 (28.67). In fact, the ratio of these two estimates is $258/28.67 = 9.00$. Recall, however, that the between-treatments approach provides a good estimate of σ^2 only if the null hypothesis is true; if the null hypothesis is false, the between-treatments approach overestimates σ^2. The within-treatments approach provides a good estimate of σ^2 in either case. Thus, if the null hypothesis is true, the two estimates will be similar and their ratio will be close to 1. If the null hypothesis is false, the between-treatments estimate will be larger than the within-treatments estimate, and their ratio will be large. In the next section we will show how large this ratio must be to reject H_0.

In summary, the logic behind ANOVA is based on the development of two independent estimates of the common population variance σ^2. One estimate of σ^2 is based on the variability among the sample means themselves, and the other estimate of σ^2 is based on the variability of the data within each sample. By comparing these two estimates of σ^2, we will be able to determine whether the population means are equal.

NOTES AND COMMENTS

In Sections 10.1 and 10.2 we presented statistical methods for testing the hypothesis that the means of two populations are equal. ANOVA can also be used to test the hypothesis that the means of two populations are equal. In practice, however, analysis of variance is usually not used except when dealing with three or more population means.

 Analysis of Variance: Testing for the Equality of k Population Means

Analysis of variance can be used to test for the equality of k population means. The general form of the hypotheses tested is

$$H_0: \mu_1 = \mu_2 = \cdots = \mu_k$$
$$H_a: \text{Not all population means are equal}$$

where

$$\mu_j = \text{mean of the } j\text{th population}$$

We assume that a simple random sample of size n_j has been selected from each of the k populations or treatments. For the resulting sample data, let

$$x_{ij} = \text{value of observation } i \text{ for treatment } j$$
$$n_j = \text{number of observations for treatment } j$$
$$\bar{x}_j = \text{sample mean for treatment } j$$
$$s_j^2 = \text{sample variance for treatment } j$$
$$s_j = \text{sample standard deviation for treatment } j$$

The formulas for the sample mean and sample variance for treatment j are as follows.

$$\bar{x}_j = \frac{\sum_{i=1}^{n_j} x_{ij}}{n_j} \tag{10.10}$$

$$s_j^2 = \frac{\sum_{i=1}^{n_j} (x_{ij} - \bar{x}_j)^2}{n_j - 1} \tag{10.11}$$

The overall sample mean, denoted $\bar{\bar{x}}$, is the sum of all the observations divided by the total number of observations. That is,

$$\bar{\bar{x}} = \frac{\sum_{j=1}^{k} \sum_{i=1}^{n_j} x_{ij}}{n_T} \tag{10.12}$$

where

$$n_T = n_1 + n_2 + \cdots + n_k \qquad \text{(10.13)}$$

If the size of each sample is n, $n_T = kn$; in this case equation (13.3) reduces to

$$\bar{\bar{x}} = \frac{\displaystyle\sum_{j=1}^{k}\sum_{i=1}^{n_j} x_{ij}}{kn} = \frac{\displaystyle\sum_{j=1}^{k}\sum_{i=1}^{n_j} x_{ij}/n}{k} = \frac{\displaystyle\sum_{j=1}^{k} \bar{x}_j}{k} \qquad \text{(10.14)}$$

In other words, whenever the sample sizes are the same, the overall sample mean is just the average of the k treatment means.

Because each sample in the NCP example consists of $n = 6$ observations, the overall sample mean can be computed by using equation (10.14). For the data in Table 10.3 we obtained the following result.

$$\bar{\bar{x}} = \frac{79 + 74 + 66}{3} = 73$$

If the null hypothesis is true ($\mu_1 = \mu_2 = \mu_3 = \mu$), the overall sample mean of 73 is the best estimate of the population mean μ.

Between-Treatments Estimate of Population Variance

In the preceding section, we introduced the concept of a between-treatments estimate of σ^2 and showed how to compute it when the sample sizes were equal. This estimate of σ^2 is called the *mean square due to treatments* and is denoted MSTR. The general formula for computing MSTR is

$$\text{MSTR} = \frac{\displaystyle\sum_{j=1}^{k} n_j(\bar{x}_j - \bar{\bar{x}})^2}{k - 1} \qquad \text{(10.15)}$$

The numerator in equation (10.15) is called the *sum of squares due to treatments* and is denoted SSTR. The denominator, $k - 1$, represents the degrees of freedom associated with SSTR. Hence, the mean square due to treatments can be computed by the following formula.

MEAN SQUARE DUE TO TREATMENTS

$$\text{MSTR} = \frac{\text{SSTR}}{k - 1} \qquad \text{(10.16)}$$

where

$$\text{SSTR} = \sum_{j=1}^{k} n_j(\bar{x}_j - \bar{\bar{x}})^2 \qquad \text{(10.17)}$$

If H_0 is true, MSTR provides an unbiased estimate of σ^2. However, if the means of the k populations are not equal, MSTR is not an unbiased estimate of σ^2; in fact, in that case, MSTR should overestimate σ^2.

For the NCP data in Table 10.3, we obtain the following results.

$$\text{SSTR} = \sum_{j=1}^{k} n_j(\bar{x}_j - \bar{\bar{x}})^2 = 6(79 - 73)^2 + 6(74 - 73)^2 + 6(66 - 73)^2 = 516$$

$$\text{MSTR} = \frac{\text{SSTR}}{k - 1} = \frac{516}{2} = 258$$

Within-Treatments Estimate of Population Variance

Earlier, we introduced the concept of a within-treatments estimate of σ^2 and showed how to compute it when the sample sizes were equal. This estimate of σ^2 is called the *mean square due to error* and is denoted MSE. The general formula for computing MSE is

$$\text{MSE} = \frac{\sum_{j=1}^{k}(n_j - 1)s_j^2}{n_T - k} \tag{10.18}$$

The numerator in equation (10.18) is called the *sum of squares due to error* and is denoted SSE. The denominator of MSE is referred to as the degrees of freedom associated with SSE. Hence, the formula for MSE can also be stated as follows.

MEAN SQUARE DUE TO ERROR

$$\text{MSE} = \frac{\text{SSE}}{n_T - k} \tag{10.19}$$

where

$$\text{SSE} = \sum_{j=1}^{k}(n_j - 1)s_j^2 \tag{10.20}$$

Note that MSE is based on the variation within each of the treatments; it is not influenced by whether the null hypothesis is true. Thus, MSE always provides an unbiased estimate of σ^2.

For the NCP data in Table 10.3 we obtain the following results.

$$\text{SSE} = \sum_{j=1}^{k}(n_j - 1)s_j^2 = (6 - 1)34 + (6 - 1)20 + (6 - 1)32 = 430$$

$$\text{MSE} = \frac{\text{SSE}}{n_T - k} = \frac{430}{18 - 3} = \frac{430}{15} = 28.67$$

Comparing the Variance Estimates: The F Test

If the null hypothesis is true, MSTR and MSE provide two independent, unbiased estimates of σ^2. When the null hypothesis is true and the ANOVA assumptions are valid, the sampling distribution of MSTR/MSE is an **F distribution** with numerator degrees of freedom equal to $k - 1$ and denominator degrees of freedom equal to $n_T - k$. In other words, if the null hypothesis is true, the value of MSTR/MSE should appear to have been selected from this F distribution. The general shape of this F distribution is shown in Figure 10.12.

If the null hypothesis is false, the value of MSTR/MSE will be inflated because MSTR overestimates σ^2. Hence, we will reject H_0 if the resulting value of MSTR/MSE appears to

FIGURE 10.12   *F* DISTRIBUTION: THE SAMPLING DISTRIBUTION OF MSTR/MSE

be too large (is in the upper tail) to have been selected from an *F* distribution with $k - 1$ numerator degrees of freedom and $n_T - k$ denominator degrees of freedom. Because the decision to reject H_0 is based on the value of MSTR/MSE, the test statistic used to test for the equality of *k* population means is as follows.

TEST STATISTIC FOR THE EQUALITY OF *k* POPULATION MEANS

$$F = \frac{\text{MSTR}}{\text{MSE}} \qquad (10.21)$$

The test statistic follows an *F* distribution with $k - 1$ degrees of freedom in the numerator and $n_T - k$ degrees of freedom in the denominator.

Let us return to the National Computer Products example and use a level of significance $\alpha = .05$ to conduct the hypothesis test. The value of the test statistic is

$$F = \frac{\text{MSTR}}{\text{MSE}} = \frac{258}{28.67} = 9$$

The numerator degrees of freedom is $k - 1 = 3 - 1 = 2$ and the denominator degrees of freedom is $n_T - k = 18 - 3 = 15$. Because we will only reject the null hypothesis for large values of the test statistic, the *p*-value is the upper tail area of the *F* distribution to the right of the test statistic $F = 9$. Figure 10.13 shows the sampling distribution of $F = \text{MSTR/MSE}$, the value of the test statistic, and the upper tail area that is the *p*-value for the hypothesis test.

From Table 4 of Appendix B we find the following areas in the upper tail of an *F* distribution with 2 numerator degrees of freedom and 15 denominator degrees of freedom.

Area in Upper Tail	.10	.05	.025	.01
F Value (df₁ = 2, df₂ = 15)	2.70	3.68	4.77	6.36

$F = 9$

Because $F = 9$ is greater than 6.36, the area in the upper tail at $F = 9$ is less than .01. Thus, the *p*-value is less than .01. Because the *p*-value $\leq \alpha = .05$, H_0 is rejected. The test provides sufficient evidence to conclude that the means of the three populations are not equal.

FIGURE 10.13   COMPUTATION OF *p*-VALUE USING THE SAMPLING DISTRIBUTION OF MSTR/MSE

In other words, analysis of variance supports the conclusion that the population mean examination scores at the three NCP plants are not equal.

Because the *F* table only provides values for upper tail areas of .10, .05, .025, and .01, we cannot determine the exact *p*-value directly from the table. Excel provides the *p*-value as part of the standard ANOVA output. In the subsection "Using Excel" we show that for the NCP example, the exact *p*-value corresponding to the test statistic $F = 9$ is .0027.

Using Excel, p-value = FDIST(9,2,15) = .0027.

As with other hypothesis testing procedures, the critical value approach may also be used. With $\alpha = .05$, the critical *F* value occurs with an area of .05 in the upper tail of an *F* distribution with 2 and 15 degrees of freedom. From the *F* distribution table, we find $F_{.05} = 3.68$. Hence, the appropriate upper tail rejection rule for the NCP example is

$$\text{Reject } H_0 \text{ if } F \geq 3.68$$

With $F = 9$, we reject H_0 and conclude that the means of the three populations are not equal. A summary of the overall procedure for testing for the equality of *k* population means follows.

TEST FOR THE EQUALITY OF *k* POPULATION MEANS

$$H_0: \mu_1 = \mu_2 = \cdots = \mu_k$$
$$H_a: \text{Not all population means are equal}$$

TEST STATISTIC

$$F = \frac{\text{MSTR}}{\text{MSE}}$$

REJECTION RULE

p-value approach:	Reject H_0 if *p*-value $\leq \alpha$
Critical value approach:	Reject H_0 if $F \geq F_\alpha$

where the value of F_α is based on an *F* distribution with $k - 1$ numerator degrees of freedom and $n_T - k$ denominator degrees of freedom.

ANOVA Table

The results of the preceding calculations can be displayed conveniently in a table referred to as the analysis of variance or **ANOVA table**. Table 10.4 is the analysis of variance table for the National Computer Products example. The sum of squares associated with the source of variation referred to as "Total" is called the total sum of squares (SST). Note that the results for the NCP example suggest that SST = SSTR + SSE, and that the degrees of freedom associated with this total sum of squares is the sum of the degrees of freedom associated with the between-treatments estimate of σ^2 and the within-treatments estimate of σ^2.

We point out that SST divided by its degrees of freedom $n_T - 1$ is nothing more than the overall sample variance that would be obtained if we treated the entire set of 18 observations as one data set. With the entire data set as one sample, the formula for computing the total sum of squares, SST, is

$$SST = \sum_{j=1}^{k}\sum_{i=1}^{n_j}(x_{ij} - \bar{\bar{x}})^2 \tag{10.22}$$

It can be shown that the results we observed for the analysis of variance table for the NCP example also apply to other problems. That is,

$$SST = SSTR + SSE \tag{10.23}$$

Analysis of variance can be thought of as a statistical procedure for partitioning the total sum of squares into separate components.

In other words, SST can be partitioned into two sums of squares: the sum of squares due to treatments and the sum of squares due to error. Note also that the degrees of freedom corresponding to SST, $n_T - 1$, can be partitioned into the degrees of freedom corresponding to SSTR, $k - 1$, and the degrees of freedom corresponding to SSE, $n_T - k$. The analysis of variance can be viewed as the process of **partitioning** the total sum of squares and the degrees of freedom into their corresponding sources: treatments and error. Dividing the sum of squares by the appropriate degrees of freedom provides the variance estimates and the F value used to test the hypothesis of equal population means.

Using Excel

Excel's Anova: Single Factor tool can be used to conduct a hypothesis test about the difference between the population means for the National Computer Products example. Refer to the Excel worksheet shown in Figure 10.14 as we describe the tasks involved.

Enter Data: Column A is used to identify the employees at each of the plants. Columns B, C, and D contain the examination scores for the three plants.

Apply Tools: The following steps describe how to use Excel's Anova: Single Factor tool to test the hypothesis that the mean examination score is the same for all three plants.

> **Step 1.** Select the **Tools** menu
> **Step 2.** Choose the **Data Analysis** option

TABLE 10.4   ANALYSIS OF VARIANCE TABLE FOR THE NCP EXAMPLE

Source of Variation	Sum of Squares	Degrees of Freedom	Mean Square	F
Treatments	516	2	258.00	9.00
Error	430	15	28.67	
Total	946	17		

FIGURE 10.14 USING EXCEL'S ANOVA: SINGLE FACTOR TOOL OUTPUT FOR THE NCP EXAMPLE

	A	B	C	D	E	F	G	H
1	Employee	Atlanta	Dallas	Seattle				
2	1	85	71	59				
3	2	75	75	64				
4	3	82	73	62				
5	4	76	74	69				
6	5	71	69	75				
7	6	85	82	67				
8								
9	Anova: Single Factor							
10								
11	SUMMARY							
12	*Groups*	*Count*	*Sum*	*Average*	*Variance*			
13	Atlanta	6	474	79	34			
14	Dallas	6	444	74	20			
15	Seattle	6	396	66	32			
16								
17								
18	ANOVA							
19	*Source of Variation*	*SS*	*df*	*MS*	*F*	*P-value*	*F crit*	
20	Between Groups	516	2	258	9	0.0027	3.6823	
21	Within Groups	430	15	28.6667				
22								
23	Total	946	17					
24								

Step 3. Choose **Anova: Single Factor** from the list of Analysis Tools

Step 4. When the Anova: Single Factor dialog box appears (see Figure 10.15):

Enter B1:D7 in the **Input Range** box

Select **Grouped By: Columns**

Select **Labels in First Row**

Enter .05 in the **Alpha** box

Select **Output Range**

Enter A9 in the **Output Range** box (to identify the upper left corner of the section of the worksheet where the output will appear)

Click **OK**

The output, titled *Anova: Single Factor,* appears in cells A9:G23 of the worksheet. Cells A11:E15 provide a summary of the data. Note that the sample mean and sample variance for each plant is the same as shown in Table 10.3. The ANOVA table, shown in cells A18:G23, is basically the same as the ANOVA table shown in Table 10.4. Excel identifies the treatments source of variation using the label *Between Groups* and the error source of variation using the label *Within Groups*. In addition, the Excel output provides the *p*-value associated with the test as well as the critical *F* value.

We can use the *p*-value shown in cell F20, 0.0027, to make the hypothesis testing decision. Thus, at the $\alpha = .05$ level of significance, we reject H_0 because the *p*-value = $0.0027 < \alpha = .05$. Hence, using the *p*-value approach we conclude that the mean examination scores differ among the three plants.

FIGURE 10.15 DIALOG BOX FOR ANOVA: SINGLE FACTOR

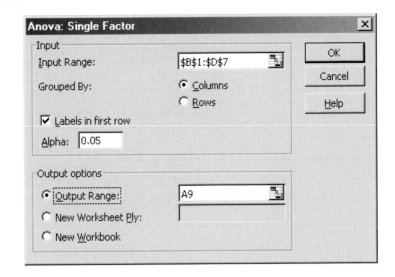

NOTES AND COMMENTS

1. The overall sample mean can also be computed as a weighted average of the k sample means.

$$\bar{\bar{x}} = \frac{n_1\bar{x}_1 + n_2\bar{x}_2 + \cdots + n_k\bar{x}_k}{n_T}$$

In problems where the sample means are provided, this formula is simpler than equation (10.12) for computing the overall mean.

2. Confidence interval estimates for each of the k population means can be developed using

$$\bar{x} \pm t_{\alpha/2}\frac{\sqrt{MSE}}{\sqrt{n}}$$

The degrees of freedom for the t value are the degrees of freedom associated with the within-treatments estimate of σ^2.

Exercises

Methods

27. Five observations were selected from each of three populations. The data obtained follow.

Observation	Sample 1	Sample 2	Sample 3
1	32	44	33
2	30	43	36
3	30	44	35
4	26	46	36
5	32	48	40
Sample mean	30	45	36
Sample variance	6.00	4.00	6.50

a. Compute the between-treatments estimate of σ^2.
b. Compute the within-treatments estimate of σ^2.

c. At the $\alpha = .05$ level of significance, can we reject the null hypothesis that the means of the three populations are equal?

d. Set up the ANOVA table for this problem.

28. Four observations were selected from each of three populations. The data obtained follow.

Observation	Sample 1	Sample 2	Sample 3
1	165	174	169
2	149	164	154
3	156	180	161
4	142	158	148
Sample mean	153	169	158
Sample variance	96.67	97.33	82.00

a. Compute the between-treatments estimate of σ^2.

b. Compute the within-treatments estimate of σ^2.

c. At the $\alpha = .05$ level of significance, can we reject the null hypothesis that the three population means are equal? Explain.

d. Set up the ANOVA table for this problem.

29. Samples were selected from three populations. The data obtained follow.

	Sample 1	Sample 2	Sample 3
	93	77	88
	98	87	75
	107	84	73
	102	95	84
		85	75
		82	
$\bar{x}_j$	100	85	79
s_j^2	35.33	35.60	43.50

a. Compute the between-treatments estimate of σ^2.

b. Compute the within-treatments estimate of σ^2.

c. At the $\alpha = .05$ level of significance, can we reject the null hypothesis that the three population means are equal? Explain.

d. Set up the ANOVA table for this problem.

30. A random sample of 16 observations was selected from each of four populations. A portion of the ANOVA table follows.

Source of Variation	Sum of Squares	Degrees of Freedom	Mean Square	F
Treatments			400	
Error				
Total	1500			

a. Provide the missing entries for the ANOVA table.

b. At the $\alpha = .05$ level of significance, can we reject the null hypothesis that the means of the four populations are equal?

4. What is the 95% confidence interval for the population mean of each model, and what is the 95% confidence interval for the difference between the means of the two populations?

5. Do you see a need for larger sample sizes and more testing with the golf balls? Discuss.

Case Problem 2   Wentworth Medical Center

As part of a long-term study of individuals 65 years of age or older, sociologists and physicians at the Wentworth Medical Center in upstate New York investigated the relationship between geographic location and depression. A sample of 60 individuals, all in reasonably good health, was selected; 20 individuals were residents of Florida, 20 were residents of New York, and 20 were residents of North Carolina. Each of the individuals sampled was given a standardized test to measure depression. The data collected follow; higher test scores indicate higher levels of depression. These data are available on the data disk in the file Medical1.

A second part of the study considered the relationship between geographic location and depression for individuals 65 years of age or older who had a chronic health condition such as arthritis, hypertension, and/or heart ailment. A sample of 60 individuals with such conditions was identified. Again, 20 were residents of Florida, 20 were residents of New York, and 20 were residents of North Carolina. The levels of depression recorded for this study follow. These data are available on the CD accompanying the text in the file named Medical2.

Medical1

Medical2

Data from Medical1			Data from Medical2		
Florida	New York	North Carolina	Florida	New York	North Carolina
3	8	10	13	14	10
7	11	7	12	9	12
7	9	3	17	15	15
3	7	5	17	12	18
8	8	11	20	16	12
8	7	8	21	24	14
8	8	4	16	18	17
5	4	3	14	14	8
5	13	7	13	15	14
2	10	8	17	17	16
6	6	8	12	20	18
2	8	7	9	11	17
6	12	3	12	23	19
6	8	9	15	19	15
9	6	8	16	17	13
7	8	12	15	14	14
5	5	6	13	9	11
4	7	3	10	14	12
7	7	8	11	13	13
3	8	11	17	11	11

Managerial Report

1. Use descriptive statistics to summarize the data from the two studies. What are your preliminary observations about the depression scores?

2. Use analysis of variance on both data sets. State the hypotheses being tested in each case. What are your conclusions?

3. Use inferences about individual treatment means where appropriate. What are your conclusions?

4. Discuss extensions of this study or other analyses that you feel might be helpful.

Case Problem 3   Compensation for ID Professionals

For the preceding 10 years *Industrial Distribution* tracked compensation of industrial distribution (ID) professionals. Results for the 358 respondents in the 1997 Annual Salary Survey showed that 27% of the respondents work for companies with sales over $40 million, with the typical ID professional working for a $12 million firm. Those who work for small to mid-sized companies (between $6 million and $20 million) report higher earnings than those in larger firms. The lowest paid employees work for firms with sales of less than $1 million. The typical outside salesperson made $50,000 in 1996, and the typical inside salesperson earned just $30,000 (*Industrial Distribution*, November 1997). Suppose that a local chapter of ID professionals in the greater San Francisco area conducted a survey of its membership to study the relationship, if any, between the years of experience and salary for individuals employed in outside and inside sales positions. On the survey, respondents were asked to specify one of three levels of years of experience: low (1–10 years), medium (11–20 years), and high (21 or more years). A portion of the data obtained follows. The complete data set, consisting of 120 observations, is available on the CD accompanying the text in the file named IDSalary.

IDSalary

Observation	Salary ($)	Position	Experience
1	28938	Inside	Medium
2	27694	Inside	Medium
3	45515	Outside	Low
4	27031	Inside	Medium
5	37283	Outside	Low
6	32718	Inside	Low
7	54081	Outside	High
8	23621	Inside	Low
9	47835	Outside	High
10	29768	Inside	Medium
.	.	.	.
.	.	.	.
.	.	.	.
115	33080	Inside	High
116	53702	Outside	Medium
117	58131	Outside	Medium
118	32788	Inside	High
119	28070	Inside	Medium
120	35259	Outside	Low

Managerial Report

1. Use descriptive statistics to summarize the data.

2. Develop a 95% confidence interval estimate of the mean annual salary for all salespersons, regardless of years of experience and type of position.

3. Develop a 95% confidence interval estimate of the mean salary for outside salespersons. Compare your results with the national value reported by *Industrial Distribution*.

4. Develop a 95% confidence interval estimate of the mean salary for inside salespersons. Compare your results with the national value reported by *Industrial Distribution.*

5. Ignoring the years of experience, develop a 95% confidence interval estimate of the mean difference between the annual salary for outside salespersons and the mean annual salary for inside salespersons. What is your conclusion?

6. Use analysis of variance to test for any significant differences due to position. Use a .05 level of significance, and for now, ignore the effect of years of experience.

7. Use analysis of variance to test for any significant differences due to years of experience. Use a .05 level of significance, and for now, ignore the effect of position.

CHAPTER 11

Comparisons Involving Proportions and a Test of Independence

UNITED WAY*
ROCHESTER, NEW YORK

United Way of Greater Rochester is a nonprofit organization dedicated to improving the quality of life for all people in the seven counties it serves by meeting the community's most important human care needs.

The annual United Way/Red Cross fund-raising campaign, conducted each spring, funds hundreds of programs offered by more than 200 service providers. These providers meet a wide variety of human needs—physical, mental, and social—and serve people of all ages, backgrounds, and economic means.

Because of enormous volunteer involvement, United Way of Greater Rochester is able to hold its operating costs at just eight cents of every dollar raised.

The United Way of Greater Rochester decided to conduct a survey to learn more about community perceptions of charities. Focus-group interviews were held with professional, service, and general worker groups to get preliminary information on perceptions. The information obtained was then used to help develop the questionnaire for the survey. The questionnaire was pretested, modified, and distributed to 440 individuals; 323 completed questionnaires were obtained.

A variety of descriptive statistics, including frequency distributions and crosstabulations, were provided from the data collected. An important part of the analysis involved the use of contingency tables and chi-square tests of independence. One use of such statistical tests was to determine whether perceptions of administrative expenses were independent of occupation.

The hypotheses for the test of independence were:

H_0: Perception of United Way administrative expenses is independent of the occupation of the respondent.

H_a: Perception of United Way administrative expenses is not independent of the occupation of the respondent.

---

*The authors are indebted to Dr. Philip R. Tyler, Marketing Consultant to the United Way, for providing this Statistics in Practice.

Statistical surveys help United Way adjust its program to better meet the needs of the people it serves. © Tony Freeman/PhotoEdit.

Two questions in the survey provided the data for the statistical test. One question obtained data on perceptions of the percentage of funds going to administrative expenses (up to 10%, 11–20%, and 21% or more). The other question asked for the occupation of the respondent.

The chi-square test at a .05 level of significance led to rejection of the null hypothesis of independence and to the conclusion that perceptions of United Way's administrative expenses did vary by occupation. Actual administrative expenses were less than 9%, but 35% of the respondents perceived that administrative expenses were 21% or more. Hence, many had inaccurate perceptions of administrative costs. In this group, production-line, clerical, sales, and professional-technical employees had more inaccurate perceptions than other groups.

The community perceptions study helped United Way of Greater Rochester to develop adjustments to its program and fund-raising activities. In this chapter, you will learn how a statistical test of independence, such as that described here, is conducted.

Many statistical applications call for a comparison of population proportions. In Section 11.1, we describe statistical inferences concerning differences in the proportions for two populations. Two samples are required, one from each population, and the statistical inference is based on the two sample proportions. The second section looks at a hypothesis test comparing the proportions of a single multinomial population with the proportions stated in a null hypothesis. One sample from the multinomial population is used, and the hypothesis test is based on comparing the sample proportions with those stated in the null hypothesis. In the last section of the chapter, we show how contingency tables can be used to test for the independence of two variables. One sample is used for the test of independence, but measures on two variables are required for each sampled element. Both Sections 11.2 and 11.3 rely on the use of a chi-square statistical test.

11.1 Inferences About the Difference Between Two Population Proportions

Letting p_1 denote the proportion for population 1 and p_2 denote the proportion for population 2, we consider inferences about the difference between the two population proportions: $p_1 - p_2$. To make an inference about this difference, we will select two independent random samples consisting of n_1 units from population 1 and n_2 units from population 2.

Interval Estimation of $p_1 - p_2$

In the following example, we show how to compute a margin of error and develop an interval estimate of the difference between two population proportions.

A tax preparation firm is interested in comparing the quality of work at two of its regional offices. By randomly selecting samples of tax returns prepared at each office and verifying the sample returns' accuracy, the firm will be able to estimate the proportion of erroneous returns prepared at each office. Of particular interest is the difference between these proportions.

$$p_1 = \text{proportion of erroneous returns for population 1 (office 1)}$$
$$p_2 = \text{proportion of erroneous returns for population 2 (office 2)}$$
$$\bar{p}_1 = \text{sample proportion for a simple random sample from population 1}$$
$$\bar{p}_2 = \text{sample proportion for a simple random sample from population 2}$$

The difference between the two population proportions is given by $p_1 - p_2$. The point estimator of $p_1 - p_2$ is as follows.

POINT ESTIMATOR OF THE DIFFERENCE BETWEEN TWO POPULATION PROPORTIONS

$$\bar{p}_1 - \bar{p}_2 \tag{11.1}$$

Thus, the point estimator of the difference between two population proportions is the difference between the sample proportions of two independent simple random samples.

As with other point estimators, the point estimator $\bar{p}_1 - \bar{p}_2$ has a sampling distribution that reflects the possible values of $\bar{p}_1 - \bar{p}_2$ if we repeatedly took two independent random samples. The mean of this sampling distribution is $p_1 - p_2$ and the standard error is as follows:

$$\sigma_{\bar{p}_1 - \bar{p}_2} = \sqrt{\frac{p_1(1 - p_1)}{n_1} + \frac{p_2(1 - p_2)}{n_2}} \tag{11.2}$$

Sample sizes involving proportions are usually large enough to use this approximation.

If the sample sizes are large enough that $n_1 p_1$, $n_1(1 - p_1)$, $n_2 p_2$, and $n_2(1 - p_2)$ are all greater than or equal to 5, the sampling distribution of $\bar{p}_1 - \bar{p}_2$ can be approximated by a normal distribution.

In the estimation of the difference between two population proportions, an interval estimate will take the following form:

$$\bar{p}_1 - \bar{p}_2 \pm \text{Margin of error}$$

With the sampling distribution of $\bar{p}_1 - \bar{p}_2$ approximated by a normal distribution, we would like to use $z_{\alpha/2} \sigma_{\bar{p}_1 - \bar{p}_2}$ as the margin of error. However, $\sigma_{\bar{p}_1 - \bar{p}_2}$ given by equation (11.2) involves the two unknown population proportions, p_1 and p_2. Thus, we use the sample proportion $\bar{p}_1$ to estimate p_1 and the sample proportion $\bar{p}_2$ to estimate p_2. The margin of error is thus.

$$\text{Margin of error} = z_{\alpha/2} \sqrt{\frac{\bar{p}_1(1 - \bar{p}_1)}{n_1} + \frac{\bar{p}_2(1 - \bar{p}_2)}{n_2}} \qquad (11.3)$$

The general form of an interval estimate of the difference between two population proportions is as follows.

INTERVAL ESTIMATE OF THE DIFFERENCE BETWEEN TWO POPULATION PROPORTIONS

$$\bar{p}_1 - \bar{p}_2 \pm z_{\alpha/2} \sqrt{\frac{\bar{p}_1(1 - \bar{p}_1)}{n_1} + \frac{\bar{p}_2(1 - \bar{p}_2)}{n_2}} \qquad (11.4)$$

where $1 - \alpha$ is the confidence coefficient.

Returning to the tax preparation example, we find that independent simple random samples from the two offices provide the following information.

Office 1	Office 2
$n_1 = 250$	$n_2 = 300$
Number of returns with errors = 35	Number of returns with errors = 27

TaxPrep

The sample proportions for the two offices follow.

$$\bar{p}_1 = \frac{35}{250} = .14$$

$$\bar{p}_2 = \frac{27}{300} = .09$$

The point estimate of the difference between the proportions of erroneous tax returns for the two populations is $\bar{p}_1 - \bar{p}_2 = .14 - .09 = .05$. Thus, we estimate that office 1 has a .05, or 5%, greater error rate than office 2.

Expression (11.4) can now be used to provide a margin of error and interval estimate of the difference between the two population proportions. Using a 90% confidence interval with $z_{\alpha/2} = z_{.05} = 1.645$, we have

$$\bar{p}_1 - \bar{p}_2 \pm z_{\alpha/2}\sqrt{\frac{\bar{p}_1(1 - \bar{p}_1)}{n_1} + \frac{\bar{p}_2(1 - \bar{p}_2)}{n_2}}$$

$$.14 - .09 \pm 1.645\sqrt{\frac{.14(1 - .14)}{250} + \frac{.09(1 - .09)}{300}}$$

$$.05 \pm .045$$

Thus, the margin of error is .045, and the 90% confidence interval is .005 to .095.

Using Excel to Construct a Confidence Interval

We can create a worksheet for developing an interval estimate of the difference between population proportions. Let us illustrate by developing an interval estimate of the difference between the proportions of erroneous tax returns at the two offices of the tax preparation firm. Refer to Figure 11.1 as we describe the tasks involved. The formula worksheet is in the background; the value worksheet is in the foreground.

Enter Data: Columns A and B contain Yes or No labels that indicate which of the tax returns from each office contain an error.

Enter Functions and Formulas: The descriptive statistics needed are provided in cells E5:F5 and E7:F8. Note that Excel's COUNTA function is used in cells E5 and F5 to count the number of observations for each of the samples. The value worksheet indicates 250 returns in the sample from office 1 and 300 returns in the sample from office 2. In cells E6 and F6, we type Yes to indicate the response of interest (an erroneous return). Excel's COUNTIF function is used in cells E7 and F7 to count the number of Yes responses from each office. Formulas entered into cells E8 and F8 compute the sample proportions. The confidence coefficient entered into cell E10 (.9) is used to compute the corresponding level of significance ($\alpha = .10$) in cell E11. In cell E12 we use the NORMSINV function to compute the z value needed to compute the margin of error for the interval estimate.

In cell E14, a point estimate of $\sigma_{\bar{p}_1 - \bar{p}_2}$, the standard error of the point estimator $\bar{p}_1 - \bar{p}_2$, is computed based on the two sample proportions (E8 and F8) and sample sizes (E5 and F5). The margin of error is then computed in cell E15 by multiplying the z value by the estimate of the standard error.

The point estimate of the difference in the two population proportions is computed in cell E17 as the difference in the sample proportions; the result, shown in the value worksheet, is .05. The lower limit of the confidence interval is computed in cell E18 by subtracting the margin of error from the point estimate. The upper limit is computed in cell E19 by adding the margin of error to the point estimate. The value worksheet shows that the 90% confidence interval estimate of the difference in the two population proportions is .0048 to .0952.

A Template for Other Problems This worksheet can be used as a template for other problems requiring an interval estimate of the difference in population proportions. The new data must be entered in columns A and B. The data ranges in the cells used to compute the sample size (E5:F5) and the cells used to compute a count of the response of interest (E7:F7) must be changed to correctly indicate the location of the new data. The response of

FIGURE 11.1   CONSTRUCTING A 90% CONFIDENCE INTERVAL FOR THE DIFFERENCE IN THE PROPORTION OF ERRONEOUS TAX RETURNS PREPARED BY TWO OFFICES

	A	B	C	D	E	F	G
1	Office 1	Office 2			Interval Estimate of Difference		
2	No	No			in Population Proportions		
3	No	No					
4	No	No			Office 1	Office 2	
5	No	No		Sample Size	=COUNTA(A2:A251)	=COUNTA(B2:B301)	
6	No	No		Response of Interest	Yes	Yes	
7	Yes	No		Count for Response	=COUNTIF(A2:A251,E6)	=COUNTIF(B2:B301,F6)	
8	No	No		Sample Proportion	=E7/E5	=F7/F5	
9	No	No					
10	No	No		Confidence Coefficient	0.9		
11	No	No		Level of Significance	=1-E10		
12	No	No		z Value	=NORMSINV(1-E11/2)		
13	No	No					
14	No	No		Standard Error	=SQRT(E8*(1-E8)/E5+F8*(1-F8)/F5)		
15	No	No		Margin of Error	=E12*E14		
16	No	No					
17	No	Yes		Point Estimate of Difference	=E8-F8		
18	Yes	No		Lower Limit	=E17-E15		
19	No	No		Upper Limit	=E17+E15		
250	Yes	No					
251	No	No					
300		No					
301		No					
302							

	A	B	C	D	E	F	G
1	Office 1	Office 2		Interval Estimate of Difference			
2	No	No		in Population Proportions			
3	No	No					
4	No	No			Office 1	Office 2	
5	No	No		Sample Size	250	300	
6	No	No		Response of Interest	Yes	Yes	
7	Yes	No		Count for Response	35	27	
8	No	No		Sample Proportion	0.14	0.09	
9	No	No					
10	No	No		Confidence Coefficient	0.9		
11	No	No		Level of Significance	0.1		
12	No	No		z Value	1.645		
13	No	No					
14	No	No		Standard Error	0.0275		
15	No	No		Margin of Error	0.0452		
16	No	No					
17	No	Yes		Point Estimate of Difference	0.05		
18	Yes	No		Lower Limit	0.0048		
19	No	No		Upper Limit	0.0952		
250	Yes	No					
251	No	No					
300		No					
301		No					
302							

Note: Rows 20–249 and 252–299 are hidden.

interest must be typed into cells E6:F6. The 90% confidence interval for the new data will then appear in cells E17:E19. If an interval estimate with a different confidence coefficient is desired, simply change the entry in cell E10.

This worksheet can also be used as a template for solving text exercises in which the sample data have already been summarized. No change in the data section is necessary. Simply type the values for the given sample sizes in cells E5:F5 and type the given values for the sample proportions in cells E8:F8. The 90% confidence interval will then appear in cells E17:E19. If an interval estimate with a different confidence coefficient is desired, simply change the entry in cell E10.

Hypothesis Tests About $p_1 - p_2$

Let us now consider hypothesis tests about the difference between the proportions of two populations. We focus on tests involving no difference between the two population proportions. In this case, the three forms for a hypothesis test are as follows:

All hypotheses considered use 0 as the difference of interest.

$$H_0: p_1 - p_2 \geq 0 \qquad H_0: p_1 - p_2 \leq 0 \qquad H_0: p_1 - p_2 = 0$$
$$H_a: p_1 - p_2 < 0 \qquad H_a: p_1 - p_2 > 0 \qquad H_a: p_1 - p_2 \neq 0$$

When we assume H_0 is true as an equality, we have $p_1 - p_2 = 0$, which is the same as saying that the population proportions are equal, $p_1 = p_2$.

We will base the test statistic on the sampling distribution of the point estimator $\bar{p}_1 - \bar{p}_2$. In equation (11.2), we showed that the standard error of $\bar{p}_1 - \bar{p}_2$ is given by

$$\sigma_{\bar{p}_1 - \bar{p}_2} = \sqrt{\frac{p_1(1 - p_1)}{n_1} + \frac{p_2(1 - p_2)}{n_2}}$$

Under the assumption H_0 is true as an equality, the population proportions are equal and $p_1 = p_2 = p$. In this case, $\sigma_{\bar{p}_1 - \bar{p}_2}$ becomes

$$\sigma_{\bar{p}_1 - \bar{p}_2} = \sqrt{\frac{p(1 - p)}{n_1} + \frac{p(1 - p)}{n_2}} = \sqrt{p(1 - p)\left(\frac{1}{n_1} + \frac{1}{n_2}\right)} \qquad (11.5)$$

With p unknown, we pool, or combine, the point estimators from the two samples ($\bar{p}_1$ and $\bar{p}_2$) to obtain a single point estimator of p as follows:

$$\bar{p} = \frac{n_1\bar{p}_1 + n_2\bar{p}_2}{n_1 + n_2} \qquad (11.6)$$

This **pooled estimator of p** is a weighted average of $\bar{p}_1$ and $\bar{p}_2$.

Substituting $\bar{p}$ for p in equation (11.5), we obtain an estimate of the standard error of $\bar{p}_1 - \bar{p}_2$. This estimate of the standard error is used in the test statistic. The general form of the test statistic for hypothesis tests about the difference between two population proportions is the point estimator divided by the estimate of $\sigma_{\bar{p}_1 - \bar{p}_2}$.

TEST STATISTIC FOR HYPOTHESIS TESTS ABOUT $p_1 - p_2$

$$z = \frac{(\bar{p}_1 - \bar{p}_2)}{\sqrt{\bar{p}(1 - \bar{p})\left(\frac{1}{n_1} + \frac{1}{n_2}\right)}} \qquad (11.7)$$

This test statistic applies to large sample situations where $n_1 p_1$, $n_1(1 - p_1)$, $n_2 p_2$, and $n_2(1 - p_2)$ are all greater than or equal to 5.

Let us return to the tax preparation firm example and assume that the firm wants to use a hypothesis test to determine whether the error proportions differ between the two offices. A two-tailed test is required. The null and alternative hypotheses are as follows:

$$H_0: p_1 - p_2 = 0$$
$$H_a: p_1 - p_2 \neq 0$$

If H_0 is rejected, the firm can conclude that the error rates at the two offices differ. We will use $\alpha = .10$ as the level of significance.

The sample data previously collected showed $\bar{p}_1 = .14$ for the $n_1 = 250$ returns sampled at office 1 and $\bar{p}_2 = .09$ for the $n_2 = 300$ returns sampled at office 2. We continue by computing the pooled estimate of p.

$$\bar{p} = \frac{n_1\bar{p}_1 + n_2\bar{p}_2}{n_1 + n_2} = \frac{250(.14) + 300(.09)}{250 + 300} = .1127$$

Using this pooled estimate and the difference between the sample proportions, the value of the test statistic is as follows.

$$z = \frac{(\bar{p}_1 - \bar{p}_2)}{\sqrt{\bar{p}(1 - \bar{p})\left(\dfrac{1}{n_1} + \dfrac{1}{n_2}\right)}} = \frac{(.14 - .09)}{\sqrt{.1127(1 - .1127)\left(\dfrac{1}{250} + \dfrac{1}{300}\right)}} = 1.85$$

In computing the p-value for this two-tailed test, we first note that $z = 1.85$ is in the upper tail of the standard normal distribution. Using $z = 1.85$ and the standard normal distribution table, we find the area in the upper tail is $1.0000 - .9678 = .0322$. Doubling this area for a two-tailed test, we find the p-value $= 2(.0322) = .0644$. With the p-value less than $\alpha = .10$, H_0 is rejected at the .10 level of significance. The firm can conclude that the error rates differ between the two offices. This hypothesis testing conclusion is consistent with the earlier 90% confidence interval results that showed the interval estimate of the difference between the population error rates at the two offices to be .005 to .095, with office 1 having the higher error rate.

Using Excel to Conduct a Hypothesis Test

We can create a worksheet for conducting a hypothesis test about the difference between population proportions. Let us illustrate by testing to see whether there is a significant difference between the proportions of erroneous tax returns at the two offices of the tax preparation firm. Refer to Figure 11.2 as we describe the tasks involved. The formula worksheet is in the background; the value worksheet is in the foreground.

Enter Data: Columns A and B contain Yes or No labels that indicate which of the tax returns from each office contain an error.

Enter Functions and Formulas: The descriptive statistics needed to perform the hypothesis test are provided in cells E5:F6 and E7:F8. They are the same as the ones used for an interval estimate (see Figure 11.1). The hypothesized value of the difference between the two populations is zero; it is entered into cell E10. In cell E11, the difference in the sample proportions is used to compute a point estimate of the difference in the two population proportions. Using the two sample proportions and sample sizes, a pooled estimate of the population proportion p is computed in cell E13; its value is .1127. Then, in cell E14, an estimate of $\sigma_{\bar{p}_1 - \bar{p}_2}$ is computed using equation (11.5), with the pooled estimate of p and the sample sizes.

The p-value here (.0649) differs from the one we found using the cumulative normal probability tables (.0644) due to rounding.

The formula =(E11−E10)/E14 entered into cell E15 computes the test statistic z (1.8462). The NORMSDIST function is then used to compute the p-value (Lower Tail) and the p-value (Upper Tail) in cells E17 and E18. The p-value (Two Tail) is computed in cell E19 as twice the minimum of the 2 one-tailed p-values. The value worksheet shows that p-value (Two Tail) $= .0649$. Because the p-value $= .0649$ is less than the level of significance, $\alpha = .10$, we have sufficient evidence to reject the null hypothesis and conclude that the population proportions are not equal.

FIGURE 11.2   HYPOTHESIS TEST CONCERNING DIFFERENCE IN PROPORTION OF ERRONEOUS TAX RETURNS PREPARED BY TWO OFFICES

	A	B	C	D	E	F	G
1	Office 1	Office 2		Hypothesis Test Concerning Difference			
2	No	No		Between Population Proportions			
3	No	No					
4	No	No			Office 1	Office 2	
5	No	No		Sample Size	=COUNTA(A2:A251)	=COUNTA(B2:B301)	
6	No	No		Response of Interest	Yes	Yes	
7	Yes	No		Count for Response	=COUNTIF(A2:A251,E6)	=COUNTIF(B2:B301,F6)	
8	No	No		Sample Proportion	=E7/E5	=F7/F5	
9	No	No					
10	No	No		Hypothesized Value	0		
11	No	No		Point Estimate of Difference	=E8-F8		
12	No	No					
13	No	No		Pooled Estimate of p	=(E5*E8+F5*F8)/(E5+F5)		
14	No	No		Standard Error	=SQRT(E13*(1-E13)*(1/E5+1/F5))		
15	No	No		Test Statistic	=(E11-E10)/E14		
16	No	No					
17	No	Yes		p-value (Lower Tail)	=NORMSDIST(E15)		
18	Yes	No		p-value (Upper Tail)	=1-NORMSDIST(E15)		
19	No	No		p-value (Two Tail)	=2*MIN(E17,E18)		
250	Yes	No					
251	No	No					
300		No					
301		No					
302							

	A	B	C	D	E	F	G
1	Office 1	Office 2		Hypothesis Test Concerning Difference			
2	No	No		Between Population Proportions			
3	No	No					
4	No	No			Office 1	Office 2	
5	No	No		Sample Size	250	300	
6	No	No		Response of Interest	Yes	Yes	
7	Yes	No		Count for Response	35	27	
8	No	No		Sample Proportion	0.14	0.09	
9	No	No					
10	No	No		Hypothesized Value	0		
11	No	No		Point Estimate of Difference	0.05		
12	No	No					
13	No	No		Pooled Estimate of p	0.1127		
14	No	No		Standard Error	0.0271		
15	No	No		Test Statistic	1.8462		
16	No	No					
17	No	Yes		p-value (Lower Tail)	0.9676		
18	Yes	No		p-value (Upper Tail)	0.0324		
19	No	No		p-value (Two Tail)	0.0649		
250	Yes	No					
251	No	No					
300		No					
301		No					
302							

Note: Rows 20–249 and 252–299 are hidden.

This worksheet can be used as a template for hypothesis testing problems involving differences between population proportions. The new data can be entered into columns A and B. The ranges for the new data and the response of interest need to be revised in cells E5:F7. The remainder of the worksheet will then be updated as needed to conduct the hypothesis test. If a hypothesized difference other than 0 is to be used, the new value must be entered in cell E10.

To use this worksheet for exercises in which the sample statistics are given, just type in the given values for cells E5:F5 and E7:F8. The remainder of the worksheet will then be updated to conduct the hypothesis test. If a hypothesized difference other than 0 is to be used, the new value must be entered in cell E10.

Exercises

Methods

1. Consider the following results for independent samples taken from two populations.

Sample 1	Sample 2
$n_1 = 400$	$n_2 = 300$
$\bar{p}_1 = .48$	$\bar{p}_2 = .36$

    a. What is the point estimate of the difference between the two population proportions?
    b. Develop a 90% confidence interval for the difference between the two population proportions.
    c. Develop a 95% confidence interval for the difference between the two population proportions.

2. Consider the hypothesis test

    $$H_0: p_1 - p_2 \le 0$$
    $$H_a: p_1 - p_2 > 0$$

    The following results are for independent samples taken from the two populations.

Sample 1	Sample 2
$n_1 = 200$	$n_2 = 300$
$\bar{p}_1 = .22$	$\bar{p}_2 = .16$

    a. What is the p-value?
    b. With $\alpha = .05$, what is your hypothesis testing conclusion?

Applications

3. A *BusinessWeek/*Harris survey asked senior executives at large corporations their opinions about the economic outlook for the future. One question was "Do you think that there will be an increase in the number of full-time employees at your company over the next 12 months?" In the current survey, 220 of 400 executives answered yes, while in a previous year's survey, 192 of 400 executives had answered yes. Provide a 95% confidence interval estimate for the difference between the proportions at the two points in time. What is your interpretation of the interval estimate?

4. In recent years, the number of people who use the Internet to obtain political news has grown. Often the political Web sites ask Internet users to register their opinions by participating in online surveys. Pew Research Center conducted a survey of its own to learn about the participation of Republicans and Democrats in online surveys (Associated Press, January 6, 2003). The following sample data apply.

Political Party	Sample Size	Participate in Online Surveys
Republican	250	115
Democrat	350	98

a. Compute the point estimate of the proportion of Republicans who indicate they would participate in online surveys. Compute the point estimate for the Democrats.
b. What is the point estimate of the difference between the two population proportions?
c. At 95% confidence, what is the margin of error?
d. Representatives of the scientific polling industry claim that the profusion of online surveys can confuse people about actual public opinion. Do you agree with this statement? Use the 95% confidence interval estimate of the difference between the Republican and Democrat population proportions to help justify your answer.

5. Slot machines are the favorite game at casinos throughout the United States (*Harrah's Survey 2002: Profile of the American Gamble*). The following sample data show the number of women and number of men who selected slot machines as their favorite game.

	Women	Men
Sample Size	320	250
Favorite Game–Slots	256	165

a. What is the point estimate of the proportion of women who say slots is their favorite game?
b. What is the point estimate of the proportion of men who say slots is their favorite game?
c. Provide a 95% confidence interval estimate of the difference between the proportion of women and proportion of men who say slots is their favorite game.

6. The Bureau of Transportation tracks the flight arrival performances of the 10 biggest airlines in the United States (*The Wall Street Journal,* March 4, 2003). Flights that arrive within 15 minutes of schedule are considered on time. Using sample data consistent with Bureau of Transportation statistics reported in January 2001 and January 2002, consider the following:

> January 2001   A sample of 924 flights showed 742 on time.
> January 2002   A sample of 841 flights showed 714 on time.

a. What is the point estimate of on-time flights in January 2001?
b. What is the point estimate of on-time flights in January 2002?
c. Let p_1 denote the population proportion of on-time flights in January 2001 and p_2 denote the population proportion of on-time flights in January 2002. State the hypotheses that could be tested to determine whether the major airlines improved on-time flight performance during the one-year period.
d. What is the p-value? At $\alpha = .05$, what is your conclusion?

7. In a test of the quality of two television commercials, each commercial was shown in a separate test area six times over a one-week period. The following week a telephone survey was conducted to identify individuals who had seen the commercials. Those individuals were asked to state the primary message in the commercials. The following results were recorded.

	Commercial A	Commercial B
Number Who Saw Commercial	150	200
Number Who Recalled Message	63	60

a. Use $\alpha = .05$ and test the hypothesis that there is no difference in the recall proportions for the two commercials.
b. Compute a 95% confidence interval for the difference between the recall proportions for the two populations.

8. During the 2003 Super Bowl, Miller Lite Beer's commercial referred to as "The Miller Lite Girls" ranked among the top three most effective advertisements aired during the Super Bowl (*USA Today,* December 29, 2003). The survey of advertising effectiveness, conducted by *USA Today*'s Ad Track poll, reported separate samples by respondent age group to learn about how the Super Bowl advertisement appealed to different age groups. The following sample data apply to the "The Miller Lite Girls" commercial.

Age Group	Sample Size	Liked the Ad a Lot
Under 30	100	49
30 to 49	150	54

a. Formulate a hypothesis test that can be used to determine whether there is a difference between the population proportions for the two age groups.
b. What is the point estimate of the difference between the two population proportions?
c. Conduct the hypothesis test and report the *p*-value. At $\alpha = .05$, what is your conclusion?
d. Discuss the appeal of the advertisements to the younger and the older age groups. Would the Miller Lite organization find the results of the *USA Today* Ad Track poll encouraging? Explain.

9. A 2003 *New York Times*/CBS News poll sampled 523 adults who were planning a vacation during the next six months and found that 141 were expecting to travel by airplane (*New York Times News Service,* March 2, 2003). A similar survey question in a May 1993 *New York Times*/CBS News poll found that of 477 adults who were planning a vacation in the next six months, 81 were expecting to travel by airplane.
a. State the hypotheses that can be used to determine whether a significant change occurred in the population proportion planning to travel by airplane over the 10-year period.
b. What is the sample proportion expecting to travel by airplane in 2003? In 1993?
c. Use $\alpha = .01$ and test for a significant difference. What is your conclusion?
d. Discuss reasons that might provide an explanation for this conclusion.

10. *Yahoo! Internet Life* sponsored surveys in several metropolitan areas to estimate the proportion of adults using the Internet at work (*USA Today,* May 7, 2000). Results showed 40% of Washington, D.C., adults use the Internet at work, while 32% of San Francisco adults use the Internet at work. If the sample sizes are 240 and 250, respectively, do the sample results indicate that the population proportion of adults using the Internet at work in Washington, D.C., is greater than the population proportion in San Francisco? What is the *p*-value? Using $\alpha = .05$, what is the conclusion?

Hypothesis Test for Proportions of a Multinomial Population

In this section we consider the case in which each element of a population is assigned to one and only one of several classes or categories. Such a population is a **multinomial population**. The multinomial distribution can be thought of as an extension of the binomial distribution to the case of three or more categories of outcomes. On each trial of a multinomial experiment, one and only one of the outcomes occurs. Each trial of the experiment is assumed to be independent, and the probabilities of the outcomes remain the same for each trial.

The assumptions for the multinomial experiment parallel those for the binomial experiment with the exception that the multinomial has three or more outcomes per trial.

As an example, consider the market share study being conducted by Scott Marketing Research. Over the past year market shares stabilized at 30% for company A, 50% for company B, and 20% for company C. Recently company C developed a "new and improved" product to replace its current entry in the market. Company C retained Scott Marketing Research to determine whether the new product will alter market shares.

In this case, the population of interest is a multinomial population; each customer is classified as buying from company A, company B, or company C. Thus, we have a multinomial population with three outcomes. Let us use the following notation for the proportions.

$$p_A = \text{market share for company A}$$
$$p_B = \text{market share for company B}$$
$$p_C = \text{market share for company C}$$

Scott Marketing Research will conduct a sample survey and compute the proportion preferring each company's product. A hypothesis test will then be conducted to see whether the new product caused a change in market shares. For the null hypothesis, we assume that company C's new product will not alter the market shares. The null and alternative hypotheses are stated as follows.

$$H_0: p_A = .30, p_B = .50, \text{ and } p_C = .20$$
$$H_a: \text{The population proportions are not}$$
$$p_A = .30, p_B = .50, \text{ and } p_C = .20$$

If the sample results lead to the rejection of H_0, Scott Marketing Research will have evidence that the introduction of the new product affects market shares.

Let us assume that the market research firm has used a consumer panel of 200 customers for the study. Each individual was asked to specify a purchase preference among the three alternatives: company A's product, company B's product, and company C's new product. The 200 responses are summarized here.

The consumer panel of 200 customers in which each individual is asked to select one of three alternatives is equivalent to a multinomial experiment consisting of 200 trials.

Observed Frequency

Company A's Product	Company B's Product	Company C's New Product
48	98	54

We now can perform a **goodness of fit test** that will determine whether the sample of 200 customer purchase preferences is consistent with the null hypothesis. The goodness of fit test is based on a comparison of the sample of *observed* results with the *expected* results under the assumption that the null hypothesis is true. Hence, the next step is to compute expected purchase preferences for the 200 customers under the assumption that $p_A = .30$, $p_B = .50$, and $p_C = .20$. Doing so provides the expected results.

Expected Frequency

Company A's Product	Company B's Product	Company C's New Product
200(.30) = 60	200(.50) = 100	200(.20) = 40

Thus, we see that the expected frequency for each category is found by multiplying the sample size of 200 by the hypothesized proportion for the category.

The goodness of fit test now focuses on the differences between the observed frequencies and the expected frequencies. Large differences between observed and expected frequencies cast doubt on the assumption that the hypothesized proportions or market shares are correct. Whether the differences between the observed and expected frequencies are "large" or "small" is a question answered with the aid of the following chi-square test statistic.

TEST STATISTIC FOR GOODNESS OF FIT

$$\chi^2 = \sum_{i=1}^{k} \frac{(f_i - e_i)^2}{e_i} \tag{11.8}$$

where

f_i = observed frequency for category i
e_i = expected frequency for category i
k = the number of categories

Note: The test statistic has a chi-square distribution with $k - 1$ degrees of freedom provided that the expected frequencies are 5 *or more* for all categories.

Tables of areas or probabilities are readily available for the chi-square distribution. Since the test statistic for goodness of fit is known to have a chi-square distribution whenever the expected frequencies are 5 or more for all categories, we can use the chi-square distribution to conduct the hypothesis test. We will use the notation χ_α^2 to denote the value of the chi-square distribution that provides an area or probability of α to the right of the χ_α^2 value. For example, refer to Table 11.1 and verify that for a chi-square distribution with 2 degrees of freedom $\chi_{.10}^2 = 4.605$, indicating that 10% of the chi-square values are to the right of 4.605.

Let us continue with the Scott Marketing Research example and use the sample data to test the hypothesis that the multinomial population retains the proportions $p_A = .30$, $p_B = .50$, and $p_C = .20$. We will use an $\alpha = .05$ level of significance. Let us proceed by using the observed and expected frequencies to compute the value of the test statistic. With the expected frequencies all 5 or more, the computation of the chi-square test statistic is shown in Table 11.2. At the bottom of the last column, we see that $\chi^2 = 7.34$.

The test for goodness of fit is always a one-tailed test with the rejection occurring in the upper tail of the chi-square distribution.

We will reject the null hypothesis if the differences between the observed and expected frequencies are *large*. Large differences between the observed and expected frequencies will result in a large value for the test statistic. Thus the test of goodness of fit will always be an upper tail test. We can use the upper tail area for the test statistic and the *p*-value approach to determine whether the null hypothesis can be rejected. With $k - 1 = 3 - 1 = 2$ degrees of freedom, Table 11.1 shows the following areas in the upper tail and their corresponding chi-square (χ^2) values:

Area in Upper Tail	.10	.05	.025	.01
χ^2 Value (2 df)	4.605	5.991	7.378	9.210

$$\chi^2 = 7.34$$

Using Excel, CHIDIST (7.34,2) = .0255.

The test statistic $\chi^2 = 7.34$ is between 5.991 and 7.378. Thus, the corresponding upper tail area or *p*-value must be between .05 and .025. Excel can be used to show that $\chi^2 = 7.34$ provides a *p*-value = .0255. With the *p*-value $\leq \alpha = .05$, we reject H_0 and conclude that the introduction of the new product by company C will alter the current market share structure.

TABLE 11.1   SELECTED VALUES FROM THE CHI-SQUARE DISTRIBUTION TABLE*

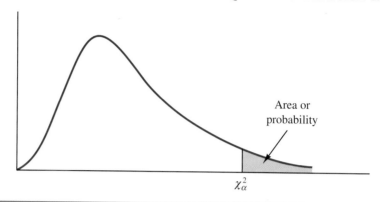

Degrees of Freedom	\.99	\.975	\.95	\.90	\.10	\.05	\.025	\.01
				Area in Upper Tail				
1	.000	.001	.004	.016	2.706	3.841	5.024	6.635
2	.020	.051	.103	.211	4.605	5.991	7.378	9.210
3	.115	.216	.352	.584	6.251	7.815	9.348	11.345
4	.297	.484	.711	1.064	7.779	9.488	11.143	13.277
5	.554	.831	1.145	1.610	9.236	11.070	12.832	15.086
6	.872	1.237	1.635	2.204	10.645	12.592	14.449	16.812
7	1.239	1.690	2.167	2.833	12.017	14.067	16.013	18.475
8	1.647	2.180	2.733	3.490	13.362	15.507	17.535	20.090
9	2.088	2.700	3.325	4.168	14.684	16.919	19.023	21.666
10	2.558	3.247	3.940	4.865	15.987	18.307	20.483	23.209
11	3.053	3.816	4.575	5.578	17.275	19.675	21.920	24.725
12	3.571	4.404	5.226	6.304	18.549	21.026	23.337	26.217
13	4.107	5.009	5.892	7.041	19.812	22.362	24.736	27.688
14	4.660	5.629	6.571	7.790	21.064	23.685	26.119	29.141
15	5.229	6.262	7.261	8.547	22.307	24.996	27.488	30.578
16	5.812	6.908	7.962	9.312	23.542	26.296	28.845	32.000
17	6.408	7.564	8.672	10.085	24.769	27.587	30.191	33.409
18	7.015	8.231	9.390	10.865	25.989	28.869	31.526	34.805
19	7.633	8.907	10.117	11.651	27.204	30.144	32.852	36.191
20	8.260	9.591	10.851	12.443	28.412	31.410	34.170	37.566
21	8.897	10.283	11.591	13.240	29.615	32.671	35.479	38.932
22	9.542	10.982	12.338	14.041	30.813	33.924	36.781	40.289
23	10.196	11.689	13.091	14.848	32.007	35.172	38.076	41.638
24	10.856	12.401	13.848	15.659	33.196	36.415	39.364	42.980
25	11.524	13.120	14.611	16.473	34.382	37.652	40.646	44.314
26	12.198	13.844	15.379	17.292	35.563	38.885	41.923	45.642
27	12.878	14.573	16.151	18.114	36.741	40.113	43.195	46.963
28	13.565	15.308	16.928	18.939	37.916	41.337	44.461	48.278
29	14.256	16.047	17.708	19.768	39.087	42.557	45.722	49.588
30	14.953	16.791	18.493	20.599	40.256	43.773	46.979	50.892
40	22.164	24.433	26.509	29.051	51.805	55.758	59.342	63.691
60	37.485	40.482	43.188	46.459	74.397	79.082	83.298	88.379
80	53.540	57.153	60.391	64.278	96.578	101.879	106.629	112.329
100	70.065	74.222	77.929	82.358	118.498	124.342	129.561	135.807

Note: A more extensive table is provided as Table 3 of Appendix B.

TABLE 11.2 COMPUTATION OF THE CHI-SQUARE TEST STATISTIC FOR THE SCOTT MARKETING RESEARCH MARKET SHARE STUDY

Category	Hypothesized Proportion	Observed Frequency (f_i)	Expected Frequency (e_i)	Difference $(f_i - e_i)$	Squared Difference $(f_i - e_i)^2$	Squared Difference Divided by Expected Frequency $(f_i - e_i)^2/e_i$
Company A	.30	48	60	−12	144	2.40
Company B	.50	98	100	−2	4	0.04
Company C	.20	54	40	14	196	4.90
Total		200				$\chi^2 = 7.34$

Instead of using the *p*-value, we could use the critical value approach to draw the same conclusion. With $\alpha = .05$ and 2 degrees of freedom, the critical value for the test statistic is $\chi^2_{.05} = 5.991$. The upper tail rejection rule becomes

$$\text{Reject } H_0 \text{ if } \chi^2 \geq 5.991$$

With $7.34 > 5.991$, we reject H_0. The *p*-value approach and critical value approach provide the same hypothesis testing conclusion.

Although no further conclusions can be made as a result of the test, we can compare the observed and expected frequencies informally to obtain an idea of how the market share structure may change. Considering company C, we find that the observed frequency of 54 is larger than the expected frequency of 40. Because the expected frequency was based on current market shares, the larger observed frequency suggests that the new product will have a positive effect on company C's market share. Comparisons of the observed and expected frequencies for the other two companies indicate that company C's gain in market share will hurt company A more than company B.

Let us summarize the general steps that can be used to conduct a goodness of fit test for a hypothesized multinomial population distribution.

MULTINOMIAL DISTRIBUTION GOODNESS OF FIT TEST: A SUMMARY

1. State the null and alternative hypotheses.

   H_0: The population follows a multinomial distribution with specified probabilities for each of the *k* categories

   H_a: The population does not follow a multinomial distribution with the specified probabilities for each of the *k* categories

2. Select a random sample and record the observed frequencies f_i for each category.
3. Assume the null hypothesis is true and determine the expected frequency e_i in each category by multiplying the category probability by the sample size.
4. Compute the value of the test statistic.

$$\chi^2 = \sum_{i=1}^{k} \frac{(f_i - e_i)^2}{e_i}$$

(continued)

5. Rejection rule:

p-value approach:	Reject H_0 if *p*-value $\leq \alpha$
Critical value approach:	Reject H_0 if $\chi^2 \geq \chi_\alpha^2$

where α is the level of significance for the test and there are $k - 1$ degrees of freedom.

Using Excel to Conduct a Goodness of Fit Test

Excel can be used to conduct a goodness of fit test for the Scott Marketing Research Study. Refer to Figure 11.3 as we describe the tasks involved. The formula worksheet is in the background; the value worksheet is in the foreground.

Research

Enter Data: Column A is used to identify each of the 200 customers who made up the consumer panel in the study. Column B shows the purchase preference (A, B, or C) for each customer. The hypothesized proportions, 0.3, 0.5, and 0.2, were entered into cells E4:E6.

Enter Functions and Formulas: The Excel formulas in cells F4:J7 are used to compute the chi-square test statistic in a fashion parallel to that shown in Table 11.2. The result is the chi-square test statistic shown in cell J7 (7.34). The number of categories, 3, was entered into

FIGURE 11.3 EXCEL WORKSHEET FOR GOODNESS OF FIT TEST CONCERNING MARKET SHARE CHANGE

	A	B	C	D	E	F	G	H	I	J	K
1	Customer	Product								Squared Diff.	
2	1	B			Hyp.	Obs.	Exp.		Squared	Divided by	
3	2	A		Category	Proportion	Freq.	Freq.	Diff.	Diff.	Exp. Freq.	
4	3	C		Company A	0.3	=COUNTIF(B2:B201,"A")	=E4*F7	=F4-G4	=H4^2	=I4/G4	
5	4	C		Company B	0.5	=COUNTIF(B2:B201,"B")	=E5*F7	=F5-G5	=H5^2	=I5/G5	
6	5	C		Company C	0.2	=COUNTIF(B2:B201,"C")	=E6*F7	=F6-G6	=H6^2	=I6/G6	
7	6	A			Total	=SUM(F4:F6)				=SUM(J4:J6)	
8	7	A									
9	8	A		Number of Categories	3						
10	9	C									
11	10	A		Test Statistic	=J7						
12	11	C		Degrees of Freedom	=F9-1						
13	12	B									
14	13	C		*p*-value	=CHIDIST(F11,F12)						
15	14	A									
200	199	C									
201	200	C									
202											

Note: Rows 16–199 are hidden.

	A	B	C	D	E	F	G	H	I	J	K
1	Customer	Product								Squared Diff.	
2	1	B			Hyp.	Obs.	Exp.		Squared	Divided by	
3	2	A		Category	Proportion	Freq.	Freq.	Diff.	Diff.	Exp. Freq.	
4	3	C		Company A	0.3	48	60	-12	144	2.4	
5	4	C		Company B	0.5	98	100	-2	4	0.04	
6	5	C		Company C	0.2	54	40	14	196	4.9	
7	6	A			Total	200				7.34	
8	7	A									
9	8	A		Number of Categories	3						
10	9	C									
11	10	A		Test Statistic	7.34						
12	11	C		Degrees of Freedom	2						
13	12	B									
14	13	C		*p*-value	0.0255						
15	14	A									
200	199	C									
201	200	C									
202											

cell F9 and the two inputs used by Excel's CHIDIST function (test statistic and degrees of freedom) are in cells F11 and F12. The value computed in cell F14 using Excel's CHIDIST function is the area in the upper tail of the chi-square distribution to the right of the test statistic. So, this value is the appropriate p-value for our upper tail hypothesis test.

The value worksheet shows that the resulting p-value is 0.0255. Thus, with $\alpha = .05$, we reject H_0 and conclude that the introduction of the new product by company C will alter the current market share structure.

Exercises

Methods

11. Test the following hypotheses by using the χ^2 goodness of fit test.

$$H_0: p_A = .40, p_B = .40, \text{ and } p_C = .20$$
$$H_a: \text{The population proportions are not}$$
$$p_A = .40, p_B = .40, \text{ and } p_C = .20$$

A sample of size 200 yielded 60 in category A, 120 in category B, and 20 in category C. Use $\alpha = .01$ and test to see whether the proportions are as stated in H_0.
a. Use the p-value approach.
b. Repeat the test using the critical value approach.

12. Suppose we have a multinomial population with four categories: A, B, C, and D. The null hypothesis is that the proportion of items is the same in every category. The null hypothesis is

$$H_0: p_A = p_B = p_C = p_D = .25$$

A sample of size 300 yielded the following results.

A: 85   B: 95   C: 50   D: 70

Use $\alpha = .05$ to determine whether H_0 should be rejected. What is the p-value?

Applications

13. During the first 13 weeks of the television season, the Saturday evening 8:00 P.M. to 9:00 P.M. audience proportions were recorded as ABC 29%, CBS 28%, NBC 25%, and independents 18%. A sample of 300 homes two weeks after a Saturday night schedule revision yielded the following viewing audience data: ABC 95 homes, CBS 70 homes, NBC 89 homes, and independents 46 homes. Test with $\alpha = .05$ to determine whether the viewing audience proportions changed.

14. M&M/MARS, makers of M&M® Chocolate Candies, conducted a national poll in which consumers indicated their preference for colors. In the brochure "Colors," made available by M&M/MARS Consumer Affairs, the traditional distribution of colors for the plain candies is as follows:

Brown	Yellow	Red	Orange	Green	Blue
30%	20%	20%	10%	10%	10%

In a follow-up study, 1-pound bags were used to determine whether the reported percentages were valid. The following results were obtained for a sample of 506 plain candies.

Brown	Yellow	Red	Orange	Green	Blue
177	135	79	41	36	38

Use $\alpha = .05$ to determine whether these data support the percentages reported by the company.

15. Where do women most often buy casual clothing? Data from the U.S. Shopper Database provided the following percentages for women shopping at each of the various outlets (*The Wall Street Journal*, January 28, 2004).

Outlet	Percentage	Outlet	Percentage
Wal-Mart	24	Kohl's	8
Traditional department stores	11	Mail order	12
J.C. Penney	8	Other	37

The other category included outlets such as Target, Kmart, and Sears as well as numerous smaller specialty outlets. No individual outlet in this group accounted for more than 5% of the women shoppers. A recent survey using a sample of 140 women shoppers in Atlanta, Georgia, found 42 Wal-Mart, 20 traditional department store, 8 J.C. Penney, 10 Kohl's, 21 mail order, and 39 other outlet shoppers. Does this sample suggest that women shoppers in Atlanta differ from the shopping preferences expressed in the U.S. Shopper Database? What is the *p*-value? Use $\alpha = .05$. What is your conclusion?

16. The American Bankers Association collects data on the use of credit cards, debit cards, personal checks, and cash when consumers pay for in-store purchases (*The Wall Street Journal*, December 16, 2003). In 1999, the following usages were reported.

In-Store Purchase	Percentage
Credit card	22
Debit card	21
Personal check	18
Cash	39

A sample taken in 2003 found that for 220 in-stores purchases, 46 used a credit card, 67 used a debit card, 33 used a personal check, and 74 used cash.

a. At $\alpha = .01$, can we conclude that a change occurred in how customers paid for in-store purchases over the four-year period from 1999 to 2003? What is the *p*-value?

b. Compute the percentage of use for each method of payment using the 2003 sample data. What appears to have been the major change or changes over the four-year period?

c. In 2003, what percentage of payments was made using plastic (credit card or debit card)?

17. *The Wall Street Journal*'s Shareholder Scoreboard tracks the performance of 1000 major U.S. companies (*The Wall Street Journal*, March 10, 2003). The performance of each company is rated based on the annual total return, including stock price changes and the reinvestment of dividends. Ratings are assigned by dividing all 1000 companies into five groups from A (top

20%), B (next 20%), to E (bottom 20%). Shown here are the one-year ratings for a sample of 60 of the largest companies. Do the largest companies differ in performance from the performance of the 1000 companies in the Shareholder Scoreboard? Use $\alpha = .05$.

A	B	C	D	E
5	8	15	20	12

18. How well do airline companies serve their customers? A study showed the following customer ratings: 3% excellent, 28% good, 45% fair, and 24% poor (*BusinessWeek*, September 11, 2000). In a follow-up study of service by telephone companies, assume that a sample of 400 adults found the following customer ratings: 24 excellent, 124 good, 172 fair, and 80 poor. Is the distribution of the customer ratings for telephone companies different from the distribution of customer ratings for airline companies? Test with $\alpha = .01$. What is your conclusion?

(11.3) Test of Independence

Another important application of the chi-square distribution involves using sample data to test for the independence of two variables. Let us illustrate the test of independence by considering the study conducted by the Alber's Brewery of Tucson, Arizona. Alber's manufactures and distributes three types of beer: light, regular, and dark. In an analysis of the market segments for the three beers, the firm's market research group raised the question of whether preferences for the three beers differ among male and female beer drinkers. If beer preference is independent of the gender of the beer drinker, one advertising campaign will be initiated for all of Alber's beers. However, if beer preference depends on the gender of the beer drinker, the firm will tailor its promotions to different target markets.

A test of independence addresses the question of whether the beer preference (light, regular, or dark) is independent of the gender of the beer drinker (male, female). The hypotheses for this test of independence are

H_0: Beer preference is independent of the gender of the beer drinker

H_a: Beer preference is not independent of the gender of the beer drinker

To test whether two variables are independent, one sample is selected and crosstabulation is used to summarize the data for the two variables simultaneously.

Table 11.3 can be used to describe the situation being studied. After identification of the population as all male and female beer drinkers, a sample can be selected and each individual asked to state his or her preference for the three Alber's beers. Every individual in the sample will be classified in one of the six cells in the table. For example, an individual may be a male preferring regular beer (cell(1,2)), a female preferring light beer (cell(2,1)),

TABLE 11.3 CONTINGENCY TABLE FOR BEER PREFERENCE AND GENDER OF BEER DRINKER

		Beer Preference		
		Light	Regular	Dark
Gender	Male	cell(1,1)	cell(1,2)	cell(1,3)
	Female	cell(2,1)	cell(2,2)	cell(2,3)

TABLE 11.4   SAMPLE RESULTS FOR BEER PREFERENCES OF MALE AND FEMALE BEER DRINKERS (OBSERVED FREQUENCIES)

| | | Beer Preference | | | |
		Light	Regular	Dark	Total
Gender	**Male**	20	40	20	80
	Female	30	30	10	70
	Total	50	70	30	150

a female preferring dark beer (cell(2,3)), and so on. Because we have listed all possible combinations of beer preference and gender or, in other words, listed all possible contingencies, Table 11.3 is called a **contingency table**. The test of independence uses the contingency table format and for that reason is sometimes referred to as a *contingency table test*.

Suppose a simple random sample of 150 beer drinkers is selected. After tasting each beer, the individuals in the sample are asked to state their preference or first choice. The crosstabulation in Table 11.4 summarizes the responses for the study. As we see, the data for the test of independence are collected in terms of counts or frequencies for each cell or category. Of the 150 individuals in the sample, 20 were men who favored light beer, 40 were men who favored regular beer, 20 were men who favored dark beer, and so on.

The data in Table 11.4 are the observed frequencies for the six classes or categories. If we can determine the expected frequencies under the assumption of independence between beer preference and gender of the beer drinker, we can use the chi-square distribution to determine whether there is a significant difference between observed and expected frequencies.

Expected frequencies for the cells of the contingency table are based on the following rationale. First we assume that the null hypothesis of independence between beer preference and gender of the beer drinker is true. Then we note that in the entire sample of 150 beer drinkers, a total of 50 prefer light beer, 70 prefer regular beer, and 30 prefer dark beer. In terms of fractions we conclude that $^{50}/_{150} = \frac{1}{3}$ of the beer drinkers prefer light beer, $^{70}/_{150} = \frac{7}{15}$ prefer regular beer, and $^{30}/_{150} = \frac{1}{5}$ prefer dark beer. If the *independence* assumption is valid, we argue that these fractions must be applicable to both male and female beer drinkers. Thus, under the assumption of independence, we would expect the sample of 80 male beer drinkers to show that $(\frac{1}{3})80 = 26.67$ prefer light beer, $(\frac{7}{15})80 = 37.33$ prefer regular beer, and $(\frac{1}{5})80 = 16$ prefer dark beer. Application of the same fractions to the 70 female beer drinkers provides the expected frequencies shown in Table 11.5.

Let e_{ij} denote the expected frequency for the contingency table category in row i and column j. With this notation, let us reconsider the expected frequency calculation for males

TABLE 11.5   EXPECTED FREQUENCIES IF BEER PREFERENCE IS INDEPENDENT OF THE GENDER OF THE BEER DRINKER

| | | Beer Preference | | | |
		Light	Regular	Dark	Total
Gender	**Male**	26.67	37.33	16.00	80
	Female	23.33	32.67	14.00	70
	Total	50.00	70.00	30.00	150

Type of Ticket	Type of Flight	
	Domestic Flights	**International Flights**
First class	29	22
Business/executive class	95	121
Full fare economy/coach class	518	135

Use $\alpha = .05$ and test for the independence of type of flight and type of ticket. What is your conclusion?

22. In a study of brand loyalty in the automotive industry, new-car customers were asked whether the make of their new car was the same as the make of their previous car (*Business Week*, May 8, 2000). The breakdown of 600 responses shows the brand loyalty for domestic, European, and Asian cars.

Purchased	Manufacturer		
	Domestic	**European**	**Asian**
Same Make	125	55	68
Different Make	140	105	107

a. Conduct a hypothesis test to determine whether brand loyalty is independent of the manufacturer. Use $\alpha = .05$. What is your conclusion?
b. If a significant difference is found, which manufacturer appears to have the greatest brand loyalty?

23. With double-digit annual percentage increases in the cost of health insurance, more and more workers are likely to lack health insurance coverage (*USA Today*, January 23, 2004). The following sample data provide a comparison of workers with and without health insurance coverage for small, medium, and large companies. For the purposes of this study, small companies are companies that have fewer than 100 employees. Medium companies have 100 to 999 employees, and large companies have 1000 or more employees. Sample data are reported for 50 employees of small companies, 75 employees of medium companies, and 100 employees of large companies.

Size of Company	Health Insurance		Total
	Yes	**No**	
Small	36	14	50
Medium	65	10	75
Large	88	12	100

a. Conduct a test of independence to determine whether employee health insurance coverage is independent of the size of the company. Use $\alpha = .05$. What is the p-value, and what is your conclusion?
b. The *USA Today* article indicated employees of small companies are more likely to lack health insurance coverage. Use percentages based on the preceding data to support this conclusion.

24. A State of Washington's Public Interest Research Group (PIRG) study showed that 46% of full-time college students work 25 or more hours per week. The PIRG study provided data on the effects of working on grades (*USA Today,* April 17, 2002). A sample of 200 students included 90 who worked 1–15 hours per week, 60 who worked 16–24 hours per week, and 50 who worked 25–34 hours per week. The sample number of students indicating their work had a positive effect, no effect, or a negative effect on grades is as follows.

	Effect on Grades			
Hours Worked per Week	Positive	None	Negative	Total
1–15 hours	26	50	14	90
16–24 hours	16	27	17	60
25–34 hours	11	19	20	50

     a. Conduct a test of independence to determine whether the effect on grades is independent of the hours worked per week. Use $\alpha = .05$. What is the *p*-value, and what is your conclusion?

     b. Use row percentages to learn more about how working affects grades. What is your conclusion?

25. Negative appeal is recognized as an effective method of persuasion in advertising. A study in *The Journal of Advertising* reported the results of a content analysis of guilt and fear advertisements in 24 magazines. The number of ads with guilt and fear appeals that appeared in selected magazine types follows.

	Type of Appeal	
Magazine Type	Number of Ads with Guilt Appeals	Number of Ads with Fear Appeals
News and opinion	20	10
General editorial	15	11
Family-oriented	30	19
Business/financial	22	17
Female-oriented	16	14
African-American	12	15

Use the chi-square test of independence with a .01 level of significance to analyze the data. What is your conclusion?

26. Businesses are increasingly placing orders online. The Performance Measurement Group collected data on the rates of correctly filled electronic orders by industry (*Investor's Business Daily,* May 8, 2000). Assume a sample of 700 electronic orders provided the following results.

	Industry			
Order	Pharmaceutical	Consumer	Computers	Telecommunications
Correct	207	136	151	178
Incorrect	3	4	9	12

     a. Conduct a hypothesis test to determine whether correctness of order fulfillment is independent of industry. Use $\alpha = .05$. What is your conclusion?

     b. Which industry has the highest percentage of correctly filled orders?

27. The National Sleep Foundation used a survey to determine whether hours of sleeping per night are independent of age (*Newsweek,* January 19, 2004). The following show the hours of sleep on weeknights for a sample of individuals age 49 and younger and for a sample of individuals age 50 and older.

Age	Hours of Sleep				Total
	Fewer than 6	6 to 6.9	7 to 7.9	8 or more	
49 or younger	38	60	77	65	240
50 or older	36	57	75	92	260

a. Conduct a test of independence to determine whether the hours of sleep on weeknights are independent of age. Use $\alpha = .05$. What is the *p*-value, and what is your conclusion?
b. What is your estimate of the percentage of people who sleep fewer than 6 hours, 6 to 6.9 hours, 7 to 7.9 hours, and 8 or more hours on weeknights?

Summary

In this chapter, we described statistical procedures for comparisons involving proportions and the contingency table test for independence of two variables. In the first section, we compared a proportion for one population with the same proportion from another population. We described how to construct an interval estimate for the difference between the proportions and how to conduct a hypothesis test to learn whether the difference between the proportions was statistically significant.

In the second section, we focused on a single multinomial population. There we saw how to conduct hypothesis tests to determine whether the sample proportions for the categories of the multinomial population were significantly different from the hypothesized values. The chi-square goodness of fit test was used to make the comparison.

The final section was concerned with tests of independence for two variables. A test of independence for two variables is an extension of the methodology employed in the goodness of fit test for a multinomial population. A contingency table is used to determine the observed and expected frequencies. Then a chi-square value is computed. Large chi-square values, caused by large differences between observed and expected frequencies, lead to the rejection of the null hypothesis of independence.

Glossary

Pooled estimator of *p* An estimator of a population proportion obtained by computing a weighted average of the sample proportions obtained from two independent samples.

Multinomial population A population in which each element is assigned to one and only one of several categories. The multinomial distribution extends the binomial distribution from two to three or more outcomes.

Goodness of fit test A statistical test conducted to determine whether to reject a hypothesized probability distribution for a population.

Contingency table A table used to summarize observed and expected frequencies for a test of independence.

Key Formulas

Point Estimator of the Difference Between Two Population Proportions

$$\bar{p}_1 - \bar{p}_2 \tag{11.1}$$

Standard Error of $\bar{p}_1 - \bar{p}_2$

$$\sigma_{\bar{p}_1 - \bar{p}_2} = \sqrt{\frac{p_1(1 - p_1)}{n_1} + \frac{p_2(1 - p_2)}{n_2}} \tag{11.2}$$

Interval Estimate of the Difference Between Two Population Proportions

$$\bar{p}_1 - \bar{p}_2 \pm z_{\alpha/2}\sqrt{\frac{\bar{p}_1(1 - \bar{p}_1)}{n_1} + \frac{\bar{p}_2(1 - \bar{p}_2)}{n_2}} \tag{11.4}$$

Standard Error of $\bar{p}_1 - \bar{p}_2$ When $p_1 = p_2 = p$

$$\sigma_{\bar{p}_1 - \bar{p}_2} = \sqrt{p(1 - p)\left(\frac{1}{n_1} + \frac{1}{n_2}\right)} \tag{11.5}$$

Pooled Estimator of p When $p_1 = p_2 = p$

$$\bar{p} = \frac{n_1\bar{p}_1 + n_2\bar{p}_2}{n_1 + n_2} \tag{11.6}$$

Test Statistic for Hypothesis Tests About $p_1 - p_2$

$$z = \frac{(\bar{p}_1 - \bar{p}_2)}{\sqrt{\bar{p}(1 - \bar{p})\left(\frac{1}{n_1} + \frac{1}{n_2}\right)}} \tag{11.7}$$

Test Statistic for Goodness of Fit

$$\chi^2 = \sum_{i=1}^{k} \frac{(f_i - e_i)^2}{e_i} \tag{11.8}$$

Expected Frequencies for Contingency Tables Under the Assumption of Independence

$$e_{ij} = \frac{(\text{Row } i \text{ Total})(\text{Column } j \text{ Total})}{\text{Sample Size}} \tag{11.9}$$

Test Statistic for Independence

$$\chi^2 = \sum_i \sum_j \frac{(f_{ij} - e_{ij})^2}{e_{ij}} \tag{11.10}$$

Supplementary Exercises

28. Jupiter Media used a survey to determine how people use their free time. Watching television was the most popular activity selected by both men and women (*The Wall Street Journal*, January 26, 2004). The proportion of men and the proportion of women who selected watching television as their most popular leisure time activity can be estimated from the following sample data.

Gender	Sample Size	Watching Television
Men	800	248
Women	600	156

a. State the hypotheses that can be used to test for a difference between the proportion for the population of men and the proportion for the population of women who selected watching television as their most popular leisure time activity.
b. What is the sample proportion of men who selected watching television as their most popular leisure time activity? What is the sample proportion of women?
c. Conduct the hypothesis test and compute the p-value. At a .05 level of significance, what is your conclusion?
d. What is the margin of error and 95% confidence interval estimate of the difference between the population proportions?

29. A large automobile insurance company selected samples of single and married male policyholders and recorded the number who made an insurance claim over the preceding three-year period.

Single Policyholders	Married Policyholders
$n_1 = 400$	$n_2 = 900$
Number making claims = 76	Number making claims = 90

a. Use $\alpha = .05$. Test to determine whether the claim rates differ between single and married male policyholders.
b. Provide a 95% confidence interval for the difference between the proportions for the two populations.

30. Medical tests were conducted to learn about drug-resistant tuberculosis. Of 142 cases tested in New Jersey, nine were found to be drug-resistant. Of 268 cases tested in Texas, five were found to be drug-resistant. Do these data suggest a statistically significant difference between the proportions of drug-resistant cases in the two states? Use a .02 level of significance. What is the p-value, and what is your conclusion?

31. In July 2001, the Harris Ad Track Research Service conducted a survey to evaluate the effectiveness of a major advertising campaign for Kodak cameras (*USA Today*, August 27, 2001). In a sample of 430 respondents, 38% thought the ads were very effective. In another sample of 285 respondents to other ad campaigns, 23% thought the ads were very effective.
a. Estimate the number of respondents who thought the Kodak ads were very effective and the number of respondents who felt the other ads were very effective.
b. Provide a 95% confidence interval for the difference in proportions.
c. On the basis of your results in part (b), do you believe the Kodak advertising campaign is more effective than most advertising campaigns?

32. In June 2001, 38% of fund managers surveyed believed that the core inflation rate would be higher in one year. One month later a similar survey revealed that 22% of fund managers expected the core inflation rate to be higher in one year (*Global Research Highlights*, Merrill Lynch, July 20, 2001). Assume that the sample size was 200 in both the June and July surveys.
a. Develop a point estimate of the difference between the June and July proportions of fund managers who felt the core inflation rate would be higher in one year.
b. Develop hypotheses such that rejection of the null hypothesis allows us to conclude that inflation expectations diminished between June and July.
c. Conduct a test of the hypotheses in part (b) using $\alpha = .01$. What is your conclusion?

33. Seven percent of mutual fund investors rate corporate stocks "very safe," 58% rate them "somewhat safe," 24% rate them "not very safe," 4% rate them "not at all safe," and 7% are "not sure." A *BusinessWeek*/Harris poll asked 529 mutual fund investors how they would rate corporate bonds on safety. The responses are as follows.

Safety Rating	Frequency
Very safe	48
Somewhat safe	323
Not very safe	79
Not at all safe	16
Not sure	63
Total	529

Do mutual fund investors' attitudes toward corporate bonds differ from their attitudes toward corporate stocks? Support your conclusion with a statistical test. Use $\alpha = .01$.

34. Since 2000, the Toyota Camry, Honda Accord, and Ford Taurus have been the three best-selling passenger cars in the United States. Based on the 2003 sales data, the market shares among the top three are as follows: Toyota Camry 37%, Honda Accord 34%, and Ford Taurus 29% (*The World Almanac,* 2004). Assume a sample of 1200 sales of passenger cars during the first quarter of 2004 shows the following.

Passenger Car	Units Sold
Toyota Camry	480
Honda Accord	390
Ford Taurus	330

Can these data be used to conclude that the market shares among the top three passenger cars have changed during the first quarter of 2004? What is the *p*-value? Use a .05 level of significance. What is your conclusion?

35. A regional transit authority is concerned about the number of riders on one of its bus routes. In setting up the route, the assumption is that the number of riders is the same on every day from Monday through Friday. Using the following data, test with $\alpha = .05$ to determine whether the transit authority's assumption is correct.

Day	Number of Riders
Monday	13
Tuesday	16
Wednesday	28
Thursday	17
Friday	16

36. The results of *Computerworld*'s Annual Job Satisfaction Survey showed that 28% of information systems (IS) managers are very satisfied with their job, 46% are somewhat satisfied, 12% are neither satisfied nor dissatisfied, 10% are somewhat dissatisfied, and 4% are very dissatisfied. Suppose that a sample of 500 computer programmers yielded the following results.

Category	Number of Respondents
Very satisfied	105
Somewhat satisfied	235
Neither	55
Somewhat dissatisfied	90
Very dissatisfied	15

Use $\alpha = .05$ and test to determine whether the job satisfaction for computer programmers is different from the job satisfaction for IS managers.

37. A sample of parts provided the following contingency table data on part quality by production shift.

Shift	Number Good	Number Defective
First	368	32
Second	285	15
Third	176	24

Use $\alpha = .05$ and test the hypothesis that part quality is independent of the production shift. What is your conclusion?

38. *The Wall Street Journal* Subscriber Study showed data on the employment status of subscribers. Sample results corresponding to subscribers of the eastern and western editions are shown here.

	Region	
Employment Status	Eastern Edition	Western Edition
Full-time	1105	574
Part-time	31	15
Self-employed/consultant	229	186
Not employed	485	344

Use $\alpha = .05$ and test the hypothesis that employment status is independent of the region. What is your conclusion?

39. A lending institution supplied the following data on loan approvals by four loan officers. Use $\alpha = .05$ and test to determine whether the loan approval decision is independent of the loan officer reviewing the loan application.

	Loan Approval Decision	
Loan Officer	Approved	Rejected
Miller	24	16
McMahon	17	13
Games	35	15
Runk	11	9

40. Data on the marital status of men and women ages 20 to 29 were obtained as part of a national survey. The results from a sample of 350 men and 400 women follow.

	Marital Status		
Gender	Never Married	Married	Divorced
Men	234	106	10
Women	216	168	16

a. Use $\alpha = .01$ and test for independence between marital status and gender. What is your conclusion?
b. Summarize the percentage in each marital status category for men and for women.

41. Barna Research Group collected data showing church attendance by age group (*USA Today*, November 20, 2003). Use the sample data to determine whether attending church is independent of age. Use a .05 level of significance. What is your conclusion? What conclusion can you draw about church attendance as individuals grow older?

	Church Attendance		
Age	Yes	No	Total
20 to 29	31	69	100
30 to 39	63	87	150
40 to 49	94	106	200
50 to 59	72	78	150

42. A salesperson makes four calls per day. A sample of 100 days gives the following frequencies of sales volumes.

Number of Sales	Observed Frequency (days)
0	30
1	32
2	25
3	10
4	3
Total	100

Records show sales are made on 30% of all sales calls. Assuming independent sales calls, the number of sales per day should follow a binomial distribution. The binomial probability function presented in Chapter 5 is

$$f(x) = \frac{n!}{x!(n - x)!} p^x (1 - p)^{n-x}$$

For this exercise, assume that the population has a binomial distribution with $n = 4$, $p = .30$, and $x = 0, 1, 2, 3,$ and 4.

a. Compute the expected frequencies for $x = 0, 1, 2, 3$, and 4 by using the binomial probability function. Combine categories if necessary to satisfy the requirement that the expected frequency is five or more for all categories.
b. Use the goodness of fit test to determine whether the assumption of a binomial distribution should be rejected. Use $\alpha = .05$. Because no parameters of the binomial distribution were estimated from the sample data, the degrees of freedom are $k - 1$ when k is the number of categories.

Case Problem   A Bipartisan Agenda for Change

In a study conducted by Zogby International for the *Democrat and Chronicle,* more than 700 New Yorkers were polled to determine whether the New York state government works. Respondents surveyed were asked questions involving pay cuts for state legislators, restrictions on lobbyists, term limits for legislators, and whether state citizens should be able to put matters directly on the state ballot for a vote (*Democrat and Chronicle,* December 7, 1997). The results regarding several proposed reforms had broad support, crossing all demographic and political lines.

Suppose that a follow-up survey of 100 individuals who live in the western region of New York was conducted. The party affiliation (Democrat, Independent, Republican) of each individual surveyed was recorded, as well as their responses to the following three questions.

1. Should legislative pay be cut for every day the state budget is late?
    Yes _____   No _____
2. Should there be more restrictions on lobbyists?
    Yes _____   No _____
3. Should there be term limits requiring that legislators serve a fixed number of years?
    Yes _____   No _____

NYReform

The responses were coded using 1 for a *yes* response and 2 for a *no* response. The complete data set is available on the data disk in the data set named NYReform.

Managerial Report

1. Use descriptive statistics to summarize the data from this study. What are your preliminary conclusions about the independence of the response (Yes or No) and party affiliation for each of the three questions in the survey?
2. With regard to question 1, test for the independence of the response (Yes and No) and party affiliation. Use $\alpha = .05$.
3. With regard to question 2, test for the independence of the response (Yes and No) and party affiliation. Use $\alpha = .05$.
4. With regard to question 3, test for the independence of the response (Yes and No) and party affiliation. Use $\alpha = .05$.
5. Does it appear that there is broad support for change across all political lines? Explain.

CHAPTER 12

Simple Linear Regression

CONTENTS

STATISTICS IN PRACTICE:
ALLIANCE DATA SYSTEMS

12.1 SIMPLE LINEAR
REGRESSION MODEL
Regression Model and
Regression Equation
Estimated Regression Equation

12.2 LEAST SQUARES METHOD
Using Excel to Develop a Scatter
Diagram and Compute
the Estimated Regression
Equation

12.3 COEFFICIENT OF
DETERMINATION
Using Excel to Compute
the Coefficient of
Determination
Correlation Coefficient

12.4 MODEL ASSUMPTIONS

12.5 TESTING FOR SIGNIFICANCE
Estimate of σ^2
t Test
Confidence Interval for β_1
F Test
Some Cautions About
the Interpretation of
Significance Tests

12.6 EXCEL'S REGRESSION TOOL
Using Excel's Regression Tool
for the Armand's Pizza Parlors
Problem
Interpretation of Estimated
Regression Equation Output
Interpretation of ANOVA Output
Interpretation of Regression
Statistics Output

12.7 USING THE ESTIMATED
REGRESSION EQUATION
FOR ESTIMATION AND
PREDICTION
Point Estimation
Interval Estimation
Confidence Interval Estimate of
the Mean Value of y
Prediction Interval Estimate of an
Individual Value of y
Using Excel to Develop
Confidence and Prediction
Interval Estimates

12.8 RESIDUAL ANALYSIS:
VALIDATING MODEL
ASSUMPTIONS
Residual Plot Against x
Residual Plot Against $\hat{y}$
Using Excel's Regression Tool to
Construct a Residual Plot

FIGURE 12.4   GRAPH OF THE ESTIMATED REGRESSION EQUATION FOR ARMAND'S
PIZZA PARLORS: $\hat{y} = 60 + 5x$

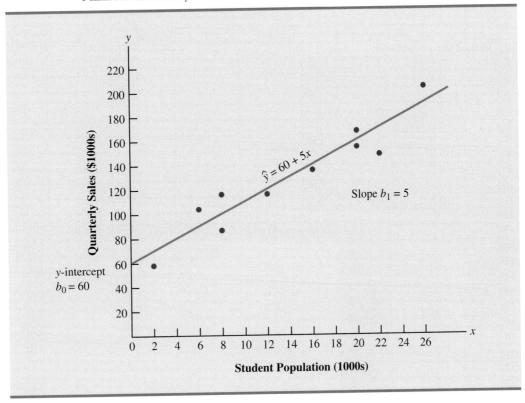

Using Excel to Develop a Scatter Diagram and Compute the Estimated Regression Equation

In Section 2.4 we showed how Excel's Chart Wizard could be used to construct a scatter diagram. Once a scatter diagram has been developed, Excel's Chart menu provides options for computing the estimated regression equation and displaying the graph of the estimated regression equation. We will demonstrate these capabilities using the Armand's Pizza Parlors data appearing in Table 12.1. Refer to Figure 12.5 as we describe the tasks involved.

Enter Data: The labels Restaurant, Population, and Sales are entered into cells A1:C1 of the worksheet. To identify each of the 10 observations, we entered the numbers 1 through 10 into cells A2:A11. The sample data have been entered into cells B2:C11.

Apply Tools: We will first use Excel's Chart Wizard to produce a scatter diagram. We will then show how options available on the Chart menu can be used to compute the estimated regression equation and to display the estimated regression line.

Step 1. Select cells B1:C11
Step 2. Click the **Chart Wizard** button on the standard toolbar (or select the **Insert** menu and choose the **Chart** option)
Step 3. When the **Chart Wizard - Step 1 of 4 - Chart Type** dialog box appears:
　　　　Choose **XY (Scatter)** in the **Chart type** list
　　　　Choose **Scatter** from the **Chart sub-type** display
　　　　Select **Next >**
Step 4. When the **Chart Wizard - Step 2 of 4 - Chart Source Data** dialog box appears:
　　　　Select **Next >**

FIGURE 12.5   SCATTER DIAGRAM, ESTIMATED REGRESSION EQUATION, AND THE ESTIMATED REGRESSION LINE FOR ARMAND'S PIZZA PARLORS

	A	B	C	D	E	F	G	H	I
1	**Restaurant**	**Population**	**Sales**						
2	1	2	58						
3	2	6	105						
4	3	8	88						
5	4	8	118						
6	5	12	117						
7	6	16	137						
8	7	20	157						
9	8	20	169						
10	9	22	149						
11	10	26	202						
12									
13									
14									
15									
16									
17									
18									
19									
20									
21									
22									
23									
24									
25									
26									
27									
28									
29									
30									

The chart embedded in the worksheet shows a scatter diagram with Quarterly Sales ($1000s) on the vertical axis (0 to 220) and Student Population (1000s) on the horizontal axis (0 to 28), with the estimated regression line labeled $y = 5x + 60$.

Step 5. When the **Chart Wizard - Step 3 of 4 - Chart Options** dialog box appears:
    Select the **Titles** tab and then
        Delete **Sales** in the Chart title box
        Enter **Student Population (1000s)** in the **Value (X) axis** box
        Enter **Quarterly Sales ($1000s)** in the **Value (Y) axis** box
    Select the **Legend** tab and then
        Remove the check in the **Show Legend** box
    Select the **Gridlines** tab
        Remove the check in the **Value (Y) axis Major Gridlines** box
    Select **Next >**

Step 6. When the **Chart Wizard - Step 4 of 4 - Chart Location** dialog box appears:
    Specify a location for the new chart (we used the default setting of the current worksheet)
    Select **Finish** to display the scatter diagram

Step 7. Position the mouse pointer over any data point and right-click to display the **Chart** menu was used to provide an overall rating for each notebook tested in the study. A score in the 90s is exceptional, while one in the 70s is above average. The performance scores and the overall ratings for the 15 notebooks follow.

PCs

Make and Model	Performance Score	Overall Rating
AMS Tech Roadster 15CTA380	115	67
Compaq Armada M700	191	78
Compaq Prosignia Notebook 150	153	79
Dell Inspiron 3700 C466GT	194	80
Dell Inspiron 7500 R500VT	236	84
Dell Latitude Cpi A366XT	184	76
Enpower ENP-313 Pro	184	77
Gateway Solo 9300LS	216	92
HP Pavilion Notebook PC	185	83
IBM ThinkPad I Series 1480	183	78
Micro Express NP7400	189	77
Micron TransPort NX PII-400	202	78
NEC Versa SX	192	78
Sceptre Soundx 5200	141	73
Sony VAIO PCG-F340	187	77

a. Develop a scatter diagram for these data with performance score as the independent variable.
b. Develop the least squares estimated regression equation.
c. Estimate the overall rating for a new PC that has a performance score of 225.

11. Although delays at major airports are now less frequent, it helps to know which airports are likely to throw off your schedule. In addition, if your plane is late arriving at a particular airport where you must make a connection, how likely is it that the departure will be late and thus increase your chances of making the connection? The following data show the percentage of late arrivals and departures during August for 13 airports (*Business 2.0*, February 2002).

Airport

Airport	Late Arrivals (%)	Late Departures (%)
Atlanta	24	22
Charlotte	20	20
Chicago	30	29
Cincinnati	20	19
Dallas	20	22
Denver	23	23
Detroit	18	19
Houston	20	16
Minneapolis	18	18
Phoenix	21	22
Pittsburgh	25	22
Salt Lake City	18	17
St. Louis	16	16

a. Develop a scatter diagram for these data with the percentage of late arrivals as the independent variable.
b. What does the scatter diagram developed in part (a) indicate about the relationship between late arrivals and late departures?
c. Use the least squares method to develop the estimated regression equation.

d. Provide an interpretation for the slope of the estimated regression equation.
e. Suppose the percentage of late arrivals at the Philadelphia airport for August was 22%. What is an estimate of the percentage of late departures?

12. The following table gives the number of employees and the revenue (in millions of dollars) for 20 companies (*Fortune*, April 17, 2000).

EmpRev

Company	Employees	Revenue ($ millions)
Sprint	77,600	19,930
Chase Manhattan	74,801	33,710
Computer Sciences	50,000	7,660
Wells Fargo	89,355	21,795
Sunbeam	12,200	2,398
CBS	29,000	7,510
Time Warner	69,722	27,333
Steelcase	16,200	2,743
Georgia-Pacific	57,000	17,796
Toro	1,275	4,673
American Financial	9,400	3,334
Fluor	53,561	12,417
Phillips Petroleum	15,900	13,852
Cardinal Health	36,000	25,034
Borders Group	23,500	2,999
MCI Worldcom	77,000	37,120
Consolidated Edison	14,269	7,491
IBP	45,000	14,075
Super Value	50,000	17,421
H&R Block	4,200	1,669

a. Develop a scatter diagram for these data with number of employees as the independent variable.
b. What does the scatter diagram developed in part (a) indicate about the relationship between number of employees and revenue?
c. Develop the estimated regression equation for these data.
d. Use the estimated regression equation to predict the revenue for a firm with 75,000 employees.

13. To the Internal Revenue Service, the reasonableness of total itemized deductions depends on the taxpayer's adjusted gross income. Large deductions, which include charity and medical deductions, are more reasonable for taxpayers with large adjusted gross incomes. If a taxpayer claims larger than average itemized deductions for a given level of income, the chances of an IRS audit are increased. Data (in thousands of dollars) on adjusted gross income and the average or reasonable amount of itemized deductions follow.

Adjusted Gross Income ($1000s)	Reasonable Amount of Itemized Deductions ($1000s)
22	9.6
27	9.6
32	10.1
48	11.1
65	13.5
85	17.7
120	25.5

a. Develop a scatter diagram for these data with adjusted gross income as the independent variable.
b. Use the least squares method to develop the estimated regression equation.
c. Estimate a reasonable level of total itemized deductions for a taxpayer with an adjusted gross income of $52,500. If this taxpayer claimed itemized deductions of $20,400, would the IRS agent's request for an audit appear justified? Explain.

14. Starting salaries for accountants and auditors in Rochester, New York, trail those of many U.S. cities. The following data show the starting salary (in thousands of dollars) and the cost of living index for Rochester and nine other metropolitan areas (*Democrat and Chronicle,* September 1, 2002). The cost of living index, based on a city's food, housing, taxes, and other costs, ranges from 0 (most expensive) to 100 (least expensive).

Salaries

Metropolitan Area	Index	Salary ($1000s)
Oklahoma City	82.44	23.9
Tampa/St. Petersburg/Clearwater	79.89	24.5
Indianapolis	55.53	27.4
Buffalo/Niagara Falls	41.36	27.7
Atlanta	39.38	27.1
Rochester	28.05	25.6
Sacramento	25.50	28.7
Raleigh/Durham/Chapel Hill	13.32	26.7
San Diego	3.12	27.8
Honolulu	0.57	28.3

a. Develop a scatter diagram for these data with the cost of living index as the independent variable.
b. Develop the estimated regression equation relating the cost of living index to the starting salary.
c. Estimate the starting salary for a metropolitan area with a cost of living index of 50.

(12.3) Coefficient of Determination

For the Armand's Pizza Parlors example, we developed the estimated regression equation $\hat{y} = 60 + 5x$ to approximate the linear relationship between the size of the student population x and quarterly sales y. A question now is: How well does the estimated regression equation fit the data? In this section, we show that the **coefficient of determination** provides a measure of the goodness of fit for the estimated regression equation.

For the ith observation, the difference between the observed value of the dependent variable, y_i, and the estimated value of the dependent variable, $\hat{y}_i$, is called the **ith residual**. The ith residual represents the error in using $\hat{y}_i$ to estimate y_i. Thus, for the ith observation, the residual is $y_i - \hat{y}_i$. The sum of squares of these residuals or errors is the quantity that is minimized by the least squares method. This quantity, also known as the *sum of squares due to error,* is denoted by SSE.

SUM OF SQUARES DUE TO ERROR

$$SSE = \Sigma(y_i - \hat{y}_i)^2 \tag{12.8}$$

The value of SSE is a measure of the error in using the estimated regression equation to estimate the values of the dependent variable in the sample.

TABLE 12.3   CALCULATION OF SSE FOR ARMAND'S PIZZA PARLORS

Restaurant i	x_i = Student Population (1000s)	y_i = Quarterly Sales ($1000s)	Predicted Sales $\hat{y}_i = 60 + 5x_i$	Error $y_i - \hat{y}_i$	Squared Error $(y_i - \hat{y}_i)^2$
1	2	58	70	−12	144
2	6	105	90	15	225
3	8	88	100	−12	144
4	8	118	100	18	324
5	12	117	120	−3	9
6	16	137	140	−3	9
7	20	157	160	−3	9
8	20	169	160	9	81
9	22	149	170	−21	441
10	26	202	190	12	144
					SSE = 1530

In Table 12.3 we show the calculations required to compute the sum of squares due to error for the Armand's Pizza Parlors example. For instance, for restaurant 1 the values of the independent and dependent variables are $x_1 = 2$ and $y_1 = 58$. Using the estimated regression equation, we find that the estimated value of quarterly sales for restaurant 1 is $\hat{y}_1 = 60 + 5(2) = 70$. Thus, the error in using $\hat{y}_1$ to estimate y_1 for restaurant 1 is $y_1 - \hat{y}_1 = 58 - 70 = -12$. The squared error, $(-12)^2 = 144$, is shown in the last column of Table 12.3. After computing and squaring the residuals for each restaurant in the sample, we sum them to obtain SSE = 1530. Thus, SSE = 1530 measures the error in using the estimated regression equation $\hat{y} = 60 + 5x$ to predict sales.

Now suppose we are asked to develop an estimate of quarterly sales without knowledge of the size of the student population. Without knowledge of any related variables, we would use the sample mean as an estimate of quarterly sales at any given restaurant. Table 12.2 shows that for the sales data, $\Sigma y_i = 1300$. Hence, the mean value of quarterly sales for the sample of 10 Armand's restaurants is $\bar{y} = \Sigma y_i / n = 1300/10 = 130$. In Table 12.4 we show the sum of squared deviations obtained by using the sample mean $\bar{y} = 130$ to estimate the value of quarterly sales for each restaurant in the sample. For the ith restaurant in the sample, the difference $y_i - \bar{y}$ provides a measure of the error involved in using $\bar{y}$ to estimate sales. The corresponding sum of squares, called the *total sum of squares,* is denoted SST.

TOTAL SUM OF SQUARES

$$\text{SST} = \Sigma(y_i - \bar{y})^2 \qquad\qquad \text{(12.9)}$$

The sum at the bottom of the last column in Table 12.4 is the total sum of squares for Armand's Pizza Parlors; it is SST = 15,730.

With SST = 15,730 and SSE = 1530, the estimated regression line provides a much better fit to the data than the line $y = \bar{y}$.

In Figure 12.6 we show the estimated regression line $\hat{y} = 60 + 5x$ and the line corresponding to $\bar{y} = 130$. Note that the points cluster more closely around the estimated regression line than they do about the line $\bar{y} = 130$. For example, for the 10th restaurant in the sample we see that the error is much larger when $\bar{y} = 130$ is used as an estimate of y_{10} than when $\hat{y}_{10} = 60 + 5(26) = 190$ is used. We can think of SST as a measure of how well the observations cluster about the $\bar{y}$ line and SSE as a measure of how well the observations cluster about the $\hat{y}$ line.

TABLE 12.4   COMPUTATION OF THE TOTAL SUM OF SQUARES FOR ARMAND'S PIZZA PARLORS

Restaurant i	x_i = Student Population (1000s)	y_i = Quarterly Sales ($1000s)	Deviation $y_i - \bar{y}$	Squared Deviation $(y_i - \bar{y})^2$
1	2	58	−72	5,184
2	6	105	−25	625
3	8	88	−42	1,764
4	8	118	−12	144
5	12	117	−13	169
6	16	137	7	49
7	20	157	27	729
8	20	169	39	1,521
9	22	149	19	361
10	26	202	72	5,184
				SST = 15,730

FIGURE 12.6   DEVIATIONS ABOUT THE ESTIMATED REGRESSION LINE AND THE LINE $y = \bar{y}$ FOR ARMAND'S PIZZA PARLORS

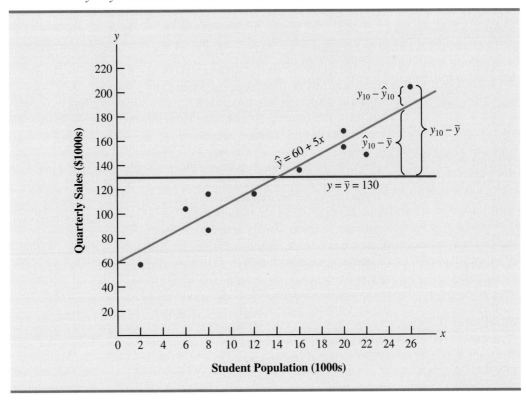

To measure how much the $\hat{y}$ values on the estimated regression line deviate from $\bar{y}$, another sum of squares is computed. This sum of squares, called the *sum of squares due to regression,* is denoted SSR.

SUM OF SQUARES DUE TO REGRESSION

$$SSR = \Sigma(\hat{y}_i - \bar{y})^2 \qquad \text{(12.10)}$$

From the preceding discussion, we should expect that SST, SSR, and SSE are related. Indeed, the relationship among these three sums of squares provides one of the most important results in statistics.

RELATIONSHIP AMONG SST, SSR, AND SSE

$$SST = SSR + SSE \qquad \text{(12.11)}$$

SSR can be thought of as the explained portion of SST, and SSE can be thought of as the unexplained portion of SST.

where

> SST = total sum of squares
> SSR = sum of squares due to regression
> SSE = sum of squares due to error

Equation (12.11) shows that the total sum of squares can be partitioned into two components, the regression sum of squares and the sum of squares due to error. Hence, if the values of any two of these sums of squares are known, the third sum of squares can be computed easily. For instance, in the Armand's Pizza Parlors example, we already know that SSE = 1530 and SST = 15,730; therefore, solving for SSR in equation (12.11), we find that the sum of squares due to regression is

$$SSR = SST - SSE = 15,730 - 1530 = 14,200$$

Now let us see how the three sums of squares, SST, SSR, and SSE, can be used to provide a measure of the goodness of fit for the estimated regression equation. The estimated regression equation would provide a perfect fit if every value of the dependent variable y_i happened to lie on the estimated regression line. In this case, $y_i - \hat{y}_i$ would be zero for each observation, resulting in SSE = 0. Because SST = SSR + SSE, we see that for a perfect fit SSR must equal SST, and the ratio (SSR/SST) must equal one. Poorer fits will result in larger values for SSE. Solving for SSE in equation (12.11), we see that SSE = SST − SSR. Hence, the largest value for SSE (and hence the poorest fit) occurs when SSR = 0 and SSE = SST.

The ratio SSR/SST, which will take values between zero and one, is used to evaluate the goodness of fit for the estimated regression equation. This ratio is called the *coefficient of determination* and is denoted by r^2.

COEFFICIENT OF DETERMINATION

$$r^2 = \frac{SSR}{SST} \qquad \text{(12.12)}$$

For the Armand's Pizza Parlors example, the value of the coefficient of determination is

$$r^2 = \frac{\text{SSR}}{\text{SST}} = \frac{14{,}200}{15{,}730} = .9027$$

The least squares method finds the estimated regression equation that maximizes r^2.

When we express the coefficient of determination as a percentage, r^2 can be interpreted as the percentage of the total sum of squares that can be explained by using the estimated regression equation. For Armand's restaurants, we can conclude that 90.27% of the total sum of squares can be explained by using the estimated regression equation $\hat{y} = 60 + 5x$ to predict quarterly sales. In other words, 90.27% of the variability in sales can be explained by the linear relationship between the size of the student population and sales. We should be pleased to find such a good fit for the estimated regression equation.

Using Excel to Compute the Coefficient of Determination

In Section 12.2 we used Excel's Chart Wizard to construct a scatter diagram for the Armand's Pizza Parlors data. We then showed how options available could be used to compute the estimated regression equation and display its graph. We will now describe how to compute the coefficient of determination.

Step 1. Position the mouse pointer over any data point in the scatter diagram and right-click to display the **Chart** menu
Step 2. Select the **Add Trendline** option
Step 3. When the Add Trendline dialog box appears:
On the **Options** tab select the **Display R-squared value on chart** box
Click **OK**

Figure 12.7 displays the scatter diagram, the estimated regression equation, the graph of the estimated regression equation, and the coefficient of determination for the Armand's Pizza Parlors data. We see that $r^2 = .9027$.

Correlation Coefficient

In Chapter 3 we introduced the **correlation coefficient** as a descriptive measure of the strength of linear association between two variables, x and y. Values of the correlation coefficient are always between -1 and $+1$. A value of $+1$ indicates that the two variables x and y are perfectly related in a positive linear sense. That is, all data points are on a straight line that has a positive slope. A value of -1 indicates that x and y are perfectly related in a negative linear sense, with all data points on a straight line that has a negative slope. Values of the correlation coefficient close to zero indicate that x and y are not linearly related.

In Section 3.5 we presented the equation for computing the sample correlation coefficient. If a regression analysis has already been performed and the coefficient of determination r^2 computed, the sample correlation coefficient can be computed as follows.

SAMPLE CORRELATION COEFFICIENT

$$r_{xy} = (\text{sign of } b_1)\sqrt{\text{Coefficient of determination}}$$
$$= (\text{sign of } b_1)\sqrt{r^2} \tag{12.13}$$

where

$$b_1 = \text{the slope of the estimated regression equation } \hat{y} = b_0 + b_1 x$$

FIGURE 12.7 USING EXCEL TO COMPUTE THE COEFFICIENT OF DETERMINATION

	A	B	C	D	E	F	G	H	I
1	Restaurant	Population	Sales						
2	1	2	58						
3	2	6	105						
4	3	8	88						
5	4	8	118						
6	5	12	117						
7	6	16	137						
8	7	20	157						
9	8	20	169						
10	9	22	149						
11	10	26	202						
12									
13									
14									
15									
16									
17									
18									
19									
20									
21									
22									
23									
24									
25									
26									
27									
28									
29									
30									

The chart displays a scatterplot titled with axes Quarterly Sales ($1000s) versus Student Population (1000s), with the fitted line $y = 5x + 60$ and $R^2 = 0.9027$.

The sign for the sample correlation coefficient is positive if the estimated regression equation has a positive slope ($b_1 > 0$) and negative if the estimated regression equation has a negative slope ($b_1 < 0$).

For the Armand's Pizza Parlors example, the value of the coefficient of determination corresponding to the estimated regression equation $\hat{y} = 60 + 5x$ is .9027. Because the slope of the estimated regression equation is positive, equation (12.13) shows that the sample correlation coefficient is $+\sqrt{.9027} = +.9501$. With a sample correlation coefficient of $r_{xy} = +.9501$, we would conclude that a strong positive linear association exists between x and y.

In the case of a linear relationship between two variables, both the coefficient of determination and the sample correlation coefficient provide measures of the strength of the relationship. The coefficient of determination provides a measure between 0 and 1, whereas the sample correlation coefficient provides a measure between -1 and $+1$. Although the sample correlation coefficient is restricted to a linear relationship between two variables, the coefficient of determination can be used for nonlinear relationships and for relationships that have two or more independent variables. Thus, the coefficient of determination provides a wider range of applicability.

NOTES AND COMMENTS

1. In developing the least squares estimated regression equation and computing the coefficient of determination, we made no probabilistic assumptions about the error term ϵ and no statistical tests for significance of the relationship between x and y were conducted. Larger values of r^2 imply that the least squares line provides a better fit to the data; that is, the observations are more closely grouped about the least squares line. But, using only r^2, we can draw no conclusion about whether the relationship between x and y is statistically significant. Such a conclusion must be based on considerations that involve the sample size and the properties of the appropriate sampling distributions of the least squares estimators.

2. As a practical matter, for typical data found in the social sciences, values of r^2 as low as .25 are often considered useful. For data in the physical and life sciences, r^2 values of .60 or greater are often found; in fact, in some cases, r^2 values greater than .90 can be found. In business applications, r^2 values vary greatly, depending on the unique characteristics of each application.

Exercises

Methods

15. The data from exercise 1 follow.

x_i	1	2	3	4	5
y_i	3	7	5	11	14

The estimated regression equation for these data is $\hat{y} = .20 + 2.60x$.
   a. Compute SSE, SST, and SSR using equations (12.8), (12.9), and (12.10).
   b. Compute the coefficient of determination r^2. Comment on the goodness of fit.
   c. Compute the sample correlation coefficient.

16. The data from exercise 2 follow.

x_i	3	12	6	20	14
y_i	55	40	55	10	15

The estimated regression equation for these data is $\hat{y} = 68 - 3x$.
   a. Compute SSE, SST, and SSR.
   b. Compute the coefficient of determination r^2. Comment on the goodness of fit.
   c. Compute the sample correlation coefficient.

17. The data from exercise 3 follow.

x_i	2	6	9	13	20
y_i	7	18	9	26	23

The estimated regression equation for these data is $\hat{y} = 7.6 + .9x$. What percentage of the total sum of squares can be accounted for by the estimated regression equation? What is the value of the sample correlation coefficient?

Applications

18. The following data are the monthly salaries y and the grade point averages x for students who obtained a bachelor's degree in business administration with a major in information systems.

GPA	Monthly Salary ($)
2.6	3300
3.4	3600
3.6	4000
3.2	3500
3.5	3900
2.9	3600

The estimated regression equation for these data is $\hat{y} = 1790.5 + 581.1x$.
   a.   Compute SST, SSR, and SSE.
   b.   Compute the coefficient of determination r^2. Comment on the goodness of fit.
   c.   What is the value of the sample correlation coefficient?

19.   The data from exercise 7 follow:

Cars

Make and Model	x = Reliability	y = Price ($)
Acura TL	4	33,150
BMW 330i	3	40,570
Lexus IS300	5	35,105
Lexus ES330	5	35,174
Mercedes-Benz C320	1	42,230
Lincoln LS Premium (V6)	3	38,225
Audi A4 3.0 Quattro	2	37,605
Cadillac CTS	1	37,695
Nissan Maxima 3.5 SE	4	34,390
Infiniti I35	5	33,845
Saab 9-3 Aero	3	36,910
Infiniti G35	4	34,695
Jaguar X-Type 3.0	1	37,995
Saab 9-5 Arc	3	36,955
Volvo S60 2.5T	3	33,890

The estimated regression equation for these data is $\hat{y} = 40,639 - 1301.2x$. What percentage of the total sum of squares can be accounted for by the estimated regression equation? Comment on the goodness of fit. What is the sample correlation coefficient?

20.   The typical household income and typical home price for a sample of 18 cities follow (*Places Rated Almanac*, 2000). Data are in thousands of dollars.

Cities

City	Income ($1000s)	Home Price ($1000s)
Akron, OH	74.1	114.9
Atlanta, GA	82.4	126.9
Birmingham, AL	71.2	130.9
Bismarck, ND	62.8	92.8
Cleveland, OH	79.2	135.8
Columbia, SC	66.8	116.7
Denver, CO	82.6	161.9
Detroit, MI	85.3	145.0
Fort Lauderdale, FL	75.8	145.3
Hartford, CT	89.1	162.1
Lancaster, PA	75.2	125.9
Madison, WI	78.8	145.2
Naples, FL	100.0	173.6

City	Income ($1000s)	Home Price ($1000s)
Nashville, TN	77.3	125.9
Philadelphia, PA	87.0	151.5
Savannah, GA	67.8	108.1
Toledo, OH	71.2	101.1
Washington, DC	97.4	191.9

a. Use these data to develop an estimated regression equation that could be used to estimate the typical home price for a city given the typical household income.

b. Compute r^2. Would you feel comfortable using this estimated regression equation to estimate the typical home price for a city?

c. Estimate the typical home price for a city with a typical household income of $95,000.

21. An important application of regression analysis in accounting is in the estimation of cost. By collecting data on production volume (units) and cost and using the least squares method to develop an estimated regression equation relating production volume and cost, an accountant can estimate the cost associated with a particular production volume. Consider the following sample of production volume and total cost data for a manufacturing operation.

Production Volume (units)	Total Cost ($)
400	4000
450	5000
550	5400
600	5900
700	6400
750	7000

a. Use these data to develop an estimated regression equation that could be used to predict the total cost for a given production volume.

b. What is the variable cost per unit produced?

c. Compute the coefficient of determination. What percentage of the variation in total cost can be explained by production volume?

d. The company's production schedule shows 500 units must be produced next month. What is the estimated total cost for this operation?

22. *PC World* provided ratings for the top five small-office laser printers and five corporate laser printers (*PC World,* February 2003). The highest rated small-office laser printer was the Minolta-QMS PagePro 1250W, with an overall rating of 91. The highest rated corporate laser printer, the Xerox Phaser 4400/N, had an overall rating of 83. The following data show the speed for plain text printing in pages per minute (ppm) and the price for each printer.

CD file

Printers

Name	Type	Speed (ppm)	Price ($)
Minolta-QMS PagePro 1250W	Small Office	12	199
Brother HL-1850	Small Office	10	499
Lexmark E320	Small Office	12.2	299
Minolta-QMS PagePro 1250E	Small Office	10.3	299
HP Laserjet 1200	Small Office	11.7	399
Xerox Phaser 4400/N	Corporate	17.8	1850
Brother HL-2460N	Corporate	16.1	1000
IBM Infoprint 1120n	Corporate	11.8	1387
Lexmark W812	Corporate	19.8	2089
Oki Data B8300n	Corporate	28.2	2200

a. Develop the estimated regression equation with speed as the independent variable.
b. Compute r^2. What percentage of the variation in price can be explained by the printing speed?
c. What is the sample correlation coefficient between speed and price? Does it reflect a strong or weak relationship between printing speed and cost?

 12.4 ## Model Assumptions

In conducting a regression analysis, we begin by making an assumption about the appropriate model for the relationship between the dependent and independent variable(s). For the case of simple linear regression, the assumed regression model is

$$y = \beta_0 + \beta_1 x + \epsilon$$

Then, the least squares method is used to develop values for b_0 and b_1, the estimates of the model parameters β_0 and β_1, respectively. The resulting estimated regression equation is

$$\hat{y} = b_0 + b_1 x$$

We saw that the value of the coefficient of determination (r^2) is a measure of the goodness of fit of the estimated regression equation. However, even with a large value of r^2, the estimated regression equation should not be used until further analysis of the appropriateness of the assumed model has been conducted. An important step in determining whether the assumed model is appropriate involves testing for the significance of the relationship. The tests of significance in regression analysis are based on the following assumptions about the error term ϵ.

ASSUMPTIONS ABOUT THE ERROR TERM ϵ IN THE REGRESSION MODEL

$$y = \beta_0 + \beta_1 x + \epsilon$$

1. The error term ϵ is a random variable with a mean or expected value of zero; that is, $E(\epsilon) = 0$.
    Implication: Because β_0 and β_1 are constants, $E(\beta_0) = \beta_0$ and $E(\beta_1) = \beta_1$; thus, for a given value of x, the expected value of y is

$$E(y) = \beta_0 + \beta_1 x \qquad \textbf{(12.14)}$$

As we indicated previously, equation (12.14) is referred to as the regression equation.
2. The variance of ϵ, denoted by σ^2, is the same for all values of x.
    Implication: The variance of y about the regression line equals σ^2 and is the same for all values of x.
3. The values of ϵ are independent.
    Implication: The value of ϵ for a particular value of x is not related to the value of ϵ for any other value of x; thus, the value of y for a particular value of x is not related to the value of y for any other value of x.
4. The error term ϵ is a normally distributed random variable.
    Implication: Because y is a linear function of ϵ, y is also a normally distributed random variable.

Figure 12.8 illustrates the model assumptions and their implications; note that in this graphical interpretation, the value of $E(y)$ changes according to the specific value of x considered. However, regardless of the x value, the probability distribution of ϵ and hence the probability distributions of y are normally distributed, each with the same variance. The specific value of the error ϵ at any particular point depends on whether the actual value of y is greater than or less than $E(y)$.

At this point, we must keep in mind that we are also making an assumption or hypothesis about the form of the relationship between x and y. That is, we assume that a straight line represented by $\beta_0 + \beta_1 x$ is the basis for the relationship between the variables. We must not lose sight of the fact that some other model, for instance, $y = \beta_0 + \beta_1 x^2 + \epsilon$, may turn out to be a better model for the underlying relationship.

12.5 Testing for Significance

In a simple linear regression equation, the mean or expected value of y is a linear function of x: $E(y) = \beta_0 + \beta_1 x$. If the value of β_1 is zero, $E(y) = \beta_0 + (0)x = \beta_0$. In this case, the mean value of y does not depend on the value of x and hence we would conclude that x and y are not linearly related. Alternatively, if the value of β_1 is not equal to zero, we would conclude that the two variables are related. Thus, to test for a significant regression relationship, we must conduct a hypothesis test to determine whether the value of β_1 is zero. Two tests are commonly used. Both require an estimate of σ^2, the variance of ϵ in the regression model.

FIGURE 12.8 ASSUMPTIONS FOR THE REGRESSION MODEL

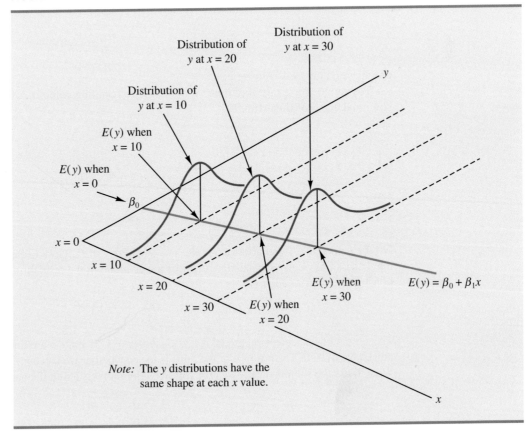

Estimate of σ^2

From the regression model and its assumptions we can conclude that σ^2, the variance of ϵ, also represents the variance of the y values about the regression line. Recall that the deviations of the y values about the estimated regression line are called residuals. Thus, SSE, the sum of squared residuals, is a measure of the variability of the actual observations about the estimated regression line. The **mean square error (MSE)** provides the estimate of σ^2; it is SSE divided by its degrees of freedom.

With $\hat{y}_i = b_0 + b_1 x_i$, SSE can be written as

$$\text{SSE} = \Sigma(y_i - \hat{y}_i)^2 = \Sigma(y_i - b_0 - b_1 x_i)^2$$

Every sum of squares is associated with a number called its degrees of freedom. Statisticians have shown that SSE has $n - 2$ degrees of freedom because two parameters (β_0 and β_1) must be estimated to compute SSE. Thus, the mean square is computed by dividing SSE by $n - 2$. MSE provides an unbiased estimator of σ^2. Because the value of MSE provides an estimate of σ^2, the notation s^2 is also used.

MEAN SQUARE ERROR (ESTIMATE OF σ^2)

$$s^2 = \text{MSE} = \frac{\text{SSE}}{n - 2} \tag{12.15}$$

In Section 12.3 we showed that for the Armand's Pizza Parlors example, SSE $= 1530$; hence,

$$s^2 = \text{MSE} = \frac{1530}{8} = 191.25$$

provides an unbiased estimate of σ^2.

To estimate σ we take the square root of s^2. The resulting value, s, is referred to as the **standard error of the estimate**.

STANDARD ERROR OF THE ESTIMATE

$$s = \sqrt{\text{MSE}} = \sqrt{\frac{\text{SSE}}{n - 2}} \tag{12.16}$$

For the Armand's Pizza Parlors example, $s = \sqrt{\text{MSE}} = \sqrt{191.25} = 13.829$. In the following discussion, we use the standard error of the estimate in the tests for a significant relationship between x and y.

t Test

The simple linear regression model is $y = \beta_0 + \beta_1 x + \epsilon$. If x and y are linearly related, we must have $\beta_1 \neq 0$. The purpose of the t test is to see whether we can conclude that $\beta_1 \neq 0$. We will use the sample data to test the following hypotheses about the parameter β_1.

$$H_0: \beta_1 = 0$$
$$H_a: \beta_1 \neq 0$$

If H_0 is rejected, we will conclude that $\beta_1 \neq 0$ and that a statistically significant relationship exists between the two variables. However, if H_0 cannot be rejected, we will have insufficient evidence to conclude that a significant relationship exists. The properties of the sampling distribution of b_1, the least squares estimator of β_1, provide the basis for the hypothesis test.

First, let us consider what would happen if we used a different random sample for the same regression study. For example, suppose that Armand's Pizza Parlors used the sales records of a different sample of 10 restaurants. A regression analysis of this new sample might result in an estimated regression equation similar to our previous estimated regression equation $\hat{y} = 60 + 5x$. However, it is doubtful that we would obtain exactly the same equation (with an intercept of exactly 60 and a slope of exactly 5). Indeed, b_0 and b_1, the least squares estimators, are sample statistics with their own sampling distributions. The properties of the sampling distribution of b_1 follow.

SAMPLING DISTRIBUTION OF b_1

Expected Value
$$E(b_1) = \beta_1$$

Standard Deviation
$$\sigma_{b_1} = \frac{\sigma}{\sqrt{\Sigma(x_i - \bar{x})^2}} \qquad \textbf{(12.17)}$$

Distribution Form
Normal

Note that the expected value of b_1 is equal to β_1, so b_1 is an unbiased estimator of β_1.

Because we do not know the value of σ, we develop an estimate of σ_{b_1}, denoted s_{b_1}, by estimating σ with s in equation (12.17). Thus, we obtain the following estimate of σ_{b_1}.

The standard deviation of b_1 is also referred to as the standard error of b_1. Thus, s_{b_1} provides an estimate of the standard error of b_1.

ESTIMATED STANDARD DEVIATION OF b_1

$$s_{b_1} = \frac{s}{\sqrt{\Sigma(x_i - \bar{x})^2}} \qquad \textbf{(12.18)}$$

For Armand's Pizza Parlors, $s = 13.829$. Hence, using $\Sigma(x_i - \bar{x})^2 = 568$ as shown in Table 12.2, we have

$$s_{b_1} = \frac{13.829}{\sqrt{568}} = .5803$$

as the estimated standard deviation of b_1.

The t test for a significant relationship is based on the fact that the test statistic

$$\frac{b_1 - \beta_1}{s_{b_1}}$$

follows a t distribution with $n - 2$ degrees of freedom. If the null hypothesis is true, then $\beta_1 = 0$ and $t = b_1/s_{b_1}$.

Let us conduct this test of significance for Armand's Pizza Parlors at the $\alpha = .01$ level of significance. The test statistic is

$$t = \frac{b_1}{s_{b_1}} = \frac{5}{.5803} = 8.62$$

The t distribution table shows that with $n - 2 = 10 - 2 = 8$ degrees of freedom, $t = 3.355$ provides an area of .005 in the upper tail. Thus, the area in the upper tail of the t distribution corresponding to the test statistic $t = 8.62$ must be less than .005. Because this test is a two-tailed test, we double this value to conclude that the p-value associated with $t = 8.62$ must be less than $2(.005) = .01$. Excel can be used to show that $t = 8.62$ provides a p-value = .0000. Because the p-value $\leq \alpha = .01$, we reject H_0 and conclude that β_1 is not equal to zero. This evidence is sufficient to conclude that a significant relationship exists between student population and quarterly sales. A summary of the t test for significance in simple linear regression follows.

Using Excel, p-value =
TDIST(8.62,8,2) = .0000.

t TEST FOR SIGNIFICANCE IN SIMPLE LINEAR REGRESSION

$$H_0: \beta_1 = 0$$
$$H_a: \beta_1 \neq 0$$

TEST STATISTIC

$$t = \frac{b_1}{s_{b_1}} \qquad\qquad (12.19)$$

REJECTION RULE

p-value approach: Reject H_0 if p-value $\leq \alpha$

Critical value approach: Reject H_0 if $t \leq -t_{\alpha/2}$ or if $t \geq t_{\alpha/2}$

where $t_{\alpha/2}$ is based on a t distribution with $n - 2$ degrees of freedom.

Confidence Interval for β_1

The form of a confidence interval for β_1 is as follows:

$$b_1 \pm t_{\alpha/2}s_{b_1}$$

The point estimator is b_1 and the margin of error is $t_{\alpha/2}s_{b_1}$. The confidence coefficient associated with this interval is $1 - \alpha$, and $t_{\alpha/2}$ is the t value providing an area of $\alpha/2$ in the upper tail of a t distribution with $n - 2$ degrees of freedom. For example, suppose that we wanted to develop a 99% confidence interval estimate of β_1 for Armand's Pizza Parlors. From Table 2 of Appendix B we find that the t value corresponding to $\alpha = .01$ and $n - 2 = 10 - 2 = 8$ degrees of freedom is $t_{.005} = 3.355$. Thus, the 99% confidence interval estimate of β_1 is

$$b_1 \pm t_{\alpha/2}s_{b_1} = 5 \pm 3.355(.5803) = 5 \pm 1.95$$

or 3.05 to 6.95.

In using the t test for significance, the hypotheses tested were

$$H_0: \beta_1 = 0$$
$$H_a: \beta_1 \neq 0$$

At the $\alpha = .01$ level of significance, we can use the 99% confidence interval as an alternative for drawing the hypothesis testing conclusion for the Armand's data. Because 0, the hypothesized value of β_1, is not included in the confidence interval (3.05 to 6.95), we can reject H_0 and conclude that a significant statistical relationship exists between the size of the student population and quarterly sales. In general, a confidence interval can be used to test any two-sided hypothesis about β_1. If the hypothesized value of β_1 is contained in the confidence interval, do not reject H_0. Otherwise, reject H_0.

F **Test**

An F test, based on the F probability distribution, can also be used to test for significance in regression. With only one independent variable, the F test will provide the same conclusion as the t test; that is, if the t test indicates $\beta_1 \neq 0$ and hence a significant relationship, the F test will also indicate a significant relationship. But with more than one independent variable, only the F test can be used to test for an overall significant relationship.

The logic behind the use of the F test for determining whether the regression relationship is statistically significant is based on the development of two independent estimates of σ^2. We explained how MSE provides an estimate of σ^2. If the null hypothesis $H_0: \beta_1 = 0$ is true, the sum of squares due to regression, SSR, divided by its degrees of freedom provides another independent estimate of σ^2. This estimate is called the *mean square due to regression,* or simply the *mean square regression,* and is denoted MSR. In general,

$$\text{MSR} = \frac{\text{SSR}}{\text{Regression degrees of freedom}}$$

For the models we consider in this text, the regression degrees of freedom is always equal to the number of independent variables in the model:

$$\text{MSR} = \frac{\text{SSR}}{\text{Number of independent variables}} \tag{12.20}$$

Because we consider only regression models with one independent variable in this chapter, we have MSR = SSR/1 = SSR. Hence, for Armand's Pizza Parlors, MSR = SSR = 14,200.

If the null hypothesis ($H_0: \beta_1 = 0$) is true, MSR and MSE are two independent estimates of σ^2 and the sampling distribution of MSR/MSE follows an F distribution with numerator degrees of freedom equal to 1 and denominator degrees of freedom equal to $n - 2$. Therefore, when $\beta_1 = 0$, the value of MSR/MSE should be close to one. However, if the null hypothesis is false ($\beta_1 \neq 0$), MSR will overestimate σ^2 and the value of MSR/MSE will be inflated; thus, large values of MSR/MSE lead to the rejection of H_0 and the conclusion that the relationship between x and y is statistically significant.

Let us conduct the F test for the Armand's Pizza Parlors example. The test statistic is

$$F = \frac{\text{MSR}}{\text{MSE}} = \frac{14,200}{191.25} = 74.25$$

*The F test and the t test
provide identical results for
simple linear regression.*

*Using Excel, p-value =
FDIST(74.25,1,8) = .0000.*

The F distribution table (Table 4 of Appendix B) shows that with 1 degree of freedom in the numerator and $n - 2 = 10 - 2 = 8$ degrees of freedom in the denominator, $F = 11.26$ provides an area of .01 in the upper tail. Thus, the area in the upper tail of the F distribution corresponding to the test statistic $F = 74.25$ must be less than .01. Thus, we conclude that the p-value must be less than .01. Excel can be used to show that $F = 74.25$ provides a p-value = .0000. Because the p-value $\leq \alpha = .01$, we reject H_0 and conclude that a significant relationship exists between the size of the student population and quarterly sales. A summary of the F test for significance in simple linear regression follows.

*If H_0 is false, MSE still
provides an unbiased
estimate of σ^2 and MSR
overestimates σ^2. If H_0 is
true, both MSE and MSR
provide unbiased estimates
of σ^2; in this case the value
of MSR/MSE should be
close to 1.*

F TEST FOR SIGNIFICANCE IN SIMPLE LINEAR REGRESSION

$$H_0: \beta_1 = 0$$
$$H_a: \beta_1 \neq 0$$

TEST STATISTIC

$$F = \frac{\text{MSR}}{\text{MSE}} \tag{12.21}$$

REJECTION RULE

      p-value approach: Reject H_0 if p-value $\leq \alpha$

      Critical value approach: Reject H_0 if $F \geq F_\alpha$

where F_α is based on an F distribution with 1 degree of freedom in the numerator and $n - 2$ degrees of freedom in the denominator.

In Chapter 10 we covered analysis of variance (ANOVA) and showed how an **ANOVA table** could be used to provide a convenient summary of the computational aspects of analysis of variance. A similar ANOVA table can be used to summarize the results of the F test for significance in regression. Table 12.5 is the general form of the ANOVA table for simple linear regression. Table 12.6 is the ANOVA table with the F test computations performed for Armand's Pizza Parlors. Regression, Error, and Total are the labels for the three sources of variation, with SSR, SSE, and SST appearing as the corresponding sum of squares in column 2. The degrees of freedom, 1 for SSR, $n - 2$ for SSE, and $n - 1$ for SST, are shown in

TABLE 12.5 GENERAL FORM OF THE ANOVA TABLE FOR SIMPLE LINEAR REGRESSION

*In every analysis of
variance table the total sum
of squares is the sum of the
regression sum of squares
and the error sum of
squares; in addition, the
total degrees of freedom is
the sum of the regression
degrees of freedom and the
error degrees of freedom.*

Source of Variation	Sum of Squares	Degrees of Freedom	Mean Square	F
Regression	SSR	1	$\text{MSR} = \dfrac{\text{SSR}}{1}$	$F = \dfrac{\text{MSR}}{\text{MSE}}$
Error	SSE	$n - 2$	$\text{MSE} = \dfrac{\text{SSE}}{n - 2}$	
Total	SST	$n - 1$		

TABLE 12.6   ANOVA TABLE FOR THE ARMAND'S PIZZA PARLORS EXAMPLE

Source of Variation	Sum of Squares	Degrees of Freedom	Mean Square	F
Regression	14,200	1	$\dfrac{14{,}200}{1} = 14{,}200$	$\dfrac{14{,}200}{191.25} = 74.25$
Error	1,530	8	$\dfrac{1530}{8} = 191.25$	
Total	15,730	9		

column 3. Column 4 contains the values of MSR and MSE and column 5 contains the value of $F = $ MSR/MSE. Almost all computer printouts of regression analysis include an ANOVA table summary of the F test for significance.

Some Cautions About the Interpretation of Significance Tests

Regression analysis, which can be used to identify how variables are associated with one another, cannot be used as evidence of a cause-and-effect relationship.

Rejecting the null hypothesis $H_0: \beta_1 = 0$ and concluding that the relationship between x and y is significant does not enable us to conclude that a cause-and-effect relationship is present between x and y. Concluding a cause-and-effect relationship is warranted only if the analyst can provide some type of theoretical justification that the relationship is in fact causal. In the Armand's Pizza Parlors example, we can conclude that there is a significant relationship between the size of the student population x and quarterly sales y; moreover, the estimated regression equation $\hat{y} = 60 + 5x$ provides the least squares estimate of the relationship. We cannot, however, conclude that changes in student population x *cause* changes in quarterly sales y just because we identified a statistically significant relationship. The appropriateness of such a cause-and-effect conclusion is left to supporting theoretical justification and to good judgment on the part of the analyst. Armand's managers felt that increases in the student population were a likely cause of increased quarterly sales. Thus, the result of the significance test enabled them to conclude that a cause-and-effect relationship was present.

In addition, just because we are able to reject $H_0: \beta_1 = 0$ and demonstrate statistical significance does not enable us to conclude that the relationship between x and y is linear. We can state only that x and y are related and that a linear relationship explains a significant portion of the variability in y over the range of values for x observed in the sample. Figure 12.9 illustrates this situation. The test for significance calls for the rejection of the null hypothesis $H_0: \beta_1 = 0$ and leads to the conclusion that x and y are significantly related, but the figure shows that the actual relationship between x and y is not linear. Although the linear approximation provided by $\hat{y} = b_0 + b_1 x$ is good over the range of x values observed in the sample, it becomes poor for x values outside that range.

Given a significant relationship, we should feel confident in using the estimated regression equation for predictions corresponding to x values within the range of the x values observed in the sample. For Armand's Pizza Parlors, this range corresponds to values of x between 2 and 26. Unless other reasons indicate that the model is valid beyond this range, predictions outside the range of the independent variable should be made with caution. For Armand's Pizza Parlors, because the regression relationship has been found significant at the .01 level, we should feel confident using it to predict sales for restaurants where the associated student population is between 2000 and 26,000.

FIGURE 12.9   EXAMPLE OF A LINEAR APPROXIMATION OF A NONLINEAR
RELATIONSHIP

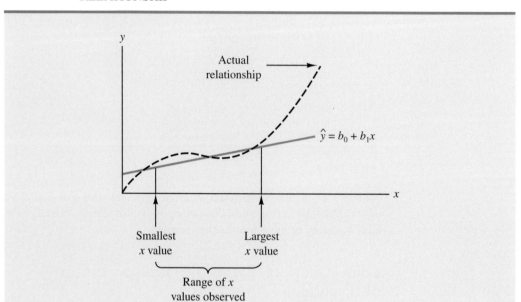

NOTES AND COMMENTS

1. The assumptions made about the error term (Section 12.4) are what allow the tests of statistical significance in this section. The properties of the sampling distribution of b_1 and the subsequent t and F tests follow directly from these assumptions.
2. Do not confuse statistical significance with practical significance. With very large sample sizes, statistically significant results can be obtained for small values of b_1; in such cases, one must exercise care in concluding that the relationship has practical significance.
3. A test of significance for a linear relationship between x and y can also be performed by using

the sample correlation coefficient r_{xy}. With ρ_{xy} denoting the population correlation coefficient, the hypotheses are as follows.

$$H_0: \rho_{xy} = 0$$
$$H_a: \rho_{xy} \neq 0$$

A significant relationship can be concluded if H_0 is rejected. However, the t and F tests presented previously in this section give the same result as the test for significance using the correlation coefficient. Conducting a test for significance using the correlation coefficient therefore is not necessary if a t or F test has already been conducted.

Exercises

Methods

23.   The data from exercise 1 follow.

x_i	1	2	3	4	5
y_i	3	7	5	11	14

a.   Compute the mean square error using equation (12.15).
b.   Compute the standard error of the estimate using equation (12.16).
c.   Compute the estimated standard deviation of b_1 using equation (12.18).
d.   Use the t test to test the following hypotheses ($\alpha = .05$):

$$H_0: \beta_1 = 0$$
$$H_a: \beta_1 \neq 0$$

e.   Use the F test to test the hypotheses in part (d) at a .05 level of significance. Present the results in the analysis of variance table format.

24.   The data from exercise 2 follow.

x_i	3	12	6	20	14
y_i	55	40	55	10	15

a.   Compute the mean square error using equation (12.15).
b.   Compute the standard error of the estimate using equation (12.16).
c.   Compute the estimated standard deviation of b_1 using equation (12.18).
d.   Use the t test to test the following hypotheses ($\alpha = .05$):

$$H_0: \beta_1 = 0$$
$$H_a: \beta_1 \neq 0$$

e.   Use the F test to test the hypotheses in part (d) at a .05 level of significance. Present the results in the analysis of variance table format.

25.   The data from exercise 3 follow.

x_i	2	6	9	13	20
y_i	7	18	9	26	23

a.   What is the value of the standard error of the estimate?
b.   Test for a significant relationship by using the t test. Use $\alpha = .05$.
c.   Use the F test to test for a significant relationship. Use $\alpha = .05$. What is your conclusion?

Applications

26.   In exercise 18 the data on grade point average and monthly salary were as follows.

GPA	Monthly Salary ($)	GPA	Monthly Salary ($)
2.6	3300	3.2	3500
3.4	3600	3.5	3900
3.6	4000	2.9	3600

a.   Does the t test indicate a significant relationship between grade point average and monthly salary? What is your conclusion? Use $\alpha = .05$.
b.   Test for a significant relationship using the F test. What is your conclusion? Use $\alpha = .05$.
c.   Show the ANOVA table.

27.   *Outside Magazine* tested 10 different models of day hikers and backpacking boots. The following data show the upper support and price for each model tested. Upper support was measured using a rating from 1 to 5, with a rating of 1 denoting average upper support and a rating of 5 denoting excellent upper support (*Outside Magazine Buyer's Guide*, 2001).

Boots

Manufacturer and Model	Upper Support	Price ($)
Salomon Super Raid	2	120
Merrell Chameleon Prime	3	125
Teva Challenger	3	130
Vasque Fusion GTX	3	135
Boreal Maigmo	3	150
L.L. Bean GTX Super Guide	5	189
Lowa Kibo	5	190
Asolo AFX 520 GTX	4	195
Raichle Mt. Trail GTX	4	200
Scarpa Delta SL M3	5	220

a. Use these data to develop an estimated regression equation to estimate the price of a day hiker and backpacking boot given the upper support rating.

b. At the .05 level of significance, determine whether upper support and price are related.

c. Would you feel comfortable using the estimated regression equation developed in part (a) to estimate the price for a day hiker or backpacking boot given the upper support rating?

d. Estimate the price for a day hiker with an upper support rating of 4.

PCs

28. Refer to exercise 10, where an estimated regression equation relating the performance score and the overall rating for notebook PCs was developed. At the .05 level of significance, test whether performance score and overall rating are related. Show the ANOVA table. What is your conclusion?

29. Refer to exercise 21, where data on production volume and cost were used to develop an estimated regression equation relating production volume and cost for a particular manufacturing operation. Use $\alpha = .05$ to test whether the production volume is significantly related to the total cost. Show the ANOVA table. What is your conclusion?

30. Refer to exercise 22 where the following data were used to determine whether the price of a printer is related to the speed for plain text printing (*PC World,* February 2003).

Printers

Name	Type	Speed (ppm)	Price ($)
Minolta-QMS PagePro 1250W	Small Office	12	199
Brother HL-1850	Small Office	10	499
Lexmark E320	Small Office	12.2	299
Minolta-QMS PagePro 1250E	Small Office	10.3	299
HP Laserjet 1200	Small Office	11.7	399
Xerox Phaser 4400/N	Corporate	17.8	1850
Brother HL-2460N	Corporate	16.1	1000
IBM Infoprint 1120n	Corporate	11.8	1387
Lexmark W812	Corporate	19.8	2089
Oki Data B8300n	Corporate	28.2	2200

Does the evidence indicate a significant relationship between printing speed and price? Conduct the appropriate statistical test and state your conclusion. Use $\alpha = .05$.

31. Refer to exercise 20, where an estimated regression equation was developed relating typical household income and typical home price. Test whether the typical household income for a city and the typical home price are related at the .01 level of significance.

Excel's Regression Tool

In previous sections of this chapter we have shown how Excel can be used for various tasks in a regression analysis. Excel also has a more comprehensive Regression tool. In this section we will illustrate how Excel's Regression tool can be used to perform a complete regression analysis, including statistical tests of significance for the Armand's Pizza Parlors data in Table 12.1.

Using Excel's Regression Tool for the Armand's Pizza Parlors Example

Refer to Figures 12.10 and 12.11 as we describe the tasks involved to use Excel's Regression tool to perform the regression analysis computations for the Armand's data.

Enter Data: The labels Restaurant, Population, and Sales are entered into cells A1:C1 of the worksheet. To identify each of the 10 observations, we entered the numbers 1 through 10 into cells A2:A11. The sample data are entered into cells B2:C11.

Apply Tools: The following steps describe how to use Excel to perform the regression analysis computations performed in Sections 12.2–12.5.

> **Step 1.** Select the **Tools** menu
> **Step 2.** Choose the **Data Analysis** option

FIGURE 12.10   REGRESSION TOOL OUTPUT FOR ARMAND'S PIZZA PARLORS

	A	**B**	**C**	**D**	**E**	**F**	**G**	**H**	**I**	**J**
1	Restaurant	Population	Sales							
2	1	2	58							
3	2	6	105							
4	3	8	88							
5	4	8	118							
6	5	12	117							
7	6	16	137							
8	7	20	157							
9	8	20	169							
10	9	22	149							
11	10	26	202							
12										
13	SUMMARY OUTPUT									
14										
15	*Regression Statistics*									
16	Multiple R	0.9501								
17	R Square	0.9027								
18	Adjusted R Square	0.8906								
19	Standard Error	13.8293								
20	Observations	10								
21										
22	ANOVA									
23		*df*	*SS*	*MS*	*F*	*Significance F*				
24	Regression	1	14200	14200	74.2484	2.55E-05				
25	Residual	8	1530	191.25						
26	Total	9	15730							
27										
28		*Coefficients*	*Standard Error*	*t Stat*	*P-value*	*Lower 95%*	*Upper 95%*	*Lower 99.0%*	*Upper 99.0%*	
29	Intercept	60	9.2260	6.5033	0.0002	38.7247	81.2753	29.0431	90.9569	
30	Population	5	0.5803	8.6167	2.55E-05	3.6619	6.3381	3.0530	6.9470	
31										

FIGURE 12.11 REGRESSION TOOL DIALOG BOX FOR THE ARMAND'S PIZZA PARLORS EXAMPLE

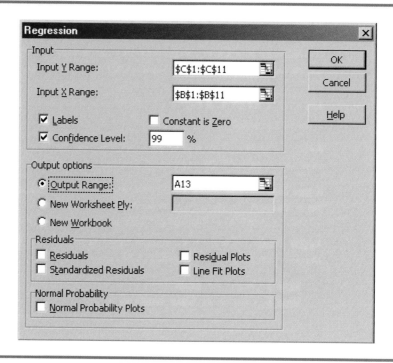

Step 3. Choose **Regression** from the list of Analysis Tools
Step 4. When the Regression dialog box appears (see Figure 12.11):
  Enter C1:C11 in the **Input Y Range** box
  Enter B1:B11 in the **Input X Range** box
  Select **Labels**
  Select **Confidence Level**
  Enter 99 in the **Confidence Level** box
  Select **Output Range**
  Enter A13 in the **Output Range** box (to identify the upper left corner of the section of the worksheet where the output will appear)
  Click **OK**

The Excel output can be reformatted to improve readability.

The regression output, titled SUMMARY OUTPUT, begins with row 13 in Figure 12.10. Because Excel initially displays the output using standard column widths, many of the row and column labels are unreadable. In several places we have reformatted to improve readability. We have also reformatted cells displaying numerical values to a maximum of four decimal places. Numbers displayed using scientific notation have not been modified. Regression output in future figures will be similarly reformatted to improve readability.

The first section of the summary output, titled *Regression Statistics,* contains summary statistics such as the coefficient of determination (R Square). The second section of the output, titled ANOVA, contains the analysis of variance table. The last section of the output, which is not titled, contains the estimated regression coefficients and related information. Let us begin our interpretation of the regression output with the information contained in cells A28:I30.

a. Develop a scatter diagram for these data; plot the vacancy rate on the horizontal axis.
b. Does there appear to be any relationship between these two variables?
c. Develop the estimated regression equation that could be used to predict the average rental rate given the overall vacancy rate.
d. Test the significance of the relationship at the .05 level of significance.
e. Did the estimated regression equation provide a good fit? Explain.

Using the Estimated Regression Equation for Estimation and Prediction

When using the simple linear regression model we are making an assumption about the relationship between x and y. We then use the least squares method to obtain the estimated simple linear regression equation. If a significant relationship exists between x and y, and the coefficient of determination shows that the fit is good, the estimated regression equation should be useful for estimation and prediction.

Point Estimation

In the Armand's Pizza Parlors example, the estimated regression equation $\hat{y} = 60 + 5x$ provides an estimate of the relationship between the size of the student population x and quarterly sales y. We can use the estimated regression equation to develop a point estimate of the mean value of y for a particular value of x or to predict an individual value of y corresponding to a given value of x. For instance, suppose Armand's managers want a point estimate of the mean quarterly sales for all restaurants located near college campuses with 10,000 students. Using the estimated regression equation $\hat{y} = 60 + 5x$, we see that for $x = 10$ (or 10,000 students), $\hat{y} = 60 + 5(10) = 110$. Thus, a point estimate of the mean quarterly sales for all restaurants located near campuses with 10,000 students is $110,000.

Now suppose Armand's managers want to predict sales for an individual restaurant located near Talbot College, a school with 10,000 students. In this case we are not interested in the mean value for all restaurants located near campuses with 10,000 students; we are just interested in predicting quarterly sales for one individual restaurant. As it turns out, the point estimate for an individual value of y is the same as the point estimate for the mean value of y. Hence, we would predict quarterly sales of $\hat{y} = 60 + 5(10) = 110$ or $110,000 for this one restaurant.

Interval Estimation

Confidence intervals and prediction intervals show the precision of the regression results. Narrower intervals provide a higher degree of precision.

Point estimates do not provide any information about the precision associated with an estimate. For that we must develop interval estimates much like those in Chapters 8, 10, and 11. The first type of interval estimate, a **confidence interval**, is an interval estimate of the *mean value of y* for a given value of x. The second type of interval estimate, a **prediction interval**, is used whenever we want an interval estimate of an *individual value of y* for a given value of x. The point estimate of the mean value of y is the same as the point estimate of an individual value of y. But, the interval estimates we obtain for the two cases are different. The margin of error is larger for a prediction interval.

Confidence Interval Estimate of the Mean Value of y

The estimated regression equation provides a point estimate of the mean value of y for a given value of x. In developing the confidence interval, we will use the following notation.

x_p = the particular or given value of the independent variable x

y_p = the value of the dependent variable y corresponding to the given x_p

$$E(y_p) = \text{the mean or expected value of the dependent variable } y$$
$$\text{corresponding to the given } x_p$$
$$\hat{y}_p = b_0 + b_1x_p = \text{the point estimate of } E(y_p) \text{ when } x = x_p$$

Using this notation to estimate the mean sales for all Armand's restaurants located near a campus with 10,000 students, we have $x_p = 10$, and $E(y_p)$ denotes the unknown mean value of sales for all restaurants where $x_p = 10$. The point estimate of $E(y_p)$ is provided by $\hat{y}_p = 60 + 5(10) = 110$.

In general, we cannot expect $\hat{y}_p$ to equal $E(y_p)$ exactly. If we want to make an inference about how close $\hat{y}_p$ is to the true mean value $E(y_p)$, we will have to estimate the variance of $\hat{y}_p$. The formula for estimating the variance of $\hat{y}_p$ given x_p, denoted by $s_{\hat{y}_p}^2$, is

$$s_{\hat{y}_p}^2 = s^2\left[\frac{1}{n} + \frac{(x_p - \bar{x})^2}{\Sigma(x_i - \bar{x})^2}\right] \tag{12.22}$$

The estimate of the standard deviation of $\hat{y}_p$ is given by the square root of equation (12.22).

$$s_{\hat{y}_p} = s\sqrt{\frac{1}{n} + \frac{(x_p - \bar{x})^2}{\Sigma(x_i - \bar{x})^2}} \tag{12.23}$$

The computational results for Armand's Pizza Parlors in Section 12.5 provided $s = 13.829$. With $x_p = 10$, $\bar{x} = 14$, and $\Sigma(x_i - \bar{x})^2 = 568$, we can use equation (12.23) to obtain

$$s_{\hat{y}_p} = 13.829\sqrt{\frac{1}{10} + \frac{(10 - 14)^2}{568}}$$
$$= 13.829\sqrt{.1282} = 4.95$$

The general expression for a confidence interval follows.

CONFIDENCE INTERVAL FOR $E(y_p)$

$$\hat{y}_p \pm t_{\alpha/2}s_{\hat{y}_p} \tag{12.24}$$

where the confidence coefficient is $1 - \alpha$ and $t_{\alpha/2}$ is based on a t distribution with $n - 2$ degrees of freedom.

Using expression (12.24) to develop a 95% confidence interval of the mean quarterly sales for all Armand's restaurants located near campuses with 10,000 students, we need the value of t for $\alpha/2 = .025$ and $n - 2 = 10 - 2 = 8$ degrees of freedom. Using Table 2 of Appendix B, we have $t_{.025} = 2.306$. Thus, with $\hat{y}_p = 110$ and a margin of error of $t_{\alpha/2}s_{\hat{y}_p} = 2.306(4.95) = 11.415$, the 95% confidence interval estimate is

$$110 \pm 11.415$$

In dollars, the 95% confidence interval for the mean quarterly sales of all restaurants near campuses with 10,000 students is $110,000 \pm $11,415$. Therefore, the 95% confidence interval for the mean quarterly sales when the student population is 10,000 is $98,585 to $121,415.

Note that the estimated standard deviation of $\hat{y}_p$ given by equation (12.23) is smallest when $x_p = \bar{x}$ and the quantity $x_p - \bar{x} = 0$. In this case, the estimated standard deviation of $\hat{y}_p$ becomes

$$s_{\hat{y}_p} = s\sqrt{\frac{1}{n} + \frac{(\bar{x} - \bar{x})^2}{\Sigma(x_i - \bar{x})^2}} = s\sqrt{\frac{1}{n}}$$

This result implies that we can make the best or most precise estimate of the mean value of y whenever $x_p = \bar{x}$. In fact, the farther x_p is from $\bar{x}$, the larger $x_p - \bar{x}$ becomes. As a result, confidence intervals for the mean value of y will become wider as x_p deviates more from $\bar{x}$. This pattern is shown graphically in Figure 12.12.

Prediction Interval Estimate of an Individual Value of y

Suppose that instead of estimating the mean value of sales for all Armand's restaurants located near campuses with 10,000 students, we want to estimate the sales for an individual restaurant located near Talbot College, a school with 10,000 students. As noted previously, the point estimate of y_p, the value of y corresponding to the given x_p, is provided by the estimated regression equation $\hat{y}_p = b_0 + b_1x_p$. For the restaurant at Talbot College, we have $x_p = 10$ and a corresponding predicted quarterly sales of $\hat{y}_p = 60 + 5(10) = 110$, or \$110,000. Note that this value is the same as the point estimate of the mean sales for all restaurants located near campuses with 10,000 students.

FIGURE 12.12   CONFIDENCE INTERVALS FOR THE MEAN SALES y AT GIVEN VALUES OF STUDENT POPULATION x

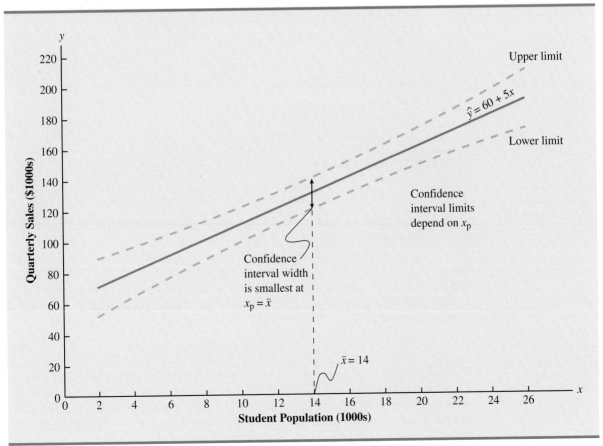

To develop a prediction interval, we must first determine the variance associated with using $\hat{y}_p$ as an estimate of an individual value of y when $x = x_p$. This variance is made up of the sum of the following two components.

1. The variance of individual y values about the mean $E(y_p)$, an estimate of which is given by s^2
2. The variance associated with using $\hat{y}_p$ to estimate $E(y_p)$, an estimate of which is given by $s_{\hat{y}_p}^2$

The formula for estimating the variance of an individual value of y_p, denoted by s_{ind}^2, is

$$
\begin{aligned}
s_{ind}^2 &= s^2 + s_{\hat{y}_p}^2 \\
&= s^2 + s^2 \left[\frac{1}{n} + \frac{(x_p - \bar{x})^2}{\Sigma(x_i - \bar{x})^2} \right] \\
&= s^2 \left[1 + \frac{1}{n} + \frac{(x_p - \bar{x})^2}{\Sigma(x_i - \bar{x})^2} \right]
\end{aligned}
\qquad \textbf{(12.25)}
$$

Hence, an estimate of the standard deviation of an individual value of y_p is given by

$$
s_{ind} = s \sqrt{1 + \frac{1}{n} + \frac{(x_p - \bar{x})^2}{\Sigma(x_i - \bar{x})^2}}
\qquad \textbf{(12.26)}
$$

For Armand's Pizza Parlors, the estimated standard deviation corresponding to the prediction of sales for one specific restaurant located near a campus with 10,000 students is computed as follows.

$$
\begin{aligned}
s_{ind} &= 13.829 \sqrt{1 + \frac{1}{10} + \frac{(10 - 14)^2}{568}} \\
&= 13.829 \sqrt{1.1282} \\
&= 14.69
\end{aligned}
$$

The general expression for a prediction interval follows.

PREDICTION INTERVAL FOR y_p

The margin of error associated with this interval estimate is $t_{\alpha/2}s_{ind}$.

$$
\hat{y}_p \pm t_{\alpha/2}s_{ind}
\qquad \textbf{(12.27)}
$$

where the confidence coefficient is $1 - \alpha$ and $t_{\alpha/2}$ is based on a t distribution with $n - 2$ degrees of freedom.

The 95% prediction interval for quarterly sales at Armand's restaurant located near Talbot College can be found by using $t_{.025} = 2.306$ and $s_{ind} = 14.69$. Thus, with $\hat{y}_p = 110$ and a margin of error of $t_{\alpha/2}s_{ind} = 2.306(14.69) = 33.875$, the 95% prediction interval is

$$
110 \pm 33.875
$$

In dollars, this prediction interval is $\$110,000 \pm \$33,875$ or $\$76,125$ to $\$143,875$. Note that the prediction interval for an individual restaurant located near a campus with 10,000 students is wider than the confidence interval for the mean sales of all restaurants located near campuses with 10,000 students. The difference reflects the fact that we are able to estimate the mean value of y more precisely than we can an individual value of y.

Both confidence interval estimates and prediction interval estimates are most precise when the value of the independent variable is $x_p = \bar{x}$. The general shapes of confidence intervals and the wider prediction intervals are shown together in Figure 12.13.

Using Excel to Develop Confidence and Prediction Interval Estimates

Excel's Regression tool does not have an option for computing confidence and prediction intervals. But, for simple linear regression, formulas can be designed to compute these intervals using equations (12.24) and (12.27) along with the output provided by the Regression tool. The general expression for a confidence or prediction interval is point estimate $\pm$ margin of error. Thus, we must develop formulas for computing a point estimate and the margin of error.

We begin by showing how to develop a 95% confidence interval estimate of the mean quarterly sales for all Armand's restaurants located near a campus with 10,000 students. In Section 12.6, we showed how Excel's Regression tool could be applied to the Armand's problem. The output provided by the Regression tool is shown again in cells A13:I30 of Figure 12.14. Now refer to cells E1:F13 of that figure as we describe the tasks involved in developing a confidence interval. The formula worksheet is in the background; the value worksheet appears in the foreground.

Enter Data: The data (cells B2:C11) and regression output (cells A13:I30) that were initially developed in Figure 12.10 are used as a starting point here.

FIGURE 12.13   CONFIDENCE AND PREDICTION INTERVALS FOR SALES y AT GIVEN VALUES OF STUDENT POPULATION x

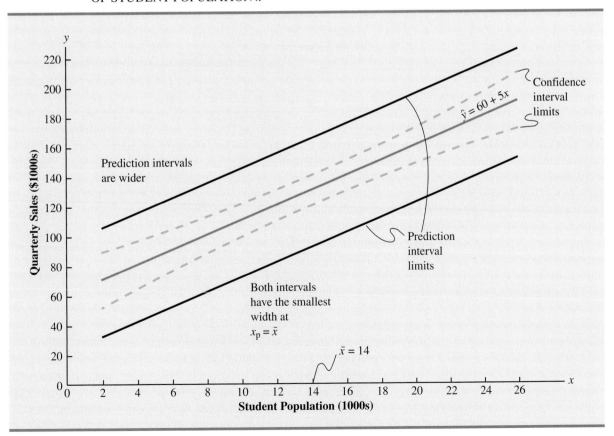

FIGURE 12.14   USING EXCEL TO COMPUTE CONFIDENCE AND PREDICTION INTERVALS

	A	B	C	D	E	F
1	Restaurant	Population	Sales		Confidence Interval	
2	1	2	58		Given value of x	10
3	2	6	105		xbar	=AVERAGE(B2:B11)
4	3	8	88		x-xbar	=F2-F3
5	4	8	118		(x-xbar)sq	=F4^2
6	5	12	117		Sum of (x-xbar)sq	=DEVSQ(B2:B11)
7	6	16	137		Var of yhat	=D25*(1/B20+F5/F6)
8	7	20	157		Stdev of yhat	=SQRT(F7)
9	8	20	169		t value	=TINV(0.05,8)
10	9	22	149		Margin of Error	=F9*F8
11	10	26	202		Point Estimate	=B29+B30*F2
12					Lower Limit	=F11-F10
13	SUMMARY OUTPUT				Upper Limit	=F11+F10
14						
15	*Regression Statistics*				Prediction Interval	
16	Multiple R	0.95012295520			Var of yind	=D25+F7
17	R Square	0.90273363000			Stdev of yind	=SQRT(F16)
18	Adjusted R Square	0.89057533375			Margin of Error	=F9*F17
19	Standard Error	13.8293166859			Lower Limit	=F11-F18
20	Observations	10			Upper Limit	=F11+F18
21						
22	ANOVA					
23		*df*				
24	Regression	1				
25	Residual	8				
26	Total	9				
27						
28		*Coefficients*				
29	Intercept	60				
30	Population	5				
31						

	A	B	C	D	E	F	G	H	I	J
1	Restaurant	Population	Sales		Confidence Interval					
2	1	2	58		Given value of x	10				
3	2	6	105		xbar	14				
4	3	8	88		x-xbar	-4				
5	4	8	118		(x-xbar)sq	16				
6	5	12	117		Sum of (x-xbar)sq	568				
7	6	16	137		Var of yhat	24.5123				
8	7	20	157		Stdev of yhat	4.9510				
9	8	20	169		t value	2.3060				
10	9	22	149		Margin of Error	11.4170				
11	10	26	202		Point Estimate	110				
12					Lower Limit	98.5830				
13	SUMMARY OUTPUT				Upper Limit	121.4170				
14										
15	*Regression Statistics*				Prediction Interval					
16	Multiple R	0.9501			Var of yind	215.7623				
17	R Square	0.9027			Stdev of yind	14.6889				
18	Adjusted R Square	0.8906			Margin of Error	33.8725				
19	Standard Error	13.8293			Lower Limit	76.1275				
20	Observations	10			Upper Limit	143.8725				
21										
22	ANOVA									
23			*df*	*SS*	*MS*	*F*	*Significance F*			
24	Regression		1	14200	14200	74.2484	2.55E-05			
25	Residual		8	1530	191.25					
26	Total		9	15730						
27										
28			*Coefficients*	*Standard Error*	*t Stat*	*P-value*	*Lower 95%*	*Upper 95%*	*Lower 99.0%*	*Upper 99.0%*
29	Intercept		60	9.2260	6.5033	0.0002	38.7247	81.2753	29.0431	90.9569
30	Population		5	0.5803	8.6167	2.55E-05	3.6619	6.3381	3.0530	6.9470
31										

Enter Functions and Formulas: Because we want to develop a 95% confidence interval estimate of the mean quarterly sales for restaurants near campuses with 10,000 students, $x_p = 10$ and we enter a value of 10 into cell F2. Excel's AVERAGE function is used to compute $\bar{x}$ in cell F3, the formula =F2-F3 is entered into cell F4 to compute the value of $x_p - \bar{x}$, and the formula =F4^2 is entered into cell F5 to compute the value of $(x_p - \bar{x})^2$. Excel's DEVSQ function can be used to compute $\Sigma(x_i - \bar{x})^2$ by entering the following formula into cell F6:

$$=DEVSQ(B2:B11)$$

To identify this sum of squares we entered the label "Sum of (x-xbar)sq" into cell E6.

We can now compute $s_{\hat{y}_p}^2$ using equation (12.22) by entering the formula =D25* (1/B20+F5/F6) into cell F7. We then enter the formula =SQRT(F7) into cell F8 to compute $s_{\hat{y}_p}$, the estimate of the standard deviation of $\hat{y}_p$. To compute the t value required by equation (12.24), we entered the formula =TINV(0.05,8) into cell F9. Finally, the margin of error $t_{\alpha/2}s_{\hat{y}_p}$ is computed by entering the formula =F9*F8 into cell F10. To compute $\hat{y}_p$, the point estimate of $E(y_p)$, we entered the formula =B29+B30*F2 into cell F11. The lower and upper limits of the 95% confidence interval are then computed by entering the formulas =F11-F10 and =F11+F10 into cells F12 and F13, respectively.

The value worksheet shows that the 95% confidence interval estimate is 98.583 to 121.417. In dollars, the 95% confidence interval for the mean quarterly sales of restaurants located near campuses with 10,000 students is $98,583 to $121,417. To develop confidence intervals for other values of x_p we simply use this worksheet as a template and enter another value for student population in cell F2. The new confidence interval will appear in cells F12 and F13. If a confidence interval for another value of α is desired, we can just insert the new value of α for the first argument of the TINV function in cell F9.

The confidence interval formulas developed here cannot be applied directly as a template for other regression problems because the number of observations will likely be different and the location of the regression output will not be in the same worksheet cells. The same cells (E1:F13) can be used to develop the confidence interval but the cell references used in cells F3, F6, F7, and F11 will need to be modified to reflect the location of the data and the regression output. The level of significance and the degrees of freedom used for TINV in cell F9 may also need to be changed.

The design of formulas to compute a prediction interval utilizes some of the same information used to develop a confidence interval. However, equation (12.27) shows that s_{ind}, instead of $s_{\hat{y}_p}$, is used in computing the margin of error. Refer to cells E15:F20 of the worksheet in Figure 12.14 as we describe the tasks involved in computing a 95% prediction interval.

Enter Functions and Formulas: To compute $s_{ind}^2 = s^2 + s_{\hat{y}_p}^2$ we entered the formula =D25+F7 into cell F16. Then, in cell F17 we entered the formula =SQRT(F16) to compute s_{ind}. The labels "Var of yind" and "Stdev of yind" were entered into cells E16 and E17 to identify these values. To compute the margin of error the formula =F9*F17 was entered into cell F18. The formulas =F11-F18 and =F11+F18 were entered into cells F19 and F20, respectively, to compute the lower and upper limits.

The 95% prediction interval is 76.127 to 143.873. In dollars, the 95% prediction interval is $76,127 to $143,873. To develop prediction intervals for other values of x_p we simply enter another value for student population in cell F2 and the new prediction interval will appear in cells F19 and F20. If a prediction interval for another value of α is desired, we can just insert the new value of α for the first argument of the TINV function in cell F9.

NOTES AND COMMENTS

1. The PredInt.xls macro, developed by Professor John O. McClain, Johnson Graduate School of Management, Cornell University, can be used to develop confidence and prediction intervals. A copy of the PredInt.xls macro is included on the data disk. Instructions for using the macro are provided as part of the macro.

2. In Appendix 12.1 we show how to use SWStat+ to develop confidence and prediction interval estimates for the Armand's Pizza Parlors data.

EXERCISES

Methods

37. The data from exercise 1 follow.

x_i	1	2	3	4	5
y_i	3	7	5	11	14

a. Use equation (12.23) to estimate the standard deviation of $\hat{y}_p$ when $x = 4$.
b. Use equation (12.24) to develop a 95% confidence interval estimate of the expected value of y when $x = 4$.
c. Use equation (12.26) to estimate the standard deviation of an individual value of y when $x = 4$.
d. Use equation (12.27) to develop a 95% prediction interval for y when $x = 4$.

38. The data from exercise 2 follow.

x_i	3	12	6	20	14
y_i	55	40	55	10	15

a. Estimate the standard deviation of $\hat{y}_p$ when $x = 8$.
b. Develop a 95% confidence interval estimate of the expected value of y when $x = 8$.
c. Estimate the standard deviation of an individual value of y when $x = 8$.
d. Develop a 95% prediction interval for y when $x = 8$.

39. The data from exercise 3 follow.

x_i	2	6	9	13	20
y_i	7	18	9	26	23

Develop the 95% confidence and prediction intervals when $x = 12$. Explain why these two intervals are different.

Applications

40. In exercise 18, the data on grade point average x and monthly salary y provided the estimated regression equation $\hat{y} = 1790.5 + 581.1x$.
   a. Develop a 95% confidence interval estimate of the mean starting salary for all students with a 3.0 GPA.
   b. Develop a 95% prediction interval estimate of the starting salary for Joe Heller, a student with a GPA of 3.0.

PCs

41. In exercise 10, data on the performance score (x) and the overall rating (y) for notebook PCs provided the estimated regression equation $\hat{y} = 51.82 + .1452x$ (*PC World*, February 2000).
   a. Develop a point estimate of the overall rating for a PC that has a performance score of 200.
   b. Develop a 95% confidence interval estimate of the mean overall score for all PCs that have a performance score of 200.
   c. Suppose that a new PC developed by Dell has a performance score of 200. Develop a 95% prediction interval estimate of the overall score for this new PC.
   d. Discuss the differences in your answers to parts (b) and (c).

42. In exercise 13, data were given on the adjusted gross income x and the amount of itemized deductions taken by taxpayers. Data were reported in thousands of dollars. With the estimated regression equation $\hat{y} = 4.68 + .16x$, the point estimate of a reasonable level of total itemized deductions for a taxpayer with an adjusted gross income of $52,500 is $13,080.
   a. Develop a 95% confidence interval estimate of the mean amount of total itemized deductions for all taxpayers with an adjusted gross income of $52,500.
   b. Develop a 95% prediction interval estimate for the amount of total itemized deductions for a particular taxpayer with an adjusted gross income of $52,500.
   c. If the particular taxpayer referred to in part (b) has claimed total itemized deductions of $20,400, would the IRS agent's request for an audit appear to be justified?
   d. Using your answer to part (b), give the IRS agent a guideline as to the amount of total itemized deductions a taxpayer with an adjusted gross income of $52,500 should have before an audit is recommended.

t Test Statistic

$$t = \frac{b_1}{s_{b_1}}$$ (12.19)

Mean Square Regression

$$MSR = \frac{SSR}{\text{Number of independent variables}}$$ (12.20)

F Test Statistic

$$F = \frac{MSR}{MSE}$$ (12.21)

Estimated Standard Deviation of $\hat{y}_p$

$$s_{\hat{y}_p} = s\sqrt{\frac{1}{n} + \frac{(x_p - \bar{x})^2}{\Sigma(x_i - \bar{x})^2}}$$ (12.23)

Confidence Interval for $E(y_p)$

$$\hat{y}_p \pm t_{\alpha/2} s_{\hat{y}_p}$$ (12.24)

Estimated Standard Deviation of an Individual Value

$$s_{\text{ind}} = s\sqrt{1 + \frac{1}{n} + \frac{(x_p - \bar{x})^2}{\Sigma(x_i - \bar{x})^2}}$$ (12.26)

Prediction Interval for y_p

$$\hat{y}_p \pm t_{\alpha/2} s_{\text{ind}}$$ (12.27)

Residual for Observation i

$$y_i - \hat{y}_i$$ (12.28)

Supplementary Exercises

50. Does a high value of r^2 imply that two variables are causally related? Explain.

51. What is the purpose of testing whether $\beta_1 = 0$? If we reject $\beta_1 = 0$, does it imply a good fit?

52. The data in the following table show the number of shares selling (millions) and the expected price (average of projected low price and projected high price) for 10 selected initial public stock offerings.

CD file

IPO

Company	Shares Selling	Expected Price ($)
American Physician	5.0	15
Apex Silver Mines	9.0	14
Dan River	6.7	15
Franchise Mortgage	8.75	17
Gene Logic	3.0	11
International Home Foods	13.6	19
PRT Group	4.6	13
Rayovac	6.7	14
RealNetworks	3.0	10
Software AG Systems	7.7	13

a. Develop an estimated regression equation with the number of shares selling as the independent variable and the expected price as the dependent variable.
b. At the .05 level of significance, is there a significant relationship between the two variables?
c. Did the estimated regression equation provide a good fit? Explain.
d. Use the estimated regression equation to estimate the expected price for a firm considering an initial public offering of 6 million shares.

53. Corporate share repurchase programs are often touted as a benefit for shareholders. But Robert Gabele, director of insider research for First Call/Thomson Financial, noted that many of these programs are undertaken solely to acquire stock for a company's incentive options for top managers. Across all companies, existing stock options in 1998 represented 6.2 percent of all common shares outstanding. The following data show the number of shares covered by option grants and the number of shares outstanding for 13 companies (*Bloomberg Personal Finance*, January/February 2000).

CD file

Options

Company	Shares of Option Grants Outstanding (millions)	Common Shares Outstanding (millions)
Adobe Systems	20.3	61.8
Apple Computer	52.7	160.9
Applied Materials	109.1	375.4
Autodesk	15.7	58.9
Best Buy	44.2	203.8
Fruit of the Loom	14.2	66.9
ITT Industries	18.0	87.9
Merrill Lynch	89.9	365.5
Novell	120.2	335.0
Parametric Technology	78.3	269.3
Reebok International	12.8	56.1
Silicon Graphics	52.6	188.8
Toys "R" Us	54.8	247.6

a. Develop the estimated regression equation that could be used to estimate the number of shares of option grants outstanding given the number of common shares outstanding.
b. Use the estimated regression equation to estimate the number of shares of option grants outstanding for a company that has 150 million shares of common stock outstanding.
c. Do you believe the estimated regression equation would provide a good prediction of the number of shares of option grants outstanding? Use r^2 to support your answer.

54. *Bloomberg Personal Finance* (July/August 2001) reported the market beta for Texas Instruments was 1.46. Market betas for individual stocks are determined by simple linear regression. For each stock, the dependent variable is its quarterly percentage return (capital appreciation plus dividends) minus the percentage return that could be obtained from a risk-free investment (the Treasury Bill rate is used as the risk-free rate). The independent variable is the quarterly percentage return (capital appreciation plus dividends) for the stock market (S&P 500) minus the percentage return from a risk-free investment. An estimated regression equation is developed with quarterly data; the market beta for the stock is the slope of the estimated regression equation (b_1). The value of the market beta is often interpreted as a measure of the risk associated with the stock. Market betas greater than 1 indicate that the stock is more volatile than the market average; market betas less than 1 indicate that the stock is less volatile than the market average. Suppose that the following figures are the differences between the percentage return and the risk-free return for 10 quarters for the S&P 500 and Horizon Technology.

MktBeta

S&P 500	Horizon
1.2	−0.7
−2.5	−2.0
−3.0	−5.5
2.0	4.7
5.0	1.8
1.2	4.1
3.0	2.6
−1.0	2.0
.5	−1.3
2.5	5.5

    a.   Develop an estimated regression equation that can be used to determine the market beta for Horizon Technology. What is Horizon Technology's market beta?

    b.   Test for a significant relationship at the .05 level of significance.

    c.   Did the estimated regression equation provide a good fit? Explain.

    d.   Use the market betas of Texas Instruments and Horizon Technology to compare the risk associated with the two stocks.

55. The Australian Public Service Commission's State of the Service Report 2002–2003 reported job satisfaction ratings for employees. One of the survey questions asked employees to choose the five most important workplace factors (from a list of factors) that most affected how satisfied they were with their job. Respondents were then asked to indicate their level of satisfaction with their top five factors. The following data show the percentage of employees who nominated the factor in their top five, and a corresponding satisfaction rating measured using the percentage of employees who nominated the factor in the top five and who were "very satisfied" or "satisfied" with the factor in their current workplace (http://www.apsc.gov.au/stateoftheservice).

JobSat

Workplace Factor	Top Five (%)	Satisfaction Rating (%)
Appropriate workload	30	49
Chance to be creative/innovative	38	64
Chance to make a useful contribution to society	40	67
Duties/expectations made clear	40	69
Flexible working arrangements	55	86
Good working relationships	60	85
Interesting work provided	48	74
Opportunities for career development	33	43
Opportunities to develop my skills	46	66
Opportunities to utilize my skills	50	70
Regular feedback/recognition for effort	42	53
Salary	47	62
Seeing tangible results from my work	42	69

    a.   Develop a scatter diagram with Top Five (%) on the horizontal axis and Satisfaction Rating (%) on the vertical axis.

    b.   What does the scatter diagram developed in part (a) indicate about the relationship between the two variables?

    c.   Develop the estimated regression equation that could be used to predict the Satisfaction Rating (%) given the Top Five (%).

    d.   Test for a significant relationship at the .05 level of significance.

e. Did the estimated regression equation provide a good fit? Explain.
f. What is the value of the sample correlation coefficient?

56. Jensen Tire & Auto is in the process of deciding whether to purchase a maintenance contract for its new computer wheel alignment and balancing machine. Managers feel that maintenance expense should be related to usage, and they collected the following information on weekly usage (hours) and annual maintenance expense (in hundreds of dollars).

Jensen

Weekly Usage (hours)	Annual Maintenance Expense ($ hundreds)
13	17.0
10	22.0
20	30.0
28	37.0
32	47.0
17	30.5
24	32.5
31	39.0
40	51.5
38	40.0

a. Develop the estimated regression equation that relates annual maintenance expense to weekly usage.
b. Test the significance of the relationship in part (a) at a .05 level of significance.
c. Jensen expects to use the new machine 30 hours per week. Develop a 95% prediction interval for the company's annual maintenance expense.
d. If the maintenance contract costs $3000 per year, would you recommend purchasing it? Why or why not?

57. In a manufacturing process the assembly line speed (feet per minute) was thought to affect the number of defective parts found during the inspection process. To test this theory, managers devised a situation in which the same batch of parts was inspected visually at a variety of line speeds. They collected the following data.

Line Speed	Number of Defective Parts Found
20	21
20	19
40	15
30	16
60	14
40	17

a. Develop the estimated regression equation that relates line speed to the number of defective parts found.
b. At a .05 level of significance, determine whether line speed and number of defective parts found are related.
c. Did the estimated regression equation provide a good fit to the data?
d. Develop a 95% confidence interval to predict the mean number of defective parts for a line speed of 50 feet per minute.

58. A sociologist was hired by a large city hospital to investigate the relationship between the number of unauthorized days that employees are absent per year and the distance (miles) between home and work for the employees. A sample of 10 employees was chosen, and the following data were collected.

Absent

Distance to Work	Number of Days Absent
1	8
3	5
4	8
6	7
8	6
10	3
12	5
14	2
14	4
18	2

   a. Develop a scatter diagram for these data. Does a linear relationship appear reasonable? Explain.
   b. Develop the least squares estimated regression equation.
   c. Is there a significant relationship between the two variables? Use $\alpha = .05$.
   d. Did the estimated regression equation provide a good fit? Explain.
   e. Use the estimated regression equation developed in part (b) to develop a 95% confidence interval for the expected number of days absent for employees living 5 miles from the company.

59. The regional transit authority for a major metropolitan area wants to determine whether there is any relationship between the age of a bus and the annual maintenance cost. A sample of 10 buses resulted in the following data.

AgeCost

Age of Bus (years)	Maintenance Cost ($)
1	350
2	370
2	480
2	520
2	590
3	550
4	750
4	800
5	790
5	950

   a. Develop the least squares estimated regression equation.
   b. Test to see whether the two variables are significantly related with $\alpha = .05$.
   c. Did the least squares line provide a good fit to the observed data? Explain.
   d. Develop a 95% prediction interval for the maintenance cost for a specific bus that is 4 years old.

60. A marketing professor at Givens College is interested in the relationship between hours spent studying and total points earned in a course. Data collected on 10 students who took the course last quarter follow.

CD file

HoursPts

Hours Spent Studying	Total Points Earned
45	40
30	35
90	75
60	65
105	90
65	50
90	90
80	80
55	45
75	65

a.   Develop an estimated regression equation showing how total points earned is related to hours spent studying.
b.   Test the significance of the model with $\alpha = .05$.
c.   Predict the total points earned by Mark Sweeney. He spent 95 hours studying.
d.   Develop a 95% prediction interval for the total points earned by Mark Sweeney.

61.   The Transactional Records Access Clearinghouse at Syracuse University reported data showing the odds of an Internal Revenue Service audit. The following table shows the average adjusted gross income reported and the percentage of the returns that were audited for 20 selected IRS districts.

CD file

IRSAudit

District	Adjusted Gross Income ($)	Percentage Audited
Los Angeles	36,664	1.3
Sacramento	38,845	1.1
Atlanta	34,886	1.1
Boise	32,512	1.1
Dallas	34,531	1.0
Providence	35,995	1.0
San Jose	37,799	0.9
Cheyenne	33,876	0.9
Fargo	30,513	0.9
New Orleans	30,174	0.9
Oklahoma City	30,060	0.8
Houston	37,153	0.8
Portland	34,918	0.7
Phoenix	33,291	0.7
Augusta	31,504	0.7
Albuquerque	29,199	0.6
Greensboro	33,072	0.6
Columbia	30,859	0.5
Nashville	32,566	0.5
Buffalo	34,296	0.5

a.   Develop the estimated regression equation that could be used to predict the percentage audited given the average adjusted gross income reported.
b.   At the .05 level of significance, determine whether the adjusted gross income and the percentage audited are related.
c.   Did the estimated regression equation provide a good fit? Explain.
d.   Use the estimated regression equation developed in part (a) to calculate a 95% confidence interval for the expected percentage audited for districts with an average adjusted gross income of $35,000.

Case Problem 1   Spending and Student Achievement

Is the educational achievement level of students related to how much the state in which they reside spends on education? In many communities taxpayers are asking this important question as school districts request tax revenue increases for education. In this case, you will be asked to analyze data on spending and achievement scores in order to determine whether there is any relationship between spending and student achievement in the public schools.

The federal government's National Assessment of Educational Progress (NAEP) program is frequently used to measure the educational achievement of students. Table 12.8

TABLE 12.8   SPENDING PER PUPIL AND COMPOSITE TEST SCORES FOR STATES THAT
PARTICIPATED IN THE NAEP PROGRAM

NAEP

State	Spending per Pupil ($)	Composite Test Score
Louisiana	4049	581
Mississippi	3423	582
California	4917	580
Hawaii	5532	580
South Carolina	4304	603
Alabama	3777	604
Georgia	4663	611
Florida	4934	611
New Mexico	4097	614
Arkansas	4060	615
Delaware	6208	615
Tennessee	3800	618
Arizona	4041	618
West Virginia	5247	625
Maryland	6100	625
Kentucky	5020	626
Texas	4520	627
New York	8162	628
North Carolina	4521	629
Rhode Island	6554	638
Washington	5338	639
Missouri	4483	641
Colorado	4772	644
Indiana	5128	649
Utah	3280	650
Wyoming	5515	657
Connecticut	7629	657
Massachusetts	6413	658
Nebraska	5410	660
Minnesota	5477	661
Iowa	5060	665
Montana	4985	667
Wisconsin	6055	667
North Dakota	4374	671
Maine	5561	675

TABLE 12.9   SPENDING PER PUPIL FOR STATES THAT DID NOT PARTICIPATE
IN THE NAEP PROGRAM

State	Spending per Pupil ($)
Idaho	3602
South Dakota	4067
Oklahoma	4265
Nevada	4658
Kansas	5164
Illinois	5297
New Hampshire	5387
Ohio	5438
Oregon	5588
Vermont	6269
Michigan	6391
Pennsylvania	6579
Alaska	7890

shows the total current spending per pupil per year, and the composite NAEP test score for 35 states that participated in the NAEP program. These data are available on the CD accompanying the text in the file named NAEP. The composite test score is the sum of the math, science, and reading scores on the 1996 (1994 for reading) NAEP test. Pupils tested are in grade 8, except for reading, which is given to fourth-graders only. The maximum possible score is 1300. Table 12.9 shows the spending per pupil for 13 states that did not participate in relevant NAEP surveys. These data were reported in an article on spending and achievement level appearing in *Forbes* (November 3, 1997).

Managerial Report

1. Develop numerical and graphical summaries of the data.
2. Use regression analysis to investigate the relationship between the amount spent per pupil and the composite score on the NAEP test. Discuss your findings.
3. Do you think that the estimated regression equation developed for these data could be used to estimate the composite test scores for the states that did not participate in the NAEP program?
4. Suppose that you only considered states that spend at least $4000 per pupil but not more than $6000 per pupil. For these states, does the relationship between the two variables appear to be any different than for the complete data set? Discuss the results of your findings and whether you think deleting states with spending less than $4000 per year and more than $6000 per pupil is appropriate.
5. Develop estimates of the composite test scores for the states that did not participate in the NAEP program.
6. Based upon your analyses, do you think that the educational achievement level of students is related to how much the state spends on education?

Case Problem 2   U.S. Department of Transportation

As part of a study on transportation safety, the U.S. Department of Transportation collected data on the number of fatal accidents per 1000 licenses and the percentage of licensed drivers under the age of 21 in a sample of 42 cities. Data collected over a one-year period follow. These data are available on the CD accompanying the text in the file named Safety.

Safety

Percentage Under 21	Fatal Accidents per 1000 Licenses	Percentage Under 21	Fatal Accidents per 1000 Licenses
13	2.962	17	4.100
12	0.708	8	2.190
8	0.885	16	3.623
12	1.652	15	2.623
11	2.091	9	0.835
17	2.627	8	0.820
18	3.830	14	2.890
8	0.368	8	1.267
13	1.142	15	3.224
8	0.645	10	1.014
9	1.028	10	0.493
16	2.801	14	1.443
12	1.405	18	3.614
9	1.433	10	1.926
10	0.039	14	1.643
9	0.338	16	2.943
11	1.849	12	1.913
12	2.246	15	2.814
14	2.855	13	2.634
14	2.352	9	0.926
11	1.294	17	3.256

Managerial Report

1. Develop numerical and graphical summaries of the data.
2. Use regression analysis to investigate the relationship between the number of fatal accidents and the percentage of drivers under the age of 21. Discuss your findings.
3. What conclusion and recommendations can you derive from your analysis?

Case Problem 3   Alumni Giving

Alumni donations are an important source of revenue for colleges and universities. If administrators could determine the factors that influence increases in the percentage of alumni who make a donation, they might be able to implement policies that could lead to increased revenues. Research shows that students who are more satisfied with their contact with teachers are more likely to graduate. As a result, one might suspect that smaller class sizes and lower student–faculty ratios might lead to a higher percentage of satisfied graduates, which in turn might lead to increases in the percentage of alumni who make a donation. Table 12.10 shows data for 48 national universities (*America's Best Colleges,* Year 2000 Edition). The

TABLE 12.10 DATA FOR 48 NATIONAL UNIVERSITIES

Alumni

	% of Classes Under 20	Student/Faculty Ratio	Alumni Giving Rate
Boston College	39	13	25
Brandeis University	68	8	33
Brown University	60	8	40
California Institute of Technology	65	3	46
Carnegie Mellon University	67	10	28
Case Western Reserve Univ.	52	8	31
College of William and Mary	45	12	27
Columbia University	69	7	31
Cornell University	72	13	35
Dartmouth College	61	10	53
Duke University	68	8	45
Emory University	65	7	37
Georgetown University	54	10	29
Harvard University	73	8	46
Johns Hopkins University	64	9	27
Lehigh University	55	11	40
Massachusetts Inst. of Technology	65	6	44
New York University	63	13	13
Northwestern University	66	8	30
Pennsylvania State Univ.	32	19	21
Princeton University	68	5	67
Rice University	62	8	40
Stanford University	69	7	34
Tufts University	67	9	29
Tulane University	56	12	17
U. of California–Berkeley	58	17	18
U. of California–Davis	32	19	7
U. of California–Irvine	42	20	9
U. of California–Los Angeles	41	18	13
U. of California–San Diego	48	19	8
U. of California–Santa Barbara	45	20	12
U. of Chicago	65	4	36
U. of Florida	31	23	19
U. of Illinois–Urbana Champaign	29	15	23
U. of Michigan–Ann Arbor	51	15	13
U. of North Carolina–Chapel Hill	40	16	26
U. of Notre Dame	53	13	49
U. of Pennsylvania	65	7	41
U. of Rochester	63	10	23
U. of Southern California	53	13	22
U. of Texas–Austin	39	21	13
U. of Virginia	44	13	28
U. of Washington	37	12	12
U. of Wisconsin–Madison	37	13	13
Vanderbilt University	68	9	31
Wake Forest University	59	11	38
Washington University–St. Louis	73	7	33
Yale University	77	7	50

column labeled % of Classes Under 20 shows the percentage of classes offered with fewer than 20 students. The column labeled Student/Faculty Ratio is the number of students enrolled divided by the total number of faculty. Finally, the column labeled Alumni Giving Rate is the percentage of alumni that made a donation to the university.

Managerial Report

1. Develop numerical and graphical summaries of the data.
2. Use regression analysis to develop an estimated regression equation that could be used to predict the alumni giving rate given the percentage of classes with fewer than 20 students.
3. Use regression analysis to develop an estimated regression equation that could be used to predict the alumni giving rate given the student–faculty ratio.
4. Which of the two estimated regression equations provides the best fit? For this estimated regression equation, perform an analysis of the residuals and discuss your findings and conclusions.
5. What conclusions and recommendations can you derive from your analysis?

Case Problem 4 # Major League Baseball Team Values

A group led by John Henry paid $700 million to purchase the Boston Red Sox in 2002, even though the Red Sox had not won the World Series since 1918 and posted an operating loss of $11.4 million for 2001. Moreover, *Forbes* magazine estimates that the current value of the team is actually $426 million. *Forbes* attributes the difference between the current value for a team and the price investors are willing to pay to the fact that the purchase of a team often includes the acquisition of a grossly undervalued cable network. For instance, in purchasing the Boston Red Sox, the new owners also got an 80% interest in the New England Sports Network. Table 12.11 shows data for the 30 major league teams (*Forbes*, April 15, 2002). The column labeled Value contains the values of the teams based on current stadium deals, without deduction for debt. The column labeled Income indicates the earnings before interest, taxes, and depreciation.

Managerial Report

1. Develop numerical and graphical summaries of the data.
2. Use regression analysis to investigate the relationship between value and income. Discuss your findings.
3. Use regression analysis to investigate the relationship between value and revenue. Discuss your findings.
4. What conclusions and recommendations can you derive from your analysis?

Appendix 12.1 # Regression Analysis with SWStat+

In Section 12.6 we showed how Excel's Regression tool can be used to perform a complete regression analysis for the Armand's Pizza Parlors data in Table 12.1. In this appendix we describe the steps required to perform regression analysis for Armand's Pizza Parlors using SWStat+. First we must create the data area for the Armand's Pizza Parlors data.

TABLE 12.11   DATA FOR MAJOR LEAGUE BASEBALL TEAMS

MLB

Team	Value	Revenue	Income
New York Yankees	730	215	18.7
New York Mets	482	169	14.3
Los Angeles Dodgers	435	143	−29.6
Boston Red Sox	426	152	−11.4
Atlanta Braves	424	160	9.5
Seattle Mariners	373	166	14.1
Cleveland Indians	360	150	−3.6
Texas Rangers	356	134	−6.5
San Francisco Giants	355	142	16.8
Colorado Rockies	347	129	6.7
Houston Astros	337	125	4.1
Baltimore Orioles	319	133	3.2
Chicago Cubs	287	131	7.9
Arizona Diamondbacks	280	127	−3.9
St. Louis Cardinals	271	123	−5.1
Detroit Tigers	262	114	12.3
Pittsburgh Pirates	242	108	9.5
Milwaukee Brewers	238	108	18.8
Philadelphia Phillies	231	94	2.6
Chicago White Sox	223	101	−3.8
San Diego Padres	207	92	5.7
Cincinnati Reds	204	87	4.3
Anaheim Angels	195	103	5.7
Toronto Blue Jays	182	91	−20.6
Oakland Athletics	157	90	6.8
Kansas City Royals	152	85	2.2
Tampa Bay Devil Rays	142	92	−6.1
Florida Marlins	137	81	1.4
Minnesota Twins	127	75	3.6
Montreal Expos	108	63	−3.4

Creating the Data Area

Step 1. Select any cell in the Armand's data set
Step 2. Select the **SWStat+** menu
Step 3. Choose **Data Area**
Step 4. Choose **Set New Data Area** from the list of Data Area options
Step 5. When the SWStat+ Data Area dialog box appears:
　　　　Select the **Set New** tab
　　　　Select **With column headers**
　　　　Select **With row headers**
　　　　Click **Set data area**

After creating the data area, the row and column labels will be highlighted in yellow and the entire data set (including labels) will have a blue border. In addition, a Results worksheet is added to the workbook. The Results worksheet will contain all the output generated using SWStat+. We are now ready to use SWStat+ to perform a complete regression analysis for the Armand's Pizza Parlors data.

where

$$SST = \text{total sum of squares} = \Sigma(y_i - \bar{y})^2$$
$$SSR = \text{sum of squares due to regression} = \Sigma(\hat{y}_i - \bar{y})^2$$
$$SSE = \text{sum of squares due to error} = \Sigma(y_i - \hat{y}_i)^2$$

Because of the computational difficulty in computing the three sums of squares, we rely on computer packages to determine those values. The analysis of variance part of the Excel output in Figure 13.4 shows the three values for the Butler Trucking example with two independent variables: SST = 23.9, SSR = 21.6006, and SSE = 2.2994. With only one independent variable (number of miles traveled), the Excel output in Figure 13.3 shows that SST = 23.9, SSR = 15.8713, and SSE = 8.0287. The value of SST is the same in both cases because it does not depend on $\hat{y}$, but SSR increases and SSE decreases when a second independent variable (number of deliveries) is added. The implication is that the estimated multiple regression equation provides a better fit for the observed data.

In Chapter 12, we used the coefficient of determination, $r^2 = SSR/SST$, to measure the goodness of fit for the estimated regression equation. The same concept applies to multiple regression. The term **multiple coefficient of determination** indicates that we are measuring the goodness of fit for the estimated multiple regression equation. The multiple coefficient of determination, denoted R^2, is computed as follows.

In the Excel Regression tool output the label R square is used to identify the value of R^2.

MULTIPLE COEFFICIENT OF DETERMINATION

$$R^2 = \frac{SSR}{SST} \tag{13.8}$$

The multiple coefficient of determination can be interpreted as the proportion of the variability in the dependent variable that can be explained by the estimated multiple regression equation. Hence, when multiplied by 100, it can be interpreted as the percentage of the variability in y that can be explained by the estimated regression equation.

In the two-independent-variable Butler Trucking example, with SSR = 21.6006 and SST = 23.9, we have

$$R^2 = \frac{21.6006}{23.9} = .9038$$

Therefore, 90.38% of the variability in travel time y is explained by the estimated multiple regression equation with miles traveled and number of deliveries as the independent variables. In Figure 13.4, we see that the multiple coefficient of determination is also provided by the Excel output; it is denoted by R square = .9038 (see cell B17).

Adding independent variables causes the prediction errors to become smaller, thus reducing the sum of squares due to error, SSE. Because SSR = SST − SSE, when SSE becomes smaller, SSR becomes larger, causing $R^2 = SSR/SST$ to increase.

Figure 13.3 shows that the R square value for the estimated regression equation with only one independent variable, number of miles traveled (x_1), is .6641. Thus, the percentage of the variability in travel times that is explained by the estimated regression equation increases from 66.41% to 90.38% when number of deliveries is added as a second independent variable. In general, R^2 always increases as independent variables are added to the model.

Many analysts prefer adjusting R^2 for the number of independent variables to avoid overestimating the impact of adding an independent variable on the amount of variability explained by the estimated regression equation. With n denoting the number of observations and p denoting the number of independent variables, the **adjusted multiple coefficient of determination** is computed as follows.

If a variable is added to the model, R^2 becomes larger even if the variable added is not statistically significant. The adjusted multiple coefficient of determination compensates for the number of independent variables in the model.

ADJUSTED MULTIPLE COEFFICIENT OF DETERMINATION

$$R_a^2 = 1 - (1 - R^2)\frac{n - 1}{n - p - 1} \qquad (13.9)$$

For the Butler Trucking example with $n = 10$ and $p = 2$, we have

$$R_a^2 = 1 - (1 - .9038)\frac{10 - 1}{10 - 2 - 1} = .8763$$

Thus, after adjusting for the two independent variables, we have an adjusted multiple coefficient of determination of .8763. This value is provided by the Excel output in Figure 13.4 as Adjusted R Square = .8763 (see cell B18).

Exercises

Methods

11. In exercise 1, the following estimated regression equation based on 10 observations was presented.

$$\hat{y} = 29.1270 + .5906x_1 + .4980x_2$$

The values of SST and SSR are 6724.125 and 6216.375, respectively.
    a. Find SSE.
    b. Compute R^2.
    c. Compute R_a^2.
    d. Comment on the goodness of fit.

12. In exercise 2, 10 observations were provided for a dependent variable y and two independent variables x_1 and x_2; for these data SST = 15,182.9, and SSR = 14,052.2.
    a. Compute R^2.
    b. Compute R_a^2.
    c. Does the estimated regression equation explain a large amount of the variability in the data? Explain.

13. In exercise 3, the following estimated regression equation based on 30 observations was presented.

$$\hat{y} = 17.6 + 3.8x_1 - 2.3x_2 + 7.6x_3 + 2.7x_4$$

The values of SST and SSR are 1805 and 1760, respectively.
    a. Compute R^2.
    b. Compute R_a^2.
    c. Comment on the goodness of fit.

Applications

14. In exercise 4, the following estimated regression equation relating sales to inventory investment and advertising expenditures was given.

$$\hat{y} = 25 + 10x_1 + 8x_2$$

The data used to develop the model came from a survey of 10 stores; for those data, SST = 16,000 and SSR = 12,000.

a.   For the estimated regression equation given, compute R^2.
b.   Compute R_a^2.
c.   Does the model appear to explain a large amount of variability in the data? Explain.

15.   In exercise 5, the owner of Showtime Movie Theaters, Inc., used multiple regression analysis to predict gross revenue (y) as a function of television advertising (x_1) and newspaper advertising (x_2). The estimated regression equation was

$$\hat{y} = 83.2 + 2.29x_1 + 1.30x_2$$

The computer solution provided SST = 25.5 and SSR = 23.435.
a.   Compute and interpret R^2 and R_a^2.
b.   When television advertising was the only independent variable, $R^2 = .653$ and $R_a^2 = .595$. Do you prefer the multiple regression results? Explain.

16.   In exercise 6, data were given on the proportion of games won, the number of team home runs, and the earned run average for the team's pitching staff for the 16 teams in the National League for the 2003 Major League Baseball season (http://www.usatoday.com, January 7, 2004).
a.   Did the estimated regression equation that uses only the number of home runs as the independent variable to predict the proportion of games won provide a good fit? Explain.
b.   Discuss the benefits of using both the number of home runs and the earned run average to predict the proportion of games won.

17.   In exercise 9, an estimated regression equation was developed relating the proportion of students who attend a four-year college to the average class size and the combined SAT score.
a.   Compute and interpret R^2 and R_a^2.
b.   Does the estimated regression equation provide a good fit to the data? Explain.

18.   Refer to exercise 10, where data were reported on a variety of statistics for the 29 teams in the National Basketball Association for a portion of the 2004 season (http://www.nba.com, January 3, 2004).
a.   In part (c) of exercise 10, an estimated regression equation was developed relating the proportion of games won given the percentage of field goals made by the team, the proportion of three-point shots made by the team's opponent, and the number of turnovers committed by the team's opponent. What are the values of R^2 and R_a^2?
b.   Does the estimated regression equation provide a good fit to the data? Explain.

(13.4) Model Assumptions

In Section 13.1 we introduced the following multiple regression model.

MULTIPLE REGRESSION MODEL

$$y = \beta_0 + \beta_1 x_1 + \beta_2 x_2 + \cdots + \beta_p x_p + \epsilon \qquad \textbf{(13.10)}$$

The assumptions about the error term ϵ in the multiple regression model parallel those for the simple linear regression model.

ASSUMPTIONS ABOUT THE ERROR TERM ϵ IN THE MULTIPLE REGRESSION MODEL $y = \beta_0 + \beta_1 x_1 + \cdots + \beta_p x_p + \epsilon$

1.   The error ϵ is a random variable with mean or expected value of zero; that is, $E(\epsilon) = 0$.

Implication: For given values of $x_1, x_2, \ldots, x_p$, the expected, or average, value of y is given by

$$E(y) = \beta_0 + \beta_1 x_1 + \beta_2 x_2 + \cdots + \beta_p x_p \qquad \textbf{(13.11)}$$

Equation (13.11) is the multiple regression equation we introduced in Section 13.1. In this equation, $E(y)$ represents the average of all possible values of y that might occur for the given values of $x_1, x_2, \ldots, x_p$.

2. The variance of ϵ is denoted by σ^2 and is the same for all values of the independent variables $x_1, x_2, \ldots, x_p$.
   Implication: The variance of y about the regression line equals σ^2 and is the same for all values of $x_1, x_2, \ldots, x_p$.

3. The values of ϵ are independent.
   Implication: The size of the error for a particular set of values for the independent variables is not related to the size of the error for any other set of values.

4. The error ϵ is a normally distributed random variable reflecting the deviation between the y value and the expected value of y given by $\beta_0 + \beta_1 x_1 + \beta_2 x_2 + \cdots + \beta_p x_p$.
   Implication: Because $\beta_0, \beta_1, \ldots, \beta_p$ are constants, for the given values of $x_1, x_2, \ldots, x_p$, the dependent variable y is also a normally distributed random variable.

To obtain more insight about the form of the relationship given by equation (13.11), consider the following two-independent-variable multiple regression equation.

$$E(y) = \beta_0 + \beta_1 x_1 + \beta_2 x_2$$

The graph of this equation is a plane in three-dimensional space. Figure 13.6 provides an example of such a graph. Note that the value of ϵ shown is the difference between the actual y value and the expected value of y, $E(y)$, when $x_1 = x_1^*$ and $x_2 = x_2^*$.

FIGURE 13.6   GRAPH OF THE REGRESSION EQUATION FOR MULTIPLE REGRESSION ANALYSIS WITH TWO INDEPENDENT VARIABLES

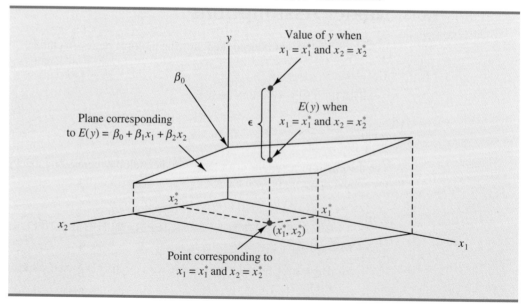

In regression analysis, the term *response variable* is often used in place of the term *dependent variable*. Furthermore, since the multiple regression equation generates a plane or surface, its graph is called a *response surface*.

13.5 Testing for Significance

In this section we show how to conduct significance tests for a multiple regression relationship. The significance tests we used in simple linear regression were a *t* test and an *F* test. In simple linear regression, both tests provide the same conclusion; that is, if the null hypothesis is rejected, we conclude that $\beta_1 \neq 0$. In multiple regression, the *t* test and the *F* test have different purposes.

1. The *F* test is used to determine whether a significant relationship exists between the dependent variable and the set of all the independent variables; we will refer to the *F* test as the test for *overall significance*.
2. If the *F* test shows an overall significance, the *t* test is used to determine whether each of the individual independent variables is significant. A separate *t* test is conducted for each of the independent variables in the model; we refer to each of these *t* tests as a test for *individual significance*.

In the material that follows, we will explain the *F* test and the *t* test and apply each to the Butler Trucking Company example.

F Test

The multiple regression model as defined in Section 13.1 is

$$y = \beta_0 + \beta_1 x_1 + \beta_2 x_2 + \cdots + \beta_p x_p + \epsilon$$

The hypotheses for the *F* test involve the parameters of the multiple regression model.

$$H_0: \beta_1 = \beta_2 = \cdots = \beta_p = 0$$
$$H_a: \text{One or more of the parameters are not equal to zero}$$

If H_0 is rejected, the test gives us sufficient statistical evidence to conclude that one or more of the parameters are not equal to zero and that the overall relationship between y and the set of independent variables $x_1, x_2, \ldots, x_p$ is significant. However, if H_0 cannot be rejected, we do not have sufficient evidence to conclude that a significant relationship is present.

Before describing the steps of the *F* test, we need to review the concept of *mean square*. A mean square is a sum of squares divided by its corresponding degrees of freedom. In the multiple regression case, the total sum of squares has $n - 1$ degrees of freedom, the sum of squares due to regression (SSR) has p degrees of freedom, and the sum of squares due to error has $n - p - 1$ degrees of freedom. Hence, the mean square due to regression (MSR) is SSR/p and the mean square due to error (MSE) is SSE/$(n - p - 1)$.

$$\text{MSR} = \frac{\text{SSR}}{p} \qquad \textbf{(13.12)}$$

and

$$\text{MSE} = \frac{\text{SSE}}{n - p - 1} \qquad \textbf{(13.13)}$$

As discussed in Chapter 13, MSE provides an unbiased estimate of σ^2, the variance of the error term ϵ. If H_0: $\beta_1 = \beta_2 = \cdots = \beta_p = 0$ is true, MSR also provides an unbiased estimate of σ^2, and the value of MSR/MSE should be close to 1. However, if H_0 is false, MSR overestimates σ^2 and the value of MSR/MSE becomes larger. To determine how large the value of MSR/MSE must be to reject H_0, we make use of the fact that if H_0 is true and the assumptions about the multiple regression model are valid, the sampling distribution of MSR/MSE is an F distribution with p degrees of freedom in the numerator and $n - p - 1$ degrees of freedom in the denominator. A summary of the F test for significance in multiple regression follows.

F TEST FOR OVERALL SIGNIFICANCE

$$H_0: \beta_1 = \beta_2 = \cdots = \beta_p = 0$$
$$H_a: \text{One or more of the parameters are not equal to zero}$$

TEST STATISTIC

$$F = \frac{\text{MSR}}{\text{MSE}} \tag{13.14}$$

REJECTION RULE

p-value approach: Reject H_0 if p-value $\leq \alpha$

Critical value approach: Reject H_0 if $F \geq F_\alpha$

where F_α is based on an F distribution with p degrees of freedom in the numerator and $n - p - 1$ degrees of freedom in the denominator.

Let us apply the F test to the Butler Trucking Company multiple regression example. With two independent variables, the hypotheses are written as follows.

$$H_0: \beta_1 = \beta_2 = 0$$
$$H_a: \beta_1 \text{ and/or } \beta_2 \text{ is not equal to zero}$$

Figure 13.7 shows a portion of the Excel output shown previously in Figure 13.4, with miles traveled (x_1) and number of deliveries (x_2) as the two independent variables. In the analysis of variance part of the output, we see that MSR = 10.8003 and MSE = .3285. Using equation (13.14), we obtain the test statistic.

$$F = \frac{10.8003}{.3285} = 32.9$$

Note that the F value in the Excel output is $F = 32.8784$; the value we calculated differs because we used rounded values for MSR and MSE in the calculation. Using $\alpha = .01$, the p-value (labeled *Significance F*) = 0.0003 in the last column of the analysis of variance table (Figure 13.7) indicates that we can reject H_0: $\beta_1 = \beta_2 = 0$ because the p-value is less than $\alpha = .01$. Alternatively, Table 4 of Appendix B shows that with two degrees of freedom in the numerator and seven degrees of freedom in the denominator, $F_{.01} = 9.55$. Because $F = 32.9 > 9.55$, we reject H_0: $\beta_1 = \beta_2 = 0$ and conclude that a significant relationship is present between travel time y and the two independent variables, miles traveled and number of deliveries.

As noted previously, the mean square error provides an unbiased estimate of σ^2, the variance of the error term ϵ. Referring to Figure 13.7, we see that the estimate of σ^2 is

FIGURE 13.7 PARTIAL EXCEL OUTPUT FOR THE BUTLER TRUCKING EXAMPLE WITH TWO INDEPENDENT VARIABLES

	A	B	C	D	E	F	G	H	I
13	SUMMARY OUTPUT								
14									
15	*Regression Statistics*								
16	Multiple R	0.9507							
17	R Square	0.9038							
18	Adjusted R Square	0.8763							
19	Standard Error	0.5731							
20	Observations	10							
21									
22	ANOVA								
23		*df*	*SS*	*MS*	*F*	*Significance F*			
24	Regression	2	21.6006	10.8003	32.8784	0.0003			
25	Residual	7	2.2994	0.3285					
26	Total	9	23.9						
27									
28		*Coefficients*	*Standard Error*	*t Stat*	*P-value*				
29	Intercept	-0.8687	0.9515	-0.9129	0.3916				
30	Miles	0.0611	0.0099	6.1824	0.0005				
31	Deliveries	0.9234	0.2211	4.1763	0.0042				
32									
33									
34									
35									
36									

The *Significance F* value in cell F24 is the *p*-value used to test for overall significance.

The *p*-value in cell E30 is used to test for the individual significance of Miles.

The *p*-value in cell E31 is used to test for the individual significance of Deliveries.

Note: Rows 1–12 are hidden.

MSE = .3285. The square root of MSE is the estimate of the standard deviation of the error term. As defined in Section 13.5, this standard deviation is called the standard error of the estimate and is denoted s. Hence, we have $s = \sqrt{MSE} = \sqrt{.3285} = .5731$. Note that the value of the standard error of the estimate appears in cell B19 of Figure 13.7.

Table 13.3 is the general analysis of variance (ANOVA) table that provides the F test results for a multiple regression model. The value of the F test statistic appears in the last

TABLE 13.3 ANOVA TABLE FOR A MULTIPLE REGRESSION MODEL WITH p INDEPENDENT VARIABLES

Source	Sum of Squares	Degrees of Freedom	Mean Square	F
Regression	SSR	p	$MSR = \dfrac{SSR}{p}$	$F = \dfrac{MSR}{MSE}$
Error	SSE	$n - p - 1$	$MSE = \dfrac{SSE}{n - p - 1}$	
Total	SST	$n - 1$		

column and can be compared to F_α with p degrees of freedom in the numerator and $n - p - 1$ degrees of freedom in the denominator to make the hypothesis test conclusion. By reviewing the Excel output for Butler Trucking Company in Figure 13.7, we see that Excel's analysis of variance table contains this information. In addition, Excel also provides the p-value corresponding to the F test statistic.

t **Test**

If the F test shows that the multiple regression relationship is significant, a t test can be conducted to determine the significance of each of the individual parameters. The t test for individual significance follows.

---

t TEST FOR INDIVIDUAL SIGNIFICANCE

For any parameter β_i

$$H_0: \beta_i = 0$$
$$H_a: \beta_i \neq 0$$

TEST STATISTIC

$$t = \frac{b_i}{s_{b_i}} \qquad (13.15)$$

REJECTION RULE

p-value approach: Reject H_0 if p-value $\leq \alpha$
Critical value approach: Reject H_0 if $t \leq t_{\alpha/2}$ or if $t \geq t_{\alpha/2}$

where $t_{\alpha/2}$ is based on a t distribution with $n - p - 1$ degrees of freedom.

In the test statistic, s_{b_i} is the estimate of the standard deviation of b_i. The value of s_{b_i} will be provided by the computer software package.

Let us conduct the t test for the Butler Trucking regression problem. Refer to cells B30:E31 in the Excel output shown in Figure 13.7. Values of b_1, b_2, s_{b_1}, and s_{b_2} are as follows.

$$b_1 = .0611 \quad s_{b_1} = .0099$$
$$b_2 = .9234 \quad s_{b_2} = .2211$$

Using equation (13.15), we obtain the test statistic for the hypotheses involving the individual parameters β_1 and β_2.

$$t = .0611/.0099 = 6.1717$$
$$t = .9234/.2211 = 4.1764$$

The t values in the Excel output are 6.1824 and 4.1763. The difference is due to rounding.

Note that both of these t-ratio values and the corresponding p-values are provided by the Excel output in Figure 13.7. Using $\alpha = .01$, the p-values of .0005 and .0042 on the Excel output indicate that we can reject $H_0: \beta_1 = 0$ and $H_0: \beta_2 = 0$. Hence, both parameters are statistically significant. Alternatively, Table 2 of Appendix B shows that with $n - p - 1 = 10 - 2 - 1 = 7$ degrees of freedom, $t_{.005} = 3.499$. Because $t = 6.1717 > 3.499$, we reject $H_0: \beta_1 = 0$. Similarly, with $4.1764 > 3.499$, we reject $H_0: \beta_2 = 0$.

Multicollinearity

We used the term *independent variable* in regression analysis to refer to any variable being used to predict or explain the value of the dependent variable. The term does not mean, however, that the independent variables themselves are independent in any statistical sense. On the contrary, most independent variables in a multiple regression problem are correlated to some degree with one another. For example, in the Butler Trucking example involving the two independent variables x_1 (miles traveled) and x_2 (number of deliveries), we could treat the miles traveled as the dependent variable and the number of deliveries as the independent variable to determine whether those two variables are themselves related. We could then compute the sample correlation coefficient $r_{x_1 x_2}$ to determine the extent to which the variables are related. Doing so yields $r_{x_1 x_2} = .16$. Thus, we find some degree of linear association between the two independent variables. In multiple regression analysis, **multicollinearity** refers to the correlation among the independent variables.

To provide a better perspective of the potential problems of multicollinearity, let us consider a modification of the Butler Trucking example. Instead of x_2 being the number of deliveries, let x_2 denote the number of gallons of gasoline consumed. Clearly, x_1 (the miles traveled) and x_2 are related; that is, we know that the number of gallons of gasoline used depends on the number of miles traveled. Hence, we would conclude logically that x_1 and x_2 are highly correlated independent variables.

Assume that we obtain the equation $\hat{y} = b_0 + b_1 x_1 + b_2 x_2$ and find that the F test shows the relationship to be significant. Then suppose we conduct a t test on β_1 to determine whether $\beta_1 \neq 0$, and we cannot reject $H_0: \beta_1 = 0$. Does this result mean that travel time is not related to miles traveled? Not necessarily. What it probably means is that with x_2 already in the model, x_1 does not make a significant additional contribution to determining the value of y. This interpretation makes sense in our example; if we know the amount of gasoline consumed, we do not gain much additional information useful in predicting y by knowing the miles traveled. Similarly, a t test might lead us to conclude $\beta_2 = 0$ on the grounds that, with x_1 in the model, knowledge of the amount of gasoline consumed does not add much.

When the independent variables are highly correlated, it is not possible to determine the separate effect of any particular independent variable on the dependent variable.

In t tests for the significance of individual parameters, the difficulty caused by multicollinearity is that it is possible to conclude that none of the individual parameters are significantly different from zero when an F test on the overall multiple regression equation indicates a significant relationship. This problem is avoided when there is little correlation among the independent variables.

Statisticians have developed several tests for determining whether multicollinearity is high enough to cause problems. According to the rule of thumb test, multicollinearity is a potential problem if the absolute value of the sample correlation coefficient exceeds .7 for any two of the independent variables. The other types of tests are more advanced and beyond the scope of this text.

If possible, every attempt should be made to avoid including independent variables that are highly correlated. In practice, however, strict adherence to this policy is rarely possible. When decision makers have reason to believe substantial multicollinearity is present, they must realize that separating the effects of the individual independent variables on the dependent variable is difficult.

NOTES AND COMMENTS

Ordinarily, multicollinearity does not affect the way in which we perform our regression analysis or interpret the output from a study. However, when multicollinearity is severe—that is, when two or more of the independent variables are highly correlated with one another—we can have difficulty

(continued)

interpreting the results of t tests on the individual parameters. In addition to the type of problem illustrated in this section, severe cases of multicollinearity have been shown to result in least squares estimates that have the wrong sign. That is, in simulated studies where researchers created the underlying regression model and then applied the least squares technique to develop estimates of β_0, β_1, β_2, and so on, it has been shown that under conditions of high multicollinearity the least squares estimates can have a sign opposite that of the parameter being estimated. For example, β_2 might actually be $+10$ and b_2, its estimate, might turn out to be -2. Thus, little faith can be placed in the individual coefficients if multicollinearity is present to a high degree.

Exercises

Methods

19. In exercise 1, the following estimated regression equation based on 10 observations was presented.

$$\hat{y} = 29.1270 + .5906x_1 + .4980x_2$$

Here SST = 6724.125, SSR = 6216.375, s_{b_1} = .0813, and s_{b_2} = .0567.
a. Compute MSR and MSE.
b. Compute F and perform the appropriate F test. Use $\alpha = .05$.
c. Perform a t test for the significance of β_1. Use $\alpha = .05$.
d. Perform a t test for the significance of β_2. Use $\alpha = .05$.

20. Refer to the data presented in exercise 2. The estimated regression equation for these data is

$$\hat{y} = -18.4 + 2.01x_1 + 4.74x_2$$

Here SST = 15,182.9, SSR = 14,052.2, s_{b_1} = .2471, and s_{b_2} = .9484.
a. Test for a significant relationship among x_1, x_2, and y. Use $\alpha = .05$.
b. Is β_1 significant? Use $\alpha = .05$.
c. Is β_2 significant? Use $\alpha = .05$.

21. The following estimated regression equation was developed for a model involving two independent variables.

$$\hat{y} = 40.7 + 8.63x_1 + 2.71x_2$$

After x_2 was dropped from the model, the least squares method was used to obtain an estimated regression equation involving only x_1 as an independent variable.

$$\hat{y} = 42.0 + 9.01x_1$$

a. Give an interpretation of the coefficient of x_1 in both models.
b. Could multicollinearity explain why the coefficient of x_1 differs in the two models? If so, how?

Applications

22. In exercise 4 the following estimated regression equation relating sales to inventory investment and advertising expenditures was given.

$$\hat{y} = 25 + 10x_1 + 8x_2$$

The data used to develop the model came from a survey of 10 stores; for these data SST = 16,000 and SSR = 12,000.

a. Compute SSE, MSE, and MSR.
b. Use an F test and a .05 level of significance to determine whether there is a relationship among the variables.

23. Refer to exercise 5.

SELF test

a. Use $\alpha = .01$ to test the hypotheses

$$H_0: \beta_1 = \beta_2 = 0$$
$$H_a: \beta_1 \text{ and/or } \beta_2 \text{ is not equal to zero}$$

CD file

Showtime

for the model $y = \beta_0 + \beta_1 x_1 + \beta_2 x_2 + \epsilon$, where

$$x_1 = \text{television advertising (\$1000s)}$$
$$x_2 = \text{newspaper advertising (\$1000s)}$$

b. Use $\alpha = .05$ to test the significance of β_1. Should x_1 be dropped from the model?
c. Use $\alpha = .05$ to test the significance of β_2. Should x_2 be dropped from the model?

24. Refer to the data in exercise 6. Use the number of team home runs and the earned run average for the team's pitching staff to predict the proportion of games won.

CD file

MLB

a. Use the F test to determine the overall significance of the relationship. What is your conclusion at the .05 level of significance?
b. Use the t test to determine the significance of each independent variable. What is your conclusion at the .05 level of significance?

25. *Barron's* conducts an annual review of online brokers, including both brokers that can be accessed via a Web browser, as well as direct-access brokers that connect customers directly with the broker's network server. Each broker's offerings and performance are evaluated in six areas, using a point value of 0–5 in each category. The results are weighted to obtain an overall score, and a final star rating, ranging from zero to five, is assigned to each broker. Trade execution, ease of use, and range of offerings are three of the areas evaluated. A point value of 5 in the trade execution area means the order entry and execution process flowed easily from one step to the next. A value of 5 in the ease of use area means that the site was easy to use and can be tailored to show what the user wants to see. A value of 5 in the range of offerings area means that all of the investment transactions can be executed online. The following data show the point values for trade execution, ease of use, range of offerings, and the star rating for a sample of 10 of the online brokers that *Barron's* evaluated (*Barron's*, March 10, 2003).

CD file

Brokers

Broker	Trade Execution	Ease of Use	Range of Offerings	Rating
Wall St. Access	3.7	4.5	4.8	4.0
E*TRADE (Power)	3.4	3.0	4.2	3.5
E*TRADE (Standard)	2.5	4.0	4.0	3.5
Preferred Trade	4.8	3.7	3.4	3.5
my Track	4.0	3.5	3.2	3.5
TD Waterhouse	3.0	3.0	4.6	3.5
Brown & Co.	2.7	2.5	3.3	3.0
Brokerage America	1.7	3.5	3.1	3.0
Merrill Lynch Direct	2.2	2.7	3.0	2.5
Strong Funds	1.4	3.6	2.5	2.0

a. Determine the estimated regression equation that can be used to predict the star rating given the point values for execution, ease of use, and range of offerings.
b. Use the F test to determine the overall significance of the relationship. What is the conclusion at the .05 level of significance?

c. Use the *t* test to determine the significance of each independent variable. What is your conclusion at the .05 level of significance?

d. Remove any independent variable that is not significant from the estimated regression equation. What is your recommended estimated regression equation? Compare the R^2 with the value of R^2 from part (a). Discuss the differences.

NBA

26. In exercise 10 an estimated regression equation was developed relating the proportion of games won given the proportion of field goals made by the team, the proportion of three-point shots made by the team's opponent, and the number of turnovers committed by the team's opponent.

a. Use the *F* test to determine the overall significance of the relationship. What is your conclusion at the .05 level of significance?

b. Use the *t* test to determine the significance of each independent variable. What is your conclusion at the .05 level of significance?

(13.6) Using the Estimated Regression Equation for Estimation and Prediction

The procedures for estimating the mean value of *y* and predicting an individual value of *y* in multiple regression are similar to those in regression analysis involving one independent variable. First, recall that in Chapter 12 we showed that the point estimate of the expected value of *y* for a given value of *x* was the same as the point estimate of an individual value of *y*. In both cases, we used $\hat{y} = b_0 + b_1 x$ as the point estimate.

In multiple regression we use the same procedure. That is, we substitute the given values of $x_1, x_2, \ldots, x_p$ into the estimated regression equation and use the corresponding value of $\hat{y}$ as the point estimate. Suppose that for the Butler Trucking example we want to use the estimated regression equation involving x_1 (miles traveled) and x_2 (number of deliveries) to develop two interval estimates:

1. A *confidence interval* of the mean travel time for all trucks that travel 100 miles and make two deliveries
2. A *prediction interval* of the travel time for *one specific* truck that travels 100 miles and makes two deliveries

Using the estimated regression equation $\hat{y} = -.8687 + .0611x_1 + .923x_2$ with $x_1 = 100$ and $x_2 = 2$, we obtain the following value of $\hat{y}$.

$$\hat{y} = -.8687 + .0611(100) + .9234(2) = 7.09$$

Hence, the point estimate of travel time in both cases is approximately seven hours.

To develop interval estimates for the mean value of *y* and for an individual value of *y*, we use a procedure similar to that for regression analysis involving one independent variable. The formulas required are beyond the scope of the text, but computer packages for multiple regression analysis will often provide confidence intervals once the values of x_1, $x_2, \ldots, x_p$ are specified by the user. Unfortunately, Excel's Regression tool does not have this capability. However, by running the PredInt.xls macro included on the data disk, you will be able to develop confidence and prediction interval estimates. In Table 13.4 we show 95% confidence and prediction interval estimates for the Butler Trucking example for selected values of x_1 and x_2; these interval estimates were obtained by using the PredInt macro. Note that the interval estimate for an individual value of *y* is wider than the interval estimate for the expected value of *y*. This difference simply reflects the fact that for given values of x_1 and x_2 we can estimate the mean travel time for all trucks with more precision than we can predict the travel time for one specific truck.

The PredInt.xls macro included on the data disk can be used to develop confidence and prediction intervals.

TABLE 13.4 THE 95% CONFIDENCE AND PREDICTION INTERVAL ESTIMATES FOR BUTLER TRUCKING

Value of x_1	Value of x_2	Value of $\hat{y}$	Confidence Interval		Prediction Interval	
			Lower Limit	Upper Limit	Lower Limit	Upper Limit
50	2	4.035	3.146	4.924	2.414	5.656
50	3	4.958	4.127	5.789	3.369	6.548
50	4	5.882	4.815	6.948	4.157	7.606
100	2	7.092	6.258	7.925	5.500	8.683
100	3	8.015	7.385	8.645	6.520	9.510
100	4	8.938	8.135	9.742	7.363	10.514

NOTES AND COMMENTS

In Appendix 13.1 we show how to use SWStat+ to develop confidence and prediction interval estimates for the Butler Trucking data.

Exercises

Methods

27. In exercise 1, the following estimated regression equation based on 10 observations was presented.

$$\hat{y} = 29.1270 + .5906x_1 + .4980x_2$$

a. Develop a point estimate of the mean value of y when $x_1 = 180$ and $x_2 = 310$.
b. Develop a point estimate for an individual value of y when $x_1 = 180$ and $x_2 = 310$.

28. Refer to the data in exercise 2. The estimated regression equation for those data is

$$\hat{y} = -18.4 + 2.01x_1 + 4.74x_2$$

a. Develop a 95% confidence interval for the mean value of y when $x_1 = 45$ and $x_2 = 15$.
b. Develop a 95% prediction interval for y when $x_1 = 45$ and $x_2 = 15$.

Applications

29. In exercise 5, the owner of Showtime Movie Theaters, Inc., used multiple regression analysis to predict gross revenue (y) as a function of television advertising (x_1) and newspaper advertising (x_2). The estimated regression equation was

Showtime

$$\hat{y} = 83.2 + 2.29x_1 + 1.30x_2$$

a. What is the gross revenue expected for a week when $3500 is spent on television advertising ($x_1 = 3.5$) and $1800 is spent on newspaper advertising ($x_2 = 1.8$)?
b. Provide a 95% confidence interval for the mean revenue of all weeks with the expenditures listed in part (a).
c. Provide a 95% prediction interval for next week's revenue, assuming that the advertising expenditures will be allocated as in part (a).

Schools

30. In exercise 9, an estimated regression equation was developed relating the percentage of students who attend a four-year college to the average class size and the combined SAT score.

a. Develop a 95% confidence interval for the mean percentage of students who attend a four-year college for a school district that has an average class size of 25 and whose students have a combined SAT score of 1000.

b. Suppose that a school district in Conway, South Carolina, has an average class size of 25 and a combined SAT score of 950. Develop a 95% prediction interval for the percentage of students who attend a four-year college.

31. The Buyer's Guide section of the Web site for *Car and Driver* magazine provides reviews and road tests for cars, trucks, SUVs, and vans. The average ratings of overall quality, vehicle styling, braking, handling, fuel economy, interior comfort, acceleration, dependability, fit and finish, transmission, and ride are summarized for each vehicle using a scale ranging from 1 (worst) to 10 (best). A portion of the data for 14 Sports/GT cars is shown here (http://www.caranddriver.com, January 7, 2004).

SportsCar

Sports/GT	Overall	Handling	Dependability	Fit and Finish
Acura 3.2CL	7.80	7.83	8.17	7.67
Acura RSX	9.02	9.46	9.35	8.97
Audi TT	9.00	9.58	8.74	9.38
BMW 3-Series/M3	8.39	9.52	8.39	8.55
Chevrolet Corvette	8.82	9.64	8.54	7.87
Ford Mustang	8.34	8.85	8.70	7.34
Honda Civic Si	8.92	9.31	9.50	7.93
Infiniti G35	8.70	9.34	8.96	8.07
Mazda RX-8	8.58	9.79	8.96	8.12
Mini Cooper	8.76	10.00	8.69	8.33
Mitsubishi Eclipse	8.17	8.95	8.25	7.36
Nissan 350Z	8.07	9.35	7.56	8.21
Porsche 911	9.55	9.91	8.86	9.55
Toyota Celica	8.77	9.29	9.04	7.97

a. Develop an estimated regression equation using handling, dependability, and fit and finish to predict overall quality.

b. Another Sports/GT car rated by *Car and Driver* is the Honda Accord. The ratings for handling, dependability, and fit and finish for the Honda Accord were 8.28, 9.06, and 8.07, respectively. Estimate the overall rating for this car.

c. Provide a 95% confidence interval for overall quality for all sports and GT cars with the characteristics listed in part (a).

d. Provide a 95% prediction interval for overall quality for the Honda Accord described in part (b).

e. The overall rating reported by *Car and Driver* for the Honda Accord was 8.65. How does this rating compare to the estimates you developed in parts (b) and (d)?

13.7 Qualitative Independent Variables

Independent variables may be qualitative or quantitative.

Thus far, the examples we have considered have involved quantitative independent variables such as student population, distance traveled, and number of deliveries. In many situations, however, we must work with **qualitative independent variables** such as gender (male, female), method of payment (cash, credit card, check), and so on. The purpose of this section is to show how qualitative variables are handled in regression analysis. To illustrate the use and interpretation of a qualitative independent variable, we will consider a problem facing the managers of Johnson Filtration, Inc.

An Example: Johnson Filtration, Inc.

Johnson Filtration, Inc., provides maintenance service for water-filtration systems throughout southern Florida. Customers contact Johnson with requests for maintenance service on their water-filtration systems. To estimate the service time and the service cost, Johnson's managers want to predict the repair time necessary for each maintenance request. Hence, repair time in hours is the dependent variable. Repair time is believed to be related to two factors, the number of months since the last maintenance service and the type of repair problem (mechanical or electrical). Data for a sample of 10 service calls are reported in Table 13.5.

Let y denote the repair time in hours and x_1 denote the number of months since the last maintenance service. The regression model that uses only x_1 to predict y is

$$y = \beta_0 + \beta_1 x_1 + \epsilon$$

Using Excel's Regression tool to develop the estimated regression equation, we obtained the partial Excel output shown in Figure 13.8. The estimated regression equation is

$$\hat{y} = 2.1473 + .3041 x_1 \tag{13.16}$$

At the .05 level of significance, the p-value of .0163 for the t (or F) test indicates that the number of months since the last service is significantly related to repair time. R Square = .5342 indicates that x_1 alone explains 53.42% of the variability in repair time.

To incorporate the type of repair into the regression model, we define the following variable.

$$x_2 = \begin{cases} 0 \text{ if the type of repair is mechanical} \\ 1 \text{ if the type of repair is electrical} \end{cases}$$

In regression analysis x_2 is called an *indicator* or **dummy variable.** Using this dummy variable, we can write the multiple regression model as

$$y = \beta_0 + \beta_1 x_1 + \beta_2 x_2 + \epsilon$$

Table 13.6 is the revised data set that includes the values of the dummy variable. Using Excel and the data in Table 13.6, we can develop estimates of the model parameters. The Excel output in Figure 13.9 shows that the estimated multiple regression equation is

$$\hat{y} = .9305 + .3876 x_1 + 1.2627 x_2 \tag{13.17}$$

TABLE 13.5   DATA FOR THE JOHNSON FILTRATION EXAMPLE

Service Call	Months Since Last Service	Type of Repair	Repair Time in Hours
1	2	Electrical	2.9
2	6	Mechanical	3.0
3	8	Electrical	4.8
4	3	Mechanical	1.8
5	2	Electrical	2.9
6	7	Electrical	4.9
7	9	Mechanical	4.2
8	8	Mechanical	4.8
9	4	Electrical	4.4
10	6	Electrical	4.5

FIGURE 13.8   PARTIAL EXCEL OUTPUT FOR THE JOHNSON FILTRATION EXAMPLE WITH MONTHS SINCE LAST SERVICE CALL AS THE INDEPENDENT VARIABLE

The Excel regression output appears in a new worksheet because we selected New Worksheet Ply as the Output option in the Regression dialog box.

	A	B	C	D	E	F	G
1	SUMMARY OUTPUT						
2							
3	*Regression Statistics*						
4	Multiple R	0.7309					
5	R Square	0.5342					
6	Adjusted R Square	0.4759					
7	Standard Error	0.7810					
8	Observations	10					
9							
10	ANOVA						
11		*df*	*SS*	*MS*	*F*	*Significance F*	
12	Regression	1	5.5960	5.5960	9.1739	0.0163	
13	Residual	8	4.8800	0.6100			
14	Total	9	10.476				
15							
16		*Coefficients*	*Standard Error*	*t Stat*	*P-value*		
17	Intercept	2.1473	0.6050	3.5493	0.0075		
18	Months	0.3041	0.1004	3.0288	0.0163		
19							

At the .05 level of significance, the Significance F or p-value of .0010 associated with the F test ($F = 21.3570$) indicates that the regression relationship is significant. The t test part of the output in Figure 13.9 shows that both months since last service (p-value = .0004) and type of repair (p-value = .0051) are statistically significant. In addition, R Square = .8592 and Adjusted R Square = .8190 indicate that the estimated regression equation does a good job of explaining the variability in repair times. Thus, equation (13.17) should prove helpful in estimating the repair time necessary for the various service calls.

TABLE 13.6   DATA FOR THE JOHNSON FILTRATION EXAMPLE WITH TYPE OF REPAIR INDICATED BY A DUMMY VARIABLE ($x_2 = 0$ FOR MECHANICAL; $x_2 = 1$ FOR ELECTRICAL)

Johnson

Customer	Months Since Last Service (x_1)	Type of Repair (x_2)	Repair Time in Hours (y)
1	2	1	2.9
2	6	0	3.0
3	8	1	4.8
4	3	0	1.8
5	2	1	2.9
6	7	1	4.9
7	9	0	4.2
8	8	0	4.8
9	4	1	4.4
10	6	1	4.5

FIGURE 13.9   PARTIAL EXCEL OUTPUT FOR THE JOHNSON FILTRATION EXAMPLE
WITH MONTHS SINCE LAST SERVICE CALL AND TYPE OF REPAIR
AS THE INDEPENDENT VARIABLES

	A	B	C	D	E	F	G
1	SUMMARY OUTPUT						
2							
3	*Regression Statistics*						
4	Multiple R	0.9269					
5	R Square	0.8592					
6	Adjusted R Square	0.8190					
7	Standard Error	0.4590					
8	Observations	10					
9							
10	ANOVA						
11		*df*	*SS*	*MS*	*F*	*Significance F*	
12	Regression	2	9.0009	4.5005	21.3570	0.0010	
13	Residual	7	1.4751	0.2107			
14	Total	9	10.476				
15							
16		*Coefficients*	*Standard Error*	*t Stat*	*P-value*		
17	Intercept	0.9305	0.4670	1.9926	0.0866		
18	Months	0.3876	0.0626	6.1954	0.0004		
19	Type	1.2627	0.3141	4.0197	0.0051		
20							

Interpreting the Parameters

The multiple regression equation for the Johnson Filtration example is

$$E(y) = \beta_0 + \beta_1 x_1 + \beta_2 x_2 \tag{13.18}$$

To understand how to interpret the parameters β_0, β_1, and β_2 when a qualitative variable is present, consider the case when $x_2 = 0$ (mechanical repair). Using $E(y \mid \text{mechanical})$ to denote the mean repair time *given* a mechanical repair, we have

$$E(y \mid \text{mechanical}) = \beta_0 + \beta_1 x_1 + \beta_2(0) = \beta_0 + \beta_1 x_1 \tag{13.19}$$

Similarly, for an electrical repair ($x_2 = 1$), we have

$$E(y \mid \text{electrical}) = \beta_0 + \beta_1 x_1 + \beta_2(1) = \beta_0 + \beta_1 x_1 + \beta_2 \tag{13.20}$$
$$= (\beta_0 + \beta_2) + \beta_1 x_1$$

Comparing equations (13.19) and (13.20), we see that the expected repair time is a linear function of x_1 for both mechanical and electrical repairs. The slope of both equations is β_1, but the y-intercept differs. The y-intercept is β_0 in equation (13.19) for mechanical repairs and ($\beta_0 + \beta_2$) in equation (13.20) for electrical repairs. The interpretation of β_2 is that it indicates the difference between the expected repair time for an electrical repair and the expected repair time for a mechanical repair.

If β_2 is positive, the expected repair time for an electrical repair will be greater than that for a mechanical repair; if β_2 is negative, the expected repair time for an electrical repair will be less than that for a mechanical repair. Finally, if $\beta_2 = 0$, there is no difference in repair time between electrical and mechanical repairs and the type of repair is not related to the repair time.

Using the estimated multiple regression equation $\hat{y} = .9305 + .3876x_1 + 1.2627x_2$, we see that .9305 is the estimate of β_0 and 1.2627 is the estimate of β_2. Thus, when $x_2 = 0$ (mechanical repair)

$$\hat{y} = .9305 + .3876x_1 \qquad \textbf{(13.21)}$$

and when $x_2 = 1$ (electrical repair)

$$\begin{aligned}\hat{y} &= .9305 + .3876x_1 + 1.2627(1) \\ &= 2.1932 + .3876x_1\end{aligned} \qquad \textbf{(13.22)}$$

In effect, the use of a dummy variable for type of repair has provided two equations that can be used to predict the repair time, one corresponding to mechanical repairs and one corresponding to electrical repairs. In addition, with $b_2 = 1.2627$, we have learned that, on average, electrical repairs require 1.2627 hours longer than mechanical repairs.

Figure 13.10 is the plot of the Johnson data from Table 13.6. Repair time in hours (y) is represented by the vertical axis and months since last service (x_1) is represented by the horizontal axis. A data point for a mechanical repair is indicated by an M and a data point for an electrical repair is indicated by an E. Equations (13.21) and (13.22) are plotted on the graph to show graphically the two equations that can be used to predict the repair time, one corresponding to mechanical repairs and one corresponding to electrical repairs.

FIGURE 13.10 SCATTER DIAGRAM FOR THE JOHNSON FILTRATION REPAIR DATA FROM TABLE 13.6

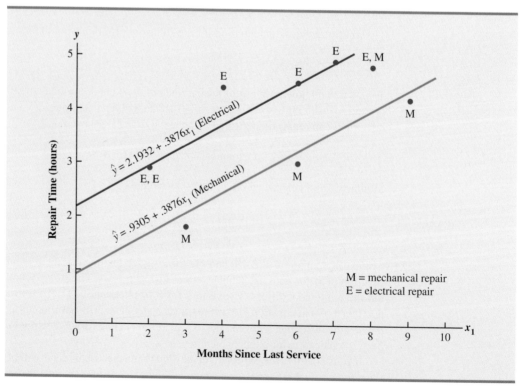

More Complex Qualitative Variables

A qualitative variable with k levels must be modeled using k − 1 dummy variables. Care must be taken in defining and interpreting the dummy variables.

Because the qualitative variable for the Johnson Filtration example had two levels (mechanical and electrical), defining a dummy variable with zero indicating a mechanical repair and one indicating an electrical repair was easy. However, when a qualitative variable has more than two levels, care must be taken in both defining and interpreting the dummy variables. As we will show, if a qualitative variable has k levels, $k − 1$ dummy variables are required, with each dummy variable being coded as 0 or 1.

For example, suppose a manufacturer of copy machines organized the sales territories for a particular state into three regions: A, B, and C. The managers want to use regression analysis to help predict the number of copiers sold per week. With the number of units sold as the dependent variable, they are considering several independent variables (the number of sales personnel, advertising expenditures, and so on). Suppose the managers believe sales region is also an important factor in predicting the number of copiers sold. Because sales region is a qualitative variable with three levels, A, B and C, we will need $3 − 1 = 2$ dummy variables to represent the sales region. Each variable can be coded 0 or 1 as follows.

$$x_1 = \begin{cases} 1 \text{ if sales region B} \\ 0 \text{ otherwise} \end{cases}$$

$$x_2 = \begin{cases} 1 \text{ if sales region C} \\ 0 \text{ otherwise} \end{cases}$$

With this definition, we have the following values of x_1 and x_2.

Region	x_1	x_2
A	0	0
B	1	0
C	0	1

Observations corresponding to region A would be coded $x_1 = 0$, $x_2 = 0$; observations corresponding to region B would be coded $x_1 = 1$, $x_2 = 0$; and observations corresponding to region C would be coded $x_1 = 0$, $x_2 = 1$.

The regression equation relating the expected value of the number of units sold, $E(y)$, to the dummy variables would be written as

$$E(y) = \beta_0 + \beta_1 x_1 + \beta_2 x_2$$

To help us interpret the parameters β_0, β_1, and β_2, consider the following three variations of the regression equation.

$$E(y \mid \text{region A}) = \beta_0 + \beta_1(0) + \beta_2(0) = \beta_0$$
$$E(y \mid \text{region B}) = \beta_0 + \beta_1(1) + \beta_2(0) = \beta_0 + \beta_1$$
$$E(y \mid \text{region C}) = \beta_0 + \beta_1(0) + \beta_2(1) = \beta_0 + \beta_2$$

Thus, β_0 is the mean or expected value of sales for region A; β_1 is the difference between the mean number of units sold in region B and the mean number of units sold in region A; and β_2 is the difference between the mean number of units sold in region C and the mean number of units sold in region A.

Two dummy variables were required because sales region is a qualitative variable with three levels. But the assignment of $x_1 = 0$, $x_2 = 0$ to indicate region A, $x_1 = 1$, $x_2 = 0$ to indicate region B, and $x_1 = 0, x_2 = 1$ to indicate region C was arbitrary. For example, we could have chosen $x_1 = 1$, $x_2 = 0$ to indicate region A, $x_1 = 0$, $x_2 = 0$ to indicate region B, and $x_1 = 0, x_2 = 1$ to indicate region C. In that case, β_1 would have been interpreted as the mean difference between regions A and B and β_2 as the mean difference between regions C and B.

The important point to remember is that when a qualitative variable has k levels, $k - 1$ dummy variables are required in the multiple regression analysis. Thus, if the sales region example had a fourth region, labeled D, three dummy variables would be necessary. For example, the three dummy variables can be coded as follows.

$$x_1 = \begin{cases} 1 \text{ if sales region B} \\ 0 \text{ otherwise} \end{cases} \qquad x_2 = \begin{cases} 1 \text{ if sales region C} \\ 0 \text{ otherwise} \end{cases} \qquad x_3 = \begin{cases} 1 \text{ if sales region D} \\ 0 \text{ otherwise} \end{cases}$$

Exercises

Methods

32. Consider a regression study involving a dependent variable y, a quantitative independent variable x_1, and a qualitative variable with two levels (level 1 and level 2).
    a. Write a multiple regression equation relating x_1 and the qualitative variable to y.
    b. What is the expected value of y corresponding to level 1 of the qualitative variable?
    c. What is the expected value of y corresponding to level 2 of the qualitative variable?
    d. Interpret the parameters in your regression equation.

33. Consider a regression study involving a dependent variable y, a quantitative independent variable x_1, and a qualitative independent variable with three possible levels (level 1, level 2, and level 3).
    a. How many dummy variables are required to represent the qualitative variable?
    b. Write a multiple regression equation relating x_1 and the qualitative variable to y.
    c. Interpret the parameters in your regression equation.

Applications

34. Management proposed the following regression model to predict sales at a fast-food outlet.

$$y = \beta_0 + \beta_1 x_1 + \beta_2 x_2 + \beta_3 x_3 + \epsilon$$

where

$$x_1 = \text{number of competitors within one mile}$$
$$x_2 = \text{population within one mile (1000s)}$$
$$x_3 = \begin{cases} 1 \text{ if drive-up window present} \\ 0 \text{ otherwise} \end{cases}$$
$$y = \text{sales (\$1000s)}$$

The following estimated regression equation was developed after 20 outlets were surveyed.

$$\hat{y} = 10.1 - 4.2x_1 + 6.8x_2 + 15.3x_3$$

a. What is the expected amount of sales attributable to the drive-up window?
b. Predict sales for a store with two competitors, a population of 8000 within one mile, and no drive-up window.
c. Predict sales for a store with one competitor, a population of 3000 within one mile, and a drive-up window.

35. Refer to the Johnson Filtration example introduced in this section. Suppose that in addition to information on the number of months since the machine was serviced and whether a mechanical or an electrical repair had occurred, the managers obtained a list showing which repairperson performed the service. The revised data follow.

Repair

Repair Time in Hours	Months Since Last Service	Type of Repair	Repairperson
2.9	2	Electrical	Dave Newton
3.0	6	Mechanical	Dave Newton
4.8	8	Electrical	Bob Jones
1.8	3	Mechanical	Dave Newton
2.9	2	Electrical	Dave Newton
4.9	7	Electrical	Bob Jones
4.2	9	Mechanical	Bob Jones
4.8	8	Mechanical	Bob Jones
4.4	4	Electrical	Bob Jones
4.5	6	Electrical	Dave Newton

a. Ignore for now the months since the last maintenance service (x_1) and the repairperson who performed the service. Develop the estimated simple linear regression equation to predict the repair time (y) given the type of repair (x_2). Recall that $x_2 = 0$ if the type of repair is mechanical and 1 if the type of repair is electrical.

b. Does the equation that you developed in part (a) provide a good fit for the observed data? Explain.

c. Ignore for now the months since the last maintenance service and the type of repair associated with the machine. Develop the estimated simple linear regression equation to predict the repair time given the repairperson who performed the service. Let $x_3 = 0$ if Bob Jones performed the service and $x_3 = 1$ if Dave Newton performed the service.

d. Does the equation that you developed in part (c) provide a good fit for the observed data? Explain.

36. This problem is an extension of the situation described in exercise 35.

a. Develop the estimated regression equation to predict the repair time given the number of months since the last maintenance service, the type of repair, and the repairperson who performed the service.

b. At the .05 level of significance, test whether the estimated regression equation developed in part (a) represents a significant relationship between the independent variables and the dependent variable.

c. Is the addition of the independent variable x_3, the repairperson who performed the service, statistically significant? Use $\alpha = .05$. What explanation can you give for the results observed?

37. The National Football League rates prospects by position on a scale that ranges from 5 to 9. The ratings are interpreted as follows: 8–9 should start the first year; 7.0–7.9 should start; 6.0–6.9 will make the team as backup; and 5.0–5.9 can make the club and contribute. The following table shows the position, weight, speed (for 40 yards), and ratings for 25 NFL prospects (*USA Today*, April 14, 2000).

Football

Player	Position	Weight (pounds)	Speed (seconds)	Rating
Cosey Coleman	Guard	322	5.38	7.4
Travis Claridge	Guard	303	5.18	7.0
Kaulana Noa	Guard	317	5.34	6.8

(*continued*)

Player	Position	Weight (pounds)	Speed (seconds)	Rating
Leander Jordan	Guard	330	5.46	6.7
Chad Clifton	Guard	334	5.18	6.3
Manula Savea	Guard	308	5.32	6.1
Ryan Johanningmeir	Guard	310	5.28	6.0
Mark Tauscher	Guard	318	5.37	6.0
Blaine Saipaia	Guard	321	5.25	6.0
Richard Mercier	Guard	295	5.34	5.8
Damion McIntosh	Guard	328	5.31	5.3
Jeno James	Guard	320	5.64	5.0
Al Jackson	Guard	304	5.20	5.0
Chris Samuels	Offensive tackle	325	4.95	8.5
Stockar McDougle	Offensive tackle	361	5.50	8.0
Chris McIngosh	Offensive tackle	315	5.39	7.8
Adrian Klemm	Offensive tackle	307	4.98	7.6
Todd Wade	Offensive tackle	326	5.20	7.3
Marvel Smith	Offensive tackle	320	5.36	7.1
Michael Thompson	Offensive tackle	287	5.05	6.8
Bobby Williams	Offensive tackle	332	5.26	6.8
Darnell Alford	Offensive tackle	334	5.55	6.4
Terrance Beadles	Offensive tackle	312	5.15	6.3
Tutan Reyes	Offensive tackle	299	5.35	6.1
Greg Robinson-Ran	Offensive tackle	333	5.59	6.0

a. Develop a dummy variable that will account for the player's position.
b. Develop an estimated regression equation to show how rating is related to position, weight, and speed.
c. At the .05 level of significance, test whether the estimated regression equation developed in part (b) indicates a significant relationship between the independent variables and the dependent variable.
d. Does the estimated regression equation provide a good fit for the observed data? Explain.
e. Is position a significant factor in the player's rating? Use $\alpha = .05$. Explain.
f. Suppose a new offensive tackle prospect who weighs 300 pounds ran the 40 yards in 5.1 seconds. Use the estimated regression equation developed in part (b) to estimate the rating for this player.

38. A 10-year study conducted by the American Heart Association provided data on how age, blood pressure, and smoking relate to the risk of strokes. Assume that the following data are from a portion of this study. Risk is interpreted as the probability (times 100) that the patient will have a stroke over the next 10-year period. For the smoking variable, define a dummy variable with 1 indicating a smoker and 0 indicating a nonsmoker.

Stroke

Risk	Age	Pressure	Smoker
12	57	152	No
24	67	163	No
13	58	155	No
56	86	177	Yes
28	59	196	No
51	76	189	Yes
18	56	155	Yes

Risk	Age	Pressure	Smoker
31	78	120	No
37	80	135	Yes
15	78	98	No
22	71	152	No
36	70	173	Yes
15	67	135	Yes
48	77	209	Yes
15	60	199	No
36	82	119	Yes
8	66	166	No
34	80	125	Yes
3	62	117	No
37	59	207	Yes

a. Develop an estimated regression equation that relates risk of a stroke to the person's age, blood pressure, and whether the person is a smoker.

b. Is smoking a significant factor in the risk of a stroke? Explain. Use $\alpha = .05$.

c. What is the probability of a stroke over the next 10 years for Art Speen, a 68-year-old smoker who has blood pressure of 175? What action might the physician recommend for this patient?

Summary

In this chapter, we introduced multiple regression analysis as an extension of simple linear regression analysis presented in Chapter 12. Multiple regression analysis enables us to understand how a dependent variable is related to two or more independent variables. The regression equation $E(y) = \beta_0 + \beta_1 x_1 + \beta_2 x_2 + \cdots + \beta_p x_p$ shows that the expected value or mean value of the dependent variable y is related to the values of the independent variables $x_1, x_2, \ldots, x_p$. Sample data and the least squares method are used to develop the estimated regression equation $\hat{y} = b_0 + b_1 x_1 + b_2 x_2 + \ldots + b_p x_p$. In effect $b_0, b_1, b_2, \ldots, b_p$ are sample statistics used to estimate the unknown model parameters $\beta_0, \beta_1, \beta_2, \ldots, \beta_p$. Excel's Regression tool was used throughout the chapter to emphasize the fact that statistical software packages are the only realistic means of performing the numerous computations required in multiple regression analysis.

The multiple coefficient of determination was presented as a measure of the goodness of fit of the estimated regression equation. It determines the proportion of the variation of y that can be explained by the estimated regression equation. The adjusted multiple coefficient of determination is a similar measure of goodness of fit that adjusts for the number of independent variables and thus avoids overestimating the impact of adding more independent variables.

An F test and a t test were presented as ways to determine statistically whether the relationship among the variables is significant. The F test is used to determine whether there is a significant overall relationship between the dependent variable and the set of all independent variables. The t test is used to determine whether there is a significant relationship between the dependent variable and an individual independent variable given the other independent variables in the regression model. Correlation among the independent variables, known as multicollinearity, was discussed.

This chapter concluded with a section that showed how dummy variables can be used to incorporate qualitative data into multiple regression analysis.

Glossary

Multiple regression analysis Regression analysis involving two or more independent variables.

Multiple regression model The mathematical equation that describes how the dependent variable y is related to the independent variables $x_1, x_2, \ldots, x_p$ and an error term ϵ.

Multiple regression equation The mathematical equation relating the expected value or mean value of the dependent variable to the values of the independent variables; that is, $E(y) = \beta_0 + \beta_1 x_1 + \beta_2 x_2 + \ldots + \beta_p x_p$.

Estimated multiple regression equation The estimate of the multiple regression equation based on sample data and the least squares method; it is $\hat{y} = b_0 + b_1 x_1 + b_2 x_2 + \ldots + b_p x_p$.

Least squares method The method used to develop the estimated regression equation. It minimizes the sum of squared residuals (the deviations between the observed values of the dependent variable, y_i, and the estimated values of the dependent variable, $\hat{y}_i$).

Multiple coefficient of determination A measure of the goodness of fit of the estimated multiple regression equation. It can be interpreted as the proportion of the variability in the dependent variable that is explained by the estimated regression equation.

Adjusted multiple coefficient of determination A measure of the goodness of fit of the estimated multiple regression equation that adjusts for the number of independent variables in the model and thus avoids overestimating the impact of adding more independent variables.

Multicollinearity The term used to describe the correlation among the independent variables.

Qualitative independent variable An independent variable with qualitative data.

Dummy variable A variable, coded as 0 or 1, used to model the effect of qualitative independent variables.

Key Formulas

Multiple Regression Model

$$y = \beta_0 + \beta_1 x_1 + \beta_2 x_2 + \cdots + \beta_p x_p + \epsilon \tag{13.1}$$

Multiple Regression Equation

$$E(y) = \beta_0 + \beta_1 x_1 + \beta_2 x_2 + \cdots + \beta_p x_p \tag{13.2}$$

Estimated Multiple Regression Equation

$$\hat{y} = b_0 + b_1 x_1 + b_2 x_2 + \cdots + b_p x_p \tag{13.3}$$

Least Squares Criterion

$$\min \Sigma (y_i - \hat{y}_i)^2 \tag{13.4}$$

Relationship Among SST, SSR, and SSE

$$SST = SSR + SSE \tag{13.7}$$

Multiple Coefficient of Determination

$$R^2 = \frac{\text{SSR}}{\text{SST}}$$

(13.8)

Adjusted Multiple Coefficient of Determination

$$R_a^2 = 1 - (1 - R^2)\frac{n-1}{n-p-1}$$

(13.9)

Mean Square Regression

$$\text{MSR} = \frac{\text{SSR}}{p}$$

(13.12)

Mean Square Error

$$\text{MSE} = \frac{\text{SSE}}{n-p-1}$$

(13.13)

F Test Statistic

$$F = \frac{\text{MSR}}{\text{MSE}}$$

(13.14)

t Test Statistic

$$t = \frac{b_i}{s_{b_i}}$$

(13.15)

Supplementary Exercises

39. The admissions officer for Clearwater College developed the following estimated regression equation relating the final college GPA to the student's SAT mathematics score and high-school GPA.

$$\hat{y} = -1.41 + .0235x_1 + .00486x_2$$

where

$$x_1 = \text{high-school grade point average}$$
$$x_2 = \text{SAT mathematics score}$$
$$y = \text{final college grade point average}$$

a. Interpret the coefficients in this estimated regression equation.
b. Estimate the final college GPA for a student who has a high-school average of 84 and a score of 540 on the SAT mathematics test.

40. The personnel director for Electronics Associates developed the following estimated regression equation relating an employee's score on a job satisfaction test to his or her length of service and wage rate.

$$\hat{y} = 14.4 - 8.69x_1 + 13.5x_2$$

where

$$x_1 = \text{length of service (years)}$$
$$x_2 = \text{wage rate (dollars)}$$
$$y = \text{job satisfaction test score (higher scores indicate greater job satisfaction)}$$

a. Interpret the coefficients in this estimated regression equation.
b. Develop an estimate of the job satisfaction test score for an employee who has four years of service and makes $6.50 per hour.

41. A partial computer output from a regression analysis using Excel's Regression tool follows.

	A	B	C	D	E	F	G
1	SUMMARY OUTPUT						
2							
3	*Regression Statistics*						
4	Multiple R						
5	R Square	0.923					
6	Adjusted R Square						
7	Standard Error	3.35					
8	Observations						
9							
10	ANOVA						
11		*df*	*SS*	*MS*	*F*	*Significance F*	
12	Regression		1612				
13	Residual	12					
14	Total						
15							
16		*Coefficients*	*Standard Error*	*t Stat*	*P-value*		
17	Intercept	8.103	2.667				
18	X1	7.602	2.105				
19	X2	3.111	0.613				
20							

a. Compute the missing entries in this output.
b. Using $\alpha = .05$, test for overall significance.
c. Use the t test and $\alpha = .05$ to test $H_0: \beta_1 = 0$ and $H_0: \beta_2 = 0$.

42. Recall that in exercise 39, the admissions officer for Clearwater College developed the following estimated regression equation relating final college GPA to the student's SAT mathematics score and high-school GPA.

$$\hat{y} = -1.41 + .0235x_1 + .00486x_2$$

where

$$x_1 = \text{high-school grade point average}$$
$$x_2 = \text{SAT mathematics score}$$
$$y = \text{final college grade point average}$$

A portion of the Excel Regression tool output follows.

	A	B	C	D	E	F	G
1	SUMMARY OUTPUT						
2							
3	*Regression Statistics*						
4	Multiple R						
5	R Square						
6	Adjusted R Square						
7	Standard Error						
8	Observations						
9							
10	ANOVA						
11		*df*	*SS*	*MS*	*F*	*Significance F*	
12	Regression		1.76209				
13	Residual						
14	Total	9	1.88				
15							
16		*Coefficients*	*Standard Error*	*t Stat*	*P-value*		
17	Intercept	-1.4053	0.4848				
18	X1	0.023467	0.0086666				
19	X2	0.00486	0.001077				
20							

a. Complete the missing entries in this output.
b. Using $\alpha = .05$, test for overall significance.
c. Did the estimated regression equation provide a good fit to the data? Explain.
d. Use the t test and $\alpha = .05$ to test $H_0\colon \beta_1 = 0$ and $H_0\colon \beta_2 = 0$.

43. Recall that in exercise 40 the personnel director for Electronics Associates developed the following estimated regression equation relating an employee's score on a job satisfaction test to length of service and wage rate.

$$\hat{y} = 14.4 - 8.69x_1 + 13.5x_2$$

where

$$x_1 = \text{length of service (years)}$$
$$x_2 = \text{wage rate (dollars)}$$
$$y = \text{job satisfaction test score (higher scores}$$
$$\text{indicate greater job satisfaction)}$$

A portion of Excel's Regression tool output follows.

	A	B	C	D	E	F	G
1	SUMMARY OUTPUT						
2							
3	*Regression Statistics*						
4	Multiple R						
5	R Square						
6	Adjusted R Square						
7	Standard Error	3.773					
8	Observations						
9							
10	ANOVA						
11		*df*	*SS*	*MS*	*F*	*Significance F*	
12	Regression						
13	Residual		71.17				
14	Total		720				
15							
16		*Coefficients*	*Standard Error*	*t Stat*	*P-value*		
17	Intercept	14.4	8.191				
18	X1	-8.69	1.555				
19	X2	13.517	2.085				
20							

a. Complete the missing entries in this output.
b. Using $\alpha = .05$, test for overall significance.
c. Did the estimated regression equation provide a good fit to the data? Explain.
d. Use the t test and $\alpha = .05$ to test $H_0: \beta_1 = 0$ and $H_0: \beta_2 = 0$.

44. *SmartMoney* magazine evaluated 65 metropolitan areas to determine where home values are headed. An ideal city would get a score of 100 if all factors measured were as favorable as possible. Areas with a score of 60 or greater are considered to be primed for price appreciation, and areas with a score of below 50 may see housing values erode. Two of the factors evaluated were the recession resistance of the area and its affordability. Both of these factors were rated using a scale ranging from 0 (low score) to 10 (high score). The data obtained for a sample of 20 cities evaluated by *SmartMoney* follow (*SmartMoney,* February 2002).

CD file

HomeValue

Metro Area	Recession Resistance	Affordability	Score
Tucson	10	7	70.7
Fort Worth	10	7	68.5
San Antonio	6	8	65.5
Richmond	8	6	63.6
Indianapolis	4	8	62.5
Philadelphia	0	10	61.9
Atlanta	2	6	60.7
Phoenix	4	5	60.3
Cincinnati	2	7	57.0

Metro Area	Recession Resistance	Affordability	Score
Miami	6	5	56.5
Hartford	0	7	56.2
Birmingham	0	8	55.7
San Diego	8	2	54.6
Raleigh	2	7	50.9
Oklahoma City	1	6	49.6
Orange County	4	2	49.1
Denver	4	4	48.6
Los Angeles	0	7	45.7
Detroit	0	5	44.3
New Orleans	0	5	41.2

a. Develop an estimated regression equation that can be used to predict the score given the recession resistance rating. At the .05 level of significance, test for a significant relationship.

b. Did the estimated regression equation developed in part (a) provide a good fit to the data? Explain.

c. Develop an estimated regression equation that can be used to predict the score given the recession resistance rating and the affordability rating. At the .05 level of significance, test for overall significance.

45. Following are data on price, curb weight, horsepower, time to go from 0 to 60 miles per hour, and the speed at $\frac{1}{4}$ mile for 16 sports and GT cars.

CD file

Auto2

Car	Price ($1000s)	Curb Weight (lb.)	Horse-power	0 to 60 (seconds)	Speed at $\frac{1}{4}$ mile (mph)
Acura Integra Type R	25.035	2577	195	7.0	90.7
Acura NSX-T	93.758	3066	290	5.0	108.0
BMW Z3 2.8	40.900	2844	189	6.6	93.2
Chevrolet Camaro Z28	24.865	3439	305	5.4	103.2
Chevrolet Corvette Convertible	50.144	3246	345	5.2	102.1
Dodge Viper RT/10	69.742	3319	450	4.4	116.2
Ford Mustang GT	23.200	3227	225	6.8	91.7
Honda Prelude Type SH	26.382	3042	195	7.7	89.7
Mercedes-Benz CLK320	44.988	3240	215	7.2	93.0
Mercedes-Benz SLK230	42.762	3025	185	6.6	92.3
Mitsubishi 3000GT VR-4	47.518	3737	320	5.7	99.0
Nissan 240SX SE	25.066	2862	155	9.1	84.6
Pontiac Firebird Trans Am	27.770	3455	305	5.4	103.2
Porsche Boxster	45.560	2822	201	6.1	93.2
Toyota Supra Turbo	40.989	3505	320	5.3	105.0
Volvo C70	41.120	3285	236	6.3	97.0

a. Develop an estimated regression equation with price, curb weight, horsepower, and time to go from 0 to 60 mph as four independent variables to predict the speed at $\frac{1}{4}$ mile.

b. Use the F test to determine the significance of the regression results. At a .05 level of significance, what is your conclusion?

c. Use the t test to determine the significance of each independent variable. At a .05 level of significance, what is your conclusion?

d. Delete any independent variable that is not significant and provide your recommended estimated regression equation.

46. The U.S. Department of Energy's *Fuel Economy Guide* provides fuel efficiency data for cars and trucks. A portion of the data for 35 standard pickup trucks produced by Chevrolet and General Motors follows (http://www.fueleconomy.gov, March 21, 2003). The column labeled Drive identifies whether the vehicle has two-wheel drive (2WD) or four-wheel drive (4WD). The column labeled Displacement shows the engine's displacement in liters, the column labeled Cylinders specifies the number of cylinders the engine has, and the column labeled Transmission shows whether the truck has an automatic transmission or a manual transmission. The column labeled City MPG shows the fuel efficiency rating for the truck for city driving in terms of miles per gallon (mpg).

CD file

FuelEcon

Truck	Name	Drive	Displacement	Cylinders	Transmission	City MPG
1	C1500 Silverado	2WD	4.3	6	Auto	15
2	C1500 Silverado	2WD	4.3	6	Manual	15
3	C1500 Silverado	2WD	4.8	8	Auto	15
4	C1500 Silverado	2WD	4.8	8	Manual	16
5	C1500 Silverado	2WD	5.3	8	Auto	11
.	.	.	.	.	.	.
.	.	.	.	.	.	.
33	K1500 Sierra	4WD	5.3	8	Auto	15
34	Sonoma	4WD	4.3	6	Auto	17
35	Sonoma	4WD	4.3	6	Manual	15

a. Develop an estimated regression equation that can be used to predict the fuel efficiency for city driving given the engine's displacement. Test for significance using $\alpha = .05$.

b. Consider the addition of the dummy variable Drive4, where the value of Drive4 is 0 if the truck has two-wheel drive and 1 if the truck has four-wheel drive. Develop the estimated regression equation that can be used to predict the fuel efficiency for city driving given the engine's displacement and the dummy variable Drive4.

c. Use $\alpha = .05$ to determine whether the dummy variable added in part (b) is significant.

d. Consider the addition of the dummy variable EightCyl, where the value of EightCyl is 0 if the truck's engine has six cylinders and 1 if the truck's engine has eight cylinders. Develop the estimated regression equation that can be used to predict the fuel efficiency for city driving given the engine's displacement and the dummy variables Drive4 and EightCyl.

e. For the estimated regression equation developed in part (d), test for overall significance and individual significance using $\alpha = .05$.

47. Today's marketplace offers a wide choice to buyers of sport utility vehicles (SUVs) and pickup trucks. An important factor to many buyers is the resale value of the vehicle. The following table shows the resale value (%) after two years and the suggested retail price for 10 SUVs, 10 small pickup trucks, and 10 large pickup trucks (*Kiplinger's New Cars & Trucks 2000 Buyer's Guide*).

Trucks

	Type of Vehicle	Suggested Retail Price ($)	Resale Value (%)
Chevrolet Blazer LS	Sport utility	19,495	55
Ford Explorer Sport	Sport utility	20,495	57
GMC Yukon XL 1500	Sport utility	26,789	67
Honda CR-V	Sport utility	18,965	65
Isuzu VehiCross	Sport utility	30,186	62
Jeep Cherokee Limited	Sport utility	25,745	57
Mercury Mountaineer Monterrey	Sport utility	29,895	59
Nissan Pathfinder XE	Sport utility	26,919	54
Toyota 4Runner	Sport utility	22,418	55
Toyota RAV4	Sport utility	17,148	55
Chevrolet S-10 Extended Cab	Small pickup	18,847	46
Dodge Dakota Club Cab Sport	Small pickup	16,870	53
Ford Ranger XLT Regular Cab	Small pickup	18,510	48
Ford Ranger XLT Supercab	Small pickup	20,225	55
GMC Sonoma Regular Cab	Small pickup	16,938	44
Isuzu Hombre Spacecab	Small pickup	18,820	41
Mazda B4000 SE Cab Plus	Small pickup	23,050	51
Nissan Frontier XE Regular Cab	Small pickup	12,110	51
Toyota Tacoma Xtracab	Small pickup	18,228	49
Toyota Tacoma Xtracab V6	Small pickup	19,318	50
Chevrolet K2500	Full-size pickup	24,417	60
Chevrolet Silverado 2500 Ext	Full-size pickup	24,140	64
Dodge Ram 1500	Full-size pickup	17,460	54
Dodge Ram Quad Cab 2500	Full-size pickup	32,770	63
Dodge Ram Regular Cab 2500	Full-size pickup	23,140	59
Ford F150 XL	Full-size pickup	22,875	58
Ford F-350 Super Duty Crew Cab XL	Full-size pickup	34,295	64
GMC New Sierra 1500 Ext Cab	Full-size pickup	27,089	68
Toyota Tundra Access Cab Limited	Full-size pickup	25,605	53
Toyota Tundra Regular Cab	Full-size pickup	15,835	58

a. Develop an estimated regression equation that can be used to predict the resale value given the suggested retail price. At the .05 level of significance, test for a significant relationship.

b. Did the estimated regression equation developed in part (a) provide a good fit to the data? Explain.

c. Develop an estimated regression equation that can be used to predict the resale value given the suggested retail price and the type of vehicle.

d. Use the F test to determine the significance of the regression results. At a .05 level of significance, what is your conclusion?

Case Problem 1   Consumer Research, Inc.

Consumer Research, Inc., is an independent agency that conducts research on consumer attitudes and behaviors for a variety of firms. In one study, a client asked for an investigation of consumer characteristics that can be used to predict the amount charged by credit card users. Data were collected on annual income, household size, and annual credit card charges for a sample of 50 consumers. The following data are on the CD accompanying the text in the data set named Consumer.

Income ($1000s)	Household Size	Amount Charged ($)	Income ($1000s)	Household Size	Amount Charged ($)
54	3	4016	54	6	5573
30	2	3159	30	1	2583
32	4	5100	48	2	3866
50	5	4742	34	5	3586
31	2	1864	67	4	5037
55	2	4070	50	2	3605
37	1	2731	67	5	5345
40	2	3348	55	6	5370
66	4	4764	52	2	3890
51	3	4110	62	3	4705
25	3	4208	64	2	4157
48	4	4219	22	3	3579
27	1	2477	29	4	3890
33	2	2514	39	2	2972
65	3	4214	35	1	3121
63	4	4965	39	4	4183
42	6	4412	54	3	3730
21	2	2448	23	6	4127
44	1	2995	27	2	2921
37	5	4171	26	7	4603
62	6	5678	61	2	4273
21	3	3623	30	2	3067
55	7	5301	22	4	3074
42	2	3020	46	5	4820
41	7	4828	66	4	5149

Consumer

Managerial Report

1. Use methods of descriptive statistics to summarize the data. Comment on the findings.
2. Develop estimated regression equations, first using annual income as the independent variable and then using household size as the independent variable. Which variable is the better predictor of annual credit card charges? Discuss your findings.
3. Develop an estimated regression equation with annual income and household size as the independent variables. Discuss your findings.
4. What is the predicted annual credit card charge for a three-person household with an annual income of $40,000?
5. Discuss the need for other independent variables that could be added to the model. What additional variables might be helpful?

Case Problem 2   Predicting Student Proficiency Test Scores

In order to predict how a school district would have scored when accounting for poverty and other income measures, *The Cincinnati Enquirer* gathered data from the Ohio Department of Education's Education Management Services and the Ohio Department of Taxation (*The Cincinnati Enquirer*, November 30, 1997). First, the newspaper obtained passage-rate data on the math, reading, science, writing, and citizenship proficiency exams given to 4th-, 6th-, 9th-, and 12th-graders in early 1996. By combining these data, they computed an overall percentage of students that passed the tests for each district.

The percentage of a school district's students on Aid for Dependent Children (ADC), the percentage who qualify for free or reduced-price lunches, and the district's median family income were also recorded. A portion of the data collected for the 608 school districts follows. The complete data set is available on the CD accompanying the text in the data set named Enquirer.

Enquirer

Rank	School District	County	% Passed	% on ADC	% Free Lunch	Median Income ($)
1	Ottawa Hills Local	Lucas	93.85	0.11	0.00	48231
2	Wyoming City	Hamilton	93.08	2.95	4.59	42672
3	Oakwood City	Montgomery	92.92	0.20	0.38	42403
4	Madeira City	Hamilton	92.37	1.50	4.83	32889
5	Indian Hill Ex Vill	Hamilton	91.77	1.23	2.70	44135
6	Solon City	Cuyahoga	90.77	0.68	2.24	34993
7	Chagrin Falls Ex Vill	Cuyahoga	89.89	0.47	0.44	38921
8	Mariemont City	Hamilton	89.80	3.00	2.97	31823
9	Upper Arlington City	Franklin	89.77	0.24	0.92	38358
10	Granville Ex Vill	Licking	89.22	1.14	0.00	36235

The data have been ranked based on the values in the column labeled % Passed; these data are the overall percentage of students passing the tests. Data in the column labeled % on ADC are the percentage of each school district's students on ADC, and the data in the column labeled % Free Lunch are the percentage of students who qualify for free or reduced-price lunches. The column labeled Median Income shows each district's median family income. Also shown for each school district is the county in which the school district is located. Note that in some cases the value in the % Free Lunch column is 0, indicating that the district did not participate in the free lunch program.

Managerial Report

Use the methods presented in this and previous chapters to analyze this data set. Present a summary of your analysis, including key statistical results, conclusions, and recommendations, in a managerial report. Include any technical material you feel is appropriate in an appendix.

Case Problem 3   Alumni Giving

Alumni donations are an important source of revenue for colleges and universities. If administrators could determine the factors that could lead to increases in the percentage of alumni who make a donation, they might be able to implement policies that could lead to increased revenues. Research shows that students who are more satisfied with their contact with teachers are more likely to graduate. As a result, one might suspect that smaller class sizes and lower student–faculty ratios might lead to a higher percentage of satisfied graduates, which in turn might lead to increases in the percentage of alumni who make a donation. Table 13.7 shows data for 48 national universities (*America's Best Colleges,* Year 2000 Edition). The column labeled Graduation Rate is the percentage of students who initially enrolled at the university and graduated. The column labeled % of Classes Under 20 shows the percentage of classes offered with fewer than 20 students. The column labeled Student-Faculty Ratio is the number of students enrolled divided by the total number of faculty. Finally, the column labeled Alumni Giving Rate is the percentage of alumni who made a donation to the university.

TABLE 13.7 DATA FOR 48 NATIONAL UNIVERSITIES

CD file

Alumni

	State	Graduation Rate (%)	% of Classes Under 20	Student-Faculty Ratio	Alumni Giving Rate (%)
Boston College	MA	85	39	13	25
Brandeis University	MA	79	68	8	33
Brown University	RI	93	60	8	40
California Institute of Technology	CA	85	65	3	46
Carnegie Mellon University	PA	75	67	10	28
Case Western Reserve Univ.	OH	72	52	8	31
College of William and Mary	VA	89	45	12	27
Columbia University	NY	90	69	7	31
Cornell University	NY	91	72	13	35
Dartmouth College	NH	94	61	10	53
Duke University	NC	92	68	8	45
Emory University	GA	84	65	7	37
Georgetown University	DC	91	54	10	29
Harvard University	MA	97	73	8	46
Johns Hopkins University	MD	89	64	9	27
Lehigh University	PA	81	55	11	40
Massachusetts Inst. of Technology	MA	92	65	6	44
New York University	NY	72	63	13	13
Northwestern University	IL	90	66	8	30
Pennsylvania State Univ.	PA	80	32	19	21
Princeton University	NJ	95	68	5	67
Rice University	TX	92	62	8	40
Stanford University	CA	92	69	7	34
Tufts University	MA	87	67	9	29
Tulane University	LA	72	56	12	17
U. of California–Berkeley	CA	83	58	17	18
U. of California–Davis	CA	74	32	19	7
U. of California–Irvine	CA	74	42	20	9
U. of California–Los Angeles	CA	78	41	18	13
U. of California–San Diego	CA	80	48	19	8
U. of California–Santa Barbara	CA	70	45	20	12
U. of Chicago	IL	84	65	4	36
U. of Florida	FL	67	31	23	19
U. of Illinois–Urbana Champaign	IL	77	29	15	23
U. of Michigan–Ann Arbor	MI	83	51	15	13
U. of North Carolina–Chapel Hill	NC	82	40	16	26
U. of Notre Dame	IN	94	53	13	49
U. of Pennsylvania	PA	90	65	7	41
U. of Rochester	NY	76	63	10	23
U. of Southern California	CA	70	53	13	22
U. of Texas–Austin	TX	66	39	21	13
U. of Virginia	VA	92	44	13	28
U. of Washington	WA	70	37	12	12
U. of Wisconsin–Madison	WI	73	37	13	13
Vanderbilt University	TN	82	68	9	31
Wake Forest University	NC	82	59	11	38
Washington University–St. Louis	MO	86	73	7	33
Yale University	CT	94	77	7	50

Managerial Report

1. Use methods of descriptive statistics to summarize the data.
2. Develop an estimated regression equation that can be used to predict the alumni giving rate given the percentage of students who graduate. Discuss your findings.
3. Develop an estimated regression equation that could be used to predict the alumni giving rate using the data provided.
4. What conclusions and recommendations can you derive from your analysis?

Appendix 13.1   Multiple Regression Analysis with SWStat+

In Appendix 12.1 we showed how SWStat+ can be used for simple linear regression. In this appendix we describe the steps required to use SWStat+ to perform multiple regression analysis for the Butler Trucking Company example. First we must create the data area for the Butler Trucking data.

Creating the Data Area

Step 1. Select any cell in the data set
Step 2. Select the **SWStat+** menu
Step 3. Choose **Data Area**
Step 4. Choose **Set New Data Area** from the list of Data Area options
Step 5. When the SWStat+ Data Area dialog box appears:
    Select the **Set New** tab
    Select **With column headers**
    Select **With row headers**
    Click **Set data area**

The Results worksheet which was created will contain all the output generated using SWStat+. We are now ready to use SWStat+ to perform multiple regression analysis for the Butler Trucking data.

Multiple Regression

The steps necessary to generate the regression analysis output in the Results worksheet shown in Figure 13.11 are as follows:

Step 1. Select the **SWStat+** menu
Step 2. Choose **Statistics**
Step 3. Choose **Regression and Correlation**
Step 4. When the SWStat+: Regression and Correlation dialog box appears:
    Select the **Regression** tab
    Choose **Time** in the **Dependent (Y)** box
    Choose **Miles** in the **Independent (X)** box
    Choose **Deliveries** in the **Independent (X)** box
    Click **Calculate**

The regression analysis output shown in Figure 13.11 is similar to the multiple regression analysis output using Excel's Regression tool. The primary difference is the order in which the results are presented.

FIGURE 13.11   SWStat+ RESULTS WORKSHEET SHOWING MULTIPLE REGRESSION OUTPUT

	A	B	C	D	E	F	G	H	I	J
1	SWStat+ Results Sheet									
2										
3	SWStat+: Regression									
4		Analysis of Variance, ANOVA								
5			Degrees Freedom, df	Sum of Squares, SS	Mean Square, MS	F-Ratio	p-Value			
6		Regression	2	21.601	10.800	32.878	0.00028			
7		Error	7	2.299	0.328					
8		Total	9	23.900						
9										
10		Regression Equation Results								
11		Dependent Variable, Y: Time								
12		Time = -0.869 + 0.061 Miles + 0.923 Deliveries								
13										
14		Indep. X Variables	Coefficient	Standard Error	t Statistic	p-Value	95% Conf. Lower	95% Conf. Upper	VIF	
15		Intercept	-0.869	0.952	-0.9129	0.39163	-3.119	1.381		
16		Miles	0.061	0.01	6.1824	0.00045	0.038	0.085	1.027	
17		Deliveries	0.923	0.221	4.1763	0.00416	0.401	1.446	1.027	
18										
19		R-squared	90.38%							
20		Multiple R	0.9507							
21		Adj. R-squared	87.63%							
22		Standard Error of Estimate	0.573							
23		Durbin-Watson	2.515							
24		Number of Observations	10							
25										

Confidence and Prediction Intervals

To develop a 95% confidence interval and a 95% prediction interval corresponding to 100 miles traveled and two deliveries, we would perform the following steps after obtaining the regression results shown in Figure 13.11.

Step 1. Select the **SWStat+** menu
Step 2. Choose **Statistics**
Step 3. Choose **Regression and Correlation**
Step 4. When the SWStat+: Regression and Correlation dialog box appears:
Select the **Predictions** tab
Select **Miles**
Enter 100 in the predictor value box
Press Enter
Select **Deliveries**
Enter 2 in the predictor value box
Press Enter
Click **Predict Y**

CHAPTER 14

Statistical Methods for Quality Control

CONTENTS

DOW CHEMICAL*
FREEPORT, TEXAS

Dow Chemical, Texas Operations, began in 1940 when The Dow Chemical Company purchased 800 acres of Texas land on the Gulf Coast to build a magnesium production facility. That original site, expanded to cover more than 5000 acres, holds one of the largest petrochemical complexes in the world. Among the products from Texas Operations are magnesium, styrene, plastics, adhesives, solvent, glycol, and chlorine. Some products are made solely for use in other processes, but many end up as essential ingredients in products such as pharmaceuticals, toothpastes, dog food, water hoses, ice chests, milk cartons, garbage bags, shampoos, and furniture.

Dow's Texas Operations produce more than 30% of the world's magnesium, an extremely lightweight metal used in products ranging from tennis rackets to suitcases to "mag" wheels. The Magnesium Department was the first group in Texas Operations to train its technical people and managers in the use of statistical quality control. Some of the earliest successful applications of statistical quality control were in chemical processing.

In one application involving the operation of a dryer, samples of the output were taken at periodic intervals; the average value for each sample was computed and recorded on a chart called an $\bar{x}$ chart. Such a chart enabled Dow analysts to monitor trends in the output that might indicate the process was not operating correctly. In one instance, analysts began to observe values for the sample mean that were not indicative of a process operating within its design limits. On further examination of the

Statistical quality control has enabled Dow Chemical to improve its processing methods and output.
© PhotoDisc, Inc.

control chart and the operation itself, the analysts found that the variation could be traced to problems involving one operator. The $\bar{x}$ chart recorded after retraining of the operator showed a significant improvement in the process quality.

Dow Chemical achieves quality improvements everywhere statistical quality control is applied. Documented savings of several hundred thousand dollars per year are realized, and new applications are continually being discovered.

In this chapter we will show how an $\bar{x}$ chart such as the one used by Dow Chemical can be developed. Such charts are a part of statistical quality control known as statistical process control. We will also discuss methods of quality control for situations in which a decision to accept or reject a group of items is based on a sample.

---

*The authors are indebted to Clifford B. Wilson, Magnesium Technical Manager, The Dow Chemical Company, for providing this Statistics in Practice.

The American Society for Quality (ASQ) defines quality as "the totality of features and characteristics of a product or service that bears on its ability to satisfy given needs." In other words, quality measures how well a product or service meets customer needs. Organizations recognize that to be competitive in today's global economy, they must strive for a high level of quality. As a result, they place increased emphasis on methods for monitoring and maintaining quality.

Today, the customer-driven focus that is fundamental to high-performing organizations has changed the scope that quality issues encompass, from simply eliminating defects on a production line to developing broad-based corporate quality strategies. Broadening the scope of quality naturally leads to the concept of **total quality (TQ)**.

Total Quality (TQ) is a people-focused management system that aims at continual increase in customer satisfaction at continually lower real cost. TQ is a total system approach (not a separate area or work program) and an integral part of high-level strategy; it works horizontally across function and departments, involves all employees, top to bottom, and extends backward and forward to include the supply chain and the customer chain. TQ stresses learning and adaptation to continual change as keys to organization success.*

Regardless of how it is implemented in different organizations, total quality is based on three fundamental principles: a focus on customers and stakeholders; participation and teamwork throughout the organization; and a focus on continuous improvement and learning. In the first section of the chapter we provide a brief introduction to the three quality management frameworks: the Malcolm Baldrige Quality Award, ISO 9000 standards, and the Six Sigma philosophy. In the last two sections we introduce two statistical tools that can be used to monitor quality: statistical process control and acceptance sampling.

14.1 Philosophies and Frameworks

Two individuals who have had great influence on quality are Dr. W. Edwards Deming and Joseph Juran. These men helped educate the Japanese in quality management shortly after World War II. Although quality is everybody's job, Deming stressed that the focus on quality must be led by managers. He developed a list of 14 points that he believed represent the key responsibilities of managers. For instance, Deming stated that managers must cease dependence on mass inspection; must end the practice of awarding business solely on the basis of price; must seek continual improvement in all production processes and service; must foster a team-oriented environment; and must eliminate goals, slogans, and work standards that prescribe numerical quotas. Perhaps most important, managers must create a work environment in which a commitment to quality and productivity is maintained at all times.

Juran proposed a simple definition of quality: *fitness for use*. Juran's approach to quality focused on three quality processes: quality planning, quality control, and quality improvement. In contrast to Deming's philosophy, which required a major cultural change in the organization, Juran's programs were designed to improve quality by working within the current organizational system. Nonetheless, the two philosophies are similar in that they both focus on the need for top management to be involved and stress the need for continuous improvement, the importance of training, and the use of quality control techniques.

Many other individuals played significant roles in the quality movement, including Philip B. Crosby, A. V. Feigenbaum, Karou Ishikawa, and Genichi Taguchi. More specialized texts dealing exclusively with quality provide details of the contributions of each of these individuals. The contributions of all individuals involved in the quality movement helped define a set of best practices and led to numerous awards and certification programs. The two most significant programs are the U.S. Malcolm Baldrige National Quality Award and the International ISO 9000 certification process. In recent years, use of Six Sigma—a methodology for improving organizational performance based on rigorous data collection and statistical analysis—has also increased.

Malcolm Baldrige National Quality Award

The Malcolm Baldrige National Quality Award is given by the president of the United States to organizations that apply and are judged to be outstanding in seven areas: leadership; strategic planning; customer and market focus; measurement, analysis, and knowledge management; human resource focus; process management; and business results. Congress established the award program in 1987 to recognize U.S. organizations for their

---

*J. R. Evans and W. M. Lindsay, *The Management and Control of Quality*, 6th ed. (Cincinnati, OH: South-Western, 2005), pp. 18–19.

The U.S. Commerce Department's National Institute of Standards and Technology (NIST) manages the Baldrige National Quality Program. More information can be obtained at www.quality.nist.gov.

achievements in quality and performance and to raise awareness about the importance of quality as a competitive edge. The award is named for Malcolm Baldrige who served as Secretary of Commerce from 1981 until his death in 1987.

Since the presentation of the first awards in 1988, the Baldrige National Quality Program has grown in stature and impact. Approximately 2 million copies of the criteria have been distributed since 1988, and wide-scale reproduction by organizations and electronic access add to that number significantly. For the eighth year in a row, a hypothetical stock index, made up of publicly traded U.S. companies that have received the Baldrige Award, outperformed the Standard & Poor's 500. In 2003, the "Baldrige Index" outperformed the S&P 500 by 4.4 to 1. At the 2003 Baldrige Award Ceremony, Bob Barnett, executive vice president of Motorola, Inc., said, "We applied for the Award, not with the idea of winning, but with the goal of receiving the evaluation of the Baldrige Examiners. That evaluation was comprehensive, professional, and insightful . . . making it perhaps the most cost-effective, value-added business consultation available anywhere in the world today."

ISO 9000

ISO 9000 is a series of five international standards published in 1987 by the International Organization for Standardization (ISO), Geneva, Switzerland. Companies can use the standards to help determine what is needed to maintain an efficient quality conformance system. For example, the standards describe the need for an effective quality system, for ensuring that measuring and testing equipment is calibrated regularly, and for maintaining an adequate record-keeping system. ISO 9000 registration determines whether a company complies with its own quality system. Overall, ISO 9000 registration covers less than 10% of the Baldrige Award criteria.

Six Sigma

In the late 1980s Motorola recognized the need to improve the quality of its products and services; their goal was to achieve a level of quality so good that, for every million opportunities, no more than 3.4 defects will occur. This level of quality is referred to as the six sigma level of quality, and the methodology created to reach this quality goal is referred to as **Six Sigma**.

An organization may undertake two kinds of Six Sigma projects:

- DMAIC (Define, Measure, Analyze, Improve, and Control) to help redesign existing processes
- DFSS (Design for Six Sigma) to design new products, processes, or services

In helping to redesign existing processes and design new processes, Six Sigma places a heavy emphasis on statistical analysis and careful measurement. Today, Six Sigma is a major tool in helping organizations achieve Baldrige levels of business performance and process quality. Many Baldrige examiners view Six Sigma as the ideal approach for implementing Baldrige improvement programs.

Six Sigma Limits and Defects per Million Opportunities   In Six Sigma terminology, a *defect* is any mistake or error that is passed on to the customer. The Six Sigma process defines quality performance as defects per million opportunities (dpmo). As we indicated previously, Six Sigma represents a quality level of at most 3.4 dpmo. To illustrate how this quality level is measured, let us consider the situation at KJW Packaging.

KJW operates a production line where boxes of cereal are filled. The filling process has a mean of $\mu = 16.05$ ounces and a standard deviation of $\sigma = .10$ ounces. In addition, assume the filling weights are normally distributed. The distribution of filling weights is shown in Figure 14.1. Suppose management considers 15.45 to 16.65 ounces to be acceptable quality

FIGURE 14.1   NORMAL DISTRIBUTION OF CEREAL BOX FILLING WEIGHTS
WITH A PROCESS MEAN $\mu = 16.05$

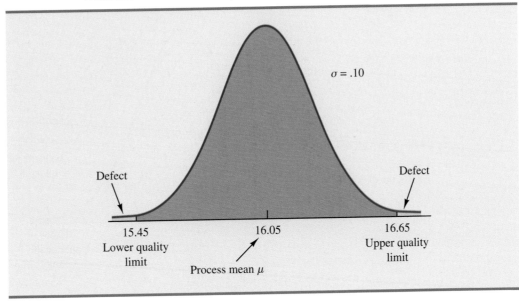

*Using Excel,
NORMSDIST(6) −
NORMSDIST(−6) =
0.999999998.*

limits for the filling process. Thus, any box of cereal that contains less than 15.45 or more than 16.65 ounces is considered to be a defect. Using Excel's NORMSDIST function it can be shown that 99.9999998% of the boxes filled will have between $16.05 − 6(.10) = 15.45$ ounces and $16.05 + 6(.10) = 16.65$ ounces. In other words, only .0000002% of the boxes filled will contain less than 15.45 ounces or more than 16.65 ounces. Thus, the likelihood of obtaining a defective box of cereal from the filling process appears to be extremely unlikely, because on average only two boxes in 10 million will be defective.

Motorola's early work on Six Sigma convinced them that a process mean can shift on average by as much as 1.5 standard deviations. For instance, suppose that the process mean for KJW increases by 1.5 standard deviations or $1.5(.10) = .15$ ounces. With such a shift, the normal distribution of filling weights would now be centered at $\mu = 16.05 + .15 = 16.20$ ounces. With a process mean of $\mu = 16.05$ ounces, the probability of obtaining a box of cereal with more than 16.65 ounces is extremely small. But how does this probability change if the mean of the process shifts up to $\mu = 16.20$ ounces? Figure 14.2 shows that for this case, the upper quality limit of 16.65 is 4.5 standard deviations to the right of the new mean $\mu = 16.20$ ounces. Using this mean and Excel's NORMSDIST function we find that the probability of obtaining a box with more than 16.65 ounces is .0000034. Thus, if the process mean shifts up by 1.5 standard deviations, approximately $1,000,000(.0000034) = 3.4$ boxes of cereal will exceed the upper limit of 16.65 ounces. In Six Sigma terminology, the quality level of the process is said to be 3.4 defects per million opportunities. If management of KJW considers 15.45 to 16.65 ounces to be acceptable quality limits for the filling process, the KJW filling process would be considered a Six Sigma process. Thus, if the process mean stays within 1.5 standard deviations of its target value $\mu = 16.05$ ounces, a maximum of only 3.4 defects per million boxes filled can be expected.

*Using Excel, 1 −
NORMSDIST(4.5) =
0.0000034.*

Organizations that want to achieve and maintain a Six Sigma level of quality must emphasize methods for monitoring and maintaining quality. *Quality assurance* refers to the entire system of policies, procedures, and guidelines established by an organization to achieve and maintain quality. Quality assurance consists of two principal functions: quality engineering and quality control. The object of *quality engineering* is to include quality in the

**FIGURE 14.2   NORMAL DISTRIBUTION OF CEREAL BOX FILLING WEIGHTS
WITH A PROCESS MEAN $\mu = 16.20$**

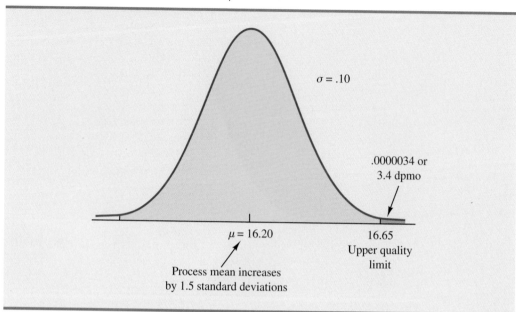

design of products and processes and to identify quality problems prior to production.
Quality control consists of a series of inspections and measurements used to determine
whether quality standards are being met. If quality standards are not being met, corrective
or preventive action can be taken to achieve and maintain conformance. In the next two sections we present two statistical methods used in quality control. The first method, *statistical process control,* uses graphical displays known as control charts to monitor a process;
the goal is to determine whether the process can be continued or whether corrective action
should be taken to achieve a desired quality level. The second method, *acceptance sampling,* is used in situations where a decision to accept or reject a group of items must be
based on the quality found in a sample.

 # Statistical Process Control

In this section we consider quality control procedures for a production process whereby
goods are manufactured continuously. On the basis of sampling and inspection of production output, a decision will be made to either continue the production process or adjust it to
bring the items or goods being produced up to acceptable quality standards.

Despite high standards of quality in manufacturing and production operations, machine
tools invariably wear out, vibrations throw machine settings out of adjustment, purchased
materials contain defects, and human operators make mistakes. Any or all of these factors
can result in poor quality output. Fortunately, procedures available to monitor production
output help detect poor quality early, which allows for the adjustment and correction of the
production process.

If the variation in the quality of the production output is due to **assignable causes** such
as tools wearing out, incorrect machine settings, poor quality raw materials, or operator
error, the process should be adjusted or corrected as soon as possible. Alternatively, if the
variation results from **common causes**—that is, randomly occurring variations in materials, temperature, humidity, and so on, which the manufacturer cannot possibly control—

the process does not need to be adjusted. The main objective of statistical process control is to determine whether variations in output are due to assignable causes or common causes.

Whenever assignable causes are detected, we conclude that the process is *out of control.* In that case, corrective action should be taken to bring the process back to an acceptable level of quality. However, if the variation in the output of a production process is due only to common causes, we conclude that the process is in *statistical control,* or simply *in control;* in such cases, no changes or adjustments are necessary.

Process control procedures are closely related to hypothesis testing procedures discussed earlier in this text. Control charts provide an ongoing test of the hypothesis that the process is in control.

The statistical procedures for process control are based on the hypothesis testing methodology presented in Chapter 9. The null hypothesis H_0 is formulated in terms of the production process being in control. The alternative hypothesis H_a is formulated in terms of the production process being out of control. Table 14.1 shows that correct decisions correspond to continuing an in-control process and adjusting an out-of-control process. However, as with other hypothesis testing procedures, both a Type I error (adjusting an in-control process) and a Type II error (allowing an out-of-control process to continue) are possible.

Control Charts

A **control chart** provides a basis for deciding whether the variation in the output is due to common causes (in control) or assignable causes (out of control). Whenever an out-of-control situation is detected, adjustments or other corrective action will be taken to bring the process back into control.

Control charts based on data that can be measured on a continuous scale are called variables control charts. The $\bar{x}$ chart is a variables control chart.

Control charts can be classified by the type of data they contain. An $\bar{x}$ **chart** is used if the quality of the output is measured in terms of a variable such as length, weight, temperature, and so on. In that case, the decision to continue or to adjust the production process will be based on the mean value found in a sample of the output. To introduce some of the concepts common to all control charts, let us consider some specific features of an $\bar{x}$ chart.

Figure 14.3 shows the general structure of an $\bar{x}$ chart. The center line of the chart corresponds to the mean of the process when the process is in control. The vertical axis measures $\bar{x}$ for the variable of interest. Each time a sample is taken from the production process, a value of the sample mean $\bar{x}$ is computed and a data point showing the value of $\bar{x}$ is plotted on the control chart.

The two lines labeled UCL and LCL are important in determining whether the process is in control or out of control. The lines are called the *upper control limit* and the *lower control limit,* respectively. They are chosen so that when the process is in control, there will be a high probability that the value of $\bar{x}$ will be between the two control limits. Values outside the control limits provide strong statistical evidence that the process is out of control and corrective action should be taken.

TABLE 14.1   DECISIONS AND STATES OF THE PROCESS

		State of Production Process	
		H_0 **True** **Process in Control**	H_0 **False** **Process Out of Control**
Decision	**Continue Process**	Correct decision	Type II error (allowing an out-of-control process to continue)
	Adjust Process	Type I error (adjusting an in-control process)	Correct decision

FIGURE 14.3   GENERAL STRUCTURE OF AN $\bar{x}$ CHART

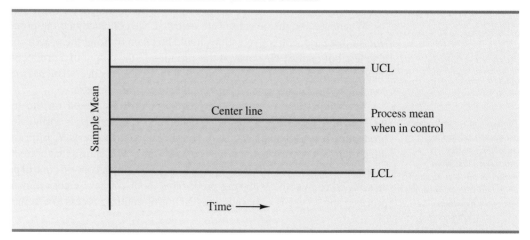

Over time, more and more data points ($\bar{x}$ values) will be added to the control chart. The order of the data points will be from left to right as the process is sampled. In essence, every time a point is plotted on the control chart, we are carrying out a hypothesis test to determine whether the process is in control.

In addition to the $\bar{x}$ chart, other control charts can be used to monitor the range of the measurements in the sample (*R* chart), the proportion of defective items in the sample (*p* chart), and the number of defective items in the sample (*np* chart). In each case, the control chart contains a LCL line, a center line, and a UCL line similar to the $\bar{x}$ chart in Figure 14.3. The major difference among the charts is what the vertical axis measures; for instance, in a *p* chart the vertical axis denotes the proportion of defective items in the sample instead of the sample mean. In the following discussion, we will illustrate the construction and use of the $\bar{x}$ chart, *R* chart, *p* chart, and *np* chart.

$\bar{x}$ Chart: Process Mean and Standard Deviation Known

We will use the KJW Packaging example introduced in Section 14.1 to illustrate the construction of an $\bar{x}$ chart. Recall that KJW operates a production line that fills cereal boxes. They designed the process so that when it is operating correctly—and hence the system is in control—the mean filling weight is $\mu = 16.05$ ounces and the process standard deviation is $\sigma = .10$ ounces. In addition, assume the filling weights (*x*) are normally distributed. The normal probability distribution of filling weights is shown in Figure 14.4.

The sampling distribution of $\bar{x}$, as presented in Chapter 7, can be used to determine the expected variation in $\bar{x}$ values for a process that is in control. Let us first briefly review the properties of the sampling distribution of $\bar{x}$. First, recall that $E(\bar{x})$, the expected value or mean of $\bar{x}$, is equal to μ, the mean filling weight when the production process is in control. For samples of size *n*, the formula for the standard deviation of $\bar{x}$, called the *standard error of the mean*, is

$$\sigma_{\bar{x}} = \frac{\sigma}{\sqrt{n}} \qquad (14.1)$$

In addition, because the filling weights (*x*) are normally distributed, the sampling distribution of $\bar{x}$ is normal for any sample size. Thus, the sampling distribution of $\bar{x}$ is a normal probability distribution with mean μ and standard deviation $\sigma_{\bar{x}}$. This probability distribu-

FIGURE 14.4   NORMAL PROBABILITY DISTRIBUTION OF CEREAL BOX FILLING
WEIGHTS WHEN THE PROCESS IS IN CONTROL

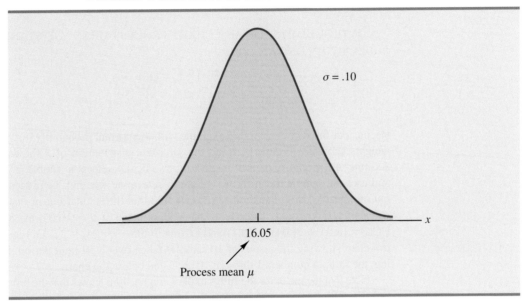

tion is shown in Figure 14.5. Note that the sampling distribution of $\bar{x}$ has the same mean
(16.05) as the probability distribution of individual filling weights.

   The sampling distribution of $\bar{x}$ is used to determine what values of $\bar{x}$ are reasonable
if the process is in control. The general practice in quality control is to define as reasonable any value of $\bar{x}$ that is within 3 standard deviations above or below the mean value μ.
Recall from the study of the normal probability distribution that approximately 99.7% of
the values of a normally distributed random variable are within ± 3 standard deviations
of its mean value. Thus, if a value of $\bar{x}$ is within the interval $\mu - 3\sigma_{\bar{x}}$ to $\mu + 3\sigma_{\bar{x}}$, we will

FIGURE 14.5   SAMPLING DISTRIBUTION OF $\bar{x}$ FOR A SAMPLE OF n FILLING WEIGHTS

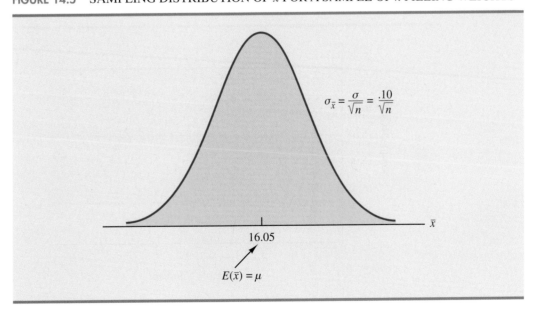

assume that the process is in control. In summary, then, the control limits for an $\bar{x}$ chart are as follows.

CONTROL LIMITS FOR AN $\bar{x}$ CHART: PROCESS MEAN AND STANDARD DEVIATION KNOWN

$$UCL = \mu + 3\sigma_{\bar{x}} \tag{14.2}$$
$$LCL = \mu - 3\sigma_{\bar{x}} \tag{14.3}$$

Reconsider the KJW Packaging example with the normal probability distribution of filling weights shown in Figure 14.4 and the sampling distribution of $\bar{x}$ shown in Figure 14.5. Assume that a quality control inspector periodically selects a sample of six cereal boxes and uses the sample mean filling weight to determine whether the process is in control or out of control. Using equation (14.1), we find that the standard error of the mean is $\sigma_{\bar{x}} = \sigma/\sqrt{n} = .10/\sqrt{6} = .04$. Thus, with the process mean at $\mu = 16.05$, the control limits are $UCL = 16.05 + 3(.04) = 16.17$ and $LCL = 16.05 - 3(.04) = 15.93$. Figure 14.6 is a control chart showing the results of 10 samples taken over a 10-hour period. For ease of reading, the sample numbers 1 through 10 are listed below the chart.

Note that the mean for the fifth sample in Figure 14.6 shows that the process is out of control. The fifth sample mean is below the LCL indicating that underfilling is occurring and that assignable causes of output variation are present. As a result, corrective action was taken at this point to bring the process back into control. The fact that the remaining points on the $\bar{x}$ chart are within the upper and lower control limits indicates that the corrective action was successful.

$\bar{x}$ Chart: Process Mean and Standard Deviation Unknown

In the KJW Packaging example, we showed how an $\bar{x}$ chart can be developed when the mean and standard deviation of the process are known before sampling. In many situations, the process mean and standard deviation must be estimated by using samples that are selected from the process when it is assumed to be operating in control. For instance, KJW might select a random sample of five boxes each morning and five boxes each afternoon for 10 days of operation. For

FIGURE 14.6 $\bar{x}$ CHART FOR THE CEREAL BOX FILLING PROCESS

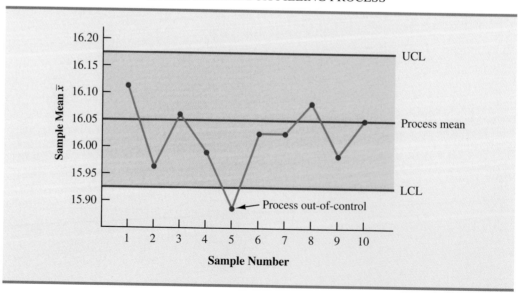

each subgroup, or sample, the mean and standard deviation of the sample are computed. The overall averages of both the sample means and the sample standard deviations can then be used to construct control charts for both the process mean and the process standard deviation.

In practice, it is common to monitor the variability of a production process by using the range instead of the standard deviation because the range is easier to compute. The range can then be used to provide good estimates of the process standard deviation; thus it can be used to construct upper and lower control limits for the $\bar{x}$ chart with little computational effort. To illustrate, let us consider the problem facing Jensen Computer Supplies, Inc.

Jensen Computer Supplies (JCS) manufactures 3.5-inch-diameter computer disks; they have just finished adjusting their production process so that it is operating in control. Suppose random samples of five disks are taken during the first hour of operation, during the second hour of operation, and so on, until 20 samples have been selected. Table 14.2 provides the diameter of each disk sampled as well as the mean $\bar{x}_j$ and range R_j for each of the samples.

The estimate of the process mean μ developed using k samples of size n is given by the overall sample mean.

OVERALL SAMPLE MEAN

$$\bar{\bar{x}} = \frac{\bar{x}_1 + \bar{x}_2 + \cdots + \bar{x}_k}{k}$$

(14.4)

where

$$\bar{x}_j = \text{mean of the } j\text{th sample } j = 1, 2, \ldots, k$$
$$k = \text{number of samples}$$

TABLE 14.2   DATA FOR JENSEN COMPUTER SUPPLIES

CD file

Jensen

Sample Number	Observations					Sample Mean $\bar{x}_j$	Sample Range R_j
1	3.5056	3.5086	3.5144	3.5009	3.5030	3.5065	.0135
2	3.4882	3.5085	3.4884	3.5250	3.5031	3.5026	.0368
3	3.4897	3.4898	3.4995	3.5130	3.4969	3.4978	.0233
4	3.5153	3.5120	3.4989	3.4900	3.4837	3.5000	.0316
5	3.5059	3.5113	3.5011	3.4773	3.4801	3.4951	.0340
6	3.4977	3.4961	3.5050	3.5014	3.5060	3.5012	.0099
7	3.4910	3.4913	3.4976	3.4831	3.5044	3.4935	.0213
8	3.4991	3.4853	3.4830	3.5083	3.5094	3.4970	.0264
9	3.5099	3.5162	3.5228	3.4958	3.5004	3.5090	.0270
10	3.4880	3.5015	3.5094	3.5102	3.5146	3.5047	.0266
11	3.4881	3.4887	3.5141	3.5175	3.4863	3.4989	.0312
12	3.5043	3.4867	3.4946	3.5018	3.4784	3.4932	.0259
13	3.5043	3.4769	3.4944	3.5014	3.4904	3.4935	.0274
14	3.5004	3.5030	3.5082	3.5045	3.5234	3.5079	.0230
15	3.4846	3.4938	3.5065	3.5089	3.5011	3.4990	.0243
16	3.5145	3.4832	3.5188	3.4935	3.4989	3.5018	.0356
17	3.5004	3.5042	3.4954	3.5020	3.4889	3.4982	.0153
18	3.4959	3.4823	3.4964	3.5082	3.4871	3.4940	.0259
19	3.4878	3.4864	3.4960	3.5070	3.4984	3.4951	.0206
20	3.4969	3.5144	3.5053	3.4985	3.4885	3.5007	.0259

For the JCS data in Table 14.2, $k = 20$ and the overall sample mean is $\bar{\bar{x}} = 3.4995$. This value will be the center line for the $\bar{x}$ chart. The range of each sample, denoted R_j, is simply the difference between the largest and smallest values in each sample. The average range for k samples is computed as follows.

AVERAGE RANGE

$$\bar{R} = \frac{R_1 + R_2 + \cdots + R_k}{k} \tag{14.5}$$

where

$$R_j = \text{range of the } j\text{th sample}, j = 1, 2, \ldots, k$$
$$k = \text{number of samples}$$

For the JCS data in Table 14.2, the average range is $\bar{R} = .0253$.

In the preceding section we showed that the upper and lower control limits for the $\bar{x}$ chart are

$$\mu \pm 3\frac{\sigma}{\sqrt{n}} \tag{14.6}$$

The overall sample mean $\bar{\bar{x}}$ is used to estimate μ and the sample ranges are used to develop an estimate of σ.

Hence, to construct the control limits for the $\bar{x}$ chart, we need to estimate μ and σ, the mean and standard deviation of the process. An estimate of μ is given by $\bar{\bar{x}}$. An estimate of σ can be developed by using the range data.

It can be shown that an estimator of the process standard deviation σ is the average range divided by d_2, a constant that depends on the sample size n. That is,

$$\text{Estimator of } \sigma = \frac{\bar{R}}{d_2} \tag{14.7}$$

The *American Society for Testing and Materials Manual on Presentation of Data and Control Chart Analysis* provides values for d_2 as shown in Table 14.3. For instance, when $n = 5$, $d_2 = 2.326$, and the estimate of σ is the average range divided by 2.326. If we substitute $\bar{\bar{x}}$ for μ and $\bar{R}/d_2$ for σ in equation (14.6), we can write the control limits for the $\bar{x}$ chart as

$$\bar{\bar{x}} \pm 3\frac{\bar{R}/d_2}{\sqrt{n}} = \bar{\bar{x}} \pm \frac{3}{d_2\sqrt{n}}\bar{R} = \bar{\bar{x}} \pm A_2\bar{R} \tag{14.8}$$

Note that $A_2 = 3/(d_2\sqrt{n})$ is a constant that depends only on the sample size. Values for A_2 are also provided in Table 14.3. For $n = 5$, $A_2 = .577$; thus, the control limits for Jensen's $\bar{x}$ chart are

$$3.4995 \pm (.577)(.0253) = 3.4995 \pm .0146$$

Hence, UCL = 3.514 and LCL = 3.485.

Figure 14.7 shows the $\bar{x}$ chart for Jensen Computer Supplies. One can use the data in Table 14.2 and Excel's Chart Wizard to construct the chart. The center line is shown at the

TABLE 14.3 FACTORS FOR $\bar{x}$ AND R CONTROL CHARTS

Observations in Sample, n	d_2	A_2	d_3	D_3	D_4
2	1.128	1.880	0.853	0	3.267
3	1.693	1.023	0.888	0	2.574
4	2.059	0.729	0.880	0	2.282
5	2.326	0.577	0.864	0	2.114
6	2.534	0.483	0.848	0	2.004
7	2.704	0.419	0.833	0.076	1.924
8	2.847	0.373	0.820	0.136	1.864
9	2.970	0.337	0.808	0.184	1.816
10	3.078	0.308	0.797	0.223	1.777
11	3.173	0.285	0.787	0.256	1.744
12	3.258	0.266	0.778	0.283	1.717
13	3.336	0.249	0.770	0.307	1.693
14	3.407	0.235	0.763	0.328	1.672
15	3.472	0.223	0.756	0.347	1.653
16	3.532	0.212	0.750	0.363	1.637
17	3.588	0.203	0.744	0.378	1.622
18	3.640	0.194	0.739	0.391	1.608
19	3.689	0.187	0.734	0.403	1.597
20	3.735	0.180	0.729	0.415	1.585
21	3.778	0.173	0.724	0.425	1.575
22	3.819	0.167	0.720	0.434	1.566
23	3.858	0.162	0.716	0.443	1.557
24	3.895	0.157	0.712	0.451	1.548
25	3.931	0.153	0.708	0.459	1.541

Source: Adapted from Table 27 of ASTM STP 15D, *ASTM Manual on Presentation of Data and Control Chart Analysis.* Copyright © 1976 American Society of Testing and Materials, Philadelphia, PA. Reprinted with permission.

overall sample mean $\bar{\bar{x}} = 3.4995$. The upper control limit (UCL) is 3.514, which is 3 "sigma limits" above $\bar{\bar{x}}$. The lower control limit (LCL) is 3.485, which is 3 "sigma limits" below $\bar{\bar{x}}$. The $\bar{x}$ chart shows the 20 sample means plotted over time. Because all 20 sample means fall within the control limits, our assumption is confirmed that the data were collected during a period the process was in control. This chart can now be used to monitor the process mean on an ongoing basis.

R Chart

Let us now consider a range chart or R chart that can be used to control the variability of a process. To develop the R chart, we need to think of the range of a sample as a random variable with its own mean and standard deviation. The average range $\bar{R}$ provides an estimate of the mean of this random variable. Moreover, it can be shown that an estimate of the standard deviation of the range, denoted $\hat{\sigma}_R$, is

$$\hat{\sigma}_R = d_3 \frac{\bar{R}}{d_2} \qquad (14.9)$$

FIGURE 14.7 $\bar{x}$ CHART FOR JENSEN COMPUTER SUPPLIES

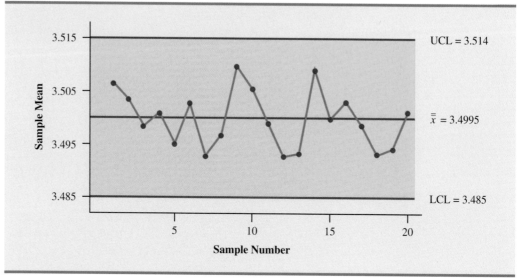

where d_2 and d_3 are constants that depend on the sample size; values of d_2 and d_3 are provided in Table 14.3. Thus, the UCL for the R chart is given by

$$\bar{R} + 3\hat{\sigma}_R = \bar{R} + 3d_3\frac{\bar{R}}{d_2} = \bar{R}\left(1 + 3\frac{d_3}{d_2}\right) \tag{14.10}$$

and the LCL is

$$\bar{R} - 3\hat{\sigma}_R = \bar{R} - 3d_3\frac{\bar{R}}{d_2} = \bar{R}\left(1 - 3\frac{d_3}{d_2}\right) \tag{14.11}$$

If we let

$$D_4 = 1 + 3\frac{d_3}{d_2} \tag{14.12}$$

$$D_3 = 1 - 3\frac{d_3}{d_2} \tag{14.13}$$

we can write the control limits for the R chart as

$$\text{UCL} = \bar{R}D_4 \tag{14.14}$$
$$\text{LCL} = \bar{R}D_3 \tag{14.15}$$

Values for D_3 and D_4 are also provided in Table 14.3. Note that for $n = 5$, $D_3 = 0$ and $D_4 = 2.114$. Thus, with $\bar{R} = .0253$, the control limits are

$$\text{UCL} = .0253(2.114) = .0535$$
$$\text{LCL} = .0253(0) = 0$$

If the R chart indicates that the process is out of control, the x̄ chart should not be interpreted until the R chart indicates the process variability is in control.

Figure 14.8 shows the R chart for Jensen Computer Suppliest. The center line is shown at the overall mean of the 20 sample ranges, $\bar{R} = .0253$. The UCL is .0535 or 3 sigma limits above $\bar{R}$. The LCL is 0.0 or 3 sigma limits below $\bar{R}$. The R chart shows the 20 sample ranges plotted over time. Because all 20 sample ranges are within the control limits, we confirm that the process was in control during the sampling period.

Using Excel to Construct an R Chart and an $\bar{x}$ Chart

The $\bar{x}$ chart in Figure 14.7 and the R chart in Figure 14.8 can be constructed using Excel. Here we show how the data in Table 14.2 can be used to construct an R chart and an $\bar{x}$ chart using Excel. Figure 14.9 is an Excel worksheet containing the Jensen Computer Supplies data. The average value for the range is needed to compute the lower and upper control limits for the $\bar{x}$ chart. So we will construct the R chart first. Our approach will be to first develop a worksheet with the needed data. Then the Chart Wizard will be used to develop the R chart. A similar procedure is followed to construct the $\bar{x}$ chart. Figure 14.10 contains the data developed for the R chart. The formula worksheet is in the background; the value worksheet appears in the foreground.

Enter Data: The data for the diameter measurements for the 20 samples selected by Jensen Computer Supplies are contained in the worksheet in Figure 14.9. We will use the data in this worksheet to construct the worksheets shown in Figures 14.10 and 14.11. For future reference, the worksheet in Figure 14.9 is named Data. The only values entered directly into the worksheets in Figures 14.10 and 14.11 are the sample numbers 1–20 in column A, the headings in cells A1:E1, and the headings in cells C23 and C24.

Enter Functions and Formulas: The worksheet in Figure 14.10 contains the formulas needed to construct an R chart using the Chart Wizard. Here we describe how this worksheet was constructed. Column A contains the sample numbers 1–20 as noted. Column B contains the Excel formulas needed to compute the range for each sample from the data in cells B2:F21 of the Data worksheet shown in Figure 14.9. Excel's MAX and MIN functions

FIGURE 14.8 *R* CHART FOR JENSEN COMPUTER SUPPLIES

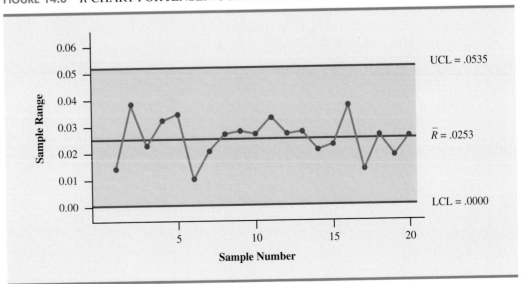

FIGURE 14.9   EXCEL DATA WORKSHEET FOR JENSEN COMPUTER SUPPLIES

	A	B	C	D	E	F	G
1	**Sample**	**Observation 1**	**Observation 2**	**Observation 3**	**Observation 4**	**Observation 5**	
2	1	3.5056	3.5086	3.5144	3.5009	3.5030	
3	2	3.4882	3.5085	3.4884	3.5250	3.5031	
4	3	3.4897	3.4898	3.4995	3.5130	3.4969	
5	4	3.5153	3.5120	3.4989	3.4900	3.4837	
6	5	3.5059	3.5113	3.5011	3.4773	3.4801	
7	6	3.4977	3.4961	3.5050	3.5014	3.5060	
8	7	3.4910	3.4913	3.4976	3.4831	3.5044	
9	8	3.4991	3.4853	3.4830	3.5083	3.5094	
10	9	3.5099	3.5162	3.5228	3.4958	3.5004	
11	10	3.4880	3.5015	3.5094	3.5102	3.5146	
12	11	3.4881	3.4887	3.5141	3.5175	3.4863	
13	12	3.5043	3.4867	3.4946	3.5018	3.4784	
14	13	3.5043	3.4769	3.4944	3.5014	3.4904	
15	14	3.5004	3.5030	3.5082	3.5045	3.5234	
16	15	3.4846	3.4938	3.5065	3.5089	3.5011	
17	16	3.5145	3.4832	3.5188	3.4935	3.4989	
18	17	3.5004	3.5042	3.4954	3.5020	3.4889	
19	18	3.4959	3.4823	3.4964	3.5082	3.4871	
20	19	3.4878	3.4864	3.4960	3.5070	3.4984	
21	20	3.4969	3.5144	3.5053	3.4985	3.4885	
22							

are used. The cell references in the formulas are to cells in the Data worksheet; note that the worksheet name followed by an exclamation point must precede a cell reference when the cells referenced are in another worksheet of the same workbook. The value worksheet shows that the ranges computed are the same as in Table 14.2. The AVERAGE function used in cell B22 computes the average of the ranges for the 20 samples.

FIGURE 14.10   EXCEL WORKSHEET SHOWING RANGE DATA AND COMPUTATION OF LCL, MEAN, AND UCL FOR AN *R* CHART

	A	B	C	D	E	F
1	Sample	R	LCL	Mean	UCL	
2	1	=MAX(Data!B2:F2)-MIN(Data!B2:F2)	=$D$23*$B$22	=$B$22	=$D$24*$B$22	
3	2	=MAX(Data!B3:F3)-MIN(Data!B3:F3)	=$D$23*$B$22	=$B$22	=$D$24*$B$22	
4	3	=MAX(Data!B4:F4)-MIN(Data!B4:F4)	=$D$23*$B$22	=$B$22	=$D$24*$B$22	
5	4	=MAX(Data!B5:F5)-MIN(Data!B5:F5)	=$D$23*$B$22	=$B$22	=$D$24*$B$22	
6	5	=MAX(Data!B6:F6)-MIN(Data!B6:F6)	=$D$23*$B$22	=$B$22	=$D$24*$B$22	
19	18	=MAX(Data!B19:F19)-MIN(Data!B19:F19)	=$D$23*$B$22	=$B$22	=$D$24*$B$22	
20	19	=MAX(Data!B20:F20)-MIN(Data!B20:F20)	=$D$23*$B$22	=$B$22	=$D$24*$B$22	
21	20	=MAX(Data!B21:F21)-MIN(Data!B21:F21)	=$D$23*$B$22	=$B$22	=$D$24*$B$22	
22	Mean(Rbar)	=AVERAGE($B$2:$B$21)				
23				D3	0	
24				D4	2.114	
25						

Note: Rows 7–18 (samples 6–17) are hidden.

	A	B	C	D	E	F
1	Sample	R	LCL	Mean	UCL	
2	1	0.0135	0.0000	0.0253	0.0534	
3	2	0.0368	0.0000	0.0253	0.0534	
4	3	0.0233	0.0000	0.0253	0.0534	
5	4	0.0316	0.0000	0.0253	0.0534	
6	5	0.0340	0.0000	0.0253	0.0534	
19	18	0.0259	0.0000	0.0253	0.0534	
20	19	0.0206	0.0000	0.0253	0.0534	
21	20	0.0259	0.0000	0.0253	0.0534	
22	Mean(Rbar)	0.0253				
23				D3	0.0000	
24				D4	2.1140	
25						

FIGURE 14.11 EXCEL WORKSHEET SHOWING $\bar{x}$ DATA AND COMPUTATION OF LCL, MEAN, AND UCL

	A	B	C	D	E	F
1	Sample	xbar	LCL	Mean	UCL	
2	1	=AVERAGE(Data!B2:F2)	=$B$22-$D$23*$D$24	=$B$22	=$B$22+$D$23*$D$24	
3	2	=AVERAGE(Data!B3:F3)	=$B$22-$D$23*$D$24	=$B$22	=$B$22+$D$23*$D$24	
4	3	=AVERAGE(Data!B4:F4)	=$B$22-$D$23*$D$24	=$B$22	=$B$22+$D$23*$D$24	
5	4	=AVERAGE(Data!B5:F5)	=$B$22-$D$23*$D$24	=$B$22	=$B$22+$D$23*$D$24	
6	5	=AVERAGE(Data!B6:F6)	=$B$22-$D$23*$D$24	=$B$22	=$B$22+$D$23*$D$24	
19	18	=AVERAGE(Data!B19:F19)	=$B$22-$D$23*$D$24	=$B$22	=$B$22+$D$23*$D$24	
20	19	=AVERAGE(Data!B20:F20)	=$B$22-$D$23*$D$24	=$B$22	=$B$22+$D$23*$D$24	
21	20	=AVERAGE(Data!B21:F21)	=$B$22-$D$23*$D$24	=$B$22	=$B$22+$D$23*$D$24	
22	Mean	=AVERAGE(B2:B21)				
23			A2	0.577		
24			Rbar	0.025275		
25						

	A	B	C	D	E	F
1	Sample	xbar	LCL	Mean	UCL	
2	1	3.5065	3.4849	3.4995	3.5141	
3	2	3.5026	3.4849	3.4995	3.5141	
4	3	3.4978	3.4849	3.4995	3.5141	
5	4	3.5000	3.4849	3.4995	3.5141	
6	5	3.4951	3.4849	3.4995	3.5141	
19	18	3.4940	3.4849	3.4995	3.5141	
20	19	3.4951	3.4849	3.4995	3.5141	
21	20	3.5007	3.4849	3.4995	3.5141	
22	Mean	3.4995				
23				A2	0.577	
24				Rbar	0.0253	
25						

Note: Rows 7–18 (samples 6–17) are hidden.

In order to compute the LCL and UCL we must know D_3 and D_4. These values are obtained from Table 14.3 and placed into cells D23 and D24, respectively. The formulas in cells C2:C21 are identical; they compute the LCL by multiplying D_3 (cell D23) times the average range (cell B22). The formulas in cells D2:D21 are also identical; they provide the average range. Finally, the formulas in cells E2:E21 (also identical) compute the UCL by multiplying D_4 (cell D24) times the average range (cell B22).

Apply Tools: The following steps describe how to use Excel's Chart Wizard to construct the R chart from the data in cells A2:E21 of Figure 14.10.

Step 1. Select cells A2:E21
Step 2. Click the **Chart Wizard** button on the Standard toolbar (or select the **Insert** menu and choose the **Chart** option)
Step 3. When the **Chart Wizard - Step 1 of 4 - Chart Type** dialog box appears:
Choose **XY (Scatter)** in the **Chart type** list
Choose **Scatter with data points connected by Lines** from the **Chart sub-type** display
Click **Next>**
Step 4. When the **Chart Wizard - Step 2 of 4 - Chart Source Data** dialog box appears:
Click **Next>**
Step 5. When the **Chart Wizard - Step 3 of 4 - Chart Options** dialog box appears:
Select the **Titles** tab and then
Type **R Chart for Jensen Computer Supplies** in the **Chart title** box
Type **Sample Number** in the **Value (X) axis** box
Type **Sample Range R** in the **Value (Y) axis** box
Select the **Legend** tab and remove the check in the **Show Legend** box
Select the **Gridlines** tab and remove the check in the **Major gridlines** box
Click **Next>**
Step 6. When the **Chart Wizard - Step 4 of 4 - Chart Location** dialog box appears:
Specify a location for the chart (we chose the **As new sheet** option)
Click **Finish**

The resulting R chart will appear in a new sheet entitled "Chart 1" in your workbook.

You will need to do some editing of your chart to make it look like Figure 14.8. To make the UCL line a solid line like it is in Figure 14.8 follow these steps:

Step 1. Right-click on the UCL line at one of the data points and select **Format Data Series**

Step 2. When the Format Data Series dialog box appears, select the **Patterns** tab:
>In the **Line** section:
>>Choose black for **Color**
>>Choose the second line from the bottom for **Weight**
>In the **Marker** section:
>>Choose the "long dash" for **Style**
>>Choose black for **Foreground**
>>Click **OK**

Control charts based on data indicating the presence of a defect or the number of defects are called attributes control charts. A p chart is an attributes control chart.

The UCL line will now appear as a solid black line. You should then follow the same steps for the average and LCL lines to make them look as they do in Figure 14.8. As a final step you will need to right-click on the vertical axis to format the axis labels as shown in Figure 14.8. You will probably also want to resize the chart to satisfy your own preference. Just select the chart and move the drag handles until the chart looks the way you want it.

The procedure for constructing an $\bar{x}$ chart is similar. Figure 14.11 shows the worksheet developed to provide the data needed to construct an $\bar{x}$ chart. It is analogous to the worksheet developed for the R chart in Figure 14.10. One can use the Chart Wizard with this worksheet to construct the $\bar{x}$ chart shown in Figure 14.7. The steps followed are almost identical to those we just described for the R chart, so we will not repeat them here.

p Chart

Let us consider the case in which the output quality is measured in terms of the items being either nondefective or defective. The decision to continue or to adjust the production process will be based on $\bar{p}$, the proportion of defective items found in a sample of the output. The control chart used to monitor the proportion of defective items is called a **p chart.**

To illustrate the construction of a p chart, consider the use of automated mail-sorting machines in a post office. These automated machines scan the zip codes on letters and divert each letter to its proper carrier route. Even when a machine is operating properly, some letters are diverted to incorrect routes. Suppose that when a machine is operating correctly, or in a state of control, 3% of the letters are incorrectly diverted. Thus p, the proportion of letters incorrectly diverted when the process is in control, is .03.

The sampling distribution of $\bar{p}$, as presented in Chapter 7, can be used to determine the variation that can be expected in $\bar{p}$ values for a process that is in control. Recall that the expected value or mean of $\bar{p}$ is p, the proportion defective when the process is in control. With samples of size n, the formula for the standard deviation of $\bar{p}$, called the standard error of the proportion, is

$$\sigma_{\bar{p}} = \sqrt{\frac{p(1 - p)}{n}} \tag{14.16}$$

We also learned in Chapter 7 that the sampling distribution of $\bar{p}$ can be approximated by a normal probability distribution whenever the following two conditions are satisfied.

$$np \geq 5$$
$$n(1 - p) \geq 5$$

Thus, if these two conditions are satisfied, the sampling distribution of $\bar{p}$ can be approximated by a normal probability distribution with mean p and standard deviation $\sigma_{\bar{p}}$. This distribution is shown in Figure 14.12.

FIGURE 14.12 SAMPLING DISTRIBUTION OF $\bar{p}$

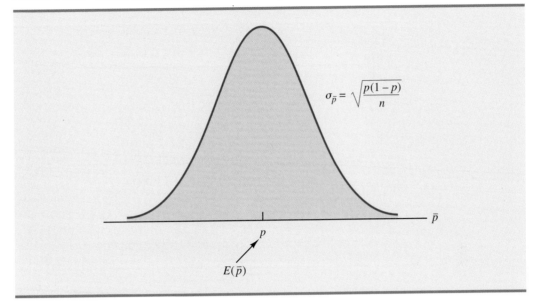

$$\sigma_{\bar{p}} = \sqrt{\frac{p(1-p)}{n}}$$

$E(\bar{p})$

To establish control limits for a p chart, we follow the same procedure we used to establish control limits for an $\bar{x}$ chart. That is, the limits for the control chart are set at 3 standard errors above and below the proportion defective when the process is in control. Thus, we have the following control limits.

CONTROL LIMITS FOR A p CHART

$$\text{UCL} = p + 3\sigma_{\bar{p}} \qquad (14.17)$$
$$\text{LCL} = p - 3\sigma_{\bar{p}} \qquad (14.18)$$

With $p = .03$ and samples of size $n = 200$, equation (14.16) shows that the standard error is

$$\sigma_{\bar{p}} = \sqrt{\frac{.03(1 - .03)}{200}} = .0121$$

Hence, the control limits are UCL = .03 + 3(.0121) = .0663, and LCL = .03 − 3(.0121) = −.0063. Whenever equation (14.18) provides a negative value, LCL is set to zero in the control chart.

Figure 14.13 is the control chart for the mail-sorting process. The points plotted show the sample proportion defective found in samples of letters taken from the process. All points are within the control limits, and the sorting process shows no evidence of being out of control.

If the proportion of defective items for a process that is in control is not known, that value is first estimated by using sample data. Suppose, for example, that k different samples, each of size n, are selected from a process that is in control. The fraction or proportion of defective items in each sample is then determined. Treating all the data collected as one large sample, we can determine the average number of defective items for all the data; that value can then be used to provide an estimate of p, the proportion of defective items observed when the process is in control. Note that this estimate of p also enables us to estimate the standard error of the proportion; upper and lower control limits can then be established.

FIGURE 14.13   *p* CHART FOR THE PROPORTION DEFECTIVE IN A MAIL-SORTING PROCESS

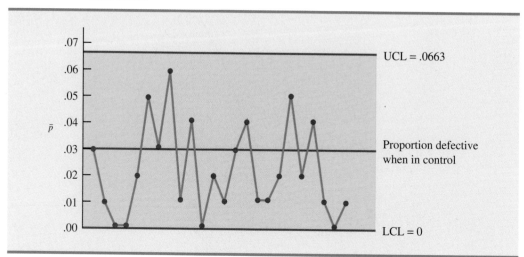

np **Chart**

An ***np* chart** is a control chart developed for the number of defective items observed in a sample. In this case, n is the sample size and p is the probability of observing a defective item when the process is in control. Whenever $np \geq 5$ and $n(1 - p) \geq 5$, the distribution of the number of defective items observed in a sample size n can be approximated by a normal probability distribution with mean np and standard deviation $\sqrt{np(1 - p)}$. Thus, for the mail-sorting example, with $n = 200$ and $p = .03$, the number of defective items observed in a sample of 200 letters can be approximated by a normal probability distribution with a mean of $200(.03) = 6$ and a standard deviation of $\sqrt{200(.03)(.97)} = 2.4125$.

The control limits for an np chart are set at 3 standard deviations above and below the expected number of defective items observed when the process is in control. Thus, we have the following control limits.

> **CONTROL LIMITS FOR AN *np* CHART**
>
> $$UCL = np + 3\sqrt{np(1 - p)} \qquad \textbf{(14.19)}$$
> $$LCL = np - 3\sqrt{np(1 - p)} \qquad \textbf{(14.20)}$$

For the mail-sorting process example, with $p = .03$ and $n = 200$, the control limits are $UCL = 6 + 3(2.4125) = 13.2375$, and $LCL = 6 - 3(2.4125) = -1.2375$. Because equation (14.20) provides a negative value for LCL, it is reset to zero in the control chart. Hence, if the number of letters diverted to incorrect routes is 14 or more, the process is concluded to be out of control.

The information provided by an np chart is equivalent to the information provided by the p chart; the only difference is that the np chart is a plot of the number of defective items observed, whereas the p chart is a plot of the proportion of defective items observed. Thus, if we were to conclude that a particular process is out of control on the basis of a p chart, the process would also be concluded to be out of control on the basis of an np chart.

Interpretation of Control Charts

Control charts are designed to identify when assignable causes of variation are present. Managers must then authorize action to eliminate the assignable cause and return the process to an in-control state.

The location and pattern of points in a control chart enable us to determine, with a small probability of error, whether a process is in statistical control. A primary indication that a process may be out of control is a data point outside the control limits, such as point 5 in Figure 14.6. Such a point is statistical evidence that the process is out of control; in such cases, corrective action should be taken as soon as possible.

Even if all points are within the upper and lower control limits, a process may not be in control. Trends in the sample data points or unusually long runs above or below the center line may also indicate out-of-control conditions.

In addition to points outside the control limits, certain patterns of the points within the control limits can be warning signals of quality control problems. For example, assume that all the data points are within the control limits but that a large number of points are on one side of the center line. This pattern may indicate that an equipment problem, a change in materials, or some other assignable cause has led to a shift in quality. Careful investigation of the production process should be undertaken to determine whether quality has changed.

Another pattern to watch for in control charts is a gradual shift, or trend, over time. For example, as tools wear out, the dimensions of machined parts will gradually deviate from their designed levels. Gradual changes in temperature or humidity, general equipment deterioration, dirt buildup, or operator fatigue may also result in a trend pattern in control charts. Six or seven points in a row that indicate either an increasing or decreasing trend should be cause for concern, even if the data points are all within the control limits. When such a pattern occurs, the process should be reviewed for possible changes or shifts in quality. Corrective action to bring the process back into control may be necessary.

NOTES AND COMMENTS

1. Because the control limits for the $\bar{x}$ chart depend on the value of the average range, these limits will not have much meaning unless the process variability is in control. In practice, the R chart is usually constructed before the $\bar{x}$ chart; if the R chart indicates that the process variability is in control, then the $\bar{x}$ chart is constructed.

2. The p and np control charts can also be constructed using Excel's Chart Wizard. For instance, to develop a p chart, start by organizing the data for $\bar{p}$, LCL, mean, and UCL in a worksheet similar to Figures 14.10 or 14.11. Then use the Chart Wizard in the same way we did earlier to construct an R chart.

Exercises

Methods

1. A process that is in control has a mean of $\mu = 12.5$ and a standard deviation of $\sigma = .8$.
   a. Construct an $\bar{x}$ chart if samples of size 4 are to be used.
   b. Repeat part (a) for samples of size 8 and 16.
   c. What happens to the limits of the control chart as the sample size is increased? Discuss why this change is reasonable.

2. Twenty-five samples, each of size 5, were selected from a process that was in control. The sum of all the data collected was 677.5 pounds.
   a. What is an estimate of the process mean (in terms of pounds per unit) when the process is in control?
   b. Develop the control chart for this process if samples of size 5 will be used. Assume that the process standard deviation is .5 when the process is in control and that the mean of the process is the estimate developed in part (a).

3. Twenty-five samples of 100 items each were inspected when a process was considered to be operating satisfactorily. In the 25 samples, 135 items were found to be defective.
   a. What is an estimate of the proportion defective when the process is in control?
   b. What is the standard error of the proportion if samples of size 100 will be used for statistical process control?
   c. Compute the upper and lower control limits for the control chart.

4. An in-control process sampled 20 times with a sample of size 8 resulted in $\bar{\bar{x}} = 28.5$ and $\bar{R} = 1.6$. Compute the upper and lower control limits for the $\bar{x}$ and R charts for this process.

Applications

5. Temperature is used to measure the output of a production process. When the process is in control, the mean of the process is $\mu = 128.5$ and the standard deviation is $\sigma = .4$.
   a. Construct an $\bar{x}$ chart if samples of size 6 are to be used.
   b. Is the process in control for a sample providing the following data?

   | 128.8 | 128.2 | 129.1 | 128.7 | 128.4 | 129.2 |

   c. Is the process in control for a sample providing the following data?

   | 129.3 | 128.7 | 128.6 | 129.2 | 129.5 | 129.0 |

6. A quality control process monitors the weight per carton of laundry detergent. Control limits are set at UCL = 20.12 ounces and LCL = 19.90 ounces. Samples of size 5 are used for the sampling and inspection process. What are the process mean and process standard deviation for the manufacturing operation?

7. The Goodman Tire and Rubber Company periodically tests its tires for tread wear under simulated road conditions. To study and control the manufacturing process, 20 samples, each containing three radial tires, were chosen from different shifts over several days of operation; the data collected are shown below. Assuming that these data were collected when the manufacturing process was believed to be operating in control, develop the R and $\bar{x}$ charts.

Tires

Sample	Tread Wear*		
1	31	42	28
2	26	18	35
3	25	30	34
4	17	25	21
5	38	29	35
6	41	42	36
7	21	17	29
8	32	26	28
9	41	34	33
10	29	17	30
11	26	31	40
12	23	19	25
13	17	24	32
14	43	35	17
15	18	25	29
16	30	42	31
17	28	36	32
18	40	29	31
19	18	29	28
20	22	34	26

*Hundredths of an inch

FIGURE 14.15 OPERATING CHARACTERISTIC CURVE FOR THE $n = 15$, $c = 0$
ACCEPTANCE SAMPLING PLAN

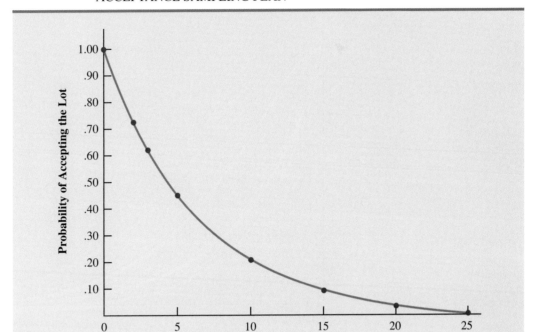

With the data in Table 14.5, a graph of the probability of accepting the lot versus the percent defective in the lot can be drawn as shown in Figure 14.15. This graph, or curve, is called the **operating characteristic (OC) curve** for the $n = 15$, $c = 0$ acceptance sampling plan.

Perhaps we should consider other sampling plans, ones with different sample sizes n and/or different acceptance criteria c. First consider the case in which the sample size remains $n = 15$ but the acceptance criterion increases from $c = 0$ to $c = 1$; that is, we will now accept the lot if zero or one defective item is found in the sample. For a lot with 5% defective items ($p = .05$), the binomial probability function in equation (14.21) can be used to compute $f(0)$ and $f(1)$. Summing these two probabilities provides the probability that the $n = 15$, $c = 1$ sampling plan will accept the lot. We find that with $n = 15$ and $p = .05$, $f(0) = .4633$ and $f(1) = .3658$. Thus, we find a $.4633 + .3658 = .8291$ probability that the $n = 15$, $c = 1$ plan will lead to the acceptance of a lot with 5% defective items.

Figure 14.16 shows the operating characteristic curves for four alternative acceptance sampling plans for the KALI example. Samples of size 15 and 20 are considered. Note that regardless of the proportion defective in the lot, the $n = 15$, $c = 1$ sampling plan provides the highest probabilities of accepting the lot. The $n = 20$, $c = 0$ sampling plan provides the lowest probabilities of accepting the lot; however, that plan also provides the highest probabilities of rejecting the lot.

Selecting an Acceptance Sampling Plan

Now that we know how to use the binomial probability distribution to compute the probability of accepting a lot with a given proportion defective, we are ready to select the values of n and c that determine the desired acceptance sampling plan for the application being studied. In formulating an acceptance plan, managers must specify two values for the proportion

FIGURE 14.16   OPERATING CHARACTERISTIC CURVES FOR FOUR ACCEPTANCE SAMPLING PLANS

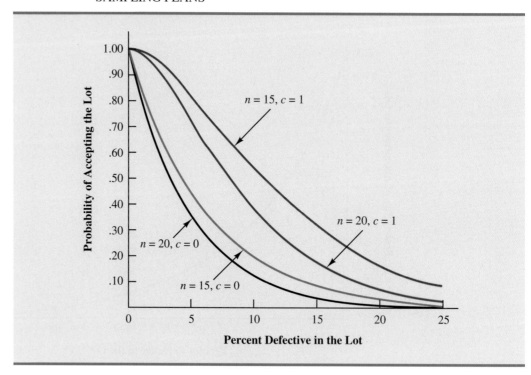

defective in the lot. One value, denoted p_0, will be used to control for the producer's risk, and the other value, denoted p_1, will be used to control for the consumer's risk.

In showing how this formulation can be done, we will use the following notation.

α = the producer's risk; the probability that a lot with p_0 defective will be rejected

β = the consumer's risk; the probability that a lot with p_1 defective will be accepted

Suppose that for the KALI example, the managers specify that $p_0 = .03$ and $p_1 = .15$. From the OC curve for $n = 15$, $c = 0$ in Figure 14.17, we see that $p_0 = .03$ provides a producer's risk of approximately $1 - .63 = .37$, and $p_1 = .15$ provides a consumer's risk of approximately .09. Thus, if the managers are willing to tolerate both a .37 probability of rejecting a lot with 3% defective items (producer's risk) and a .09 probability of accepting a lot with 15% defective items (consumer's risk), the $n = 15$, $c = 0$ acceptance sampling plan would be acceptable.

Suppose, however, that the managers request a producer's risk of $\alpha = .10$ and a consumer's risk of $\beta = .20$. We see that now the $n = 15$, $c = 0$ sampling plan offers a better-than-desired consumer's risk but an unacceptably large producer's risk. The fact that $\alpha = .37$ indicates that 37% of the lots will be erroneously rejected when only 3% of the items in them are defective. The producer's risk is too high, and a different acceptance sampling plan should be considered.

Using $p_0 = .03$, $\alpha = .10$, $p_1 = .15$, and $\beta = .20$ in Figure 14.16 shows that the acceptance sampling plan with $n = 20$ and $c = 1$ comes closest to meeting both the producer's and the consumer's risk requirements. Exercise 13 at the end of this section will ask you to compute the producer's risk and the consumer's risk for the $n = 20$, $c = 1$ sampling plan.

As shown in this section, several computations and several operating characteristic curves may need to be considered to determine the sampling plan with the desired pro-

FIGURE 14.17 OPERATING CHARACTERISTIC CURVE FOR $n = 15$, $c = 0$ WITH $p_0 = .03$ AND $p_1 = .15$

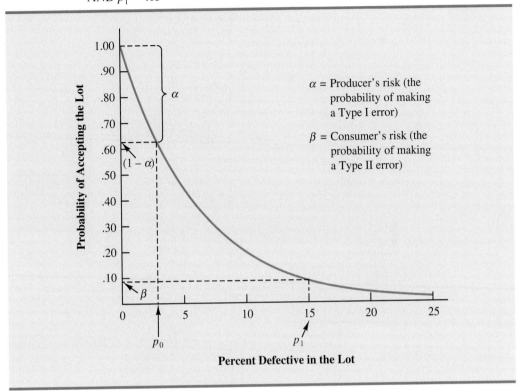

ducer's and consumer's risks. Fortunately, tables of sampling plans are published. For example, the American Military Standard Table, MIL-STD-105D, provides information helpful in designing acceptance sampling plans. More advanced texts on quality control, such as those listed in the bibliography, describe the use of such tables. The advanced texts also discuss the role of sampling costs in determining the optimal sampling plan.

Multiple Sampling Plans

The acceptance sampling procedure presented for the KALI example is called a *single-sample plan,* because only one sample or sampling stage is used. After the number of defective components in the sample is determined, a decision must be made to accept or reject the lot. An alternative to the single-sample plan is a **multiple sampling plan,** in which two or more stages of sampling are used. At each stage a decision is made among three possibilities: stop sampling and accept the lot, stop sampling and reject the lot, or continue sampling. Although more complex, multiple sampling plans often result in a smaller total sample size than single-sample plans with the same α and β probabilities.

The logic of a two-stage, or double-sample, plan is shown in Figure 14.18. Initially a sample of n_1 items is selected. If the number of defective components x_1 is less than or equal to c_1, accept the lot. If x_1 is greater than or equal to c_2, reject the lot. If x_1 is between c_1 and c_2 ($c_1 < x_1 < c_2$), select a second sample of n_2 items. Determine the total number of defects from the first sample (x_1) and the second sample (x_2). If $x_1 + x_2 \leq c_3$, accept the lot; otherwise reject the lot. The development of the double-sample plan is more difficult because the sample sizes n_1 and n_2 and the acceptance numbers c_1, c_2, and c_3 must meet acceptable levels of both the producer's and consumer's risks.

FIGURE 14.18   A TWO-STAGE ACCEPTANCE SAMPLING PLAN

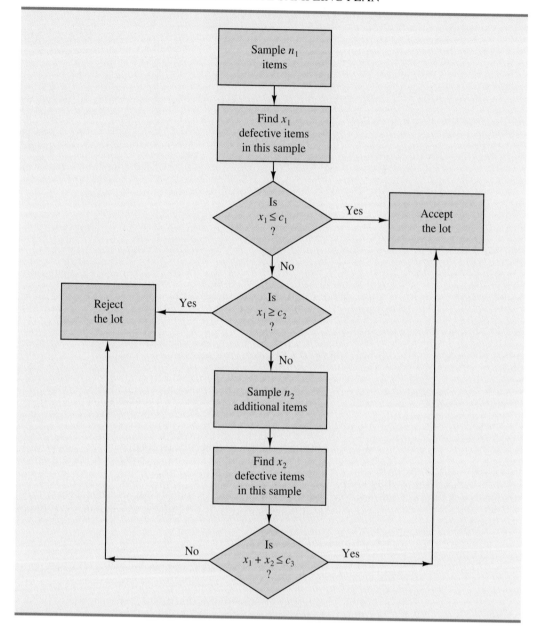

NOTES AND COMMENTS

1. The use of the binomial probability distribution for acceptance sampling is based on the assumption of large lots. If the lot size is small, the hypergeometric probability distribution is the appropriate distribution.

2. In the MIL-STD-105D sampling tables, p_0 is called the acceptable quality level (AQL). In some sampling tables, p_1 is called the lot tolerance percent defective (LTPD) or the rejectable

quality level (RQL). Many of the published sampling plans also use quality indexes such as the indifference quality level (IQL) and the average outgoing quality limit (AOQL). The more advanced texts listed in the bibliography provide a complete discussion of these other indexes.

3. In this section we provided an introduction to *attributes sampling plans*. In these plans each item sampled is classified as nondefective or de-

fective. In *variables sampling plans,* a sample is taken and a measurement of the quality characteristic is taken. For example, for gold jewelry a measurement of quality may be the amount of gold it contains. A simple statistic such as the average amount of gold in the sample jewelry is computed and compared with an allowable value to determine whether to accept or reject the lot.

Exercises

Methods

10. For an acceptance sampling plan with $n = 25$ and $c = 0$, find the probability of accepting a lot when the defect rate is 2%. What is the probability of accepting the lot if the defect rate is 6%?

11. Consider an acceptance sampling plan with $n = 20$ and $c = 0$. Compute the producer's risk for each of the following cases.
    a. The lot has a defect rate of 2%.
    b. The lot has a defect rate of 6%.

12. Repeat exercise 11 for the acceptance sampling plan with $n = 20$ and $c = 1$. What happens to the producer's risk as the acceptance number c is increased? Explain.

Applications

13. Refer to the KALI example presented in this section. The quality control manager requested a producer's risk of .10 or less when p_0 was .03 and a consumer's risk of .20 or less when p_1 was .15. Consider the acceptance sampling plan based on a sample size of 20 and an acceptance criterion of $c = 1$. Answer the following questions.
    a. What is the producer's risk for the $n = 20$, $c = 1$ sampling plan?
    b. What is the consumer's risk for the $n = 20$, $c = 1$ sampling plan?
    c. Does the $n = 20$, $c = 1$ sampling plan satisfy the risk limits as requested by the quality control manager? Discuss.

14. To inspect incoming shipments of raw materials, a manufacturer is considering samples of sizes 10, 15, and 20. Use binomial probabilities to select a sampling plan that provides a producer's risk of $\alpha = .03$ when p_0 is .05 and a consumer's risk of $\beta = .12$ when p_1 is .30.

15. A domestic manufacturer of watches purchases quartz crystals from a Swiss firm. The crystals are shipped in lots of 1000. The acceptance sampling procedure uses 20 randomly selected crystals.
    a. Construct operating characteristic curves for acceptance criteria of 0, 1, and 2.
    b. If p_0 is .01 and $p_1 = .08$, what are the producer's and consumer's risks for each sampling plan in part (a)?

Summary

In this chapter we discussed how statistical methods can be used to assist in the control of quality. First, we presented a brief introduction to three quality management frameworks: the Malcolm Baldrige Quality Award, ISO 9000 standards, and the Six Sigma philosophy. In Six Sigma terminology a defect is any mistake or error passed on to the customer, and Six Sigma represents a quality level of at most 3.4 defects per million opportunities.

Quality control consists of a series of inspections and measurements used to determine whether quality standards are being met. Two of the statistical methods used in quality control are statistical process control and acceptance sampling. We first presented the $\bar{x}$, R, p, and np control charts as graphical aids in monitoring process quality. Control limits are established for each chart; samples are selected periodically and the data plotted on the control chart. Data outside the control limits indicate that the process is out of control and that corrective action should be taken. Patterns of data within the control limits can also indicate potential quality control problems and suggest that corrective action may be warranted.

With the technique known as acceptance sampling, a sample is selected and inspected. The number of defective items in the sample provides the basis for accepting or rejecting the lot. The sample size and the acceptance criterion can be adjusted to control both the producer's risk (Type I error) and the consumer's risk (Type II error).

Glossary

Total quality (TQ) A people-focused management system that aims at continual increase in customer satisfaction at continually lower real cost.

Six Sigma A methodology used to provide a level of quality so good that for every 1 million opportunities, no more than 3.4 defects will occur. This level of quality is referred to as the Six Sigma level of quality.

Quality control A series of inspections and measurements used to determine whether quality standards are being met.

Assignable causes Variations in process outputs that are due to factors such as machine tools wearing out, incorrect machine settings, poor-quality raw materials, operator error, and so on. Corrective action should be taken whenever assignable causes are detected.

Common causes Normal or natural variations in process outputs that are due purely to chance. No corrective action is necessary when output variations are due to common causes.

Control chart A graphical tool used to help determine whether a process is in control or out of control.

$\bar{x}$ chart A control chart used to monitor the mean value of a variable such as a length, weight, temperature, and so on.

R chart A control chart used to control the variability of a process.

p chart A control chart used to monitor the proportion of defective items generated by a process.

np chart A control chart used to monitor the number of defective items generated by a process.

Lot A group of items such as an incoming shipment of raw materials, a shipment of purchased parts, or a batch of finished goods from final assembly.

Acceptance sampling A statistical procedure in which the number of defective items found in a sample is used to determine whether a lot should be accepted or rejected.

Producer's risk The risk of rejecting a good-quality lot; a Type I error.

Consumer's risk The risk of accepting a poor-quality lot; a Type II error.

Acceptance criterion The maximum number of defective items that can be found in the sample and still indicate an acceptable lot.

Operating characteristic (OC) curve A graph showing the probability of accepting the lot as a function of the percent defective in the lot. This curve can be used to determine whether a particular acceptance sampling plan meets both the producer's and the consumer's risk requirements.

Multiple sampling plan A form of acceptance sampling in which more than one sample or stage is used. On the basis of the number of defective items found in a sample, a decision will be made to accept the lot, reject the lot, or continue sampling.

Key Formulas

Standard Error of the Mean

$$\sigma_{\bar{x}} = \frac{\sigma}{\sqrt{n}} \qquad (14.1)$$

Control Limits for an $\bar{x}$ Chart: Process Mean and Standard Deviation Known

$$\text{UCL} = \mu + 3\sigma_{\bar{x}} \qquad (14.2)$$
$$\text{LCL} = \mu - 3\sigma_{\bar{x}} \qquad (14.3)$$

Overall Sample Mean

$$\bar{\bar{x}} = \frac{\bar{x}_1 + \bar{x}_2 + \cdots + \bar{x}_k}{k} \qquad (14.4)$$

Average Range

$$\bar{R} = \frac{R_1 + R_2 + \cdots + R_k}{k} \qquad (14.5)$$

Control Limits for an $\bar{x}$ Chart: Process Mean and Standard Deviation Unknown

$$\bar{\bar{x}} \pm A_2\bar{R} \qquad (14.8)$$

Control Limits for an R Chart

$$\text{UCL} = \bar{R}D_4 \qquad (14.14)$$
$$\text{LCL} = \bar{R}D_3 \qquad (14.15)$$

Standard Error of the Proportion

$$\sigma_{\bar{p}} = \sqrt{\frac{p(1 - p)}{n}} \qquad (14.16)$$

Control Limits for a p Chart

$$\text{UCL} = p + 3\sigma_{\bar{p}} \qquad (14.17)$$
$$\text{LCL} = p - 3\sigma_{\bar{p}} \qquad (14.18)$$

Control Limits for an np Chart

$$\text{UCL} = np + 3\sqrt{np(1 - p)} \qquad (14.19)$$
$$\text{LCL} = np - 3\sqrt{np(1 - p)} \qquad (14.20)$$

Binomial Probability Function for Acceptance Sampling

$$f(x) = \frac{n!}{x!(n - x)!} p^x(1 - p)^{(n-x)} \qquad (14.21)$$

Supplementary Exercises

16. Samples of size 5 provided the following 20 sample means for a production process that is believed to be in control.

95.72	95.24	95.18
95.44	95.46	95.32
95.40	95.44	95.08
95.50	95.80	95.22
95.56	95.22	95.04
95.72	94.82	95.46
95.60	95.78	

   a. Based on these data, what is an estimate of the mean when the process is in control?
   b. Assuming that the process standard deviation is $\sigma = .50$, develop an $\bar{x}$ control chart for this production process. Assume that the mean of the process is the estimate developed in part (a).
   c. Are any of the 20 sample means outside the control limits?

17. Product filling weights are normally distributed with a mean of 350 grams and a standard deviation of 15 grams.
   a. Develop the control limits for samples of size 10, 20, and 30.
   b. What happens to the control limits as the sample size is increased?
   c. What happens when a Type I error is made?
   d. What happens when a Type II error is made?
   e. What is the probability of a Type I error for samples of size 10, 20, and 30?
   f. What is the advantage of increasing the sample size for control chart purposes? What error probability is reduced as the sample size is increased?

18. Twenty-five samples of size 5 resulted in $\bar{\bar{x}} = 5.42$ and $\bar{R} = 2.0$. Compute control limits for the $\bar{x}$ and R charts, and estimate the standard deviation of the process.

19. The following quality control data for a manufacturing process at Kensport Chemical Company show the temperature in degrees centigrade at five points in time during a manufacturing cycle. The company is interested in using control charts to monitor the temperature of its manufacturing process. Construct the $\bar{x}$ and R charts. What conclusions can be drawn about the quality of the process?

Sample	$\bar{x}$	R	Sample	$\bar{x}$	R
1	95.72	1.0	11	95.80	.6
2	95.24	.9	12	95.22	.2
3	95.18	.8	13	95.56	1.3
4	95.44	.4	14	95.22	.5
5	95.46	.5	15	95.04	.8
6	95.32	1.1	16	95.72	1.1
7	95.40	.9	17	94.82	.6
8	95.44	.3	18	95.46	.5
9	95.08	.2	19	95.60	.4
10	95.50	.6	20	95.74	.6

20. The following data were collected for the Master Blend Coffee production process. The data show the filling weights based on samples of 3-pound cans of coffee. Use these data to construct the $\bar{x}$ and R charts. What conclusions can be drawn about the quality of the production process?

			Observations		
Sample	**1**	**2**	**3**	**4**	**5**
1	3.05	3.08	3.07	3.11	3.11
2	3.13	3.07	3.05	3.10	3.10
3	3.06	3.04	3.12	3.11	3.10
4	3.09	3.08	3.09	3.09	3.07
5	3.10	3.06	3.06	3.07	3.08
6	3.08	3.10	3.13	3.03	3.06
7	3.06	3.06	3.08	3.10	3.08
8	3.11	3.08	3.07	3.07	3.07
9	3.09	3.09	3.08	3.07	3.09
10	3.06	3.11	3.07	3.09	3.07

Coffee

21. Consider the following situations and comment on whether the sample results might cause concern about the quality of the process.
   a. A p chart has LCL = 0 and UCL = .068. When the process is in control, the proportion defective is .033. Plot the following seven sample results: .035, .062, .055, .049, .058, .066, and .055. Discuss.
   b. An $\bar{x}$ chart has LCL = 22.2 and UCL = 24.5. The mean is μ = 23.35 when the process is in control. Plot the following seven sample results: 22.4, 22.6, 22.65, 23.2, 23.4, 23.85, and 24.1. Discuss.

22. Managers of 1200 different retail outlets make twice-a-month restocking orders from a central warehouse. Past experience shows 4% of the orders contain one or more errors such as wrong item shipped, wrong quantity shipped, and item requested but not shipped. Random samples of 200 orders are selected monthly and checked for accuracy.
   a. Construct a control chart for this situation.
   b. Six months of data show the following numbers of orders with one or more errors: 10, 15, 6, 13, 8, and 17. Plot the data on the control chart. What does your plot indicate about the order process?

23. An n = 10, c = 2 acceptance sampling plan is being considered; assume that p_0 = .05 and p_1 = .20.
   a. Compute both the producer's and the consumer's risks for this acceptance sampling plan.
   b. Would the producer, the consumer, or both be unhappy with the proposed sampling plan?
   c. What change in the sampling plan, if any, would you recommend?

24. An acceptance sampling plan with n = 15 and c = 1 was designed with a producer's risk of .075.
   a. Was the value of p_0 equal to .01, .02, .03, .04, or .05? What does this value mean?
   b. What is the consumer's risk associated with this plan if p_1 is .25?

25. A manufacturer produces lots of a canned food product. Let p denote the proportion of the lots that do not meet the product quality specifications. An n = 25, c = 0 acceptance sampling plan will be used.
   a. Compute points on the operating characteristic curve when p = .01, .03, .10, and .20.
   b. Plot the operating characteristic curve.
   c. What is the probability that the acceptance sampling plan will reject a lot that has .01 defective?

APPENDIXES

Appendix A: References and Bibliography

General

Bowerman, B. L., and R. T. O'Connell. *Applied Statistics: Improving Business Processes.* Irwin, 1996.

Freedman, D., R. Pisani, and R. Purves. *Statistics,* 3rd ed. W. W. Norton, 1997.

Hogg, R. V., and A. T. Craig. *Introduction to Mathematical Statistics,* 5th ed. Prentice Hall, 1994.

Hogg, R. V., and E. A. Tanis. *Probability and Statistical Inference,* 6th ed. Prentice Hall, 2001.

Joiner, B. L., and B. F. Ryan. *Minitab Handbook.* Brooks/Cole, 2000.

Miller, I., and M. Miller. *John E. Freund's Mathematical Statistics.* Prentice Hall, 1998.

Moore, D. S., and G. P. McCabe. *Introduction to the Practice of Statistics,* 4th ed. Freeman, 2003.

Roberts, H. *Data Analysis for Managers with Minitab.* Scientific Press, 1991.

Tanur, J. M. *Statistics: A Guide to the Unknown,* 4th ed. Brooks/Cole, 2002.

Tukey, J. W. *Exploratory Data Analysis.* Addison-Wesley, 1977.

Probability

Hogg, R. V., and E. A. Tanis. *Probability and Statistical Inference,* 6th ed. Prentice Hall, 2001.

Ross, S. M. *Introduction to Probability Models,* 7th ed. Academic Press, 2000.

Wackerly, D. D., W. Mendenhall, and R. L. Scheaffer. *Mathematical Statistics with Applications,* 6th ed. Duxbury Press, 2002.

Sampling

Cochran, W. G. *Sampling Techniques,* 3rd ed. Wiley, 1977.

Deming, W. E. *Some Theory of Sampling.* Dover, 1984.

Hansen, M. H., W. N. Hurwitz, W. G. Madow, and M. N. Hanson. *Sample Survey Methods and Theory.* Wiley, 1993.

Kish, L. *Survey Sampling.* Wiley, 1995.

Levy, P. S., and S. Lemeshow. *Sampling of Populations: Methods and Applications,* 3rd ed. Wiley, 1999.

Scheaffer, R. L., W. Mendenhall, and L. Ott. *Elementary Survey Sampling,* 5th ed. Duxbury Press, 1996.

Experimental Design

Cochran, W. G., and G. M. Cox. *Experimental Designs,* 2nd ed. Wiley, 1992.

Hicks, C. R., and K. V. Turner. *Fundamental Concepts in the Design of Experiments,* 5th ed. Oxford University Press, 1999.

Montgomery, D. C. *Design and Analysis of Experiments,* 5th ed. Wiley, 2000.

Winer, B. J., K. M. Michels, and D. R. Brown. *Statistical Principles in Experimental Design,* 3rd ed. McGraw-Hill, 1991.

Wu, C. F. Jeff, and M. Hamada. *Experiments: Planning, Analysis, and Parameter Optimization.* Wiley, 2000.

Regression Analysis

Belsley, D. A. *Conditioning Diagnostics: Collinearity and Weak Data in Regression.* Wiley, 1991.

Chatterjee, S., and B. Price. *Regression Analysis by Example,* 3rd ed. Wiley, 1999.

Draper, N. R., and H. Smith. *Applied Regression Analysis,* 3rd ed. Wiley, 1998.

Graybill, F. A., and H. Iyer. *Regression Analysis: Concepts and Applications.* Duxbury Press, 1994.

Hosmer, D. W., and S. Lemeshow. *Applied Logistic Regression,* 2nd ed. Wiley, 2000.

Kleinbaum, D. G., L. L. Kupper, and K. E. Muller. *Applied Regression Analysis and Other Multivariate Methods,* 3rd ed. Duxbury Press, 1997.

Kutner, M. H., C. J. Nachtschiem, W. Wasserman, and J. Neter. *Applied Linear Statistical Models,* 4th ed. Irwin, 1996.

Mendenhall, M., and T. Sincich. *A Second Course in Statistics: Regression Analysis,* 5th ed. Prentice Hall, 1996.

Myers, R. H. *Classical and Modern Regression with Applications,* 2nd ed. PWS, 1990.

Nonparametric Methods

Conover, W. J. *Practical Nonparametric Statistics,* 3rd ed. Wiley, 1998.

Gibbons, J. D., and S. Chakraborti. *Nonparametric Statistical Inference,* 3rd ed. Marcel Dekker, 1992.

Siegel, S., and N. J. Castellan. *Nonparametric Statistics for the Behavioral Sciences,* 2nd ed. McGraw-Hill, 1990.

Sprent, P. *Applied Non-Parametric Statistical Methods.* CRC, 1993.

Quality Control

Deming, W. E. *Quality, Productivity, and Competitive Position.* MIT, 1982.

Evans, J. R., and W. M. Lindsay. *The Management and Control of Quality,* 6th ed. South-Western, 2005.

Gryna, F. M., and I. M. Juran. *Quality Planning and Analysis: From Product Development Through Use,* 3rd ed. McGraw-Hill, 1993.

Ishikawa, K. *Introduction to Quality Control.* Kluwer Academic, 1991.

Montgomery, D. C. *Introduction to Statistical Quality Control,* 4th ed. Wiley, 2000.

Decision Analysis

Chernoff, H., and L. E. Moses. *Elementary Decision Theory.* Dover, 1987.

Clemen, R. T., and T. Reilly. *Making Hard Decisions with Decision Tools.* Duxbury Press, 2001.

Goodwin, P., and G. Wright. *Decision Analysis for Management Judgment,* 2nd ed. Wiley, 1999.

Pratt, J. W., H. Raiffa, and R. Schlaifer. *Introduction to Statistical Decision Theory.* MIT Press, 1995.

Raiffa, H. *Decision Analysis.* McGraw-Hill, 1997.

Appendix B: Tables

TABLE 1 CUMULATIVE PROBABILITIES FOR THE STANDARD NORMAL DISTRIBUTION

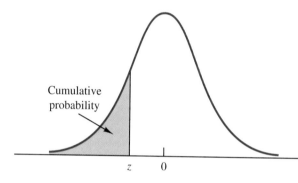

Entries in the table give the area under the curve to the left of the z value. For example, for $z = -.85$, the cumulative probability is .1977.

z	.00	.01	.02	.03	.04	.05	.06	.07	.08	.09
−3.0	.0013	.0013	.0013	.0012	.0012	.0011	.0011	.0011	.0010	.0010
−2.9	.0019	.0018	.0018	.0017	.0016	.0016	.0015	.0015	.0014	.0014
−2.8	.0026	.0025	.0024	.0023	.0023	.0022	.0021	.0021	.0020	.0019
−2.7	.0035	.0034	.0033	.0032	.0031	.0030	.0029	.0028	.0027	.0026
−2.6	.0047	.0045	.0044	.0043	.0041	.0040	.0039	.0038	.0037	.0036
−2.5	.0062	.0060	.0059	.0057	.0055	.0054	.0052	.0051	.0049	.0048
−2.4	.0082	.0080	.0078	.0075	.0073	.0071	.0069	.0068	.0066	.0064
−2.3	.0107	.0104	.0102	.0099	.0096	.0094	.0091	.0089	.0087	.0084
−2.2	.0139	.0136	.0132	.0129	.0125	.0122	.0119	.0116	.0113	.0110
−2.1	.0179	.0174	.0170	.0166	.0162	.0158	.0154	.0150	.0146	.0143
−2.0	.0228	.0222	.0217	.0212	.0207	.0202	.0197	.0192	.0188	.0183
−1.9	.0287	.0281	.0274	.0268	.0262	.0256	.0250	.0244	.0239	.0233
−1.8	.0359	.0351	.0344	.0336	.0329	.0322	.0314	.0307	.0301	.0294
−1.7	.0446	.0436	.0427	.0418	.0409	.0401	.0392	.0384	.0375	.0367
−1.6	.0548	.0537	.0526	.0516	.0505	.0495	.0485	.0475	.0465	.0455
−1.5	.0668	.0655	.0643	.0630	.0618	.0606	.0594	.0582	.0571	.0559
−1.4	.0808	.0793	.0778	.0764	.0749	.0735	.0721	.0708	.0694	.0681
−1.3	.0968	.0951	.0934	.0918	.0901	.0885	.0869	.0853	.0838	.0823
−1.2	.1151	.1131	.1112	.1093	.1075	.1056	.1038	.1020	.1003	.0985
−1.1	.1357	.1335	.1314	.1292	.1271	.1251	.1230	.1210	.1190	.1170
−1.0	.1587	.1562	.1539	.1515	.1492	.1469	.1446	.1423	.1401	.1379
−.9	.1841	.1814	.1788	.1762	.1736	.1711	.1685	.1660	.1635	.1611
−.8	.2119	.2090	.2061	.2033	.2005	.1977	.1949	.1922	.1894	.1867
−.7	.2420	.2389	.2358	.2327	.2296	.2266	.2236	.2206	.2177	.2148
−.6	.2743	.2709	.2676	.2643	.2611	.2578	.2546	.2514	.2483	.2451
−.5	.3085	.3050	.3015	.2981	.2946	.2912	.2877	.2843	.2810	.2776
−.4	.3446	.3409	.3372	.3336	.3300	.3264	.3228	.3192	.3156	.3121
−.3	.3821	.3783	.3745	.3707	.3669	.3632	.3594	.3557	.3520	.3483
−.2	.4207	.4168	.4129	.4090	.4052	.4013	.3974	.3936	.3897	.3859
−.1	.4602	.4562	.4522	.4483	.4443	.4404	.4364	.4325	.4286	.4247
−.0	.5000	.4960	.4920	.4880	.4840	.4801	.4761	.4721	.4681	.4641

TABLE 1   CUMULATIVE PROBABILITIES FOR THE STANDARD NORMAL DISTRIBUTION (*Continued*)

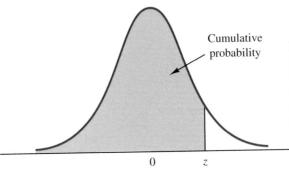

Cumulative probability

Entries in the table give the area under the curve to the left of the z value. For example, for $z = 1.25$, the cumulative probability is .8944.

z	.00	.01	.02	.03	.04	.05	.06	.07	.08	.09
.0	.5000	.5040	.5080	.5120	.5160	.5199	.5239	.5279	.5319	.5359
.1	.5398	.5438	.5478	.5517	.5557	.5596	.5636	.5675	.5714	.5753
.2	.5793	.5832	.5871	.5910	.5948	.5987	.6026	.6064	.6103	.6141
.3	.6179	.6217	.6255	.6293	.6331	.6368	.6406	.6443	.6480	.6517
.4	.6554	.6591	.6628	.6664	.6700	.6736	.6772	.6808	.6844	.6879
.5	.6915	.6950	.6985	.7019	.7054	.7088	.7123	.7157	.7190	.7224
.6	.7257	.7291	.7324	.7357	.7389	.7422	.7454	.7486	.7517	.7549
.7	.7580	.7611	.7642	.7673	.7704	.7734	.7764	.7794	.7823	.7852
.8	.7881	.7910	.7939	.7967	.7995	.8023	.8051	.8078	.8106	.8133
.9	.8159	.8186	.8212	.8238	.8264	.8289	.8315	.8340	.8365	.8389
1.0	.8413	.8438	.8461	.8485	.8508	.8531	.8554	.8577	.8599	.8621
1.1	.8643	.8665	.8686	.8708	.8729	.8749	.8770	.8790	.8810	.8830
1.2	.8849	.8869	.8888	.8907	.8925	.8944	.8962	.8980	.8997	.9015
1.3	.9032	.9049	.9066	.9082	.9099	.9115	.9131	.9147	.9162	.9177
1.4	.9192	.9207	.9222	.9236	.9251	.9265	.9279	.9292	.9306	.9319
1.5	.9332	.9345	.9357	.9370	.9382	.9394	.9406	.9418	.9429	.9441
1.6	.9452	.9463	.9474	.9484	.9495	.9505	.9515	.9525	.9535	.9545
1.7	.9554	.9564	.9573	.9582	.9591	.9599	.9608	.9616	.9625	.9633
1.8	.9641	.9649	.9656	.9664	.9671	.9678	.9686	.9693	.9699	.9706
1.9	.9713	.9719	.9726	.9732	.9738	.9744	.9750	.9756	.9761	.9767
2.0	.9772	.9778	.9783	.9788	.9793	.9798	.9803	.9808	.9812	.9817
2.1	.9821	.9826	.9830	.9834	.9838	.9842	.9846	.9850	.9854	.9857
2.2	.9861	.9864	.9868	.9871	.9875	.9878	.9881	.9884	.9887	.9890
2.3	.9893	.9896	.9898	.9901	.9904	.9906	.9909	.9911	.9913	.9913
2.4	.9918	.9920	.9922	.9925	.9927	.9929	.9931	.9932	.9934	.9936
2.5	.9938	.9940	.9941	.9943	.9945	.9946	.9948	.9949	.9951	.9952
2.6	.9953	.9955	.9956	.9957	.9959	.9960	.9961	.9962	.9963	.9964
2.7	.9965	.9966	.9967	.9968	.9969	.9970	.9971	.9972	.9973	.9974
2.8	.9974	.9975	.9976	.9977	.9977	.9978	.9979	.9979	.9980	.9981
2.9	.9981	.9982	.9982	.9983	.9984	.9984	.9985	.9985	.9986	.9986
3.0	.9986	.9987	.9987	.9988	.9988	.9989	.9989	.9989	.9990	.9990

TABLE 2   *t* DISTRIBUTION

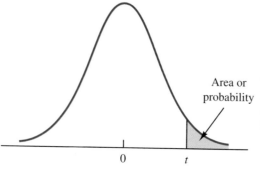

Entries in the table give the *t* values for an area or probability in the upper tail of the *t* distribution. For example, with 10 degrees of freedom and a .05 area in the upper tail, $t_{.05} = 1.812$.

Area or probability

0   *t*

Degrees of Freedom	Area in Upper Tail					
	.20	**.10**	**.05**	**.025**	**.01**	**.005**
1	1.376	3.078	6.314	12.706	31.821	63.656
2	1.061	1.886	2.920	4.303	6.965	9.925
3	.978	1.638	2.353	3.182	4.541	5.841
4	.941	1.533	2.132	2.776	3.747	4.604
5	.920	1.476	2.015	2.571	3.365	4.032
6	.906	1.440	1.943	2.447	3.143	3.707
7	.896	1.415	1.895	2.365	2.998	3.499
8	.889	1.397	1.860	2.306	2.896	3.355
9	.883	1.383	1.833	2.262	2.821	3.250
10	.879	1.372	1.812	2.228	2.764	3.169
11	.876	1.363	1.796	2.201	2.718	3.106
12	.873	1.356	1.782	2.179	2.681	3.055
13	.870	1.350	1.771	2.160	2.650	3.012
14	.868	1.345	1.761	2.145	2.624	2.977
15	.866	1.341	1.753	2.131	2.602	2.947
16	.865	1.337	1.746	2.120	2.583	2.921
17	.863	1.333	1.740	2.110	2.567	2.898
18	.862	1.330	1.734	2.101	2.552	2.878
19	.861	1.328	1.729	2.093	2.539	2.861
20	.860	1.325	1.725	2.086	2.528	2.845
21	.859	1.323	1.721	2.080	2.518	2.831
22	.858	1.321	1.717	2.074	2.508	2.819
23	.858	1.319	1.714	2.069	2.500	2.807
24	.857	1.318	1.711	2.064	2.492	2.797
25	.856	1.316	1.708	2.060	2.485	2.787
26	.856	1.315	1.706	2.056	2.479	2.779
27	.855	1.314	1.703	2.052	2.473	2.771
28	.855	1.313	1.701	2.048	2.467	2.763
29	.854	1.311	1.699	2.045	2.462	2.756
30	.854	1.310	1.697	2.042	2.457	2.750
31	.853	1.309	1.696	2.040	2.453	2.744
32	.853	1.309	1.694	2.037	2.449	2.738
33	.853	1.308	1.692	2.035	2.445	2.733
34	.852	1.307	1.691	2.032	2.441	2.728

TABLE 2   *t* DISTRIBUTION (*Continued*)

Degrees of Freedom	Area in Upper Tail					
	.20	.10	.05	.025	.01	.005
35	.852	1.306	1.690	2.030	2.438	2.724
36	.852	1.306	1.688	2.028	2.434	2.719
37	.851	1.305	1.687	2.026	2.431	2.715
38	.851	1.304	1.686	2.024	2.429	2.712
39	.851	1.304	1.685	2.023	2.426	2.708
40	.851	1.303	1.684	2.021	2.423	2.704
41	.850	1.303	1.683	2.020	2.421	2.701
42	.850	1.302	1.682	2.018	2.418	2.698
43	.850	1.302	1.681	2.017	2.416	2.695
44	.850	1.301	1.680	2.015	2.414	2.692
45	.850	1.301	1.679	2.014	2.412	2.690
46	.850	1.300	1.679	2.013	2.410	2.687
47	.849	1.300	1.678	2.012	2.408	2.685
48	.849	1.299	1.677	2.011	2.407	2.682
49	.849	1.299	1.677	2.010	2.405	2.680
50	.849	1.299	1.676	2.009	2.403	2.678
51	.849	1.298	1.675	2.008	2.402	2.676
52	.849	1.298	1.675	2.007	2.400	2.674
53	.848	1.298	1.674	2.006	2.399	2.672
54	.848	1.297	1.674	2.005	2.397	2.670
55	.848	1.297	1.673	2.004	2.396	2.668
56	.848	1.297	1.673	2.003	2.395	2.667
57	.848	1.297	1.672	2.002	2.394	2.665
58	.848	1.296	1.672	2.002	2.392	2.663
59	.848	1.296	1.671	2.001	2.391	2.662
60	.848	1.296	1.671	2.000	2.390	2.660
61	.848	1.296	1.670	2.000	2.389	2.659
62	.847	1.295	1.670	1.999	2.388	2.657
63	.847	1.295	1.669	1.998	2.387	2.656
64	.847	1.295	1.669	1.998	2.386	2.655
65	.847	1.295	1.669	1.997	2.385	2.654
66	.847	1.295	1.668	1.997	2.384	2.652
67	.847	1.294	1.668	1.996	2.383	2.651
68	.847	1.294	1.668	1.995	2.382	2.650
69	.847	1.294	1.667	1.995	2.382	2.649
70	.847	1.294	1.667	1.994	2.381	2.648
71	.847	1.294	1.667	1.994	2.380	2.647
72	.847	1.293	1.666	1.993	2.379	2.646
73	.847	1.293	1.666	1.993	2.379	2.645
74	.847	1.293	1.666	1.993	2.378	2.644
75	.846	1.293	1.665	1.992	2.377	2.643
76	.846	1.293	1.665	1.992	2.376	2.642
77	.846	1.293	1.665	1.991	2.376	2.641
78	.846	1.292	1.665	1.991	2.375	2.640
79	.846	1.292	1.664	1.990	2.374	2.639

(*Continued*)

TABLE 2 *t* DISTRIBUTION (*Continued*)

Degrees of Freedom	Area in Upper Tail					
	.20	.10	.05	.025	.01	.005
80	.846	1.292	1.664	1.990	2.374	2.639
81	.846	1.292	1.664	1.990	2.373	2.638
82	.846	1.292	1.664	1.989	2.373	2.637
83	.846	1.292	1.663	1.989	2.372	2.636
84	.846	1.292	1.663	1.989	2.372	2.636
85	.846	1.292	1.663	1.988	2.371	2.635
86	.846	1.291	1.663	1.988	2.370	2.634
87	.846	1.291	1.663	1.988	2.370	2.634
88	.846	1.291	1.662	1.987	2.369	2.633
89	.846	1.291	1.662	1.987	2.369	2.632
90	.846	1.291	1.662	1.987	2.368	2.632
91	.846	1.291	1.662	1.986	2.368	2.631
92	.846	1.291	1.662	1.986	2.368	2.630
93	.846	1.291	1.661	1.986	2.367	2.630
94	.845	1.291	1.661	1.986	2.367	2.629
95	.845	1.291	1.661	1.985	2.366	2.629
96	.845	1.290	1.661	1.985	2.366	2.628
97	.845	1.290	1.661	1.985	2.365	2.627
98	.845	1.290	1.661	1.984	2.365	2.627
99	.845	1.290	1.660	1.984	2.364	2.626
100	.845	1.290	1.660	1.984	2.364	2.626
∞	.842	1.282	1.645	1.960	2.326	2.576

TABLE 3   CHI-SQUARE DISTRIBUTION

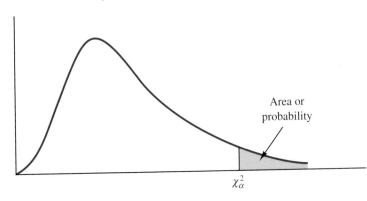

Entries in the table give χ_a^2 values, where α is the area or probability in the upper tail of the chi-square distribution. For example, with 10 degrees of freedom and a .01 area in the upper tail, $\chi_{.01}^2 = 23.209$.

Area or probability

χ_α^2

Degrees of Freedom	Area in Upper Tail									
	.995	.99	.975	.95	.90	.10	.05	.025	.01	.005
1	.000	.000	.001	.004	.016	2.706	3.841	5.024	6.635	7.879
2	.010	.020	.051	.103	.211	4.605	5.991	7.378	9.210	10.597
3	.072	.115	.216	.352	.584	6.251	7.815	9.348	11.345	12.838
4	.207	.297	.484	.711	1.064	7.779	9.488	11.143	13.277	14.860
5	.412	.554	.831	1.145	1.610	9.236	11.070	12.832	15.086	16.750
6	.676	.872	1.237	1.635	2.204	10.645	12.592	14.449	16.812	18.548
7	.989	1.239	1.690	2.167	2.833	12.017	14.067	16.013	18.475	20.278
8	1.344	1.647	2.180	2.733	3.490	13.362	15.507	17.535	20.090	21.955
9	1.735	2.088	2.700	3.325	4.168	14.684	16.919	19.023	21.666	23.589
10	2.156	2.558	3.247	3.940	4.865	15.987	18.307	20.483	23.209	25.188
11	2.603	3.053	3.816	4.575	5.578	17.275	19.675	21.920	24.725	26.757
12	3.074	3.571	4.404	5.226	6.304	18.549	21.026	23.337	26.217	28.300
13	3.565	4.107	5.009	5.892	7.041	19.812	22.362	24.736	27.688	29.819
14	4.075	4.660	5.629	6.571	7.790	21.064	23.685	26.119	29.141	31.319
15	4.601	5.229	6.262	7.261	8.547	22.307	24.996	27.488	30.578	32.801
16	5.142	5.812	6.908	7.962	9.312	23.542	26.296	28.845	32.000	34.267
17	5.697	6.408	7.564	8.672	10.085	24.769	27.587	30.191	33.409	35.718
18	6.265	7.015	8.231	9.390	10.865	25.989	28.869	31.526	34.805	37.156
19	6.844	7.633	8.907	10.117	11.651	27.204	30.144	32.852	36.191	38.582
20	7.434	8.260	9.591	10.851	12.443	28.412	31.410	34.170	37.566	39.997
21	8.034	8.897	10.283	11.591	13.240	29.615	32.671	35.479	38.932	41.401
22	8.643	9.542	10.982	12.338	14.041	30.813	33.924	36.781	40.289	42.796
23	9.260	10.196	11.689	13.091	14.848	32.007	35.172	38.076	41.638	44.181
24	9.886	10.856	12.401	13.848	15.659	33.196	36.415	39.364	42.980	45.558
25	10.520	11.524	13.120	14.611	16.473	34.382	37.652	40.646	44.314	46.928
26	11.160	12.198	13.844	15.379	17.292	35.563	38.885	41.923	45.642	48.290
27	11.808	12.878	14.573	16.151	18.114	36.741	40.113	43.195	46.963	49.645
28	12.461	13.565	15.308	16.928	18.939	37.916	41.337	44.461	48.278	50.994
29	13.121	14.256	16.047	17.708	19.768	39.087	42.557	45.722	49.588	52.335

(Continued)

TABLE 3   CHI-SQUARE DISTRIBUTION (*Continued*)

Degrees of Freedom	Area in Upper Tail									
	.995	.99	.975	.95	.90	.10	.05	.025	.01	.005
30	13.787	14.953	16.791	18.493	20.599	40.256	43.773	46.979	50.892	53.672
35	17.192	18.509	20.569	22.465	24.797	46.059	49.802	53.203	57.342	60.275
40	20.707	22.164	24.433	26.509	29.051	51.805	55.758	59.342	63.691	66.766
45	24.311	25.901	28.366	30.612	33.350	57.505	61.656	65.410	69.957	73.166
50	27.991	29.707	32.357	34.764	37.689	63.167	67.505	71.420	76.154	79.490
55	31.735	33.571	36.398	38.958	42.060	68.796	73.311	77.380	82.292	85.749
60	35.534	37.485	40.482	43.188	46.459	74.397	79.082	83.298	88.379	91.952
65	39.383	41.444	44.603	47.450	50.883	79.973	84.821	89.177	94.422	98.105
70	43.275	45.442	48.758	51.739	55.329	85.527	90.531	95.023	100.425	104.215
75	47.206	49.475	52.942	56.054	59.795	91.061	96.217	100.839	106.393	110.285
80	51.172	53.540	57.153	60.391	64.278	96.578	101.879	106.629	112.329	116.321
85	55.170	57.634	61.389	64.749	68.777	102.079	107.522	112.393	118.236	122.324
90	59.196	61.754	65.647	69.126	73.291	107.565	113.145	118.136	124.116	128.299
95	63.250	65.898	69.925	73.520	77.818	113.038	118.752	123.858	129.973	134.247
100	67.328	70.065	74.222	77.929	82.358	118.498	124.342	129.561	135.807	140.170

TABLE 4 F DISTRIBUTION

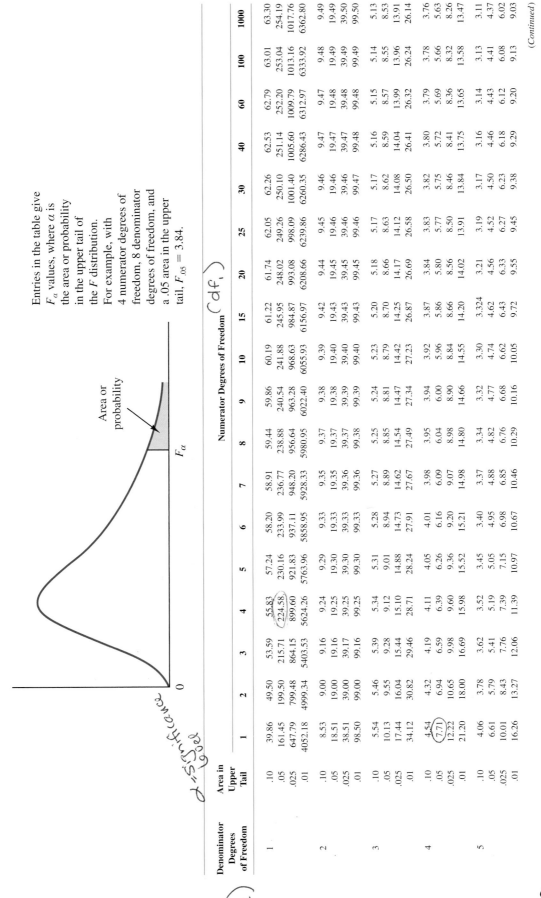

Entries in the table give F_α values, where α is the area or probability in the upper tail of the F distribution. For example, with 4 numerator degrees of freedom, 8 denominator degrees of freedom, and a .05 area in the upper tail, $F_{.05} = 3.84$.

Area or probability

F_α

$\alpha = $ significance level

Denominator Degrees of Freedom (df_2)	Area in Upper Tail	\multicolumn{18}{c}{Numerator Degrees of Freedom (df_1)}																	
		1	2	3	4	5	6	7	8	9	10	15	20	25	30	40	60	100	1000
1	.10	39.86	49.50	53.59	55.83	57.24	58.20	58.91	59.44	59.86	60.19	61.22	61.74	62.05	62.26	62.53	62.79	63.01	63.30
	.05	161.45	199.50	215.71	224.58	230.16	233.99	236.77	238.88	240.54	241.88	245.95	248.02	249.26	250.10	251.14	252.20	253.04	254.19
	.025	647.79	799.48	864.15	899.60	921.83	937.11	948.20	956.64	963.28	968.63	984.87	993.08	998.09	1001.40	1005.60	1009.79	1013.16	1017.76
	.01	4052.18	4999.34	5403.53	5624.26	5763.96	5858.95	5928.33	5980.95	6022.40	6055.93	6156.97	6208.66	6239.86	6260.35	6286.43	6312.97	6333.92	6362.80
2	.10	8.53	9.00	9.16	9.24	9.29	9.33	9.35	9.37	9.38	9.39	9.42	9.44	9.45	9.46	9.47	9.47	9.48	9.49
	.05	18.51	19.00	19.16	19.25	19.30	19.33	19.35	19.37	19.38	19.40	19.43	19.45	19.46	19.46	19.47	19.48	19.49	19.49
	.025	38.51	39.00	39.17	39.25	39.30	39.33	39.36	39.37	39.39	39.40	39.43	39.45	39.46	39.46	39.47	39.48	39.49	39.50
	.01	98.50	99.00	99.16	99.25	99.30	99.33	99.36	99.38	99.39	99.40	99.43	99.45	99.46	99.47	99.48	99.48	99.49	99.50
3	.10	5.54	5.46	5.39	5.34	5.31	5.28	5.27	5.25	5.24	5.23	5.20	5.18	5.17	5.17	5.16	5.15	5.14	5.13
	.05	10.13	9.55	9.28	9.12	9.01	8.94	8.89	8.85	8.81	8.79	8.70	8.66	8.63	8.62	8.59	8.57	8.55	8.53
	.025	17.44	16.04	15.44	15.10	14.88	14.73	14.62	14.54	14.47	14.42	14.25	14.17	14.12	14.08	14.04	13.99	13.96	13.91
	.01	34.12	30.82	29.46	28.71	28.24	27.91	27.67	27.49	27.34	27.23	26.87	26.69	26.58	26.50	26.41	26.32	26.24	26.14
4	.10	4.54	4.32	4.19	4.11	4.05	4.01	3.98	3.95	3.94	3.92	3.87	3.84	3.83	3.82	3.80	3.79	3.78	3.76
	.05	7.71	6.94	6.59	6.39	6.26	6.16	6.09	6.04	6.00	5.96	5.86	5.80	5.77	5.75	5.72	5.69	5.66	5.63
	.025	12.22	10.65	9.98	9.60	9.36	9.20	9.07	8.98	8.90	8.84	8.66	8.56	8.50	8.46	8.41	8.36	8.32	8.26
	.01	21.20	18.00	16.69	15.98	15.52	15.21	14.98	14.80	14.66	14.55	14.20	14.02	13.91	13.84	13.75	13.65	13.58	13.47
5	.10	4.06	3.78	3.62	3.52	3.45	3.40	3.37	3.34	3.32	3.30	3.324	3.21	3.19	3.17	3.16	3.14	3.13	3.11
	.05	6.61	5.79	5.41	5.19	5.05	4.95	4.88	4.82	4.77	4.74	4.62	4.56	4.52	4.50	4.46	4.43	4.41	4.37
	.025	10.01	8.43	7.76	7.39	7.15	6.98	6.85	6.76	6.68	6.62	6.43	6.33	6.27	6.23	6.18	6.12	6.08	6.02
	.01	16.26	13.27	12.06	11.39	10.97	10.67	10.46	10.29	10.16	10.05	9.72	9.55	9.45	9.38	9.29	9.20	9.13	9.03

(Continued)

TABLE 4 _F_ DISTRIBUTION (_Continued_)

Denominator Degrees of Freedom	Area in Upper Tail	Numerator Degrees of Freedom																	
		1	2	3	4	5	6	7	8	9	10	15	20	25	30	40	60	100	1000
6	.10	3.78	3.46	3.29	3.18	3.11	3.05	3.01	2.98	2.96	2.94	2.87	2.84	2.81	2.80	2.78	2.76	2.75	2.72
	.05	5.99	5.14	4.76	4.53	4.39	4.28	4.21	4.15	4.10	4.06	3.94	3.87	3.83	3.81	3.77	3.74	3.71	3.67
	.025	8.81	7.26	6.60	6.23	5.99	5.82	5.70	5.60	5.52	5.46	5.27	5.17	5.11	5.07	5.01	4.96	4.92	4.86
	.01	13.75	10.92	9.78	9.15	8.75	8.47	8.26	8.10	7.98	7.87	7.56	7.40	7.30	7.23	7.14	7.06	6.99	6.89
7	.10	3.59	3.26	3.07	2.96	2.88	2.83	2.78	2.75	2.72	2.70	2.63	2.59	2.57	2.56	2.54	2.51	2.50	2.47
	.05	5.59	4.74	4.35	4.12	3.97	3.87	3.79	3.73	3.68	3.64	3.51	3.44	3.40	3.38	3.34	3.30	3.27	3.23
	.025	8.07	6.54	5.89	5.52	5.29	5.12	4.99	4.90	4.82	4.76	4.57	4.47	4.40	4.36	4.31	4.25	4.21	4.15
	.01	12.25	9.55	8.45	7.85	7.46	7.19	6.99	6.84	6.72	6.62	6.31	6.16	6.06	5.99	5.91	5.82	5.75	5.66
8	.10	3.46	3.11	2.92	2.81	2.73	2.67	2.62	2.59	2.56	2.54	2.46	2.42	2.40	2.38	2.36	2.34	2.32	2.30
	.05	5.32	4.46	4.07	3.84	3.69	3.58	3.50	3.44	3.39	3.35	3.22	3.15	3.11	3.08	3.04	3.01	2.97	2.93
	.025	7.57	6.06	5.42	5.05	4.82	4.65	4.53	4.43	4.36	4.30	4.10	4.00	3.94	3.89	3.84	3.78	3.74	3.68
	.01	11.26	8.65	7.59	7.01	6.63	6.37	6.18	6.03	5.91	5.81	5.52	5.36	5.26	5.20	5.12	5.03	4.96	4.87
9	.10	3.36	3.01	2.81	2.69	2.61	2.55	2.51	2.47	2.44	2.42	2.34	2.30	2.27	2.25	2.23	2.21	2.19	2.16
	.05	5.12	4.26	3.86	3.63	3.48	3.37	3.29	3.23	3.18	3.14	3.01	2.94	2.89	2.86	2.83	2.79	2.76	2.71
	.025	7.21	5.71	5.08	4.72	4.48	4.32	4.20	4.10	4.03	3.96	3.77	3.67	3.60	3.56	3.51	3.45	3.40	3.34
	.01	10.56	8.02	6.99	6.42	6.06	5.80	5.61	5.47	5.35	5.26	4.96	4.81	4.71	4.65	4.57	4.48	4.41	4.32
10	.10	3.29	2.92	2.73	2.61	2.52	2.46	2.41	2.38	2.35	2.32	2.24	2.20	2.17	2.16	2.13	2.11	2.09	2.06
	.05	4.96	4.10	3.71	3.48	3.33	3.22	3.14	3.07	3.02	2.98	2.85	2.77	2.73	2.70	2.66	2.62	2.59	2.54
	.025	6.94	5.46	4.83	4.47	4.24	4.07	3.95	3.85	3.78	3.72	3.52	3.42	3.35	3.31	3.26	3.20	3.15	3.09
	.01	10.04	7.56	6.55	5.99	5.64	5.39	5.20	5.06	4.94	4.85	4.56	4.41	4.31	4.25	4.17	4.08	4.01	3.92
11	.10	3.23	2.86	2.66	2.54	2.45	2.39	2.34	2.30	2.27	2.25	2.17	2.12	2.10	2.08	2.05	2.03	2.01	1.98
	.05	4.84	3.98	3.59	3.36	3.20	3.09	3.01	2.95	2.90	2.85	2.72	2.65	2.60	2.57	2.53	2.49	2.46	2.41
	.025	6.72	5.26	4.63	4.28	4.04	3.88	3.76	3.66	3.59	3.53	3.33	3.23	3.16	3.12	3.06	3.00	2.96	2.89
	.01	9.65	7.21	6.22	5.67	5.32	5.07	4.89	4.74	4.63	4.54	4.25	4.10	4.01	3.94	3.86	3.78	3.71	3.61
12	.10	3.18	2.81	2.61	2.48	2.39	2.33	2.28	2.24	2.21	2.19	2.10	2.06	2.03	2.01	1.99	1.96	1.94	1.91
	.05	4.75	3.89	3.49	3.26	3.11	3.00	2.91	2.85	2.80	2.75	2.62	2.54	2.50	2.47	2.43	2.38	2.35	2.30
	.025	6.55	5.10	4.47	4.12	3.89	3.73	3.61	3.51	3.44	3.37	3.18	3.07	3.01	2.96	2.91	2.85	2.80	2.73
	.01	9.33	6.93	5.95	5.41	5.06	4.82	4.64	4.50	4.39	4.30	4.01	3.86	3.76	3.70	3.62	3.54	3.47	3.37
13	.10	3.14	2.76	2.56	2.43	2.35	2.28	2.23	2.20	2.16	2.14	2.05	2.01	1.98	1.96	1.93	1.90	1.88	1.85
	.05	4.67	3.81	3.41	3.18	3.03	2.92	2.83	2.77	2.71	2.67	2.53	2.46	2.41	2.38	2.34	2.30	2.26	2.21
	.025	6.41	4.97	4.35	4.00	3.77	3.60	3.48	3.39	3.31	3.25	3.05	2.95	2.88	2.84	2.78	2.72	2.67	2.60
	.01	9.07	6.70	5.74	5.21	4.86	4.62	4.44	4.30	4.19	4.10	3.82	3.66	3.57	3.51	3.43	3.34	3.27	3.18
14	.10	3.10	2.73	2.52	2.39	2.31	2.24	2.19	2.15	2.12	2.10	2.01	1.96	1.93	1.91	1.89	1.86	1.83	1.80
	.05	4.60	3.74	3.34	3.11	2.96	2.85	2.76	2.70	2.65	2.60	2.46	2.39	2.34	2.31	2.27	2.22	2.19	2.14
	.025	6.30	4.86	4.24	3.89	3.66	3.50	3.38	3.29	3.21	3.15	2.95	2.84	2.78	2.73	2.67	2.61	2.56	2.50
	.01	8.86	6.51	5.56	5.04	4.69	4.46	4.28	4.14	4.03	3.94	3.66	3.51	3.41	3.35	3.27	3.18	3.11	3.02
15	.10	3.07	2.70	2.49	2.36	2.27	2.21	2.16	2.12	2.09	2.06	1.97	1.92	1.89	1.87	1.85	1.82	1.79	1.76
	.05	4.54	3.68	3.29	3.06	2.90	2.79	2.71	2.64	2.59	2.54	2.40	2.33	2.28	2.25	2.20	2.16	2.12	2.07
	.025	6.20	4.77	4.15	3.80	3.58	3.41	3.29	3.20	3.12	3.06	2.86	2.76	2.69	2.64	2.59	2.52	2.47	2.40
	.01	8.68	6.36	5.42	4.89	4.56	4.32	4.14	4.00	3.89	3.80	3.52	3.37	3.28	3.21	3.13	3.05	2.98	2.88

TABLE 4 *F* DISTRIBUTION (*Continued*)

Denominator Degrees of Freedom	Area in Upper Tail	Numerator Degrees of Freedom																	
		1	2	3	4	5	6	7	8	9	10	15	20	25	30	40	60	100	1000
16	.10	3.05	2.67	2.46	2.33	2.24	2.18	2.13	2.09	2.06	2.03	1.94	1.89	1.86	1.84	1.81	1.78	1.76	1.72
	.05	4.49	3.63	3.24	3.01	2.85	2.74	2.66	2.59	2.54	2.49	2.35	2.28	2.23	2.19	2.15	2.11	2.07	2.02
	.025	6.12	4.69	4.08	3.73	3.50	3.34	3.22	3.12	3.05	2.99	2.79	2.68	2.61	2.57	2.51	2.45	2.40	2.32
	.01	8.53	6.23	5.29	4.77	4.44	4.20	4.03	3.89	3.78	3.69	3.41	3.26	3.16	3.10	3.02	2.93	2.86	2.76
17	.10	3.03	2.64	2.44	2.31	2.22	2.15	2.10	2.06	2.03	2.00	1.91	1.86	1.83	1.81	1.78	1.75	1.73	1.69
	.05	4.45	3.59	3.20	2.96	2.81	2.70	2.61	2.55	2.49	2.45	2.31	2.23	2.18	2.15	2.10	2.06	2.02	1.97
	.025	6.04	4.62	4.01	3.66	3.44	3.28	3.16	3.06	2.98	2.92	2.72	2.62	2.55	2.50	2.44	2.38	2.33	2.26
	.01	8.40	6.11	5.19	4.67	4.34	4.10	3.93	3.79	3.68	3.59	3.31	3.16	3.07	3.00	2.92	2.83	2.76	2.66
18	.10	3.01	2.62	2.42	2.29	2.20	2.13	2.08	2.04	2.00	1.98	1.89	1.84	1.80	1.78	1.75	1.72	1.70	1.66
	.05	4.41	3.55	3.16	2.93	2.77	2.66	2.58	2.51	2.46	2.41	2.27	2.19	2.14	2.11	2.06	2.02	1.98	1.92
	.025	5.98	4.56	3.95	3.61	3.38	3.22	3.10	3.01	2.93	2.87	2.67	2.56	2.49	2.44	2.38	2.32	2.27	2.20
	.01	8.29	6.01	5.09	4.58	4.25	4.01	3.84	3.71	3.60	3.51	3.23	3.08	2.98	2.92	2.84	2.75	2.68	2.58
19	.10	2.99	2.61	2.40	2.27	2.18	2.11	2.06	2.02	1.98	1.96	1.86	1.81	1.78	1.76	1.73	1.70	1.67	1.64
	.05	4.38	3.52	3.13	2.90	2.74	2.63	2.54	2.48	2.42	2.38	2.23	2.16	2.11	2.07	2.03	1.98	1.94	1.88
	.025	5.92	4.51	3.90	3.56	3.33	3.17	3.05	2.96	2.88	2.82	2.62	2.51	2.44	2.39	2.33	2.27	2.22	2.14
	.01	8.18	5.93	5.01	4.50	4.17	3.94	3.77	3.63	3.52	3.43	3.15	3.00	2.91	2.84	2.76	2.67	2.60	2.50
20	.10	2.97	2.59	2.38	2.25	2.16	2.09	2.04	2.00	1.96	1.94	1.84	1.79	1.76	1.74	1.71	1.68	1.65	1.61
	.05	4.35	3.49	3.10	2.87	2.71	2.60	2.51	2.45	2.39	2.35	2.20	2.12	2.07	2.04	1.99	1.95	1.91	1.85
	.025	5.87	4.46	3.86	3.51	3.29	3.13	3.01	2.91	2.84	2.77	2.57	2.46	2.40	2.35	2.29	2.22	2.17	2.09
	.01	8.10	5.85	4.94	4.43	4.10	3.87	3.70	3.56	3.46	3.37	3.09	2.94	2.84	2.78	2.69	2.61	2.54	2.43
21	.10	2.96	2.57	2.36	2.23	2.14	2.08	2.02	1.98	1.95	1.92	1.83	1.78	1.74	1.72	1.69	1.66	1.63	1.59
	.05	4.32	3.47	3.07	2.84	2.68	2.57	2.49	2.42	2.37	2.32	2.18	2.10	2.05	2.01	1.96	1.92	1.88	1.82
	.025	5.83	4.42	3.82	3.48	3.25	3.09	2.97	2.87	2.80	2.73	2.53	2.42	2.36	2.31	2.25	2.18	2.13	2.05
	.01	8.02	5.78	4.87	4.37	4.04	3.81	3.64	3.51	3.40	3.31	3.03	2.88	2.79	2.72	2.64	2.55	2.48	2.37
22	.10	2.95	2.56	2.35	2.22	2.13	2.06	2.01	1.97	1.93	1.90	1.81	1.76	1.73	1.70	1.67	1.64	1.61	1.57
	.05	4.30	3.44	3.05	2.82	2.66	2.55	2.46	2.40	2.34	2.30	2.15	2.07	2.02	1.98	1.94	1.89	1.85	1.79
	.025	5.79	4.38	3.78	3.44	3.22	3.05	2.93	2.84	2.76	2.70	2.50	2.39	2.32	2.27	2.21	2.14	2.09	2.01
	.01	7.95	5.72	4.82	4.31	3.99	3.76	3.59	3.45	3.35	3.26	2.98	2.83	2.73	2.67	2.58	2.50	2.42	2.32
23	.10	2.94	2.55	2.34	2.21	2.11	2.05	1.99	1.95	1.92	1.89	1.80	1.74	1.71	1.69	1.66	1.62	1.59	1.55
	.05	4.28	3.42	3.03	2.80	2.64	2.53	2.44	2.37	2.32	2.27	2.13	2.05	2.00	1.96	1.91	1.86	1.82	1.76
	.025	5.75	4.35	3.75	3.41	3.18	3.02	2.90	2.81	2.73	2.67	2.47	2.36	2.29	2.24	2.18	2.11	2.06	1.98
	.01	7.88	5.66	4.76	4.26	3.94	3.71	3.54	3.41	3.30	3.21	2.93	2.78	2.69	2.62	2.54	2.45	2.37	2.27
24	.10	2.93	2.54	2.33	2.19	2.10	2.04	1.98	1.94	1.91	1.88	1.78	1.73	1.70	1.67	1.64	1.61	1.58	1.54
	.05	4.26	3.40	3.01	2.78	2.62	2.51	2.42	2.36	2.30	2.25	2.11	2.03	1.97	1.94	1.89	1.84	1.80	1.74
	.025	5.72	4.32	3.72	3.38	3.15	2.99	2.87	2.78	2.70	2.64	2.44	2.33	2.26	2.21	2.15	2.08	2.02	1.94
	.01	7.82	5.61	4.72	4.22	3.90	3.67	3.50	3.36	3.26	3.17	2.89	2.74	2.64	2.58	2.49	2.40	2.33	2.22

(*Continued*)

TABLE 4 *F* DISTRIBUTION (*Continued*)

		Numerator Degrees of Freedom																	
Denominator Degrees of Freedom	Area in Upper Tail	1	2	3	4	5	6	7	8	9	10	15	20	25	30	40	60	100	1000
25	.10	2.92	2.53	2.32	2.18	2.09	2.02	1.97	1.93	1.89	1.87	1.77	1.72	1.68	1.66	1.63	1.59	1.56	1.52
	.05	4.24	3.39	2.99	2.76	2.60	2.49	2.40	2.34	2.28	2.24	2.09	2.01	1.96	1.92	1.87	1.82	1.78	1.72
	.025	5.69	4.29	3.69	3.35	3.13	2.97	2.85	2.75	2.68	2.61	2.41	2.30	2.23	2.18	2.12	2.05	2.00	1.91
	.01	7.77	5.57	4.68	4.18	3.85	3.63	3.46	3.32	3.22	3.13	2.85	2.70	2.60	2.54	2.45	2.36	2.29	2.18
26	.10	2.91	2.52	2.31	2.17	2.08	2.01	1.96	1.92	1.88	1.86	1.76	1.71	1.67	1.65	1.61	1.58	1.55	1.51
	.05	4.23	3.37	2.98	2.74	2.59	2.47	2.39	2.32	2.27	2.22	2.07	1.99	1.94	1.90	1.85	1.80	1.76	1.70
	.025	5.66	4.27	3.67	3.33	3.10	2.94	2.82	2.73	2.65	2.59	2.39	2.28	2.21	2.16	2.09	2.03	1.97	1.89
	.01	7.72	5.53	4.64	4.14	3.82	3.59	3.42	3.29	3.18	3.09	2.81	2.66	2.57	2.50	2.42	2.33	2.25	2.14
27	.10	2.90	2.51	2.30	2.17	2.07	2.00	1.95	1.91	1.87	1.85	1.75	1.70	1.66	1.64	1.60	1.57	1.54	1.50
	.05	4.21	3.35	2.96	2.73	2.57	2.46	2.37	2.31	2.25	2.20	2.06	1.97	1.92	1.88	1.84	1.79	1.74	1.68
	.025	5.63	4.24	3.65	3.31	3.08	2.92	2.80	2.71	2.63	2.57	2.36	2.25	2.18	2.13	2.07	2.00	1.94	1.86
	.01	7.68	5.49	4.60	4.11	3.78	3.56	3.39	3.26	3.15	3.06	2.78	2.63	2.54	2.47	2.38	2.29	2.22	2.11
28	.10	2.89	2.50	2.29	2.16	2.06	2.00	1.94	1.90	1.87	1.84	1.74	1.69	1.65	1.63	1.59	1.56	1.53	1.48
	.05	4.20	3.34	2.95	2.71	2.56	2.45	2.36	2.29	2.24	2.19	2.04	1.96	1.91	1.87	1.82	1.77	1.73	1.66
	.025	5.61	4.22	3.63	3.29	3.06	2.90	2.78	2.69	2.61	2.55	2.34	2.23	2.16	2.11	2.05	1.98	1.92	1.84
	.01	7.64	5.45	4.57	4.07	3.75	3.53	3.36	3.23	3.12	3.03	2.75	2.60	2.51	2.44	2.35	2.26	2.19	2.08
29	.10	2.89	2.50	2.28	2.15	2.06	1.99	1.93	1.89	1.86	1.83	1.73	1.68	1.64	1.62	1.58	1.55	1.52	1.47
	.05	4.18	3.33	2.93	2.70	2.55	2.43	2.35	2.28	2.22	2.18	2.03	1.94	1.89	1.85	1.81	1.75	1.71	1.65
	.025	5.59	4.20	3.61	3.27	3.04	2.88	2.76	2.67	2.59	2.53	2.32	2.21	2.14	2.09	2.03	1.96	1.90	1.82
	.01	7.60	5.42	4.54	4.04	3.73	3.50	3.33	3.20	3.09	3.00	2.73	2.57	2.48	2.41	2.33	2.23	2.16	2.05
30	.10	2.88	2.49	2.28	2.14	2.05	1.98	1.93	1.88	1.85	1.82	1.72	1.67	1.63	1.61	1.57	1.54	1.51	1.46
	.05	4.17	3.32	2.92	2.69	2.53	2.42	2.33	2.27	2.21	2.16	2.01	1.93	1.88	1.84	1.79	1.74	1.70	1.63
	.025	5.57	4.18	3.59	3.25	3.03	2.87	2.75	2.65	2.57	2.51	2.31	2.20	2.12	2.07	2.01	1.94	1.88	1.80
	.01	7.56	5.39	4.51	4.02	3.70	3.47	3.30	3.17	3.07	2.98	2.70	2.55	2.45	2.39	2.30	2.21	2.13	2.02
40	.10	2.84	2.44	2.23	2.09	2.00	1.93	1.87	1.83	1.79	1.76	1.66	1.61	1.57	1.54	1.51	1.47	1.43	1.38
	.05	4.08	3.23	2.84	2.61	2.45	2.34	2.25	2.18	2.12	2.08	1.92	1.84	1.78	1.74	1.69	1.64	1.59	1.52
	.025	5.42	4.05	3.46	3.13	2.90	2.74	2.62	2.53	2.45	2.39	2.18	2.07	1.99	1.94	1.88	1.80	1.74	1.65
	.01	7.31	5.18	4.31	3.83	3.51	3.29	3.12	2.99	2.89	2.80	2.52	2.37	2.27	2.20	2.11	2.02	1.94	1.82
60	.10	2.79	2.39	2.18	2.04	1.95	1.87	1.82	1.77	1.74	1.71	1.60	1.54	1.50	1.48	1.44	1.40	1.36	1.30
	.05	4.00	3.15	2.76	2.53	2.37	2.25	2.17	2.10	2.04	1.99	1.84	1.75	1.69	1.65	1.59	1.53	1.48	1.40
	.025	5.29	3.93	3.34	3.01	2.79	2.63	2.51	2.41	2.33	2.27	2.06	1.94	1.87	1.82	1.74	1.67	1.60	1.49
	.01	7.08	4.98	4.13	3.65	3.34	3.12	2.95	2.82	2.72	2.63	2.35	2.20	2.10	2.03	1.94	1.84	1.75	1.62
100	.10	2.76	2.36	2.14	2.00	1.91	1.83	1.78	1.73	1.69	1.66	1.56	1.49	1.45	1.42	1.38	1.34	1.29	1.22
	.05	3.94	3.09	2.70	2.46	2.31	2.19	2.10	2.03	1.97	1.93	1.77	1.68	1.62	1.57	1.52	1.45	1.39	1.30
	.025	5.18	3.83	3.25	2.92	2.70	2.54	2.42	2.32	2.24	2.18	1.97	1.85	1.77	1.71	1.64	1.56	1.48	1.36
	.01	6.90	4.82	3.98	3.51	3.21	2.99	2.82	2.69	2.59	2.50	2.22	2.07	1.97	1.89	1.80	1.69	1.60	1.45
1000	.10	2.71	2.31	2.09	1.95	1.85	1.78	1.72	1.68	1.64	1.61	1.49	1.43	1.38	1.35	1.30	1.25	1.20	1.08
	.05	3.85	3.00	2.61	2.38	2.22	2.11	2.02	1.95	1.89	1.84	1.68	1.58	1.52	1.47	1.41	1.33	1.26	1.11
	.025	5.04	3.70	3.13	2.80	2.58	2.42	2.30	2.20	2.13	2.06	1.85	1.72	1.64	1.58	1.50	1.41	1.32	1.13
	.01	6.66	4.63	3.80	3.34	3.04	2.82	2.66	2.53	2.43	2.34	2.06	1.90	1.79	1.72	1.61	1.50	1.38	1.16

Summation

Definition

$$\sum_{i=1}^{n} x_i = x_1 + x_2 + \cdots + x_n \tag{C.1}$$

Example for $x_1 = 5$, $x_2 = 8$, $x_3 = 14$:

$$\sum_{i=1}^{3} x_i = x_1 + x_2 + x_3$$
$$= 5 + 8 + 14$$
$$= 27$$

Result 1

For a constant c:

$$\sum_{i=1}^{n} c = \underbrace{(c + c + \cdots + c)}_{n \text{ times}} = nc \tag{C.2}$$

Example for $c = 5$, $n = 10$:

$$\sum_{i=1}^{10} 5 = 10(5) = 50$$

Example for $c = \bar{x}$:

$$\sum_{i=1}^{n} \bar{x} = n\bar{x}$$

Result 2

$$\sum_{i=1}^{n} cx_i = cx_1 + cx_2 + \cdots + cx_n$$
$$= c(x_1 + x_2 + \cdots + x_n) = c\sum_{i=1}^{n} x_i \tag{C.3}$$

Example for $x_1 = 5$, $x_2 = 8$, $x_3 = 14$, $c = 2$:

$$\sum_{i=1}^{3} 2x_i = 2\sum_{i=1}^{3} x_i = 2(27) = 54$$

Result 3

$$\sum_{i=1}^{n} (ax_i + by_i) = a\sum_{i=1}^{n} x_i + b\sum_{i=1}^{n} y_i \tag{C.4}$$

Example for $x_1 = 5$, $x_2 = 8$, $x_3 = 14$, $a = 2$, $y_1 = 7$, $y_2 = 3$, $y_3 = 8$, $b = 4$:

$$\sum_{i=1}^{3} (2x_i + 4y_i) = 2 \sum_{i=1}^{3} x_i + 4 \sum_{i=1}^{3} y_i$$
$$= 2(27) + 4(18)$$
$$= 54 + 72$$
$$= 126$$

Double Summation

Consider the following data involving the variable x_{ij}, where i is the subscript denoting the row position and j is the subscript denoting the column position:

		Column		
		1	2	3
Row	1	$x_{11} = 10$	$x_{12} = 8$	$x_{13} = 6$
	2	$x_{21} = 7$	$x_{22} = 4$	$x_{23} = 12$

Definition

$$\sum_{i=1}^{n} \sum_{j=1}^{m} x_{ij} = (x_{11} + x_{12} + \cdots + x_{1m}) + (x_{21} + x_{22} + \cdots + x_{2m})$$
$$+ (x_{31} + x_{32} + \cdots + x_{3m}) + \cdots + (x_{n1} + x_{n2} + \cdots + x_{nm}) \qquad \textbf{(C.5)}$$

Example:

$$\sum_{i=1}^{2} \sum_{j=1}^{3} x_{ij} = x_{11} + x_{12} + x_{13} + x_{21} + x_{22} + x_{23}$$
$$= 10 + 8 + 6 + 7 + 4 + 12$$
$$= 47$$

Definition

$$\sum_{i=1}^{n} x_{ij} = x_{1j} + x_{2j} + \cdots + x_{nj} \qquad \textbf{(C.6)}$$

Example:

$$\sum_{i=1}^{2} x_{i2} = x_{12} + x_{22}$$
$$= 8 + 4$$
$$= 12$$

Shorthand Notation

Sometimes when a summation is for all values of the subscript, we use the following shorthand notations:

$$\sum_{i=1}^{n} x_i = \sum_i x_i \qquad \textbf{(C.7)}$$

$$\sum_{i=1}^{n} \sum_{j=1}^{m} x_{ij} = \sum \sum x_{ij} \qquad \textbf{(C.8)}$$

$$\sum_{i=1}^{n} x_{ij} = \sum_i x_{ij} \qquad \textbf{(C.9)}$$

Chapter 1

2. a. 9

  b. 4

  c. Qualitative: country and room rate
  Quantitative: number of rooms and overall score

  d. Country is nominal; room rate is ordinal; number of rooms is ratio; overall score is interval

3. a. Average number of rooms = 808/9 = 89.78, or approximately 90 rooms

  b. Average overall score = 732.1/9 = 81.3

  c. 2 of 9 are located in England; approximately 22%

  d. 4 of 9 have a room rate of $$; approximately 44%

4. a. 10

  b. All brands of minisystems manufactured

  c. $314

  d. $314

6. Questions a, c, and d provide quantitative data
  Questions b and e provide qualitative data

8. a. 1005

  b. Qualitative

  c. Percentages

  d. Approximately 291

10. a. Quantitative; ratio

  b. Qualitative; nominal

  c. Qualitative; ordinal

  d. Quantitative; ratio

  e. Qualitative; nominal

12. a. All visitors to Hawaii

  b. Yes

  c. First and fourth questions provide quantitative data
  Second and third questions provide qualitative data

13. a. Quantitative

  b. Time series with 6 observations

  c. Earnings for Volkswagen

  d. An increase would be expected in 2003, but it appears that the rate of increase is slowing

14. a. Qualitative

16. a. Product taste tests and test marketing

  b. Specially designed statistical studies

18. a. 36%

  b. 189

  c. Qualitative

20. a. 43% of managers were bullish or very bullish, and 21% of managers expected health care to be the leading industry over the next 12 months

  b. The average 12-month return estimate is 11.2% for the population of investment managers

  c. The sample average of 2.5 years is an estimate of how long the population of investment managers think it will take to resume sustainable growth

22. a. All registered voters in California

  b. Registered voters contacted by the Policy Institute

  c. Too time consuming and costly to reach the entire population

24. a. Correct

  b. Incorrect

  c. Correct

  d. Incorrect

  e. Incorrect

Chapter 2

2. a. .20

  b. 40

  c/d.

Class	Frequency	Percent Frequency
A	44	22
B	36	18
C	80	40
D	40	20
Total	200	100

3. a. $360° \times 58/120 = 174°$

  b. $360° \times 42/120 = 126°$

  c.

  d.

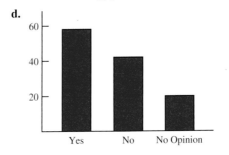

4. a. Qualitative

b.

TV Show	Frequency	Percent Frequency
CSI	18	36
ER	11	22
Friends	15	30
Raymond	6	12
Total	50	100

d. CSI had the largest; Friends was second

6. a.

Book	Frequency	Percent Frequency
7 Habits	10	16.66
Millionaire	16	26.67
Motley	9	15.00
Dad	13	21.67
WSJ Guide	6	10.00
Other	6	10.00
Total	60	100.00

b. First 5: *Millionaire, Dad, 7 Habits, Motley, WSJ Guide*
c. 48.33%

7.

Rating	Frequency	Relative Frequency
Outstanding	19	.38
Very good	13	.26
Good	10	.20
Average	6	.12
Poor	2	.04

Management should be pleased with these results: 64% of the ratings are very good to outstanding, and 84% of the ratings are good or better; comparing these ratings to previous results will show whether the restaurant is making improvements in its customers' ratings of food quality

8. a.

Position	Frequency	Relative Frequency
Pitcher	17	.309
Catcher	4	.073
1st Base	5	.091
2nd Base	4	.073
3rd Base	2	.036
Shortstop	5	.091
Left Field	6	.109
Center Field	5	.091
Right Field	7	.127
Total	55	1.000

b. Pitcher
c. 3rd base

d. Right field
e. Infielders 16 to outfielders 18

10. a. The data are ordinal; they simply provide quality classifications

b.

Response	Frequency	Relative Frequency
3	2	.03
4	4	.07
5	12	.20
6	24	.40
7	18	.30
Total	60	1.00

12.

Class	Cumulative Frequency	Cumulative Relative Frequency
≤19	10	.20
≤29	24	.48
≤39	41	.82
≤49	48	.96
≤59	50	1.00

14. b/c.

Class	Frequency	Percent Frequency
6.0–7.9	4	20
8.0–9.9	2	10
10.0–11.9	8	40
12.0–13.9	3	15
14.0–15.9	3	15
Total	20	100

15. a/b.

Waiting Time	Frequency	Relative Frequency
0–4	4	.20
5–9	8	.40
10–14	5	.25
15–19	2	.10
20–24	1	.05
Total	20	1.00

c/d.

Waiting Time	Cumulative Frequency	Cumulative Relative Frequency
≤4	4	.20
≤9	12	.60
≤14	17	.85
≤19	19	.95
≤24	20	1.00

e. $12/20 = .60$

16. a. Adjusted Gross Income

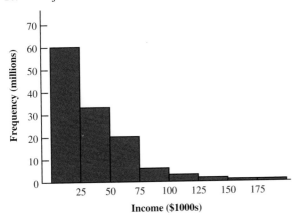

Histogram is skewed to the right

b. Exam Scores

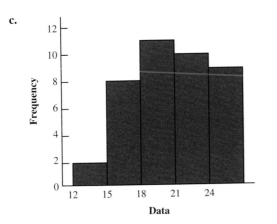

Histogram is skewed to the left

c.

Histogram skewed slightly to the left, but roughly symmetric

18. a. Lowest salary: $93,000
Highest salary: $178,000

b.

Salary ($1000s)	Frequency	Relative Frequency	Percent Frequency
91–105	4	0.08	8
106–120	5	0.10	10
121–135	11	0.22	22
136–150	18	0.36	36
151–165	9	0.18	18
166–180	3	0.06	6
Total	50	1.00	100

c. 20/50
d. 24%

20. a.

Price	Frequency	Percent Frequency
30–39.99	7	35
40–49.99	5	25
50–59.99	2	10
60–69.99	3	15
70–79.99	3	15
Total	20	100

c. Fleetwood Mac, Harper/Johnson

22.
```
5 | 7  8
6 | 4  5  8
7 | 0  2  2  5  5  6  8
8 | 0  2  3  5
```

23. Leaf unit = .1
```
 6 | 3
 7 | 5  5  7
 8 | 1  3  4  8
 9 | 3  6
10 | 0  4  5
11 | 3
```

24. Leaf unit = 10
```
11 | 6
12 | 0  2
13 | 0  6  7
14 | 2  2  7
15 | 5
16 | 0  2  8
17 | 0  2  3
```

25.

```
 9 | 8  9
10 | 2  4  6  6
11 | 4  5  7  8  8  9
12 | 2  4  5  7
13 | 1  2
14 | 4
15 | 1
```

26. a.

```
1 | 0  3  7  7
2 | 4  5  5
3 | 0  0  5  5  9
4 | 0  0  0  5  5  8
5 | 0  0  0  4  5  5
```

b.

```
0 | 5  7
1 | 0  1  1  3  4
1 | 5  5  5  8
2 | 0  0  0  0  0  0
2 | 5  5
3 | 0  0  0
3 | 6
4 |
4 |
5 |
5 |
6 | 3
```

28. a.

```
2 | 1  4
2 | 6  7
3 | 0  1  1  1  2  3
3 | 5  6  7  7
4 | 0  0  3  3  3  3  3  4  4
4 | 6  6  7  9
5 | 0  0  0  2  2
5 | 5  6  7  9
6 | 1  4
6 | 6
7 | 2
```

b. 40–44 with 9

c. 43 with 5

d. 10%; relative small participation in the race

29. a.

		y		
		1	2	Total
x	A	5	0	5
	B	11	2	13
	C	2	10	12
	Total	18	12	30

b.

		y		
		1	2	Total
x	A	100.0	0.0	100.0
	B	84.6	15.4	100.0
	C	16.7	83.3	100.0

c.

		y	
		1	2
x	A	27.8	0.0
	B	61.1	16.7
	C	11.1	83.3
	Total	100.0	100.0

d. A values are always in *y* = 1
     B values are most often in *y* = 1
     C values are most often in *y* = 2

30. a.

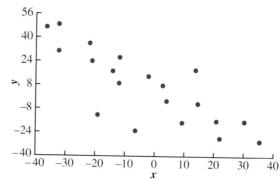

b. A negative relationship between *x* and *y*; *y* decreases as *x* increases

32. a.

	Household Income ($1000s)					
Education Level	Under 25	25.0– 49.9	50.0– 74.9	75.0– 99.9	100 or more	Total
Not H.S. Graduate	32.70	14.82	8.27	5.02	2.53	15.86
H.S. Graduate	35.74	35.56	31.48	25.39	14.47	30.78
Some College	21.17	29.77	30.25	29.82	22.26	26.37
Bachelor's Degree	7.53	14.43	20.56	25.03	33.88	17.52
Beyond Bach. Deg.	2.86	5.42	9.44	14.74	26.86	9.48
Total	100.00	100.00	100.00	100.00	100.00	100.00

15.86% of the heads of households did not graduate from high school

b. 26.86%, 39.72%

34. a.

Sales/ Margins/ ROE	EPS Rating					
	0– 19	20– 39	40– 59	60– 79	80– 100	Total
A				1	8	9
B		1	4	5	2	12
C	1		1	2	3	7
D	3	1		1		5
E		2	1			3
Total	4	4	6	9	13	36

b.

Sales/ Margins/ ROE	EPS Rating					
	0– 19	20– 39	40– 59	60– 79	80– 100	**Total**
A				11.11	88.89	100
B		8.33	33.33	41.67	16.67	100
C	14.29		14.29	28.57	42.86	100
D	60.00	20.00		20.00		100
E		66.67	33.33			100

Higher EPS ratings seem to be associated with higher ratings on Sales/Margins/ROE

36. b. No apparent relationship

38. a.

Vehicle	Frequency	Percent Frequency
Accord	6	12
Camry	7	14
F-Series	14	28
Ram	10	20
Silverado	13	26

b. Ford F-Series and the Toyota Camry

40. a.

Response	Frequency	Percent Frequency
Accuracy	16	16
Approach shots	3	3
Mental approach	17	17
Power	8	8
Practice	15	15
Putting	10	10
Short game	24	24
Strategic decisions	7	7
Total	100	100

b. Poor short game, poor mental approach, lack of accuracy, and limited practice

42. a/b.

Closing Price	Freq.	Rel. Freq.	Cum. Freq.	Cum. Rel. Freq.
0–9.99	9	.225	9	.225
10–19.99	10	.250	19	.475
20–29.99	5	.125	24	.600
30–39.99	11	.275	35	.875
40–49.99	2	.050	37	.925
50–59.99	2	.050	39	.975
60–69.99	0	.000	39	.975
70–79.99	1	.025	40	1.000
Total	40	1.000		

44.

Income ($)	Frequency	Relative Frequency
18,000–21,999	13	0.255
22,000–25,999	20	0.392
26,000–29,999	12	0.235
30,000–33,999	4	0.078
34,000–37,999	2	0.039
Total	51	1.000

46. a. High Temperature

```
3 |
4 |
5 | 7
6 | 1  4  4  4  4  6  8
7 | 3  5  7  9
8 | 0  1  1  4  6
9 | 0  2  3
```

b. Low Temperature

```
3 | 9
4 | 3  6  8
5 | 0  0  0  2  4  4  5  5  7  9
6 | 1  8
7 | 2  4  5  5
8 |
9 |
```

c. The range of low temperatures is below the range of high temperatures

d. 8 cities

e.

Temperature	Frequency	
	High Temp.	Low Temp.
30–39	0	1
40–49	0	3
50–59	1	10
60–69	7	2
70–79	4	4
80–89	5	0
90–99	3	0
Total	20	20

48. a.

Occupation	Satisfaction Score						
	30– 39	40– 49	50– 59	60– 69	70– 79	80– 89	Total
Cabinetmaker			2	4	3	1	10
Lawyer	1	5	2	1	1		10
Physical Therapist			5	2	1	2	10
Systems Analyst		2	1	4	3		10
Total	1	7	10	11	8	3	40

b.

Occupation	Satisfaction Score						Total
	30–39	40–49	50–59	60–69	70–79	80–89	
Cabinetmaker			20	40	30	10	100
Lawyer	10	50	20	10	10		100
Physical Therapist			50	20	10	20	100
Systems Analyst		20	10	40	30		100

c. Cabinetmakers seem to have the highest job satisfaction scores; lawyers seem to have the lowest

50. a. Row totals: 247; 54; 82; 121
Column totals: 149; 317; 17; 7; 14

b.

Year	Freq.	Fuel	Freq.
1973 or before	247	Elect.	149
1974–79	54	Nat. Gas	317
1980–86	82	Oil	17
1987–91	121	Propane	7
Total	504	Other	14
		Total	504

c. Crosstabulation of column percentages

Year Constructed	Fuel Type				
	Elect.	Nat. Gas	Oil	Propane	Other
1973 or before	26.9	57.7	70.5	71.4	50.0
1974–1979	16.1	8.2	11.8	28.6	0.0
1980–1986	24.8	12.0	5.9	0.0	42.9
1987–1991	32.2	22.1	11.8	0.0	7.1
Total	100.0	100.0	100.0	100.0	100.0

d. Crosstabulation of row percentages.

Year Constructed	Fuel Type					Total
	Elect.	Nat. Gas	Oil	Propane	Other	
1973 or before	16.2	74.1	4.9	2.0	2.8	100.0
1974–1979	44.5	48.1	3.7	3.7	0.0	100.0
1980–1986	45.1	46.4	1.2	0.0	7.3	100.0
1987–1991	39.7	57.8	1.7	0.0	0.8	100.0

52. a. Crosstabulation of market value and profit

Market Value ($1000s)	Profit ($1000s)				Total
	0–300	300–600	600–900	900–1200	
0–8000	23	4			27
8000–16,000	4	4	2	2	12
16,000–24,000		2	1	1	4
24,000–32,000		1	2	1	4
32,000–40,000		2	1		3
Total	27	13	6	4	50

b. Crosstabulation of row percentages

Market Value ($1000s)	Profit ($1000s)				Total
	0–300	300–600	600–900	900–1200	
0–8000	85.19	14.81	0.00	0.00	100
8000–16,000	33.33	33.33	16.67	16.67	100
16,000–24,000	0.00	50.00	25.00	25.00	100
24,000–32,000	0.00	25.00	50.00	25.00	100
32,000–40,000	0.00	66.67	33.33	0.00	100

c. A positive relationship is indicated between profit and market value; as profit goes up, market value goes up

54. b. A positive relationship is demonstrated between market value and stockholders' equity

Chapter 3

2. 16, 16.5

3. Arrange data in order: 15, 20, 25, 25, 27, 28, 30, 34

$i = \dfrac{20}{100}(8) = 1.6$; round up to position 2

20th percentile = 20

$i = \dfrac{25}{100}(8) = 2$; use positions 2 and 3

25th percentile $= \dfrac{20 + 25}{2} = 22.5$

$i = \dfrac{65}{100}(8) = 5.2$; round up to position 6

65th percentile = 28

$i = \dfrac{75}{100}(8) = 6$; use positions 6 and 7

75th percentile $= \dfrac{28 + 30}{2} = 29$

4. 59.727, 57, 53

6. a. 422
b. 380
c. 690
d. Not using capacity

8. a. $\bar{x} = \dfrac{\Sigma x_i}{n} = \dfrac{695}{20} = 34.75$

Mode = 25 (appears three times)

b. Data in order: 18, 20, 25, 25, 25, 26, 27, 27, 28, 33, 36, 37, 40, 40, 42, 45, 46, 48, 53, 54

Median (10th and 11th positions)

$\dfrac{33 + 36}{2} = 34.5$

At-home workers are slightly younger

c. $i = \dfrac{25}{100}(20) = 5$; use positions 5 and 6

$Q_1 = \dfrac{25 + 26}{2} = 25.5$

$i = \dfrac{75}{100}(20) = 15$; use positions 15 and 16

$Q_3 = \dfrac{42 + 45}{2} = 43.5$

d. $i = \dfrac{32}{100}(20) = 6.4$; round up to position 7

32nd percentile = 27
At least 32% of the people are 27 or younger

10. a. 76, 76
 b. 39, 37.5
 c. Yes; emergency wait too long

12. a. $639
 b. 98.8 pictures
 c. 110.2 minutes

14. 16, 4

15. Range = $34 - 15 = 19$
Arrange data in order: 15, 20, 25, 25, 27, 28, 30, 34

$i = \dfrac{25}{100}(8) = 2$; $Q_1 = \dfrac{20 + 25}{2} = 22.5$

$i = \dfrac{75}{100}(8) = 6$; $Q_3 = \dfrac{28 + 30}{2} = 29$

IQR $= Q_3 - Q_1 = 29 - 22.5 = 6.5$

$\bar{x} = \dfrac{\sum x_i}{n} = \dfrac{204}{8} = 25.5$

x_i	$(x_i - \bar{x})$	$(x_i - \bar{x})^2$
27	1.5	2.25
25	−.5	.25
20	−5.5	30.25
15	−10.5	110.25
30	4.5	20.25
34	8.5	72.25
28	2.5	6.25
25	−.5	.25
		242.00

$$s^2 = \dfrac{\sum(x_i - \bar{x})^2}{n - 1} = \dfrac{242}{8 - 1} = 34.57$$

$$s = \sqrt{34.57} = 5.88$$

16. a. Range $= 190 - 168 = 22$
 b. $\bar{x} = \dfrac{\sum x_i}{n} = \dfrac{1068}{6} = 178$

$s^2 = \dfrac{\sum(x_i - \bar{x})^2}{n - 1}$

$= \dfrac{4^2 + (-10)^2 + 6^2 + 12^2 + (-8)^2 + (-4)^2}{6 - 1}$

$= \dfrac{376}{5} = 75.2$

 c. $s = \sqrt{75.2} = 8.67$
 d. $\dfrac{s}{\bar{x}}(100) = \dfrac{8.67}{178}(100\%) = 4.87\%$

18. a. 38, 97, 9.85
 b. Eastern shows more variation

20. *Dawson:* range = 2, $s = .67$
 Clark: range = 8, $s = 2.58$

22. a. 45.05, 23.98; 57.50, 11.475
 b. 190.67, 13.81; 140.63, 11.86
 c. 38.02%; 57.97%
 d. Greater for broker-assisted trades

24. *Quarter-milers:* $s = .0564$, Coef. of Var. = 5.8%
 Milers: $s = .1295$, Coef. of Var. = 2.9%

26. .20, 1.50, 0, −.50, −2.20

27. Chebyshev's theorem: *at least* $(1 - 1/z^2)$

 a. $z = \dfrac{40 - 30}{5} = 2$; $1 - \dfrac{1}{(2)^2} = .75$

 b. $z = \dfrac{45 - 30}{5} = 3$; $1 - \dfrac{1}{(3)^2} = .89$

 c. $z = \dfrac{38 - 30}{5} = 1.6$; $1 - \dfrac{1}{(1.6)^2} = .61$

 d. $z = \dfrac{42 - 30}{5} = 2.4$; $1 - \dfrac{1}{(2.4)^2} = .83$

 e. $z = \dfrac{48 - 30}{5} = 3.6$; $1 - \dfrac{1}{(3.6)^2} = .92$

28. a. 95%
 b. Almost all
 c. 68%

29. a. $z = 2$ standard deviations

$1 - \dfrac{1}{z^2} = 1 - \dfrac{1}{2^2} = \dfrac{3}{4}$; at least 75%

 b. $z = 2.5$ standard deviations

$1 - \dfrac{1}{z^2} = 1 - \dfrac{1}{2.5^2} = .84$; at least 84%

 c. $z = 2$ standard deviations
Empirical rule: 95%

30. a. 68%
 b. 81.5%
 c. 2.5%

32. a. −.67
 b. 1.50
 c. Neither is an outlier
 d. Yes; $z = 8.25$

34. a. 76.5, 7
 b. 16%, 2.5%
 c. 12.2, 7.89; no outliers

36. 15, 22.5, 26, 29, 34

38. Arrange data in order: 5, 6, 8, 10, 10, 12, 15, 16, 18

$i = \dfrac{25}{100}(9) = 2.25$; round up to position 3

$Q_1 = 8$
Median (5th position) = 10

$i = \dfrac{75}{100}(9) = 6.75$; round up to position 7

$Q_3 = 15$

5-number summary: 5, 8, 10, 15, 18

40. a. 619, 725, 1016, 1699, 4450
  b. Limits: 0, 3160
  c. Yes
  d. No

41. a. Arrange data in order low to high

$i = \dfrac{25}{100}(21) = 5.25$; round up to 6th position

$Q_1 = 1872$

Median (11th position) $= 4019$

$i = \dfrac{75}{100}(21) = 15.75$; round up to 16th position

$Q_3 = 8305$

5-number summary: 608, 1872, 4019, 8305, 14138

  b. $IQR = Q_3 - Q_1 = 8305 - 1872 = 6433$
Lower limit: $1872 - 1.5(6433) = -7777$
Upper limit: $8305 + 1.5(6433) = 17,955$

  c. No outliers; data are within limits

  d. $41,138 > 27,604$; $41,138$ would be an outlier; data value would be reviewed and corrected

  e.

42. a. 61
  b. 34, 45, 61, 90, 126
  c. No; upper limit $= 157.5$

44. a. 18.2, 15.35
  b. 11.7, 23.5
  c. 3.4, 11.7, 15.35, 23.5, 41.3
  d. Yes; Alger Small Cap 41.3

45. b. There appears to be a negative linear relationship between x and y
  c.

x_i	y_i	$x_i - \bar{x}$	$y_i - \bar{y}$	$(x_i - \bar{x})(y_i - \bar{y})$
4	50	−4	4	−16
6	50	−2	4	−8
11	40	3	−6	−18
3	60	−5	14	−70
16	30	8	−16	−128
40	230	0	0	−240

$\bar{x} = 8$; $\bar{y} = 46$

$s_{xy} = \dfrac{\Sigma(x_i - \bar{x})(y_i - \bar{y})}{n - 1} = \dfrac{-240}{4} = -60$

The sample covariance indicates a negative linear association between x and y

d. $r_{xy} = \dfrac{s_{xy}}{s_x s_y} = \dfrac{-60}{(5.43)(11.40)} = -.969$

The sample correlation coefficient of $-.969$ is indicative of a strong negative linear relationship

46. b. There appears to be a positive linear relationship between x and y
  c. $s_{xy} = 26.5$
  d. $r_{xy} = .693$

48. $-.91$; strong negative relationship

50. a. .92
  b. Strong positive linear relationship

52. a. 3.69
  b. 3.175

53. a.

f_i	M_i	$f_i M_i$
4	5	20
7	10	70
9	15	135
5	20	100
25		325

$\bar{x} = \dfrac{\Sigma f_i M_i}{n} = \dfrac{325}{25} = 13$

b.

f_i	M_i	$(M_i - \bar{x})$	$(M_i - \bar{x})^2$	$f_i (M_i - \bar{x})^2$
4	5	−8	64	256
7	10	−3	9	63
9	15	2	4	36
5	20	7	49	245
25				600

$s^2 = \dfrac{\Sigma f_i (M_i - \bar{x})^2}{n - 1} = \dfrac{600}{25 - 1} = 25$

$s = \sqrt{25} = 5$

54. a.

Grade x_i	Weight w_i
4 (A)	9
3 (B)	15
2 (C)	33
1 (D)	3
0 (F)	0
	60 credit hours

$\bar{x} = \dfrac{\Sigma w_i x_i}{\Sigma w_i} = \dfrac{9(4) + 15(3) + 33(2) + 3(1)}{9 + 15 + 33 + 3}$

$= \dfrac{150}{60} = 2.5$

b. Yes

56. 10.74, 25.63, 5.06; estimate $= 1288.8$

58. a. 1800, 1351
   b. 387, 1710
   c. 7280, 1323
   d. 3,675,303, 1917
   e. High positive skewness
   f. yes; 4135 and 7450

60. a. 2.3, 1.85
   b. 1.90, 1.38
   c. Altria Group 5%
   d. $-.51$, about ½ a standard deviation below mean
   e. 1.02, about one standard deviation above mean
   f. No outliers

62. a. $\bar{x} = 83.135$, $s = 16.173$
   b. \$50,789 to \$115,481
   c. Same range as in part (b); higher probability
   d. Danbury, CT, is an outlier

64. a. 502.67; positive linear relationship
   b. .933; strong linear relationship

66. b. .9856, strong positive linear relationship

68. a. 817
   b. 833

70. a. 60.68
   b. $s^2 = 31.23$; $s = 5.59$

Chapter 4

2. $\binom{6}{3} = \dfrac{6!}{3!3!} = \dfrac{6 \cdot 5 \cdot 4 \cdot 3 \cdot 2 \cdot 1}{(3 \cdot 2 \cdot 1)(3 \cdot 2 \cdot 1)} = 20$

ABC	ACE	BCD	BEF
ABD	ACF	BCE	CDE
ABE	ADE	BCF	CDF
ABF	ADF	BDE	CEF
ACD	AEF	BDF	DEF

4. b. (H,H,H), (H,H,T), (H,T,H), (H,T,T),
   (T,H,H), (T,H,T), (T,T,H), (T,T,T)
   c. ⅛

6. $P(E_1) = .40$, $P(E_2) = .26$, $P(E_3) = .34$
   The relative frequency method was used

8. a. 4: Commission Positive—Council Approves
   Commission Positive—Council Disapproves
   Commission Negative—Council Approves
   Commission Negative—Council Disapproves

9. $\binom{50}{4} = \dfrac{50!}{4!46!} = \dfrac{50 \cdot 49 \cdot 48 \cdot 47}{4 \cdot 3 \cdot 2 \cdot 1} = 230,300$

10. a. Use the relative frequency approach
   $P(\text{California}) = 1,434/2,374 = .60$
   b. Number not from four states
   $\qquad = 2,374 - 1,434 - 390 - 217 - 112$
   $\qquad = 221$
   $P(\text{Not from 4 states}) = 221/2,374 = .09$
   c. $P(\text{Not in early stages}) = 1 - .22 = .78$
   d. Estimate of number of Massachusetts' companies in early stage of development $= (.22)390 \approx 86$

e. If we assume the size of the awards did not differ by state, we can multiply the probability an award went to Colorado by the total venture funds disbursed to get an estimate
   Estimate of Colorado funds $= (112/2374)(\$32.4)$
   $\qquad\qquad\qquad\qquad = \$1.53$ billion
   Authors' Note: The actual amount going to Colorado was \$1.74 billion

12. a. 2,869,685
   b. $1/(2,869,685) = .0000003485$
   c. $1/(120,526,770) = .0000000083$

14. a. ¼
   b. ½
   c. ¾

15. a. $S =$ (ace of clubs, ace of diamonds, ace of hearts, ace of spades)
   b. $S =$ (2 of clubs, 3 of clubs, . . . , 10 of clubs, J of clubs, Q of clubs, K of clubs, A of clubs)
   c. There are 12; jack, queen, or king in each of the four suits
   d. For (a): $4/52 = 1/13 = .08$
   For (b): $13/52 = 1/4 = .25$
   For (c): $12/52 = .23$

16. a. 36
   c. ⅙
   d. ⁵⁄₁₈
   e. No; $P(\text{odd}) = P(\text{even}) = ½$
   f. Classical

17. a. (4, 6), (4, 7), (4, 8)
   b. $.05 + .10 + .15 = .30$
   c. (2, 8), (3, 8), (4, 8)
   d. $.05 + .05 + .15 = .25$
   e. .15

18. a. $P(0) = .05$
   b. $P(4 \text{ or } 5) = .20$
   c. $P(0, 1, \text{ or } 2) = .55$

20. a. .112
   b. .086
   c. .49

22. a. .40, .40, .60
   b. .80, yes
   c. $A^c = (E_3, E_4, E_5)$; $C^c = (E_1, E_4)$;
   $P(A^c) = .60$; $P(C^c) = .40$
   d. (E_1, E_2, E_5); .60
   e. .80

23. a. $P(A) = P(E_1) + P(E_4) + P(E_6)$
   $\qquad = .05 + .25 + .10 = .40$
   $P(B) = P(E_2) + P(E_4) + P(E_7)$
   $\qquad = .20 + .25 + .05 = .50$
   $P(C) = P(E_2) + P(E_3) + P(E_5) + P(E_7)$
   $\qquad = .20 + .20 + .15 + .05 = .60$
   b. $A \cup B = \{E_1, E_2, E_4, E_6, E_7\}$;
   $P(A \cup B) = P(E_1) + P(E_2) + P(E_4) + P(E_6) + P(E_7)$
   $\qquad = .05 + .20 + .25 + .10 + .05$
   $\qquad = .65$
   c. $A \cap B = \{E_4\}$; $P(A \cap B) = P(E_4) = .25$

d. Yes, they are mutually exclusive

e. $B^c = \{E_1, E_3, E_5, E_6\}$;
$$P(B^c) = P(E_1) + P(E_3) + P(E_5) + P(E_6)$$
$$= .05 + .20 + .15 + .10$$
$$= .50$$

24. a. .05

 b. .70

26. a. .30, .23

 b. .17

 c. .64

28. Let B = rented a car for business reasons
 P = rented a car for personal reasons

 a. $P(B \cup P) = P(B) + P(P) - P(B \cap P)$
$$= .540 + .458 - .300$$
$$= .698$$

 b. $P(\text{Neither}) = 1 - .698 = .302$

30. a. $P(A \mid B) = \dfrac{P(A \cap B)}{P(B)} = \dfrac{.40}{.60} = .6667$

 b. $P(B \mid A) = \dfrac{P(A \cap B)}{P(A)} = \dfrac{.40}{.50} = .80$

 c. No, because $P(A \mid B) \neq P(A)$

32. a.

Age	Yes	No	Total
18 to 34	.375	.085	.46
35 and over	.475	.065	.54
Total	.850	.150	1.00

 b. 46% 18 to 34; 54% 35 and over

 c. .15

 d. .1848

 e. .1204

 f. .5667

 g. Higher probability of No for 18 to 34

33. a.

	Reason for Applying			
Status	Quality	Cost/ Convenience	Other	Total
Full-time	.218	.204	.039	.461
Part-time	.208	.307	.024	.539
Total	.426	.511	.063	1.000

 b. A student is most likely to cite cost or convenience as the first reason (probability = .511); school quality is the reason cited by the second largest number of students (probability = .426)

 c. $P(\text{quality} \mid \text{full-time}) = .218/.461 = .473$

 d. $P(\text{quality} \mid \text{part-time}) = .208/.539 = .386$

 e. For independence, we must have $P(A)P(B) = P(A \cap B)$; from the table
$$P(A \cap B) = .218, \ P(A) = .461, \ P(B) = .426$$
$$P(A)P(B) = (.461)(.426) = .196$$
Because $P(A)P(B) \neq P(A \cap B)$, the events are not independent

34. a. .44

 b. .15

 c. .136

 d. .106

 e. .0225

 f. .0025

36. a. .7921

 b. .9879

 c. .0121

 d. .3364, .8236, .1764
 Don't foul Reggie Miller

38. a. .0209

 b. .0141, .027

 c. No

 d. .0202, .0458

 e. Yes

39. a. Yes, because $P(A_1 \cap A_2) = 0$

 b. $P(A_1 \cap B) = P(A_1)P(B \mid A_1) = .40(.20) = .08$
$P(A_2 \cap B) = P(A_2)P(B \mid A_2) = .60(.05) = .03$

 c. $P(B) = P(A_1 \cap B) + P(A_2 \cap B) = .08 + .03 = .11$

 d. $P(A_1 \mid B) = \dfrac{.08}{.11} = .7273$
$$P(A_2 \mid B) = \dfrac{.03}{.11} = .2727$$

40. a. .10, .20, .09

 b. .51

 c. .26, .51, .23

42. M = missed payment
 D_1 = customer defaults
 D_2 = customer does not default
 $P(D_1) = .05, P(D_2) = .95, P(M \mid D_2) = .2, P(M \mid D_1) = 1$

 a. $P(D_1 \mid M) = \dfrac{P(D_1)P(M \mid D_1)}{P(D_1)P(M \mid D_1) + P(D_2)P(M \mid D_2)}$
$$= \dfrac{(.05)(1)}{(.05)(1) + (.95)(.2)}$$
$$= \dfrac{.05}{.24} = .21$$

 b. Yes, the probability of default is greater than .20

44. a. .47, .53, .50, .45

 b. .4963

 c. .4463

 d. 47%, 53%

46. a. .68

 b. 52

 c. 10

48. a. 315

 b. .29

 c. No

 d. Republicans

50. a. .76

 b. .24

52. b. .2022
  c. .4618
  d. .4005

54. a. .49
  b. .44
  c. .54
  d. No
  e. Yes

56. a. .25
  b. .125
  c. .0125
  d. .10
  e. No

58. 3.44%

60. a. .40
  b. .67

Chapter 5

1. a. Head, Head (H, H)
  Head, Tail (H, T)
  Tail, Head (T, H)
  Tail, Tail (T, T)
  b. x = number of heads on two coin tosses
  c.

Outcome	Values of x
(H, H)	2
(H, T)	1
(T, H)	1
(T, T)	0

  d. Discrete; it may assume 3 values: 0, 1, and 2

2. a. x = time in minutes to assemble product
  b. Any positive value: $x > 0$
  c. Continuous

3. Let Y = position is offered
    N = position is not offered
  a. $S = \{(Y, Y, Y), (Y, Y, N), (Y, N, Y), (Y, N, N), (N, Y, Y),$
    $(N, Y, N), (N, N, Y), (N, N, N)\}$
  b. Let N = number of offers made; N is a discrete random
    variable
  c.

Experimental Outcome	(Y, Y, Y)	(Y, Y, N)	(Y, N, Y)	(Y, N, N)	(N, Y, Y)	(N, Y, N)	(N, N, Y)	(N, N, N)
Value of N	3	2	2	1	2	1	1	0

4. $x = 0, 1, 2, \ldots, 12$

6. a. 0, 1, 2, . . . , 20; discrete
  b. 0, 1, 2, . . . ; discrete
  c. 0, 1, 2, . . . , 50; discrete
  d. $0 \leq x \leq 8$; continuous
  e. $x > 0$; continuous

7. a. $f(x) \geq 0$ for all values of x
    $\Sigma f(x) = 1$; therefore, it is a valid probability
    distribution
  b. Probability $x = 30$ is $f(30) = .25$
  c. Probability $x \leq 25$ is $f(20) + f(25) = .20 + .15 = .35$
  d. Probability $x > 30$ is $f(35) = .40$

8. a.

x	$f(x)$
1	3/20 = .15
2	5/20 = .25
3	8/20 = .40
4	4/20 = .20
	Total 1.00

  b.

  c. $f(x) \geq 0$ for $x = 1, 2, 3, 4$
    $\Sigma f(x) = 1$

10. a.

x	1	2	3	4	5
$f(x)$	.05	.09	.03	.42	.41

  b.

x	1	2	3	4	5
$f(x)$	.04	.10	.12	.46	.28

  c. .83
  d. .28
  e. Senior executives more satisfied

12. a. Yes
  b. .65

14. a. .05
  b. .70
  c. .40

16. a.

y	$f(y)$	$yf(y)$
2	.20	.40
4	.30	1.20
7	.40	2.80
8	.10	.80
Totals	1.00	5.20

$E(y) = \mu = 5.20$

b.

y	$y - \mu$	$(y - \mu)^2$	$f(y)$	$(y - \mu)^2 f(y)$
2	-3.20	10.24	.20	2.048
4	-1.20	1.44	.30	.432
7	1.80	3.24	.40	1.296
8	2.80	7.84	.10	.784
		Total		4.560

$$\text{Var}(y) = 4.56$$
$$\sigma = \sqrt{4.56} = 2.14$$

18. a/b.

x	$f(x)$	$xf(x)$	$x - \mu$	$(x - \mu)^2$	$(x - \mu)^2 f(x)$
0	0.04	0.00	-1.84	3.39	0.12
1	0.34	0.34	-0.84	0.71	0.24
2	0.41	0.82	0.16	0.02	0.01
3	0.18	0.53	1.16	1.34	0.24
4	0.04	0.15	2.16	4.66	0.17
Total	1.00	1.84			0.79
		↑			↑
		$E(x)$			Var(x)

c/d.

y	$f(y)$	$yf(y)$	$y - \mu$	$(y - \mu)^2$	$y - \mu^2 f(y)$
0	0.00	0.00	-2.93	8.58	0.01
1	0.03	0.03	-1.93	3.72	0.12
2	0.23	0.45	-0.93	0.86	0.20
3	0.52	1.55	0.07	0.01	0.00
4	0.22	0.90	1.07	1.15	0.26
Total	1.00	2.93			0.59
		↑			↑
		$E(y)$			Var(y)

e. The number of bedrooms in owner-occupied houses is greater than in renter-occupied houses; the expected number of bedrooms is 1.09 = 2.93 − 1.84 greater and the variability in the number of bedrooms is less for the owner-occupied houses

20. a. 166
b. −94; concern is to protect against the expense of a big accident

22. a. 445
b. $1250 loss

24. a. Medium: 145; large: 140
b. Medium: 2725; large: 12,400

25. a.

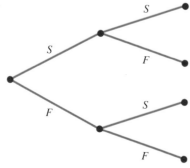

b. $f(1) = \binom{2}{1}(.4)^1(.6)^1 = \dfrac{2!}{1!1!}(.4)(.6) = .48$

Using Excel: BINOMDIST(1,2,.4,FALSE) = .48

c. $f(0) = \binom{2}{0}(.4)^0(.6)^2 = \dfrac{2!}{0!2!}(1)(.36) = .36$

Using Excel: BINOMDIST(0,2,.4,FALSE) = .36

d. $f(2) = \binom{2}{2}(.4)^2(.6)^0 = \dfrac{2!}{2!0!}(.16)(.1) = .16$

Using Excel: BINOMDIST(2,2,.4,FALSE) = .16

e. $P(x \geq 1) = f(1) + f(2) = .48 + .16 = .64$
f. $E(x) = np = 2(.4) = .8$
$\text{Var}(x) = np(1 - p) = 2(.4)(.6) = .48$
$\sigma = \sqrt{.48} = .6928$

26. a. $f(0) = .3487$
b. $f(2) = .1937$
c. .9298
d. .6513
e. 1
f. $\sigma^2 = .9000, \sigma = .9487$

28. a. .2789
b. .4181
c. .0733

30. a. Probability of a defective part being produced must be .03 for each part selected; parts must be selected independently
b. Let D = defective
G = not defective

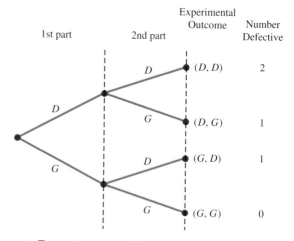

c. Two outcomes result in exactly one defect
d. $P(\text{no defects}) = (.97)(.97) = .9409$
$P(1 \text{ defect}) = 2(.03)(.97) = .0582$
$P(2 \text{ defects}) = (.03)(.03) = .0009$

32. a. .90
b. .99
c. .999
d. Yes

34. a. .0634
b. .0634
c. .9729

38. a. $f(x) = \dfrac{3^x e^{-3}}{x!}$

   b. .224

   c. .149

   d. .801

39. a. $f(x) = \dfrac{2^x e^{-2}}{x!}$

   b. $\mu = 6$ for 3 time periods

   c. $f(x) = \dfrac{6^x e^{-6}}{x!}$

   d. $f(2) = \dfrac{2^2 e^{-2}}{2!} = \dfrac{4(.1353)}{2} = .2706$

   Using Excel: POISSON(2,2,FALSE) = .2707

   e. $f(6) = \dfrac{6^6 e^{-6}}{6!} = .1606$

   Using Excel: POISSON(6,6,FALSE) = .1606

   f. $f(5) = \dfrac{4^5 e^{-4}}{5!} = .1563$

   Using Excel: POISSON(5,4,FALSE) = .1563

40. a. $\mu = 48(5/60) = 4$

   $f(3) = \dfrac{4^3 e^{-4}}{3!} = \dfrac{(64)(.0183)}{6} = .1952$

   b. $\mu = 48(15/60) = 12$

   $f(10) = \dfrac{12^{10} e^{-12}}{10!} = .1048$

   c. $\mu = 48(5/60) = 4$; one can expect four callers to be waiting after 5 minutes

   $f(0) = \dfrac{4^0 e^{-4}}{0!} = .0183$; the probability none will be waiting after 5 minutes is .0183

   d. $\mu = 48(3/60) = 2.4$

   $f(0) = \dfrac{2.4^0 e^{-2.4}}{0!} = .0907$; the probability of no interruptions in 3 minutes is .0907

42. a. $f(0) = \dfrac{7^0 e^{-7}}{0!} = e^{-7} =$POISSON(0,7,FALSE)

   $= .0009$

   b. Probability $= 1 - [f(0) + f(1)]$
   $= 1 -$ POISSON(1,7,TRUE) $= .9927$

   c. $\mu = 3.5$

   $f(0) = \dfrac{3.5^0 e^{-3.5}}{0!} = e^{-3.5} =$POISSON(0,3.5,FALSE)

   $= .0302$

   Probability $= 1 - f(0) = 1 - .0302 = .9698$

   d.

   Probability $= 1 - [f(0) + f(1) + f(2) + f(3) + f(4)]$
   $= 1 -$ POISSON(4,7,TRUE)
   $= .8270$

44. a. $\mu = 1.25$

   b. .2865

   c. .3581

   d. .3554

46. a. $f(1) = \dfrac{\binom{3}{1}\binom{10-3}{4-1}}{\binom{10}{4}} = \dfrac{\left(\frac{3!}{1!2!}\right)\left(\frac{7!}{3!4!}\right)}{\frac{10!}{4!6!}}$

   $= \dfrac{(3)(35)}{210} = .50$

   Using Excel: HYPGEOMDIST(1,4,3,10) = .5000

   b. $f(2) = \dfrac{\binom{3}{2}\binom{10-3}{2-2}}{\binom{10}{2}} = \dfrac{(3)(1)}{45} = .0667$

   Using Excel: HYPGEOMDIST(2,2,3,10) = .0667

   c. $f(0) = \dfrac{\binom{3}{0}\binom{10-3}{2-0}}{\binom{10}{2}} = \dfrac{(1)(21)}{45} = .4667$

   Using Excel: HYPGEOMDIST(0,2,3,10) = .4667

   d. $f(2) = \dfrac{\binom{3}{2}\binom{10-3}{4-2}}{\binom{10}{4}} = \dfrac{(3)(21)}{210} = .30$

   Using Excel: HYPGEOMDIST(2,4,3,10) = .3000

48. a. .5250

   b. .8167

50. $N = 60, n = 10$

   a. $r = 20, x = 0$

   $f(0) = \dfrac{\binom{20}{0}\binom{40}{10}}{\binom{60}{10}} = \dfrac{(1)\left(\frac{40!}{10!30!}\right)}{\frac{60!}{10!50!}}$

   $= \left(\dfrac{40!}{10!30!}\right)\left(\dfrac{10!50!}{60!}\right)$

   $= \dfrac{40\cdot39\cdot38\cdot37\cdot36\cdot35\cdot34\cdot33\cdot32\cdot31}{60\cdot59\cdot58\cdot57\cdot56\cdot55\cdot54\cdot53\cdot52\cdot51}$

   $\approx .01$

   Using Excel: HYPGEOMDIST(1,10,20,60) = .0112

   b. $r = 20, x = 1$

   $f(1) = \dfrac{\binom{20}{1}\binom{40}{9}}{\binom{60}{10}} = 20\left(\dfrac{40!}{9!31!}\right)\left(\dfrac{10!50!}{60!}\right)$

   $\approx .07$

   Using Excel: HYPGEOMDIST(1,10,20,60) = .0725

   c. $1 - f(0) - f(1) = 1 - .08 = .92$

   d. Same as the probability one will be from Hawaii; in part (b) it was equal to approximately .07

52. a. .5333

   b. .6667

   c. .7778

   d. $n = 7$

54. a.

x	1	2	3	4	5
$f(x)$	.24	.21	.10	.21	.24

b. 3.00, 2.34

c. Bonds: $E(x) = 1.36$, $\text{Var}(x) = .23$
Stocks: $E(x) = 4$, $\text{Var}(x) = 1$

56. a. .0596

b. .3585

c. 100

d. 95, 9.7468

58. a. .9510

b. .0480

c. .0490

60. a. 240

b. 12.9615

c. 12.9615

62. .1912

64. a. .2240

b. .5767

66. a. .4667

b. .4667

c. .0667

Chapter 6

1. a.

$f(x)$

b. $P(x = 1.25) = 0$; the probability of any single point is zero because the area under the curve above any single point is zero

c. $P(1.0 \le x \le 1.25) = 2(.25) = .50$

d. $P(1.20 < x < 1.5) = 2(.30) = .60$

2. b. .50

c. .60

d. 15

e. 8.33

4. a.

$f(x)$

b. $P(.25 < x < .75) = 1(.50) = .50$

c. $P(x \le .30) = 1(.30) = .30$

d. $P(x > .60) = 1(.40) = .40$

6. a. .40

b. .64

c. .68

10. a. .9332

b. .8413

c. .0919

d. .4938

12. a. .2967

b. .4418

c. .3300

d. .5910

e. .8849

f. .2389

13. a. $.6879 - .0239 = .6640$

b. $.8888 - .6985 = .1903$

c. $.1492 - .0401 = .1091$

14. a. $z = 1.96$

b. $z = 1.96$

c. $z = .61$

d. $z = 1.12$

e. $z = .44$

f. $z = .44$

15. a. The z-value corresponding to a cumulative probability of .2119 is $z = -.80$

b. Compute $.9030/2 = .4515$; the cumulative probability of $.5000 + .4515 = .9515$ corresponds to $z = 1.66$

c. Compute $.2052/2 = .1026$; z corresponds to a cumulative probability of $.5000 + .1026 = .6026$, so $z = .26$

d. The z-value corresponding to a cumulative probability of .9948 is $z = 2.56$

e. The area to the left of z is $1 - .6915 = .3085$, so $z = -.50$

16. a. $z = 2.33$

b. $z = 1.96$

c. $z = 1.645$

d. $z = 1.28$

18. $\mu = 30$ and $\sigma = 8.2$

a. At $x = 40$, $z = \dfrac{40 - 30}{8.2} = 1.22$

$P(z \le 1.22) = .8888$

$P(x \ge 40) = 1.000 - .8888 = .1112$

b. At $x = 20$, $z = \dfrac{20 - 30}{8.2} = -1.22$

$P(z \le -1.22) = .1112$

$P(x \le 20) = .1112$

c. A z-value of 1.28 cuts off an area of approximately 10% in the upper tail

$x = 30 + 8.2(1.28)$

$= 40.50$

A stock price of $40.50 or higher will put a company in the top 10%

20. a. .0885

b. 12.51%

c. 93.8 hours or more

22. a. .4194; using NORMDIST: .4199

b. $517.44 or more; using NORMINV: $517.59

c. .0166; using NORMDIST: .0165

24. a. 902.75, 114.185
   b. .1841
   c. .1977; using NORMDIST: .1972
   d. 1,091 million

26. a. .5276
   b. .3935
   c. .4724
   d. .1341; using EXPONDIST: .1342

27. a. $P(x \leq x_0) = 1 - e^{-x_0/3}$
   b. $P(x \leq 2) = 1 - e^{-2/3} = 1 - .5134 = .4866$
   c. $P(x \geq 3) = 1 - P(x \leq 3) = 1 - (1 - e^{-3/3})$
         $= e^{-1} = .3679$
   d. $P(x \leq 5) = 1 - e^{-5/3} = 1 - .1889 = .8111$
   e. $P(2 \leq x \leq 5) = P(x \leq 5) - P(x \leq 2)$
         $= .8111 - .4866 = .3245$

28. a. .3935
   b. .2231
   c. .3834

29. a.

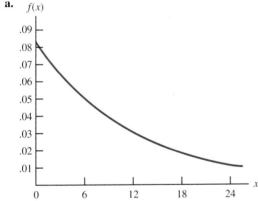

$f(x)$

   b. $P(x \leq 12) = 1 - e^{-12/12} = 1 - .3679 = .6321$
   c. $P(x \leq 6) = 1 - e^{-6/12} = 1 - .6065 = .3935$
   d. $P(x \geq 30) = 1 - P(x < 30)$
         $= 1 - (1 - e^{-30/12})$
         $= .0821$

30. a. 50 hours
   b. .3935
   c. .1353

32. a. $f(x) = 30e^{-30x}$
   b. .0821
   c. .7135

34. a. $3780 or less
   b. 19.22%
   c. $8167.50

36. a. 3229
   b. .2244
   c. $12,382 or more

38. a. .0228
   b. $50

40. a. 38.3%
   b. 3.59% better, 96.41% worse
   c. 38.21%

42. $\mu = 19.23$ ounces

44. a. $\frac{1}{7}$ minute
   b. $7e^{-7x}$
   c. .0009
   d. .2466

46. a. 2 minutes
   b. .2212
   c. .3935
   d. .0821

Chapter 7

1. a. AB, AC, AD, AE, BC, BD, BE, CD, CE, DE
   b. With 10 samples, each has a $\frac{1}{10}$ probability
   c. B and D because the two smallest random numbers are
         .0476 and .0957

2. Elements 2, 3, 5, and 10

3. The simple random sample consists of New York, Detroit,
      Oakland, Boston, and Kansas City

4. Step 1. Generate a random number for each company
      Step 2. Sort with respect to random numbers and select the
              first three companies

6. Finite, infinite, infinite, infinite, finite

7. a. $\bar{x} = \dfrac{\Sigma x_i}{n} = \dfrac{54}{6} = 9$

   b. $s = \sqrt{\dfrac{\Sigma(x_i - \bar{x})^2}{n - 1}}$

      $\Sigma(x_i - \bar{x})^2 = (-4)^2 + (-1)^2 + 1^2 + (-2)^2 + 1^2 + 5^2$
         $= 48$

      $s = \sqrt{\dfrac{48}{6 - 1}} = 3.1$

8. a. .50
   b. .3667

9. a. $\bar{x} = \dfrac{\Sigma x_i}{n} = \dfrac{465}{5} = 93$

   b.

x_i	$(x_i - \bar{x})$	$(x_i - \bar{x})^2$
94	+1	1
100	+7	49
85	−8	64
94	+1	1
92	−1	1
Totals 465	0	116

$$s = \sqrt{\frac{\Sigma(x_i - \bar{x})^2}{n - 1}} = \sqrt{\frac{116}{4}} = 5.39$$

10. a. .45
   b. .15
   c. .45

12. a. .10
   b. 20
   c. .72

15. a. The sampling distribution is normal with:
$$E(\bar{x}) = \mu = 200$$
$$\sigma_{\bar{x}} = \frac{\sigma}{\sqrt{n}} = \frac{50}{\sqrt{100}} = 5$$

For ± 5, $(\bar{x} - \mu) = 5$,
$$z = \frac{\bar{x} - \mu}{\sigma_{\bar{x}}} = \frac{5}{5} = 1$$
$$\text{Area} = .8413 - .1587 = .6826$$

   b. For ± 10, $(\bar{x} - \mu) = 10$,
$$z = \frac{\bar{x} - \mu}{\sigma_{\bar{x}}} = \frac{10}{5} = 2$$
$$\text{Area} = .9772 - .0228 = .9544$$

16. 3.54, 2.50, 2.04, 1.77
$\sigma_{\bar{x}}$ decreases as n increases

18. a. Normal with $E(\bar{x}) = 51{,}800$ and $\sigma_{\bar{x}} = 516.40$
   b. $\sigma_{\bar{x}}$ decreases to 365.15
   c. $\sigma_{\bar{x}}$ decreases as n increases

19. a.

51,300   51,800   52,300

$$\sigma_{\bar{x}} = \frac{\sigma}{\sqrt{n}} = \frac{4000}{\sqrt{60}} = 516.40$$

At $\bar{x} = 52{,}300$, $z = \dfrac{52{,}300 - 51{,}800}{516.40} = .97$
$$P(\bar{x} \le 52{,}300) = P(z \le .97) = .8340$$

At $\bar{x} = 51{,}300$, $z = \dfrac{51{,}300 - 51{,}800}{516.40} = -.97$
$$P(\bar{x} < 51{,}300) = P(z < -.97) = .1660$$
$$P(51{,}300 \le \bar{x} \le 52{,}300) = .8340 - .1660 = .6680$$
Using Excel:
=NORMDIST(52300,51800,516.40,TRUE)-
   NORMDIST(51300,51800,516.40,TRUE) = .6671

   b. $\sigma_{\bar{x}} = \dfrac{\sigma}{\sqrt{n}} = \dfrac{4000}{\sqrt{120}} = 365.15$

At $\bar{x} = 52{,}300$, $z = \dfrac{52{,}300 - 51{,}800}{365.15} = 1.37$
$$P(\bar{x} \le 52{,}300) = P(z \le 1.37) = .9147$$

At $\bar{x} = 51{,}300$, $z = \dfrac{51{,}300 - 51{,}800}{365.15} = -1.37$
$$P(\bar{x} < 51{,}300) = P(z < -1.37) = .0853$$
$$P(51{,}300 \le \bar{x} \le 52{,}300) = .9147 - .0853 = .8294$$

Using Excel:
=NORMDIST(52300,51800,365.15,TRUE)-
   NORMDIST(51300,51800,365.15,TRUE) = .8291

20. a. Normal with $E(\bar{x}) = 4260$ and $\sigma_{\bar{x}} = 127.28$
   b. .95
   c. .5704

22. a. Using table: .5034, .6212, .7888, .9232, .9876
   b. Higher probability within ± 250

24. a. Normal with $E(\bar{x}) = 687$ and $\sigma_{\bar{x}} = 34.29$
   b. Using table: .9964; using NORMDIST: .9965
   c. Using table: .5346; using NORMDIST: .5340
   d. Increase the sample size

26. a. $n/N = .01$; no
   b. 1.29, 1.30; little difference
   c. Using table: .8764

28. a. $E(\bar{p}) = .40$
$$\sigma_{\bar{p}} = \sqrt{\frac{p(1-p)}{n}} = \sqrt{\frac{(.40)(.60)}{200}} = .0346$$
Within $\pm .03$ means $.37 \le \bar{p} \le .43$
Using table: $z = \dfrac{\bar{p} - p}{\sigma_{\bar{p}}} = \dfrac{.03}{.0346} = .87$
$$P(.37 \le \bar{p} \le .43) = P(-.87 \le z \le .87)$$
$$= .8078 - .1922$$
$$= .6156$$
Using Excel:
=NORMDIST(.43,.40,.0346,TRUE)-
   NORMDIST(.37,.40,.0346,TRUE) = .6141

   b. Using table: $z = \dfrac{\bar{p} - p}{\sigma_{\bar{p}}} = \dfrac{.05}{.0346} = 1.44$
$$P(.35 \le \bar{p} \le .45) = P(-1.44 \le z \le 1.44)$$
$$= .9251 - .0749$$
$$= .8502$$
Using Excel:
=NORMDIST(.45,.40,.0346,TRUE)-
   NORMDIST(.35,.40,.0346,TRUE) = .8516

30. a. Using table: .6156; using NORMDIST: .6175
   b. Using table: .7814; using NORMDIST: .7830
   c. Using table: .9488; using NORMDIST: .9490
   d. Using table: .9942; using NORMDIST: .9942
   e. Higher probability with larger n

31. a.

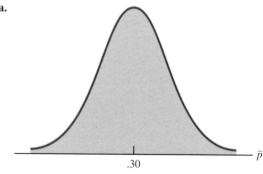

.30

$$\sigma_{\bar{p}} = \sqrt{\frac{p(1-p)}{n}} = \sqrt{\frac{.30(.70)}{100}} = .0458$$

The normal distribution is appropriate because $np = 100(.30) = 30$ and $n(1-p) = 100(.70) = 70$ are both greater than 5

b. $P(.20 \le \bar{p} \le .40) = ?$

$$z = \frac{.40 - .30}{.0458} = 2.18$$

$$P(.20 \le \bar{p} \le .40) = P(-2.18 \le z \le 2.18)$$
$$= .9854 - .0146$$
$$= .9708$$

Using Excel:
=NORMDIST(.40,.30,.0458,TRUE)-
        NORMDIST(.20,.30,.0458,TRUE) = .9710

c. $P(.25 \le \bar{p} \le .35) = ?$

$$z = \frac{.35 - .30}{.0458} = 1.09$$

$$P(.25 \le \bar{p} \le .35) = P(-1.09 \le z \le 1.09)$$
$$= .8621 - .1379$$
$$= .7242$$

Using Excel:
=NORMDIST(.35,.30,.0458,TRUE)-
        NORMDIST(.25,.30,.0458,TRUE) = .7250

32. a. Normal with $E(\bar{p}) = .56$ and $\sigma_{\bar{p}} = .0287$
b. Using table: .7062; using NORMDIST: .7041
c. Using table: .8612; using NORMDIST: .8605
     Using table: .9438; using NORMDIST: .9440

34. a. Normal with $E(\bar{p}) = .56$ and $\sigma_{\bar{p}} = .0248$
b. Using table: .5820; using NORMDIST: .5800
c. Using table: .8926; using NORMDIST: .8932

36. a. Normal with $E(\bar{p}) = .76$ and $\sigma_{\bar{p}} = .0214$
b. Using table: .8384; using NORMDIST: .8390
c. Using table: .9452; using NORMDIST: .9455

38. Thoroughbreds, The Marker, Officers Club, SeaBlue, Crickets

40. a. Normal with $E(\bar{x}) = 115.50$ and $\sigma_{\bar{x}} = 5.53$
b. Using table: .9298; using NORMDIST: .9292
c. Using table: $z = -2.71$, .0034;
     using NORMDIST: .0025

42. a. 707
b. .50
c. Using table: $z = \pm 1.41$, .8414;
     using NORMDIST: .8428
d. .9544

44. a. 625
b. .7888

46. a. Normal with $E(\bar{p}) = .305$ and $\sigma_{\bar{p}} = .0326$
b. Using table: $z = \pm 1.23$, .7814;
     using NORMDIST: .7802
c. Using table: $z = \pm .61$, .4582;
     using NORMDIST: .4605

48. a. Using table: $z = \pm 2.06$, .9606; using NORMDIST: .9604
b. Using table: $z = 1.65$, .0495; using NORMDIST: .0499

50. a. 48
b. Normal, $E(\bar{p}) = .25$, $\sigma_{\bar{p}} = .0625$
c. .2119

Chapter 8

2. Use $\bar{x} \pm z_{\alpha/2}(\sigma/\sqrt{n})$
a. $32 \pm 1.645 (6/\sqrt{50})$
     32 ± 1.4; 30.6 to 33.4
b. $32 \pm 1.96(6/\sqrt{50})$
     32 ± 1.66; 30.34 to 33.66
c. $32 \pm 2.576(6/\sqrt{50})$
     32 ± 2.19; 29.81 to 34.19

4. 54

5. a. $1.96\sigma/\sqrt{n} = 1.96(5/\sqrt{49}) = 1.40$
b. 24.80 ± 1.40; 23.40 to 26.20

6. 8.1 to 8.9

8. a. Population is at least approximately normal
b. 3.1
c. 4.1

10. a. \$113,638 to \$124,672
b. \$112,581 to \$125,729
c. \$110,515 to \$127,795
d. Width increases as confidence level increases

12. a. 2.179
b. -1.676
c. 2.457
d. -1.708 and 1.708
e. -2.014 and 2.014

13. a. $\bar{x} = \dfrac{\Sigma x_i}{n} = \dfrac{80}{8} = 10$

b. $s = \sqrt{\dfrac{\Sigma(x_i - \bar{x})^2}{n-1}} = \sqrt{\dfrac{84}{7}} = 3.464$

c. $t_{.025}\left(\dfrac{s}{\sqrt{n}}\right) = 2.365\left(\dfrac{3.46}{\sqrt{8}}\right) = 2.9$

d. $\bar{x} \pm t_{.025}\left(\dfrac{s}{\sqrt{n}}\right)$

     10 ± 2.9 (7.1 to 12.9)

14. a. 21.5 to 23.5
b. 21.3 to 23.7
c. 20.9 to 24.1
d. A larger margin of error and a wider interval

15. $\bar{x} \pm t_{\alpha/2}(s/\sqrt{n})$
     90% confidence: $df = 64$ and $t_{.05} = 1.669$

     $19.5 \pm 1.669\left(\dfrac{5.2}{\sqrt{65}}\right)$

     19.5 ± 1.08 (18.42 to 20.58)
     95% confidence: $df = 64$ and $t_{.025} = 1.998$

     $19.5 \pm 1.998\left(\dfrac{5.2}{\sqrt{65}}\right)$

     19.5 ± 1.29 (18.21 to 20.79)

16. a. 1.69
  b. 47.31 to 50.69
  c. Fewer hours and higher cost for United

18. a. 3.8
  b. .8429
  c. 2.96 to 4.64
  d. Larger n next time

20. 6.27 to 6.78

22. a. 3.348%
  b. 2.40% to 4.29%

24. a. Planning value of $\sigma = \dfrac{\text{Range}}{4} = \dfrac{36}{4} = 9$

  b. $n = \dfrac{z_{.025}^2 \sigma^2}{E^2} = \dfrac{(1.96)^2(9)^2}{(3)^2} = 34.57$; use $n = 35$

  c. $n = \dfrac{(1.96)^2(9)^2}{(2)^2} = 77.79$; use $n = 78$

25. a. Use $n = \dfrac{z_{\alpha/2}^2 \sigma^2}{E^2}$

  $n = \dfrac{(1.96)^2(6.84)^2}{(1.5)^2} = 79.88$; use $n = 80$

  b. $n = \dfrac{(1.645)^2(6.84)^2}{(2)^2} = 31.65$; use $n = 32$

26. a. 340
  b. 1358
  c. 8487

28. a. 343
  b. 487
  c. 840
  d. n gets larger; no to 99% confidence

30. 81

31. a. $\bar{p} = \dfrac{100}{400} = .25$

  b. $\sqrt{\dfrac{\bar{p}(1 - \bar{p})}{n}} = \sqrt{\dfrac{.25(.75)}{400}} = .0217$

  c. $\bar{p} \pm z_{.025}\sqrt{\dfrac{\bar{p}(1 - \bar{p})}{n}}$
    $.25 \pm 1.96(.0217)$
    $.25 \pm .0424$; .2076 to .2924

32. a. .6733 to .7267
  b. .6682 to .7318

34. 1068

35. a. $\bar{p} = \dfrac{281}{611} = .4599\ (46\%)$

  b. $z_{.05}\sqrt{\dfrac{\bar{p}(1 - \bar{p})}{n}} = 1.645\sqrt{\dfrac{4599(1 - .4599)}{611}} = .0332$

  c. $\bar{p} \pm .0332$
    $.4599 \pm .0332\ (.4267\text{ to }.4931)$

36. a. .4393
  b. .3870 to .4916

38. a. .0430
  b. .2170 to .3030
  c. 822

39. a. $n = \dfrac{1.96^2 p^*(1 - p^*)}{E^2}$

  $n = \dfrac{1.96^2(.33)(.67)}{(.03)^2} = 943.75$; use $n = 944$

  b. $n = \dfrac{2.576^2(.33)(.67)}{(.03)^2} = 1630.19$; use $n = 1631$

40. .0267, .8333 to .8867

42. a. .0442
  b. 601, 1068, 2401, 9604

44. a. 2009
  b. 47,991 to 52,009

46. a. 998
  b. \$24,479 to \$26,455
  c. \$93.5 million
  d. Yes; \$21.4 (30%) over *Lost World*

48. a. 14 minutes
  b. 13.38 to 14.62
  c. 32 per day
  d. Staff reduction

50. 37

52. 176

54. a. .5420
  b. .0508
  c. .4912 to .5928

56. a. .68
  b. .6391 to .7209

58. a. 1267
  b. 1509

60. a. .3101
  b. .2898 to .3304
  c. 8219; no, this sample size is unnecessarily large

Chapter 9

2. a. $H_0: \mu \leq 14$
    $H_a: \mu > 14$
  b. No evidence that the new plan increases sales
  c. The research hypothesis $\mu > 14$ is supported; the new plan increases sales

4. a. $H_0: \mu \geq 220$
    $H_a: \mu < 220$

5. a. Rejecting $H_0: \mu \leq 56.2$ when it is true
  b. Accepting $H_0: \mu \leq 56.2$ when it is false

6. a. $H_0: \mu \leq 1$
    $H_a: \mu > 1$
  b. Claiming $\mu > 1$ when it is not true
  c. Claiming $\mu \leq 1$ when it is not true

8. a. $H_0: \mu \geq 220$
$H_a: \mu < 220$

   b. Claiming $\mu < 220$ when it is not true

   c. Claiming $\mu \geq 220$ when it is not true

10. a. $z = \dfrac{\bar{x} - \mu_0}{\sigma/\sqrt{n}} = \dfrac{26.4 - 25}{6/\sqrt{40}} = 1.48$

   b. Using normal table with $z = 1.48$: p-value = $1.0000 - .9306 = .0694$
Using Excel: p-value = $1 - \text{NORMSDIST}(1.48)$
$= .0694$

   c. p-value $> .01$, do not reject H_0

   d. Reject H_0 if $z \geq 2.33$
$1.48 < 2.33$, do not reject H_0

11. a. $z = \dfrac{\bar{x} - \mu_0}{\sigma/\sqrt{n}} = \dfrac{14.15 - 15}{3/\sqrt{50}} = -2.00$

   b. p-value = $2(.0228) = .0456$

   c. p-value $\leq .05$, reject H_0

   d. Reject H_0 if $z \leq -1.96$ or $z \geq 1.96$
$-2.00 \leq -1.96$, reject H_0

12. a. .1056; do not reject H_0

   b. .0062; reject H_0

   c. ≈ 0; reject H_0

   d. .7967; do not reject H_0

14. a. .3844; do not reject H_0

   b. .0074; reject H_0

   c. .0836; do not reject H_0

15. a. $H_0: \mu \geq 1056$
$H_a: \mu < 1056$

   b. $z = \dfrac{\bar{x} - \mu_0}{\sigma/\sqrt{n}} = \dfrac{910 - 1056}{1600/\sqrt{400}} = -1.83$
p-value = .0336

   c. p-value $\leq .05$, reject H_0; the mean refund of "last-minute" filers is less than $1056

   d. Reject H_0 if $z \leq -1.645$
$-1.83 \leq -1.645$; reject H_0

16. a. $H_0: \mu \leq 895$
$H_a: \mu > 895$

   b. .1170

   c. Do not reject H_0

   d. Withhold judgment; collect more data

18. a. $H_0: \mu = 4.1$
$H_a: \mu \neq 4.1$

   b. -2.21, .0272

   c. Reject H_0

20. a. $H_0: \mu \geq 181,900$
$H_a: \mu < 181,900$

   b. -2.93

   c. .0017

   d. Reject H_0

22. a. $H_0: \mu = 8$
$H_a: \mu \neq 8$

   b. .1706

   c. Do not reject H_0

   d. 7.83 to 8.97; yes

24. a. $t = \dfrac{\bar{x} - \mu_0}{s/\sqrt{n}} = \dfrac{17 - 18}{4.5/\sqrt{48}} = -1.54$

   b. Degrees of freedom = $n - 1 = 47$
Area in lower tail is between .05 and .10
p-value (two-tail) is between .10 and .20
Using Excel: p-value = TDIST(1.54,47,2) = .1303

   c. p-value $> .05$; do not reject H_0

   d. With $df = 47$, $t_{.025} = 2.012$
Reject H_0 if $t \leq -2.012$ or $t \geq 2.012$
$t = -1.54$; do not reject H_0

26. a. Between .02 and .05; using Excel: p-value = TDIST(2.10,64,2) = .0397; reject H_0

   b. Between .01 and .02; using Excel: p-value = TDIST(2.57,64,2) = .0125; reject H_0

   c. Between .10 and .20; using Excel: p-value = TDIST(1.54,64,2) = .1285; do not reject H_0

27. a. $H_0: \mu \geq 238$
$H_a: \mu < 238$

   b. $t = \dfrac{\bar{x} - \mu_0}{s/\sqrt{n}} = \dfrac{231 - 238}{80/\sqrt{100}} = -.88$
Degrees of freedom = $n - 1 = 99$
p-value is between .10 and .20
Using Excel: p-value = TDIST(.88,99,1) = .1905

   c. p-value $> .05$; do not reject H_0
Cannot conclude mean weekly benefit in Virginia is less than the national mean

   d. $df = 99$, $t_{.05} = -1.66$
Reject H_0 if $t \leq -1.66$
$-.88 > -1.66$; do not reject H_0

28. a. $H_0: \mu \leq 3530$
$H_a: \mu > 3530$

   b. Between .005 and .01
Using Excel: p-value = TDIST(2.49,91,1) = .0072

   c. Reject H_0

30. a. $H_0: \mu = 600$
$H_a: \mu \neq 600$

   b. Between .20 and .40
Using Excel: p-value = TDIST(1.17,39,2) = .2491

   c. Do not reject H_0

   d. A larger sample size

32. a. $H_0: \mu = 10,192$
$H_a: \mu \neq 10,192$

   b. Between .02 and .05
Using Excel: p-value = TDIST(2.23,49,2) = .0304

   c. Reject H_0

34. a. $H_0: \mu = 2$
$H_a: \mu \neq 2$

   b. 2.2

   c. .516

   d. Between .20 and .40
Using Excel: p-value = TDIST(1.22,9,2) = .2535

   e. Do not reject H_0

36. a. $z = \dfrac{\bar{p} - p_0}{\sqrt{\dfrac{p_0(1 - p_0)}{n}}} = \dfrac{.68 - .75}{\sqrt{\dfrac{.75(1 - .75)}{300}}} = -2.80$

p-value $= .0026$

p-value $\leq .05$; reject H_0

b. $z = \dfrac{.72 - .75}{\sqrt{\dfrac{.75(1 - .75)}{300}}} = -1.20$

p-value $= .1151$

p-value $> .05$; do not reject H_0

c. $z = \dfrac{.70 - .75}{\sqrt{\dfrac{.75(1 - .75)}{300}}} = -2.00$

p-value $= .0228$

p-value $\leq .05$; reject H_0

d. $z = \dfrac{.77 - .75}{\sqrt{\dfrac{.75(1 - .75)}{300}}} = .80$

p-value $= .7881$

p-value $> .05$; do not reject H_0

38. a. $H_0: p = .64$
$H_a: p \neq .64$

b. $\bar{p} = 52/100 = .52$

$z = \dfrac{\bar{p} - p_0}{\sqrt{\dfrac{p_0(1 - p_0)}{n}}} = \dfrac{.52 - .64}{\sqrt{\dfrac{.64(1 - .64)}{100}}} = -2.50$

p-value $= 2(.0062) = .0124$

c. p-value $\leq .05$; reject H_0
Proportion differs from the reported .64

d. Yes, because $\bar{p} = .52$ indicates that fewer believe the supermarket brand is as good as the name brand

40. a. .2702
b. $H_0: p \leq .22$
$H_a: p > .22$
p-value ≈ 0; reject H_0
c. Helps evaluate the effectiveness of commercials

42. $H_0: p \leq .24$
$H_a: p > .24$
p-value $= .0023$; reject H_0

44. a. $H_0: p \leq .51$
$H_a: p > .51$
b. $\bar{p} = .58$, p-value $= .0026$
c. Reject H_0

46. a. $H_0: \mu = 16$
$H_a: \mu \neq 16$
b. .0286; reject H_0
Readjust line
c. .2186; do not reject H_0
Continue operation
d. $z = 2.19$; reject H_0
$z = -1.23$; do not reject H_0
Yes, same conclusion

48. a. $H_0: \mu \leq 45{,}250$
$H_a: \mu > 45{,}250$
b. .0034
c. Reject H_0

50. $t = -.93$
p-value between .20 and .40
Using Excel: p-value $=$ TDIST(.93,31,2) $= .3596$
Do not reject H_0

52. $t = 2.26$
p-value between .01 and .025
Using Excel: p-value $=$ TDIST(2.26,31,1) $= .0155$
Reject H_0

54. a. $H_0: p \leq .50$
$H_a: p > .50$
b. .64
c. .0026; reject H_0

56. a. $H_0: p \leq .50$
$H_a: p > .50$
b. .6381
c. .0023; reject H_0

58. $H_0: p \geq .90$
$H_a: p < .90$
p-value $= .0808$
Do not reject H_0

Chapter 10

1. a. $\bar{x}_1 - \bar{x}_2 = 13.6 - 11.6 = 2$
b. $z_{\alpha/2} = z_{.05} = 1.645$

$\bar{x}_1 - \bar{x}_2 \pm 1.645 \sqrt{\dfrac{\sigma_1^2}{n_1} + \dfrac{\sigma_2^2}{n_2}}$

$2 \pm 1.645 \sqrt{\dfrac{(2.2)^2}{50} + \dfrac{(3)^2}{35}}$

$2 \pm .98 \quad (1.02 \text{ to } 2.98)$

c. $z_{\alpha/2} = z_{.05} = 1.96$

$2 \pm 1.96 \sqrt{\dfrac{(2.2)^2}{50} + \dfrac{(3)^2}{35}}$

$2 \pm 1.17 \quad (.83 \text{ to } 3.17)$

2. a. $z = \dfrac{(\bar{x}_1 - \bar{x}_2) - D_0}{\sqrt{\dfrac{\sigma_1^2}{n_1} + \dfrac{\sigma_2^2}{n_2}}} = \dfrac{(25.2 - 22.8) - 0}{\sqrt{\dfrac{(5.2)^2}{40} + \dfrac{(6)^2}{50}}} = 2.03$

b. p-value $= 1.0000 - .9788 = .0212$
c. p-value $\leq .05$; reject H_0

4. a. $\bar{x}_1 - \bar{x}_2 = 2.04 - 1.72 = .32$

b. $z_{.025} \sqrt{\dfrac{\sigma_1^2}{n_1} + \dfrac{\sigma_2^2}{n_2}} = 1.96 \sqrt{\dfrac{(.10)^2}{40} + \dfrac{(.08)^2}{35}} = .04$

c. $.32 \pm .04 \quad (.28 \text{ to } .36)$

6. p-value $= .015$
Reject H_0; an increase

8. a. 1.08
b. .2802
c. Do not reject H_0; cannot conclude a difference exists

9. a. $\bar{x}_1 - \bar{x}_2 = 22.5 - 20.1 = 2.4$

b. $df = \dfrac{\left(\dfrac{s_1^2}{n_1} + \dfrac{s_2^2}{n_2}\right)^2}{\dfrac{1}{n_1 - 1}\left(\dfrac{s_1^2}{n_1}\right)^2 + \dfrac{1}{n_2 - 1}\left(\dfrac{s_2^2}{n_2}\right)^2}$

$= \dfrac{\left(\dfrac{2.5^2}{20} + \dfrac{4.8^2}{30}\right)^2}{\dfrac{1}{19}\left(\dfrac{2.5^2}{20}\right)^2 + \dfrac{1}{29}\left(\dfrac{4.8^2}{30}\right)^2} = 45.8$

c. $df = 45, t_{.025} = 2.014$

$t_{.025}\sqrt{\dfrac{s_1^2}{n_1} + \dfrac{s_2^2}{n_2}} = 2.014\sqrt{\dfrac{2.5^2}{20} + \dfrac{4.8^2}{30}} = 2.1$

d. 2.4 ± 2.1 (.3 to 4.5)

10. a. $t = \dfrac{(\bar{x}_1 - \bar{x}_2) - 0}{\sqrt{\dfrac{s_1^2}{n_1} + \dfrac{s_2^2}{n_2}}} = \dfrac{(13.6 - 10.1) - 0}{\sqrt{\dfrac{5.2^2}{35} + \dfrac{8.5^2}{40}}} = 2.18$

b. $df = \dfrac{\left(\dfrac{s_1^2}{n_1} + \dfrac{s_2^2}{n_2}\right)^2}{\dfrac{1}{n_1 - 1}\left(\dfrac{s_1^2}{n_1}\right)^2 + \dfrac{1}{n_2 - 1}\left(\dfrac{s_2^2}{n_2}\right)^2}$

$= \dfrac{\left(\dfrac{5.2^2}{35} + \dfrac{8.5^2}{40}\right)^2}{\dfrac{1}{34}\left(\dfrac{5.2^2}{35}\right)^2 + \dfrac{1}{39}\left(\dfrac{8.5^2}{40}\right)^2} = 65.7$

Use $df = 65$

c. $df = 65$, area in tail is between .01 and .025; two-tailed p-value is between .02 and .05

d. p-value $\leq$ .05; reject H_0

12. a. $\bar{x}_1 - \bar{x}_2 = 22.5 - 18.6 = 3.9$ miles

b. $df = \dfrac{\left(\dfrac{s_1^2}{n_1} + \dfrac{s_2^2}{n_2}\right)^2}{\dfrac{1}{n_1 - 1}\left(\dfrac{s_1^2}{n_1}\right)^2 + \dfrac{1}{n_2 - 1}\left(\dfrac{s_2^2}{n_2}\right)^2}$

$= \dfrac{\left(\dfrac{8.4^2}{50} + \dfrac{7.4^2}{40}\right)^2}{\dfrac{1}{49}\left(\dfrac{8.4^2}{50}\right)^2 + \dfrac{1}{39}\left(\dfrac{7.4^2}{40}\right)^2} = 87.1$

Use $df = 87, t_{.025} = 1.988$

$3.9 \pm 1.988\sqrt{\dfrac{8.4^2}{50} + \dfrac{7.4^2}{40}}$

3.9 ± 3.3 (.6 to 7.2)

14. a. $H_0: \mu_1 - \mu_2 = 0$
$H_a: \mu_1 - \mu_2 \neq 0$

b. 2.18

c. Between .02 and .05

d. Reject H_0; mean ages differ

16. a. $H_0: \mu_1 - \mu_2 \leq 0$
$H_a: \mu_1 - \mu_2 > 0$

b. 38

c. $t = 1.80, df = 25$
p-value between .025 and .05

d. Reject H_0; conclude higher mean score if college grad

18. a. $H_0: \mu_1 - \mu_2 \geq 120$
$H_a: \mu_1 - \mu_2 < 120$

b. -2.10
Between .01 and .025

c. 32 to 118

d. Larger sample size

19. a. 1, 2, 0, 0, 2

b. $\bar{d} = \Sigma d_i/n = 5/5 = 1$

c. $s_d = \sqrt{\dfrac{\Sigma(d_i - \bar{d})^2}{n - 1}} = \sqrt{\dfrac{4}{5 - 1}} = 1$

d. $t = \dfrac{\bar{d} - \mu}{s_d/\sqrt{n}} = \dfrac{1 - 0}{1/\sqrt{5}} = 2.24$

$df = n - 1 = 4$
p-value is between .025 and .05
p-value $\leq$ .05; reject H_0

20. a. 3, -1, 3, 5, 3, 0, 1

b. 2

c. 2.08

d. 2

e. .07 to 3.93

21. $H_0: \mu_d \leq 0$
$H_a: \mu_d > 0$
$\bar{d} = .625$
$s_d = 1.30$
$t = \dfrac{\bar{d} - \mu_d}{s_d/\sqrt{n}} = \dfrac{.625 - 0}{1.30/\sqrt{8}} = 1.36$
$df = n - 1 = 7$
p-value is between .10 and .20
p-value $>$ .05; do not reject H_0

22. .16 to .35

24. $t = 1.63$
p-value between .10 and .20
Do not reject H_0

26. a. $t = -.60$
p-value greater than .40
Do not reject H_0

b. $-.103$

c. .39; larger sample size

27. a. $\bar{\bar{x}} = (30 + 45 + 36)/3 = 37$

$\text{SSTR} = \sum_{j=1}^{k} n_j(\bar{x}_j - \bar{\bar{x}})^2$
$= 5(30 - 37)^2 + 5(45 - 37)^2 + 5(36 - 37)^2$
$= 570$

$\text{MSTR} = \dfrac{\text{SSTR}}{k - 1} = \dfrac{570}{2} = 285$

b. $\text{SSE} = \sum_{j=1}^{k}(n_j - 1)s_j^2$

$= 4(6) + 4(4) + 4(6.5) = 66$

$\text{MSE} = \dfrac{\text{SSE}}{n_T - k} = \dfrac{66}{15 - 3} = 5.5$

c. $F = \dfrac{\text{MSTR}}{\text{MSE}} = \dfrac{285}{5.5} = 51.82$

From the F table (2 degrees of freedom numerator and 12 denominator), p-value is less than .01

Because the p-value $\leq \alpha = .05$, we reject the null hypothesis that the means of the three populations are equal

d.

Source of Variation	Sum of Squares	Degrees of Freedom	Mean Square	F
Treatments	570	2	285	51.82
Error	66	12	5.5	
Total	636	14		

28. a. $\text{MSTR} = 268$
  b. $\text{MSE} = 92$
  c. Cannot reject H_0 because p-value is greater than .10
  d.

Source of Variation	Sum of Squares	Degrees of Freedom	Mean Square	F
Treatments	536	2	268	2.91
Error	828	9	92	
Total	1364	11		

30. b. Reject H_0 because p-value is less than .01

32.

	Mfg 1	Mfg 2	Mfg 3
Sample mean	23	28	21
Sample variance	6.67	4.67	3.33

$\bar{\bar{x}} = (23 + 28 + 21)/3 = 24$

$\text{SSTR} = \sum_{j=1}^{k}n_j(\bar{x}_j - \bar{\bar{x}})^2$

$= 4(23 - 24)^2 + 4(28 - 24)^2$
$+ 4(21 - 24)^2 = 104$

$\text{MSTR} = \dfrac{\text{SSTR}}{k - 1} = \dfrac{104}{2} = 52$

$\text{SSE} = \sum_{j=1}^{k}(n_j - 1)s_j^2$

$= 3(6.67) + 3(4.67) + 3(3.33) = 44.01$

$\text{MSE} = \dfrac{\text{SSE}}{n_T - k} = \dfrac{44.01}{12 - 3} = 4.89$

$F = \dfrac{\text{MSTR}}{\text{MSE}} = \dfrac{52}{4.89} = 10.63$

From the F table (2 degrees of freedom numerator and 9 denominator), p-value is less than .01

Actual p-value $= .0043$

Because the p-value $\leq \alpha = .05$, we reject the null hypothesis that the mean time needed to mix a batch of material is the same for each manufacturer

34. Significant; p-value is less than .05

36. Significant; p-value $= .0419$

38. 8934 to 11,066

40. a. $H_0: \mu_1 - \mu_2 \leq 0$
  $H_a: \mu_1 - \mu_2 > 0$
  b. $t = .60$, $df = 57$
  p-value greater than .20
  Do not reject H_0

42. a. 15 (or \$15,000)
  b. 9.81 to 20.19
  c. 11.5%

44. Sample means: 58.6, 48.8, 60.1; $F = 18.59$
  p-value ≈ 0; significant difference

46. Sample means: 7.41, 6.11, 7.06; $F = 9.33$
  p-value $\leq .01$; significant difference

Chapter 11

2. a. $\bar{p} = \dfrac{n_1\bar{p}_1 + n_2\bar{p}_2}{n_1 + n_2} = \dfrac{200(.22) + 300(.16)}{200 + 300} = .1840$

$z = \dfrac{\bar{p}_1 - \bar{p}_2}{\sqrt{\bar{p}(1 - \bar{p})\left(\dfrac{1}{n_1} + \dfrac{1}{n_2}\right)}}$

$= \dfrac{.22 - .16}{\sqrt{.1840(1 - .1840)\left(\dfrac{1}{200} + \dfrac{1}{300}\right)}} = 1.70$

p-value $= 1.0000 - .9554 = .0446$
  b. p-value $\leq .05$; reject H_0

3. $\bar{p}_1 = 220/400 = .55$ $\qquad \bar{p}_2 = 192/400 = .48$

$\bar{p}_1 - \bar{p}_2 \pm z_{.025}\sqrt{\dfrac{\bar{p}_1(1 - \bar{p}_1)}{n_1} + \dfrac{\bar{p}_2(1 - \bar{p}_2)}{n_2}}$

$.55 - .48 \pm 1.96\sqrt{\dfrac{.55(1 - .55)}{400} + \dfrac{.48(1 - .48)}{400}}$

$.07 \pm .0691 \qquad (.0009 \text{ to } .1391)$

7% more executives are predicting an increase in full-time jobs; the confidence interval shows the difference may be from 0% to 14%

4. a. .46, .28
  b. .18
  c. .0777
  d. .1023 to .2577, higher for Republicans

6. a. .803
  b. .849

c. $H_0: p_1 - p_2 \geq 0$
   $H_a: p_1 - p_2 < 0$
d. p-value $= .0055$
   Reject H_0

8. a. $H_0: p_1 - p_2 = 0$
   $H_a: p_1 - p_2 \neq 0$
b. .13
c. p-value $= .0404$

10. p-value $= .0322$
   Proportion in Washington greater

11. a. Expected frequencies: $e_1 = 200(.40) = 80$
   $e_2 = 200(.40) = 80$
   $e_3 = 200(.20) = 40$
   Actual frequencies: $f_1 = 60, f_2 = 120, f_3 = 20$

   $$\chi^2 = \frac{(60-80)^2}{80} + \frac{(120-80)^2}{80} + \frac{(20-40)^2}{40}$$

   $$= \frac{400}{80} + \frac{1600}{80} + \frac{400}{40}$$

   $$= 5 + 20 + 10 = 35$$

   Degrees of freedom: $k - 1 = 2$
   $\chi^2 = 35$ shows p-value ≈ 0
   p-value $\leq .01$; reject H_0
b. Reject H_0 if $\chi^2 \geq 9.210$
   $\chi^2 = 35$; reject H_0

12. $\chi^2 = 15.33, df = 3$
   p-value less than .005
   Reject H_0

13. $H_0: p_{ABC} = .29, p_{CBS} = .28, p_{NBC} = .25, p_{IND} = .18$
   $H_a:$ The proportions are not
   $\quad p_{ABC} = .29, p_{CBS} = .28, p_{NBC} = .25, p_{IND} = .18$
   Expected frequencies: $300(.29) = 87, 300(.28) = 84$
   $\qquad\qquad\qquad\qquad 300(.25) = 75, 300(.18) = 54$
   $e_1 = 87, e_2 = 84, e_3 = 75, e_4 = 54$
   Actual frequencies: $f_1 = 95, f_2 = 70, f_3 = 89, f_4 = 46$

   $$\chi^2 = \frac{(95-87)^2}{87} + \frac{(70-84)^2}{84} + \frac{(89-75)^2}{75}$$

   $$+ \frac{(46-54)^2}{54} = 6.87$$

   Degrees of freedom: $k - 1 = 3$
   $\chi^2 = 6.87$, p-value between .05 and .10
   Do not reject H_0

14. $\chi^2 = 29.51, df = 5$
   p-value ≈ 0
   Reject H_0

16. a. $\chi^2 = 12.21, df = 3$
   p-value is between .005 and .01
   Conclude difference for 2003
b. 21%, 30%, 15%, 34%
   Increased use of debit card
c. 51%

18. $\chi^2 = 16.31, df = 3$
   p-value less than .005
   Reject H_0

19. $H_0:$ The column variable is independent of the row variable
   $H_a:$ The column variable is not independent of the row variable
   Expected frequencies:

	A	B	C
P	28.5	39.9	45.6
Q	21.5	30.1	34.4

$$\chi^2 = \frac{(20-28.5)^2}{28.5} + \frac{(44-39.9)^2}{39.9} + \frac{(50-45.6)^2}{45.6}$$

$$+ \frac{(30-21.5)^2}{21.5} + \frac{(26-30.1)^2}{30.1} + \frac{(30-34.4)^2}{34.4}$$

$$= 7.86$$

Degrees of freedom: $(2-1)(3-1) = 2$
$\chi^2 = 7.86$, p-value between .01 and .025
Reject H_0

20. $\chi^2 = 19.77, df = 4$
   p-value less than .005
   Reject H_0

21. $H_0:$ Type of ticket purchased is independent of the type of flight
   $H_a:$ Type of ticket purchased is not independent of the type of flight
   Expected frequencies:
   $e_{11} = 35.59 \qquad e_{12} = 15.41$
   $e_{21} = 150.73 \qquad e_{22} = 65.27$
   $e_{31} = 455.68 \qquad e_{32} = 197.32$

Ticket	Flight	Observed Frequency (f_i)	Expected Frequency (e_i)	$(f_i - e_i)^2/e_i$
First	Domestic	29	35.59	1.22
First	International	22	15.41	2.82
Business	Domestic	95	150.73	20.61
Business	International	121	65.27	47.59
Full-fare	Domestic	518	455.68	8.52
Full-fare	International	135	197.32	19.68
Totals		920		$\chi^2 = 100.43$

Degrees of freedom: $(3-1)(2-1) = 2$
$\chi^2 = 100.43$, p-value ≈ 0
Reject H_0

22. a. $\chi^2 = 7.36, df = 2$
   p-value between .025 and .05
   Reject H_0
b. Domestic 47.2%

24. a. $\chi^2 = 10.60, df = 4$
   p-value between .025 and .05
   Reject H_0; not independent
b. Higher negative effect on grades as hours increase

26. a. $\chi^2 = 7.85, df = 3$
   p-value between .025 and .05
   Reject H_0
b. Pharmaceutical, 98.6%

28. a. $H_0: p_1 - p_2 = 0$
$H_a: p_1 - p_2 \neq 0$
b. .31, .26
c. $z = 2.04$; p-value $= .0414$
Reject H_0; conclude difference
d. .0475, .0025 to .0975

30. $z = 2.37$; p-value $= .0178$
Reject H_0

32. a. .16
b. $H_0: p_1 - p_2 \leq 0$
$H_a: p_1 - p_2 > 0$
c. $z = 3.49$; p-value ≈ 0
Reject H_0

34. $\chi^2 = 4.64$, $df = 2$
p-value between .05 and .10
Do not reject H_0

36. $\chi^2 = 42.53$, $df = 4$
p-value ≈ 0
Reject H_0

38. $\chi^2 = 23.37$, $df = 3$
p-value ≈ 0
Reject H_0

40. a. $\chi^2 = 12.86$, $df = 2$
p-value less than .005
Reject H_0
b. 66.9, 30.3, 2.9
54.0, 42.0, 4.0

42. a. 24.01, 41.16, 26.46, 8.37
Last entry combines 3 and 4
b. $\chi^2 = 6.17$, $df = 3$
p-value greater than .10
Do not reject H_0; binomial

Chapter 12

1. a.

y

14 —
12 —
10 —
8 —
6 —
4 —
2 —
0 ——┼——┼——┼——┼——┼—— x
0   1   2   3   4   5

b. There appears to be a positive linear relationship between x and y
c. Many different straight lines can be drawn to provide a linear approximation of the relationship between x and y; in part (d) we will determine the equation of a straight line that "best" represents the relationship according to the least squares criterion

d. $\bar{x} = \Sigma x_i / n = 15/5 = 3$, $\quad \bar{y} = \Sigma y_i / n = 40/5 = 8$,
$\Sigma(x_i - \bar{x})(y_i - \bar{y}) = 26$, $\quad \Sigma(x_i - \bar{x})^2 = 10$
$$b_1 = \frac{\Sigma(x_i - \bar{x})(y_i - \bar{y})}{\Sigma(x_i - \bar{x})^2} = \frac{26}{10} = 2.6$$
$b_0 = \bar{y} - b_1 \bar{x} = 8 - (2.6)(3) = 0.2$
$\hat{y} = 0.2 - 2.6x$
e. $\hat{y} = .2 + 2.6x = .2 + 2.6(4) = 10.6$

2. b. There appears to be a negative linear relationship between x and y
d. $\hat{y} = 68 - 3x$
e. 38

4. a.

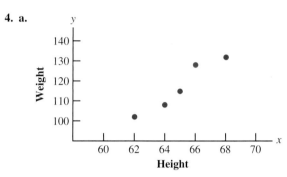

b. It indicates there may be a positive linear relationship between height and weight
c. Many different straight lines can be drawn to provide a linear approximation of the relationship between height and weight; in part (d) we will determine the equation of a straight line that "best" represents the relationship according to the least squares criterion
d. Summations needed to compute the slope and y-intercept:
$\bar{x} = \Sigma x_i / n = 325/5 = 65$,
$\bar{y} = \Sigma y_i / n = 585/5 = 117$,
$\Sigma(x_i - \bar{x})(y_i - \bar{y}) = 110$, $\quad \Sigma(x_i - \bar{x})^2 = 20$
$$b_1 = \frac{\Sigma(x_i - \bar{x})(y_i - \bar{y})}{\Sigma(x_i - \bar{x})^2} = \frac{110}{20} = 5.5$$
$b_0 = \bar{y} - b_1 \bar{x} = 117 - (5.5)(65) = -240.5$
$\hat{y} = -240.5 + 5.5x$
e. $\hat{y} = -240.5 + 5.5(63) = 106$
The estimate of weight is 106 pounds

6. c. $\hat{y} = -10.16 + .18x$
e. 11.95 or approximately \$12,000

8. c. $\hat{y} = 490.21 + 204.24x$
d. \$1307

10. b. $\hat{y} = 51.8273 + .1452x$
c. 84.4973 or approximately 84

12. c. $\hat{y} = 1293.3190 + .3165x$
d. 25,031

14. b. $\hat{y} = 28.30 - .0415x$
c. 26.2

15. a. $\hat{y}_i = .2 + 2.6x_i$ and $\bar{y} = 8$

x_i	y_i	$\hat{y}_i$	$y_i - \hat{y}_i$	$(y_i - \hat{y}_i)^2$	$y_i - \bar{y}$	$(y_i - \bar{y})^2$
1	3	2.8	.2	.04	-5	25
2	7	5.4	1.6	2.56	-1	1
3	5	8.0	-3.0	9.00	-3	9
4	11	10.6	.4	.16	3	9
5	14	13.2	.8	.64	6	36
				SSE = 12.40		SST = 80

$$SSR = SST - SSE = 80 - 12.4 = 67.6$$

b. $r^2 = \dfrac{SSR}{SST} = \dfrac{67.6}{80} = .845$

The least squares line provided a good fit; 84.5% of the variability in y has been explained by the least squares line

c. $r = \sqrt{.845} = +.9192$

16. a. SSE = 230, SST = 1850, SSR = 1620

b. $r^2 = .876$

c. $r = -.936$

18. a. The estimated regression equation and the mean for the dependent variable:

$$\hat{y} = 1790.5 + 581.1x, \quad \bar{y} = 3650$$

The sum of squares due to error and the total sum of squares:

$$SSE = \Sigma(y_i - \hat{y}_i)^2 = 85,135.14$$
$$SST = \Sigma(y_i - \bar{y})^2 = 335,000$$

Thus, SSR = SST − SSE
$$= 335,000 - 85,135.14 = 249,864.86$$

b. $r^2 = \dfrac{SSR}{SST} = \dfrac{249,864.86}{335,000} = .746$

The least squares line accounted for 74.6% of the total sum of squares

c. $r = \sqrt{.746} = +.8637$

20. a. $\hat{y} = -48.111111 + 2.332505x$

b. $r^2 = .82$; yes, we should feel comfortable

c. $173,500

22. a. $\hat{y} = -745.480627 + 117.917320x$

b. $r^2 = .7071$

c. $r = +.84$

23. a. $s^2 = MSE = \dfrac{SSE}{n-2} = \dfrac{12.4}{3} = 4.133$

b. $s = \sqrt{MSE} = \sqrt{4.133} = 2.033$

c. $\Sigma(x_i - \bar{x})^2 = 10$

$$s_{b_1} = \dfrac{s}{\sqrt{\Sigma(x_i - \bar{x})^2}} = \dfrac{2.033}{\sqrt{10}} = .643$$

d. $t = \dfrac{b_1 - \beta_1}{s_{b_1}} = \dfrac{2.6 - 0}{.643} = 4.04$

From the t table (3 degrees of freedom), area in tail is between .01 and .025

p-value is between .02 and .05

Actual *p*-value = .0272

Because the *p*-value $\leq \alpha$, we reject H_0: $\beta_1 = 0$

e. $MSR = \dfrac{SSR}{1} = 67.6$

$$F = \dfrac{MSR}{MSE} = \dfrac{67.6}{4.133} = 16.36$$

From the F table (1 degree of freedom numerator and 3 denominator), *p*-value is between .025 and .05

Actual *p*-value = .0272

Because the *p*-value $\leq \alpha$, we reject H_0: $\beta_1 = 0$

Source of Variation	Sum of Squares	Degrees of Freedom	Mean Square	F
Regression	67.6	1	67.6	16.36
Error	12.4	3	4.133	
Total	80	4		

24. a. 76.6667

b. 8.7560

c. .6526

d. Significant; *p*-value is .0193

e. Significant; *p*-value is .0193

26. a. $s^2 = MSE = \dfrac{SSE}{n-2} = \dfrac{85,135.14}{4} = 21,283.79$

$s = \sqrt{MSE} = \sqrt{21,283.79} = 145.89$

$\Sigma(x_i - \bar{x})^2 = .74$

$$s_{b_1} = \dfrac{s}{\sqrt{\Sigma(x_i - \bar{x})^2}} = \dfrac{145.89}{\sqrt{.74}} = 169.59$$

$$t = \dfrac{b_1 - \beta_1}{s_{b_1}} = \dfrac{581.08 - 0}{169.59} = 3.43$$

From the t table (4 degrees of freedom), area in tail is between .01 and .025

p-value is between .02 and .05

Actual *p*-value = .0266

Because the *p*-value $\leq \alpha$, we reject H_0: $\beta_1 = 0$

b. $MSR = \dfrac{SSR}{1} = \dfrac{249,864.86}{1} = 249,864.86$

$$F = \dfrac{MSR}{MSE} = \dfrac{249,864.86}{21,283.79} = 11.74$$

From the F table (1 degree of freedom numerator and 4 denominator), *p*-value is between .025 and .05

Actual *p*-value = .0266

Because the *p*-value $\leq \alpha$, we reject H_0: $\beta_1 = 0$

c.

Source of Variation	Sum of Squares	Degrees of Freedom	Mean Square	F
Regression	29,864.86	1	29,864.86	11.74
Error	85,135.14	4	21,283.79	
Total	335,000	5		

28. They are related; p-value is .0006

30. Significant; p-value is .0024

32. a. $\hat{y} = 6.1092 + .8951x$
   b. Significant relationship
   c. $r^2 = .82$; a good fit

34. a. $\hat{y} = 80.0 + 50.0x$
   b. p-value $\le \alpha$; reject H_0: $\beta_1 = 0$
   c. p-value $\le \alpha$; reject H_0: $\beta_1 = 0$
   d. p-value $= .000$

36. b. There appears to be a negative linear relationship between the two variables
   c. $\hat{y} = 37.0747 - 0.7792x$
   d. Significant relationship
   e. 0.43; not a very good fit

37. a. $s = 2.033$

$$\bar{x} = 3, \Sigma(x_i - \bar{x})^2 = 10$$

$$s_{\hat{y}_p} = s\sqrt{\frac{1}{n} + \frac{(x_p - \bar{x})^2}{\Sigma(x_i - \bar{x})^2}}$$

$$= 2.033\sqrt{\frac{1}{5} + \frac{(4 - 3)^2}{10}} = 1.11$$

   b. $\hat{y} = .2 + 2.6x = .2 + 2.6(4) = 10.6$

$$\hat{y}_p \pm t_{\alpha/2}s_{\hat{y}_p}$$
$$10.6 \pm 3.182(1.11)$$
$$10.6 \pm 3.53, \text{ or } 7.07 \text{ to } 14.13$$

   c. $s_{\text{ind}} = s\sqrt{1 + \frac{1}{n} + \frac{(x_p - \bar{x})^2}{\Sigma(x_i - \bar{x})^2}}$

$$= 2.033\sqrt{1 + \frac{1}{5} + \frac{(4 - 3)^2}{10}} = 2.32$$

   d. $\hat{y}_p \pm t_{\alpha/2}s_{\text{ind}}$
$$10.6 \pm 3.182(2.32)$$
$$10.6 \pm 7.38, \text{ or } 3.22 \text{ to } 17.98$$

38. a. 8.7560
   b. 24.07 to 51.93
   c. 9.7895
   d. 6.85 to 69.15

40. a. $s = 145.89$, $\bar{x} = 3.2$, $\Sigma(x_i - \bar{x})^2 = .74$
$$\hat{y} = 1790.5 + 581.1x = 1790.5 + 581.1(3)$$
$$= 3533.8$$

$$s_{\hat{y}_p} = s\sqrt{\frac{1}{n} + \frac{(x_p - \bar{x})^2}{\Sigma(x_i - \bar{x})^2}}$$

$$= 145.89\sqrt{\frac{1}{6} + \frac{(3 - 3.2)^2}{.74}} = 68.54$$

$$\hat{y}_p \pm t_{\alpha/2}s_{\hat{y}_p}$$
$$3533.8 \pm 2.776(68.54)$$
$$3533.8 \pm 190.27, \text{ or } \$3343.53 \text{ to } \$3724.07$$
   b. $\hat{y} = 1790.5 + 581.1x = 1790.5 + 581.1(3)$
$$= 3533.8$$

$$s_{\text{ind}} = s\sqrt{1 + \frac{1}{n} + \frac{(x_p - \bar{x})^2}{\Sigma(x_i - \bar{x})^2}}$$

$$= 145.89\sqrt{1 + \frac{1}{6} + \frac{(3 - 3.2)^2}{0.74}} = 161.19$$

$$\hat{y}_p \pm t_{\alpha/2}s_{\text{ind}}$$
$$3533.8 \pm 2.776(161.19)$$
$$3533.8 \pm 447.46, \text{ or } \$3086.34 \text{ to } \$3981.26$$

42. a. $11,740 to $14,420
   b. $9,300 to $16,860
   c. Yes, $20,400 is much larger than anticipated
   d. Any deductions exceeding $16,800

44. a. $\hat{y} = -6.76 + 1.755x$
   b. $r^2 = .713$; a good fit
   c. 31.8 to 60
   d. 6.3 to 85.5

45. a. Using Excel's Regression tool the estimated regression equation is $\hat{y} = -7.0222 + 1.5873x$ or $\hat{y} = -7.02 + 1.59x$

   b.

x_i	y_i	$\hat{y}_i$	$y_i - \hat{y}_i$
6	6	2.52	3.48
11	8	10.47	-2.47
15	12	16.83	-4.83
18	20	21.60	-1.60
20	30	24.78	5.22

   c.

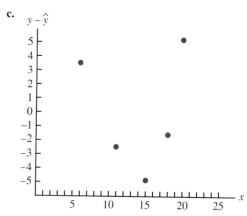

With only five observations, it is difficult to determine whether the assumptions are satisfied; however, the plot does suggest curvature in the residuals, which would indicate that the error term assumptions are not satisfied; the scatter diagram for these data also indicates that the underlying relationship between x and y may be curvilinear

46. a. $\hat{y} = 2.322 + .6366x$
   b. Assumption that variance is the same for all values of x is questionable; the variance appears to increase for larger values of x

47. Using Excel's Regression tool, the estimated regression equation is $\hat{y} = 29.3991 + 1.5475x$ or $\hat{y} = 29.40 + 1.55x$

  b. Significant relationship: Significance F (or p-value) $< \alpha = .05$

  c.

x_i	y_i	$\hat{y}_i = 29.40 + 1.55x_i$	$y_i - \hat{y}_i$
1	19	30.95	−11.95
2	32	32.50	−.50
4	44	35.60	8.40
6	40	38.70	1.30
10	52	44.90	7.10
14	53	51.10	1.90
20	54	60.40	−6.40

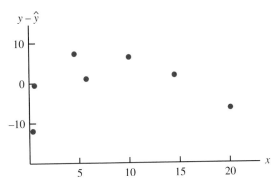

  d. The residual plot leads us to question the assumption of a linear relationship between x and y; even though the relationship is significant at the $\alpha = .05$ level, it would be extremely dangerous to extrapolate beyond the range of the data (e.g., $x > 20$)

48. **b.** The assumptions concerning the error terms appear reasonable

50. No; regression or correlation can never prove that two variables are casually related

52. **a.** $\hat{y} = 9.2649 + 0.7105$ Shares

  b. Significant; p-value $= .0013$

  c. $r^2 = .744$; good fit

  d. 13.53

54. **a.** $\hat{y} = 0.2747 + 0.9498$ S&P

  b. Significant; p-value $= .029$

  c. $r^2 = .470$; not a good fit

  d. Woolworth has a higher risk with a market beta of 1.25

56. **a.** $\hat{y} = 10.528 + .9534x$

  b. Significant; p-value $= .0001$

  c. \$2874 to \$4952

  d. Yes; expected expense is \$3913

58. **a.** Negative linear relationship

  b. $\hat{y} = 8.0978 - 0.3442$ Distance to Work

  c. Significant; p-value $= .0022$

  d. $r^2 = .711$; reasonably good fit

  e. 5.2 to 7.6

60. **a.** $\hat{y} = 5.8470 + 0.8295$ Hours Studying

  b. Significant; p-value $= .000$

  c. 84.65 points

  d. 63.35 to 103.96

Chapter 13

2. **a.** The estimated regression equation is
  $\hat{y} = 45.0594 + 1.9436x_1$
  An estimate of y when $x_1 = 45$ is
  $\hat{y} = 45.0594 + 1.9436(45) = 132.52$

  b. The estimated regression equation is
  $\hat{y} = 85.2171 + 4.3215x_2$
  An estimate of y when $x_2 = 15$ is
  $\hat{y} = 85.2171 + 4.3215(15) = 150.04$

  c. The estimated regression equation is
  $\hat{y} = -18.3683 + 2.0102x_1 + 4.7378x_2$
  An estimate of y when $x_1 = 45$ and $x_2 = 15$ is
  $\hat{y} = -18.3683 + 2.0102(45) + 4.7378(15) = 143.16$

4. **a.** \$255,000

5. **a.** The Excel output is shown in Figure D13.5a

  b. The Excel output is shown in Figure D13.5b

  c. It is 1.6039 in part (a) and 2.2902 in part (b); in part (a) the coefficient is an estimate of the change in revenue due to a one-unit change in television advertising expenditures; in part (b) it represents an estimate of the change in revenue due to a one-unit change in television advertising expenditures when the amount of newspaper advertising is held constant

  d. Revenue $= 83.2301 + 2.2902(3.5) + 1.3010(1.8)$
  $= 93.59$ or \$93,590

6. **a.** $\hat{y} = .3540 + .0009$ HR

  b. $\hat{y} = .8647 - .0837$ ERA

  c. $\hat{y} = .7092 + .0014$ HR $- .1026$ ERA

  d. .551

8. **a.** Return $= 247.3579 - 32.8445$ Safety $+ 34.5887$ ExpRatio

  b. 70.2

10. **a.** $\hat{y} = -1.2207 + 3.9576$ FG%

  b. .04

  c. $\hat{y} = -1.2346 + 4.8166$ FG% $- 2.5895$ Opp 3 Pt% $+ .0344$ Opp TO

  e. .6372

12. **a.** $R^2 = \dfrac{\text{SSR}}{\text{SST}} = \dfrac{14,052.2}{15,182.9} = .926$

  b. $R_a^2 = 1 - (1 - R^2)\dfrac{n-1}{n-p-1}$
  $= 1 - (1 - .926)\dfrac{10-1}{10-2-1} = .905$

  c. Yes; after adjusting for the number of independent variables in the model, we see that 90.5% of the variability in y has been accounted for

14. **a.** .75

  b. .68

FIGURE D13.5a

Regression Statistics	
Multiple R	0.8078
R Square	0.6526
Adjusted R Square	0.5946
Standard Error	1.2152
Observations	8

ANOVA

	df	SS	MS	F	Significance F
Regression	1	16.6401	16.6401	11.2688	0.0153
Residual	6	8.8599	1.4767		
Total	7	25.5			

	Coefficients	Standard Error	t Stat	P-value
Intercept	88.6377	1.5824	56.0159	2.174E-09
Television Advertising ($1000s)	1.6039	0.4778	3.3569	0.0153

15. a. $R^2 = \dfrac{SSR}{SST} = \dfrac{23.435}{25.5} = .919$

$R_a^2 = 1 - (1 - R^2)\dfrac{n-1}{n-p-1}$

$= 1 - (1 - .919)\dfrac{8-1}{8-2-1} = .887$

b. Multiple regression analysis is preferred because both R^2 and R_a^2 show an increased percentage of the variability of y explained when both independent variables are used

16. a. No, $R^2 = .1532$

    b. Using both independent variables provides a better fit

18. a. $R^2 = .5638$, $R_a^2 = .5114$

    b. The fit is not very good; but it does explain over 50% of the variability in y

19. a. $MSR = \dfrac{SSR}{p} = \dfrac{6216.375}{2} = 3108.188$

$MSE = \dfrac{SSE}{n-p-1} = \dfrac{507.75}{10-2-1} = 72.536$

FIGURE D13.5b

Regression Statistics	
Multiple R	0.9587
R Square	0.9190
Adjusted R Square	0.8866
Standard Error	0.6426
Observations	8

ANOVA

	df	SS	MS	F	Significance F
Regression	2	23.4354	11.7177	28.3778	0.0019
Residual	5	2.0646	0.4129		
Total	7	25.5			

	Coefficients	Standard Error	t Stat	P-value
Intercept	83.2301	1.5739	52.8825	4.57E-08
Television Advertising ($1000s)	2.2902	0.3041	7.5319	0.0007
Newspaper Advertising ($1000s)	1.3010	0.3207	4.0567	0.0098

b. $F = \dfrac{\text{MSR}}{\text{MSE}} = \dfrac{3108.188}{72.536} = 42.85$

p-value (2 degrees of freedom numerator and 7 denominator) = .0001

Because the p-value $\leq \alpha = .05$, the overall model is significant

c. $t = \dfrac{b_1}{s_{b_1}} = \dfrac{.5906}{.0813} = 7.26$

p-value (7 degrees of freedom) = .0002

Because the p-value $\leq \alpha = .05$, β_1 is significant

d. $t = \dfrac{b_2}{s_{b_2}} = \dfrac{.4980}{.0567} = 8.78$

p-value (7 degrees of freedom) = .0001

Because the p-value $\leq \alpha = .05$, β_2 is significant

20. a. Significant; p-value = .0001
   b. Significant; p-value = .0000
   c. Significant; p-value = .0016

22. a. SSE = 4000, MSE = 571.43,
   MSR = 6000
   b. Significant; p-value = .0078

23. a. $F = 28.38$

p-value (2 degrees of freedom numerator and 1 denominator) = .0019

Because the p-value $\leq \alpha = .01$, reject H_0

b. $t = 7.53$

p-value = .0007

Because p-value $\leq \alpha = .05$, β_1 is significant and x_1 should not be dropped from the model

c. $t = 4.06$

$t_{.025} = 2.571$

With $t > t_{.025} = 2.571$, β_2 is significant and x_2 should not be dropped from the model

24. a. Significant relationship
   b. Both independent variables are significant

26. a. Significant; p-value = .0000
   b. All of the independent variables are significant

28. a. Using the PredInt macro, the 95% confidence interval is 132.16 to 154.16
   b. Using the PredInt macro, the 95% prediction interval is 111.13 to 175.18

29. a. See Excel output in Figure D13.5b
   $\hat{y} = 83.2301 + 2.2902(3.5) + 1.3010(1.8) = 93.588$
   or $93,588
   b. Using the PredInt macro: 92.840 to 94.335, or $92,840 to $94,335
   c. Using the PredInt macro: 91.774 to 95.401, or $91,774 to $95,401

30. a. 58.37% to 75.03%
   b. 35.24% to 90.59%

32. a. $E(y) = \beta_0 + \beta_1 x_1 + \beta_2 x_2$

where $x_2 = \begin{cases} 0 \text{ if level 1} \\ 1 \text{ if level 2} \end{cases}$

b. $E(y) = \beta_0 + \beta_1 x_1 + \beta_2(0) = \beta_0 + \beta_1 x_1$
   c. $E(y) = \beta_0 + \beta_1 x_1 + \beta_2(1) = \beta_0 + \beta_1 x_1 + \beta_2$
   d. $\beta_2 = E(y \mid \text{level 2}) - E(y \mid \text{level 1})$
   β_1 is the change in $E(y)$ for a one-unit change in x_1 holding x_2 constant

34. a. $15,300
   b. $\hat{y} = 10.1 - 4.2(2) + 6.8(8) + 15.3(0) = 56.1$
   Sales prediction: $56,100
   c. $\hat{y} = 10.1 - 4.2(1) + 6.8(3) + 15.3(1) = 41.6$
   Sales prediction: $41,600

36. a. $\hat{y} = 1.8602 + 0.2914\,\text{Months} + 1.1024\,\text{Type} - 0.6091\,\text{Person}$
   b. Significant; p-value = .0021 $< \alpha = .05$
   c. Person is not significant

38. a. $\hat{y} = -91.7595 + 1.0767\,\text{Age} + .2518\,\text{Pressure} + 8.7399\,\text{Smoker}$
   b. Significant; p-value = .0102 $< \alpha = .05$
   c. 95% prediction interval is 21.35 to 47.18 or a probability of .2135 to .4718; quit smoking and begin some type of treatment to reduce his blood pressure

40. a. Job satisfaction can be expected to decrease by 8.69 units with a one-unit increase in length of service if the wage rate does not change; a dollar increase in the wage rate is associated with a 13.5 point increase in the job satisfaction score when the length of service does not change
   b. $\hat{y} = 14.4 - 8.69(4) + 13.5(6.5) = 67.39$

42. a. $\hat{y} = -1.4053 + 0.0235\,X1 + 0.0049\,X2$
   b. Significant; p-value = .0000
   c. $R^2 = \dfrac{\text{SSR}}{\text{SST}} = .937$

   $R_a^2 = 1 - (1 - .937)\dfrac{9}{7} = .919$; good fit

   d. For β_1: significant (p-value = .0303)
   For β_2: significant (p-value = .0028)

44. a. $\hat{y} = 50.6095 + 1.5621\,\text{RecRes}$
   b. No; only 43.15% of the variability in Score is explained by the RecRes
   c. $\hat{y} = 33.4848 + 1.8998\,\text{RecRes} + 2.6108\,\text{Afford}$
   Significant; p-value = .000

46. a. $\hat{y} = 24.1207 - 2.1019\,\text{Displacement}$
   Significant; p-value = .0001
   b. $\hat{y} = 26.3827 - 2.4387\,\text{Displacement} - 1.2015\,\text{Drive4}$
   c. Because p-value = .0160, Drive4 is significant
   d. $\hat{y} = 33.3328 - 4.1492\,\text{Displacement} - 1.2368\,\text{Drive4} + 2.1615\,\text{EightCyl}$
   e. Because the p-value = .0000 $< \alpha = .05$, there is a significant overall relationship
   For Displacement: Because the p-value = .0000, Displacement is significant

For Drive4: Because the p-value = .0073, Drive4 is significant
For EightCyl: Because the p-value = .0104, EightCyl is significant

Chapter 14

2. a. 5.42
   b. UCL = 6.09, LCL = 4.75

4. R chart:
   UCL = $\bar{R}D_4$ = 1.6(1.864) = 2.98
   LCL = $\bar{R}D_3$ = 1.6(.136) = .22
   $\bar{x}$ chart:
   UCL = $\bar{\bar{x}} + A_2\bar{R}$ = 28.5 + .373(1.6) = 29.10
   LCL = $\bar{\bar{x}} - A_2\bar{R}$ = 28.5 − .373(1.6) = 27.90

6. 20.01, .082

8. a. .0470
   b. UCL = .0989, LCL = −.0049 (use LCL = 0)
   c. $\bar{p}$ = .08; in control
   d. UCL = 14.826, LCL = −0.726 (use LCL = 0)
      Process is out of control if more than 14 defective
   e. In control with 12 defective
   f. np chart

10. $f(x) = \dfrac{n!}{x!(n-x)!} p^x(1-p)^{n-x}$

When p = .02, the probability of accepting the lot is

$$f(0) = \frac{25!}{0!(25-0)!}(.02)^0(1-.02)^{25} = .6035$$

When p = .06, the probability of accepting the lot is

$$f(0) = \frac{25!}{0!(25-0)!}(.06)^0(1-.06)^{25} = .2129$$

12. p_0 = .02; producer's risk = .0599
   p_0 = .06; producer's risk = .3396
   Producer's risk decreases as the acceptance criterion c is increased

14. n = 20, c = 3

16. a. 95.4
   b. UCL = 96.07, LCL = 94.73
   c. No

18.

	R Chart	$\bar{x}$ Chart
UCL	4.23	6.57
LCL	0	4.27

Estimate of standard deviation = .86

20.

	R Chart	$\bar{x}$ Chart
UCL	.1121	3.112
LCL	0	3.051

22. a. UCL = .0817, LCL = −.0017 (use LCL = 0)

24. a. .03
   b. β = .0802

Excel provides a wealth of functions for data management and statistical analysis. If we know what function is needed, and how to use it, we can simply enter the function into the appropriate worksheet cell. However, if we are not sure what functions are available to accomplish a task or are not sure how to use a particular function, Excel can provide assistance.

Finding the Right Excel Function

*In earlier versions of Excel, the **Paste Function** dialog box serves the same purpose as the **Insert Function** dialog box in Excel 2003.*

To identify the functions available in Excel, select the **Insert** menu and then choose **Function** from the list of options. Alternatively, select the f_x button on the formula bar. Either approach provides the **Insert Function** dialog box shown in Figure 1.

The **Search for a function** box at the top of the Insert Function dialog box enables us to type a brief description of what we want to do. After doing so and clicking **Go**, Excel will search for and display, in the **Select a function** box, the functions that may accomplish our task. In many situations, however, we may want to browse through an entire category of functions to see what is available. For this task, the **Or select a category** box is helpful. It contains a drop-down list of several categories of functions provided by Excel. Figure 1 shows that we selected the **Statistical** category. As a result, Excel's statistical functions

FIGURE 1   INSERT FUNCTION DIALOG BOX

appear in alphabetic order in the Select a function box. We see the AVEDEV function listed first, followed by the AVERAGE function, and so on.

The AVEDEV function is highlighted in Figure 1, indicating it is the function currently selected. The proper syntax for the function and a brief description of the function appear below the Select a function box. We can scroll through the list in the Select a function box to display the syntax and a brief description for each of the statistical functions available. For instance, scrolling down farther, we select the COUNTIF function. See Figure 2. Note that COUNTIF is now highlighted, and that immediately below the Select a function box we see **COUNTIF(range,criteria)**, which indicates that the COUNTIF function contains two arguments, range and criteria. In addition, we see that the description of the COUNTIF function is "Counts the number of cells within a range that meet the given condition."

If the function selected (highlighted) is the one we want to use, we click **OK**; the **Function Arguments** dialog box then appears. The Function Arguments dialog box for the COUNTIF function is shown in Figure 3. This dialog box assists in creating the appropriate arguments for the function selected. When finished entering the arguments, we click **OK**; Excel then inserts the function into a worksheet cell.

*In earlier versions of Excel, a similar dialog box will appear. It serves the same purpose as the **Function Arguments** dialog box in Excel 2003.*

Inserting a Function into a Worksheet Cell

We will now show how to use the Insert Function and Function Arguments dialog boxes to select a function, develop its arguments, and insert the function into a worksheet cell.

In Section 2.1, we used Excel's COUNTIF function to construct a frequency distribution for soft drink purchases. Figure 4 displays an Excel worksheet containing the soft drink

**FIGURE 2   DESCRIPTION OF THE COUNTIF FUNCTION IN THE INSERT FUNCTION
DIALOG BOX**

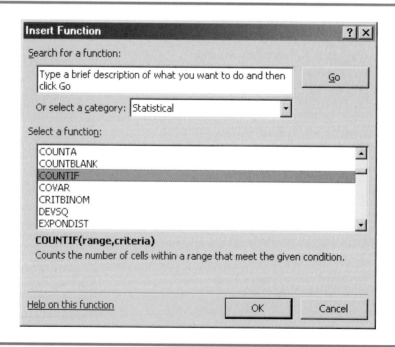

FIGURE 3   FUNCTION ARGUMENTS DIALOG BOX FOR THE COUNTIF FUNCTION

Function Arguments   ☒

┌─ COUNTIF ──┐
│   │
│   **Range** [▦] = reference   │
│   │
│   **Criteria** [▦] = any   │
│   │
│   =   │
│   Counts the number of cells within a range that meet the given condition. │
│   │
│   │
│   **Range** is the range of cells from which you want to count nonblank cells. │
│   │
│   │
│   Formula result =   │
│   │
│   Help on this function   [OK]   [Cancel]   │
└──┘

FIGURE 4   EXCEL WORKSHEET WITH SOFT DRINK DATA AND LABELS FOR THE
FREQUENCY DISTRIBUTION WE WOULD LIKE TO CONSTRUCT

CD file

SoftDrink

*Note: Rows 11–44
are hidden.*

	A	B	C	D	E
1	**Brand Purchased**		**Soft Drink**	**Frequency**	
2	Coke Classic		Coke Classic		
3	Diet Coke		Diet Coke		
4	Pepsi-Cola		Dr. Pepper		
5	Diet Coke		Pepsi-Cola		
6	Coke Classic		Sprite		
7	Coke Classic				
8	Dr. Pepper				
9	Diet Coke				
10	Pepsi-Cola				
45	Pepsi-Cola				
46	Pepsi-Cola				
47	Pepsi-Cola				
48	Coke Classic				
49	Dr. Pepper				
50	Pepsi-Cola				
51	Sprite				
52					

data and labels for the frequency distribution we would like to construct. We see that the frequency of Coke Classic purchases will go into cell D2, the frequency of Diet Coke purchases will go into cell D3, and so on. Suppose we want to use the COUNTIF function to compute the frequencies for these cells and would like some assistance from Excel.

Step 1. Select cell D2

Step 2. Click f_x on the formula bar (or select **Insert** and then choose **Function**)

Step 3. When the **Insert Function** dialog box appears:
Select **Statistical** in the **Or select a category box**
Select **COUNTIF** in the **Select a function box**
Click **OK**

Step 4. When the **Function Arguments** box appears (see Figure 5):
Enter $A$2:$A$51 in the **Range** box
Enter C2 in the **Criteria** box (At this point, the value of the function will appear on the next-to-last line of the dialog box. Its value is 19.)
Click **OK**

Step 5. Copy cell D2 to cells D3:D6

The worksheet then appears as in Figure 6. The formula worksheet is in the background; the value worksheet appears in the foreground. The formula worksheet shows that the COUNTIF function was inserted into cell D2. We copied the contents of cell D2 into cells D3:D6. The value worksheet shows the proper class frequencies as computed.

We illustrated the use of Excel's capability to provide assistance in using the COUNTIF function. The procedure is similar for all Excel functions. This capability is especially helpful if you do not know what function to use or forget the proper name and/or syntax for a function.

FIGURE 5   COMPLETED FUNCTION ARGUMENTS DIALOG BOX
FOR THE COUNTIF FUNCTION

FIGURE 6   EXCEL WORKSHEET SHOWING THE USE OF EXCEL'S COUNTIF FUNCTION TO CONSTRUCT A FREQUENCY DISTRIBUTION

	A	B	C	D	E
1	**Brand Purchased**		**Soft Drink**	**Frequency**	
2	Coke Classic		Coke Classic	=COUNTIF($A$2:$A$51,C2)	
3	Diet Coke		Diet Coke	=COUNTIF($A$2:$A$51,C3)	
4	Pepsi-Cola		Dr. Pepper	=COUNTIF($A$2:$A$51,C4)	
5	Diet Coke		Pepsi-Cola	=COUNTIF($A$2:$A$51,C5)	
6	Coke Classic		Sprite	=COUNTIF($A$2:$A$51,C6)	
7	Coke Classic				
8	Dr. Pepper				
9	Diet Coke				
10	Pepsi-Cola				
45	Pepsi-Cola				
46	Pepsi-Cola				
47	Pepsi-Cola				
48	Coke Classic				
49	Dr. Pepper				
50	Pepsi-Cola				
51	Sprite				
52					

Note: Rows 11–44 are hidden.

	A	B	C	D	E
1	**Brand Purchased**		**Soft Drink**	**Frequency**	
2	Coke Classic		Coke Classic	19	
3	Diet Coke		Diet Coke	8	
4	Pepsi-Cola		Dr. Pepper	5	
5	Diet Coke		Pepsi-Cola	13	
6	Coke Classic		Sprite	5	
7	Coke Classic				
8	Dr. Pepper				
9	Diet Coke				
10	Pepsi-Cola				
45	Pepsi-Cola				
46	Pepsi-Cola				
47	Pepsi-Cola				
48	Coke Classic				
49	Dr. Pepper				
50	Pepsi-Cola				
51	Sprite				
52					